Conference Proceedings:

Lubrication Management and Technology 2006

LUBMAT 2006

Edited by:

I. Sherrington, F. Velasco, R. D. Arnell, E. H. Smith, T. Sperring

Proceedings of the 1st European Conference on Lubrication Management and Technology

Held at the University of Central Lancashire, Preston, UK

14th - 16th June 2006

Lubrication Management and Technology 2006

Published by

Jost Institute for Tribotechnology
University of Central Lancashire
Preston PR1 2HE
United Kingdom
http:/www.uclan.ac.uk/lubmat

Printed by

Emerald Group Publishing Limited
60-62 Toller Lane
Bradford, BD8 9BY
United Kingdom
http://www.emeraldinsight.com

The views expressed in the papers bound in these proceedings are entirely those of individual authors. The organisers of LUBMAT assume no liability for any injury or damage resulting as a consequence of the use of the information presented in these proceedings.

First edition 2007

ISBN: 978-1-901922-64-6

LUBMAT 2006
FORWARD BY THE CONFERENCE CHAIRMAN

Over the past two decades the use of lubrication management has become increasingly important in sustaining the operation of industrial assets and the cost effectiveness of many processes in industry. At the same time there has also been dramatic development in the technologies for evaluating lubricant performance and condition. These developments have gone hand in hand with changes in health and safety legislation, improved environmental practice, increased demands on lubricated systems from customers and the drive to manage lubricated systems at reduced cost. It is, therefore, more than timely to introduce the First European Conference on Lubrication Management and Technology, in the form of LUBMAT '06 to provide a forum to present and discuss new ideas and current practice in the subject and to debate the principal issues and challenges facing practioners in this area.

LUBMAT focuses on four themes, namely: lubrication management, lubrication technology, lubricants and additives and lubricant testing with the emphasis of the meeting being toward industrial applications, but nonetheless also incorporating a significant input from academics and aiming to encourage knowledge transfer in both directions.

This inaugural meeting of LUBMAT takes place on the 40th anniversary of the emergence of the subject of tribology. The discipline arose following the publication of a UK Government Report, "Lubrication (Tribology) Education and Research" on the 9th March 1966 which introduced the word "tribology", formed from the Greek roots "tribos" meaning "rubbing" and "ology" meaning "study of". The report also defined the subject as "the study of interacting surfaces in relative motion and the practices related thereto". In view of this important anniversary, I am especially honoured that Dr H. P. Jost, the Chairman of the Government Committee producing the report, has been able to accept my invitation to deliver the Opening Address for LUBMAT '06. Dr Jost's tireless, forthright and pioneering approach to encourage government, academic and industrial partners to work together in focussed co-operation to find ways to reduce wear and control friction should be inspiration and motivation for us all.

As Chairman of both the Organising Committee and the Scientific Committee I have been pleased to see a wide span of contributions of a high standard from both industrial and academic authors. We received abstracts from almost 60 authors representing 18 countries. A large proportion of these offers were accepted by the scientific committee and I thank contributors for the part they have played in making LUBMAT '06 a diverse and relevant meeting which with the potential to enrich and initiate new developments in this area in the future.

My thanks also go to many people who have contributed to the organisation of LUBMAT '06. These include: the members of the Organising Committee and the Scientific Committee for their contributions to the organisation, operation and planning of this meeting, the Plenary Speakers for their commitment to bring us concise summaries of the "state of the art" in their specialist areas and the Conference and Events Management service from UCLAN for their competent and professional approach in making the practical arrangements for the conference, particularly in association with the Conference Dinner and Social Event. My thanks also go to our meeting sponsors, the US Office of Naval Research (ONRG) and Shell Global Solutions, who have generously supported LUBMAT '06 by their attendance and through their financial contributions. Finally, a special acknowledgement is reserved for Mr Francisco Velasco, the Conference Co-ordinator, for his diligent and thorough management of the event planning and his part in forming the communication channel with our Spanish partners Tekniker. He has played a key and indispensable role in the effective planning, organisation and smooth operation of the meeting and the production of this volume of proceedings.

This volume of proceedings contains papers from the first meeting of LUBMAT. However, it was always intended that the conference would become a regular calendar fixture, taking place in the UK and Spain alternately, once every two years. Accordingly, the next meeting of LUBMAT will be held in San Sebastián in Spain, in June 2008. If you have found LUBMAT '06 to be informative and enjoyable, I hope very much that you will be able to join us again.

Prof. Ian Sherrington
Chairman of the Scientific and Organising Committees

MEMBERS OF THE SCIENTIFIC COMMITTEE

Chairman: Prof. Ian Sherrington, Jost Institute for Tribotechnology, UK

Dr. Ana Aranzabe, Fundación Tekniker, Spain

Prof. R. Derek Arnell, Jost Institute for Tribotechnology, UK

Mr. Richard Atkinson, Kluber Lubrication Great Britain Ltd, UK

Mr. Javier Barriga, Fundación Tekniker, Spain

Mr. Bob Cutler, WearCheck, UK

Dr. Ramón Gallifa, Fuchs Lubricantes S. A., Spain

Dr. Amaia Igartua, Fundación Tekniker, Spain

Mr. Javier Laucirica, Fundación Tekniker, Spain

Prof. Martin Priest, University of Leeds, UK

Prof. Edward H. Smith, Jost Institute for Tribotechnology, UK

Dr. Trevor Sperring, Jost Institute for Tribotechnology, UK

Mr. Jesús Terradillos, Fundación Tekniker, Spain

Mr. Francisco Velasco, Jost Institute for Tribotechnology, UK

Prof. Jože Vižintin, Centre for Tribology and Technical Diagnostics, University of Ljubljana, Slovenia

MEMBERS OF THE ORGANISING COMMITTEE

Chairman: Prof. Ian Sherrington, Jost Institute for Tribotechnology, UK

Co-ordinator: Mr. Francisco Velasco, Jost Institute for Tribotechnology, UK

Dr. Ana Aranzabe, Fundación Tekniker, Spain

Mr. Javier Barriga, Fundación Tekniker, Spain

Mr. Alex Bengoa, Fundación Tekniker, Spain

Mr. Javier García, Fundación Tekniker, Spain

Prof. Edward H. Smith, Jost Institute for Tribotechnology, UK

Dr. Trevor Sperring, Jost Institute for Tribotechnology, UK

SPONSORS

Office of Naval Research Global (ONRG)

Edison House
221/223 Old Marylebone Road
London NW1 5TH
United Kingdom

Shell Global Solutions

Cheshire Innovation Park
PO Box 1
Chester CH1 3SH
United Kingdom

CO-SPONSORS

Institution of Mechanical Engineers (IMechE)

1 Birdcage Walk
Westminster
London SW1H 9JJ
United Kingdom

CONTENTS

Plenary Session 1
KEYNOTE ADDRESSES

Chair: Prof. Ian Sherrington

Opening Address
H. P. JOST

Industrial Lubricants and Market Trends
R. GALLIFA

Opening Address

H. Peter Jost

International Tribology Council

Lubrication management and technology are two inter-connected subjects of considerable economic and environmental importance. The Jost Institute for Tribotechnology and the Fundación Tekniker are, therefore, to be congratulated for staging this event to highlight some of the important facets in these areas.

Before relating to the subject of the Conference, I have been asked to spend a few minutes on the important economic and wider environmental background aspects of our subject.

ECONOMIC ASPECTS

The economics of tribology are often overlooked, this in spite of the significant effect that the application of tribological knowledge can have. It is well known that investigations in the UK, Germany, United States, Canada and China have shown that the application of tribological principles and practices can lead to savings of between 1% and 1.4% of an industrial country's GNP, requiring an investment in R&D on average as low as 1 in 50 of the savings obtainable. It is also estimated that savings in the UK falling under this heading can be between £10 and £11 billion per annum (2005 values), lubrication accounting for approximately 20% of such savings, with the remainder falling under the headings of materials technology engineering design and miscellaneous, including **condition monitoring**.

In the UK lubrication field we are, therefore, dealing with a value in the region of **£2.0 - £2.2** billion savings per annum by the application of tribology. Even if this figure was 20% or 50% inaccurate, the savings would still be massive. The trouble is that they are so thinly spread over a large spectrum of applications.

Personally, I do not believe that these estimates are **optimistically inaccurate**. As an example, take Hatfield. The **technological causes** of the Hatfield **disaster were tribological ones**, viz: the effects of the **inter-action** of wheel and rail that caused cracks, which eventually led not only to large costs, estimated by the Strategic Rail Authority to be at least £250 million, but in addition, to a massive network-wide inspection and re-railing exercise. Not only did this entail huge financial cost, but it also cost several lives and led – as you may remember – to **manslaughter proceedings**.

On the economic side of tribology we are, therefore, dealing with very high figures, with design and materials technology playing a major part.*

---

* The macro and micro economics of which were outlined in the Presidential Address at last year's 3rd World Tribology Congress. Copies are available on the ITC website www.itctribology.org and from the ITC secretariat (email: itcsecretariat@aol.com).

ENVIRONMENTAL CONSIDERATIONS

In addition to the important part of the tribological aspects on our **economy**, tribology has a **not insignificant** influence on the environmental issue facing the world

Some of you will know **of the environmental aspect** endeavours to create a long-term road map for the United Nations framework, and giving important guides to the subject that were expounded by the Lord May of Oxford OM AC Kt., then President of the Royal Society. Also, that the International Academic Conference represented by senior officers from 50 national academies of science (AP Conferences) and being a mechanism whereby the world's academics can speak on behalf of science, came to the conclusion that something drastic needed to be done about the climate changes, which from the year **1000** – before your time and mine - and about 1940 averaged plus/minus 0.25°C, and had started to rise in the middle of the last century. In the Northern Hemisphere it had reached a rise of around 0.4°C after which it increased dramatically until last year, in 2005, it reached a rise of nearly 1%.

The forecast scenarios between now and 2100 show at the end of that period an increase of between 2.2°C at the best and, at the worst, 5.5°C and that will make life, as we know it, almost impossible.

What does this mean in practice? One of the practical effects, causing great concern, as Lord May pointed out, would be that unless the environmental pollution loss was remedied, already in the year 2050 the demand for fresh water would exceed the supply (on the basis that 21% of fresh water being used by industry and 69% by agriculture). 2050 is only **44 years** ahead. Just compare this gap with that between the emergence of tribology in 1966, i.e. 40 years ago, and you can see how very quickly time passes.

These are the world's major problems and I was, therefore, pleased that the organisers asked me to give weight to the economics and the tribological influence on the environment, with special reference to lubricants and their influence on the environment, although in this short address, I can only refer to some of the areas involved, as I see them, and **that** only rather superficially, in a way skimming the surface, which is normally not my style.

Seen against this background the subject of this Conference although a small part, but in reality may be of greater importance than the title of the Conference would suggest.

LET US LOOK AT THE COMPATIBILITY OF LUBRICANTS AND NATURE

About 1% of our total mineral oil consumption is used to formulate lubricants. Everywhere the production, management including operation and disposal of lubricants have to cover the requirements of the best possible protection of our nature, the environment in general and of the living beings especially. In **this** context, safety considerations play an ever increasing role.

The importance of environmental compatibility and of connected tests **has to be** understood by all those engaged in the fields of production, management and disposal of lubricants. Health and water hazards have to be minimised – not only in respect of conventional lubricants - but also of "coolants and metal working lubricants", "engine oils", "fast biodegradable lubricants" and not forgetting the operation of fluids. These are some important aspects that can influence the degree of impairment of the environment.

There are, of course, lubricants that have little or no detrimental environmental effect. Fluids like air and water are foremost of these, not to mention magnetic levitation. However, for materials technology and engineering design reasons, neither water nor air can be used in a vast majority of lubrication applications. We have, therefore, to aim to rely on non-environmental damaging lubricants of a higher viscosity than gases, including synthetic oils, but even when using these, the environmental aspects have to be given careful consideration.

Basically, scientists and engineers have not only to find the answers to a number of problems, but also to find a means to measure and reduce the impairment of the environment. The task of tribologists is, therefore, to solve, or at least reduce, the problems caused by contacts of lubricants with the environment.

WHAT ARE THE ROUTES WE CAN TAKE?

Firstly, environmental facts, some of which will feature at this conference, public awareness, industrial involvement, government directives and regulations, globalisation of markets and last – but not least – economic incentives, are important routes, particularly the last, for it is easier to introduce a restriction or a different route, when economic advantages can be gained by it, than by merely stating scientific and technological facts, however logical and important. If public awareness can be strengthened in many areas and more facts dealing with the lubrication impact on the environment can be made public, then the easier it will be to implement the necessary solutions.

Furthermore, governments will generally act only either on advice for necessary actions, or by public pressure. Sometimes on neither. Tribologists feature in both of these areas. There have been moves during the last few years and particularly the last two years and not merely in one country, but throughout the industrial world. Some of you will remember that even in the United States, where interference by government is frowned upon, two regulations were made years ago which had a considerable impact. One was the Executive Order 12873 and the other, the Great Lakes Water Quality Initiative.

Since then countries including Germany, Austria and many others in Europe, including the United Kingdom, have introduced regulations, in general falling under two headings: materials and lubricant contamination, with water protection playing an important part.

I have to say that many of these regulations are extremely complex and are not always easily understood, at least not by ordinary mortals like us.

In addition to water and air, lubricants that assist us in our environmental endeavours are non-petroleum products, including those that are (1) fast biodegradable, (2) non-toxic to human beings, (3) non-toxic to fish and (4) non-toxic to bacteria.

In addition to the environmental aspects, health hazards and water hazards can also be encountered, particularly by coolants and metal working lubricants, by fast biodegradable lubricants and the operation of fluids, as well as by engine oils.

METAL CUTTING FLUIDS

Metal cutting coolants are worth special mention. According to Kaldos, in the United Kingdom the machine tool population is around 250,000 units, consuming a vast amount of energy-generated by power stations and thereby causing environmental problems, both regionally and on a global basis. Almost 100% of energy input in metal cutting is converted into heat and dissipated into the environment.

Cutting fluids not only represent additional environmental problems, but generate separation, cleaning, treatment and health hazard problems. To combat some of these, **minimum cutting** fluid applications have recently emerged which show **considerable** savings, not only in cutting fluids, but consequently in cleaning treatment, separation equipment and labour.

In addition, considerable progress has been made in the application of **biodegradable, multi-layered cutting fluids**, tests of which have yielded promising results. In general, however, the potentials of tribology in the field of metal cutting forces are, to **a large extent**, still **unexplored.** Investigations are, therefore, needed to meet, not only their operational efficiency, but also **the** environmental health and safety requirements involved.

AS TO DANGEROUS SUBSTANCES

Not overlooked must be a danger of using lubricants that have carcinogenic effects. There are many of these: the main ones were listed by Professor Bartz under three headings:

1)   Cancer generating, such as n-nitro samines, polychlorinated biphenyles

2)   Definite cancer generating (as shown in animal tests) such as benzo   (a) pyrene

3)   Materials suspected of cancerous potentials such as chlorine, paraffins and formaldehydes.

There are also other substances that have to be treated with great caution, for instance: lead or boron containing components and zinc-dithioposphates which are very popular additives, but have also been evaluated for their toxicological potential, not to mention cadmium, mercury and hexavalent chromium.

CONCLUSION

So, what should be borne in mind in the field of lubrication management and technology, broadly falling under the heading of environmental effects.

There are nine conclusions.

Firstly, to protect the environment. The good news is that lubricants which are environmentally more acceptable have gained in importance and this trend will continue.

Secondly, in some countries, including European Union members, several laws and regulations have been enacted to control the management, i.e. the production, application and disposal of lubricants and these must be observed.

Thirdly, consideration of environmental aspects of lubricants, focusing on health habits and water hazards is essential. To define and classify the impairment of the environment, numerous different **terms** are used, revealing the fact that the whole matter is **still confusing** and at the moment **not at all clear**. Some groups of watermissible and non-watermissible fluids have to be used as base fluids for environmental acceptable fluids, including watermissible fluids that are categorised by some polyethylene glycols and non-watermissible fluids such as synthetic ester fluids and natural or vegetable oils, e.g. rape oils.

Fourthly, a relative comparison of base fluids will reveal that they are characterised by advantages and disadvantages. Some of these environmental disadvantages will unfortunately prevent their use, and to a certain extent, this has already happened.

Fifthly, lubricating **greases** based on some of the above-mentioned fluids can be formulated conforming to requirements regarded as having fast biodegradable abilities and that should not be unattainable.

Sixthly, disposal of environmentally acceptable lubricants can be complex and depends on the type of fluids. Some countries, including the UK, have already enacted special laws and regulations. More will follow.

Seventhly, in addition to technical requirements, aspects of toxicology and industrial biological considerations will exert an increasingly important future influence on the formulation of coolants.

Eighthly, high disposal costs and improved design will result in the use of products with high service life data and constant long term properties, as well as better maintenance procedures.

Finally, there is a **down side**. As more knowledge becomes available, it will become increasingly difficult in our management function to find a balance between the economic advantages and ecological requirements. On the one hand, toxicologically and ecologically questionable products must be excluded from further use in lubricants and coolants if they pose any significant health risks during the application; on the other hand, it seems inevitable that the technological development level of lubricants and coolants will decrease, if **unnecessary** restrictions are imposed and that is highly undesirable.

Having said all this, let us put the theme of the Conference in perspective. Lubrication technology and management are believed to constitute approximately 20% of tribology, but an extremely important 20% they are. The management and technology of lubrication can play a crucial part in the development of that part of tribology which could have perhaps not the major, but a significant aspect of the environmental scenario of the future.

To achieve our aims, close co-operation between academia, industry and government is not only desirable, but essential. Joint activities and organisational groupings, on global bases, must form important means to achieve our objectives. This requirement cannot be over emphasised.

Let us not forget the purpose of tribology is to create **national wealth** and **improve the quality of life**. In our endeavours in these spheres, the subject of this Conference can play an important part.

ACKNOWLEDGEMENTS

In the preparation of this address, I acknowledge and express appreciation to Lord May of Oxford, Professor Wilfried Bartz and Dr Kaldos for their papers having drawn my attention to some of the important points used by me in this address.

Lubrication Management and Technology *LUBMAT '06. Preston, UK*

Industrial Lubricants and Market Trends

R. Gallifa

Fuchs Lubricantes, S.A., P.I. San Vicente, s.n. 08755 Castellbisbal - Barcelona, Spain

ABSTRACT

The main drivers affecting the cost of lubricants are described: the cost of raw materials due to significant shortages of some basic petrochemicals and also, the increasing costs associated to health, safety and environmental regulations. Despite the cost of raw materials is a limitative problem for the competitiveness of the Lubricant Specialists and the Industry in general, the actual and coming strict demand of more friendly lubricants together with the continuously need of new technical performance requirements are and must be seen as a booster for lubricants innovation.

1. INTRODUCTION

From the point of view of the application, lubricants are generally classified in two big areas: Industrial Lubricants and Automotive Lubricants.

The Metal Industry is the main sector responsible for lubricant consumption and that is why the majority of classifications of Industrial Lubricants regarding statistics are influenced by the metal applications.

It is common to divide the Industrial Lubricants in the following categories:

- Process Lubricants: Such as metalworking lubricants for cutting, grinding, forming, drawing, rolling…The common characteristic of the Process Lubricants is that there is always contact between the lubricant, the tool and the processed material.

- Lubricants for Processing Machinery / Equipments: Hydraulic and gear oils, slide way oils, chain lubricants…In this case there is no contact between the lubricant and the manufactured good.

- Lubricants that have been designed to be a permanent component of the manufactured goods. There are many examples in the vehicles: lubricants of all moving parts, such as window regulators, door hinges, back mirrors, electrical switches, power train components…in fact in a car there are hundreds of lubricated points.

Automotive Lubricants refers mainly to engine oils.

The weight consumption of Lubricants by sectors in a developed country as Spain is shown in Table 1. These data may be extrapolated as an indicative of western European countries. In rough figures, the 40% of the Lubricants are Industrial Lubricants and the 60% Automotive Lubricants. [1]

Table 1. Aselube 2005 in K Tones

ASELUBE 2005 IN KTONES			
SPAIN			
	2005	2004	VARIATION
Automotive Engine, Transmission and Gear Oils			
- Passenger Cars and Motor Bikes	97,9	100,2	-2,3%
- Public and GoodsTansport	93,3	97,0	-3,8%
- Gear and Transm. Oils	28,0	30,1	-6,8%
	219,3	227,3	-3,5%
Industrial Oils	153,8	150,2	2,4%
Marine / Aircraft	22,7	22,5	1,1%
Process Oils	13,8	16,1	-14,4%
Greases	10,2	10,2	-0,4%
Total	**419,8**	**426,3**	**-1,5%**

This paper concerns mainly to Industrial Lubricants but the discussion may be extrapolated to Automotive Lubricants too.

The cost of Lubricants depends of the following factors:

- Lubricants Design: Research, Development and Innovation costs (R+D+I).
- Raw Materials of the Formulation or Receipt
- Manufacturing Costs
- Distribution
- Services

The weight of the different factors is not the same and strongly depends whether the Lubricant is a Commodity or a Specialty. In simple terms, Commodities are normally following old standards with very well known technical formulations and normally the weight of the raw material cost is the most determinant. Contrary Specialties are following special requirements meaning very expensive tests with not always an obvious investment payback. Specialties are also referred as Customized Lubricants or Taylor Made Lubricants and despite the important contribution of the raw material cost , the cost of Development may be prominent.

2. PETROCHEMICAL RAW MATERIALS

The cost of Petrochemicals is strongly related to the crude oil prices but also to the general worldwide demand. [2]

The extractive capacity of petroleum reserves, the regional conflicts, the evolution of the parity of the most significant currencies and some effects of globalization are determinants.

Table 2 shows a historical view on the crude oil prices from 1946 to present, indicating a strong influence of reserves, geopolitical factors and general consumption. Yom Kipur, the conflicts of the Gulf area, the wars in Iran and Irak and the current problems of instability were known in the near past as causing cost peaks and general complications in the growing of the general economy as well as in the final consumers.

Table 2. Historical evolution of crude oil prices from 1946 to present
[Financial Date Forecaster, March 2006, www.InflationData.com]

Year	Ave Nominal Price	% Incr.Nom.Pr.	Ave Annual Inflation Adj.Price	% Incr.Infl.Adj. Pr.
U.S.Ave $/bl				
1946	1,63		16,18	
1947	2,16	32,5	19,01	17,5
1951	2,77	69,9	21,00	29,8
1955	2,93	79,8	21,50	32,9
1959	3,00	84,0	20,25	25,2
1963	2,91	78,5	18,71	15,6
1967	3,12	91,4	18,41	13,8
1971	3,60	120,9	17,50	8,2
1975	12,21	649,1	44,63	175,8
1979	25,10	1439,9	67,42	316,7
1983	29,08	1684,0	57,48	255,3
1987	17,75	989,0	30,74	90,0
1991	20,20	1139,3	29,19	80,4
1995	16,75	927,6	21,64	33,7
1999	16,56	916,0	19,52	20,6
2003	27,69	1598,8	29,63	83,1
2004	37,66	2210,4	39,21	142,3
2005	50,04	2969,9	50,38	211,4

At present, besides geopolitical issues the highly increasing demand of countries like China, India, Pakistan... is a determinant factor and will not stop. There is a big backlog between developed countries and countries having a great pace of development. The 40% of the increase of consumption during the last 5 years in the world was due to the consumption in China.

A lack of investment in exploration to find new reserves, problems in some extraction fields due to weather conditions, closures in several refineries due to technical reasons, a lack of logistic media for the increasing need of transport and the interest of the hedge funds are influencing the petrol price and its derivatives.

Few governments have criticized the lack of investment by the oil companies on exploration for new oil reserves and on the required refining capacity to cater for the growing demands of the emerging markets in Asia. The Eastern European countries are also starting to increase their demand of crude oil and all indicators show that these demands will continue to grow very significantly. The new international political context creates uncertainties that affect investment policies, and the lack of these policies in turn creates uncertainties.

The market is suffering from large distortions due to the temporary imbalances that occur between the supply and demand and the exchange rates between the strongest currencies that have affected the trading relationships between regions with a long-standing tradition of trading. Since its creation, the Euro zone has faced with economical measures to absorb some sharp changes in petrol prices, this causes great difficulties in exporting at the times of its greatest strength and therefore leading to a lack of competitiveness of European industry and of the manufacturing industry, which consumes lubricants. The companies do not want changes and they must design safety scenarios, which will allow for the projecting of long-term plans which are sustainable and subject to the fewest possible surprises.

Solvent Neutral SN 150 is one of the base oils generally accepted in the Industry as a raw materials cost reference or indicator of the evolution of the mineral oil lubricants. The analysis of the cost of SN150 versus the crude oil cost from beginning of last year to present, shows a trend change (see Figure 1). The cost of SN 150 does not progress along with the cost of the barrel anymore. The point of change in October 2005 is seen as a consequence of petrol refineries being favoring the fuel production in detriment of base oils.

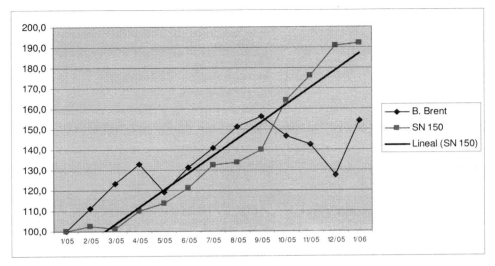

Figure 1. Evolution of cost vs. crude oil cost in year (2005-2006)

From January 2005, the petrol has increased the price in 40% and the base oil has increased about 200%!

3. HEALTH, SAFETY AND ENVIRONMENT

People and society are the priority, and as a consequence, so are aspects relating to personal safety and environment.

In the last years, there has been increasing administrative and public mandatory regulations and this must and will continue.

The current Material Safety Data Sheet of chemicals, the End-of-Live Vehicles (ELV) Directive, the International Material Data System (IMDS) of the Car Industry mean daily work at the offices of Chemist and for Engineers of the industrial sites and centers of development. In addition, REACH is approaching and is accentuating this daily work.

3.1. Material Safety Data Sheet (MSDS)

The use of the MSDS is required by national law and must meet the European directive 1991/155 EC. The form has the following 16 parts regarding:

1. Identification substance
2. Composition / data on components
3. Hazards identification
4. First aid measures
5. Fire fighting measures
6. Accidental release measures
7. Handling and storage
8. Exposure controls and personal protection
9. Physical and chemical properties
10. Stability and reactivity
11. Toxicological information
12. Ecological information
13. Disposal consideration
14. Transport information
15. Regulatory information
16. Other information

A person and telephone contact is provided in case of necessity. The MSDS is a document to be consulted before the use of the product or in case of need if there is any incident and defines pictograms and risk and safety phrases for the labelling of products.

Additionally, the 1999/45 EC states that the consumers must be informed if there is any significant change in the MSDS due to new knowledge about some aspect influencing health, safety and environment meaning a change in the picture expressing hazard or the corresponding risk phrases.

3.2.   End-of-Live Vehicles Directive (ELV)

The End-of-Life Directive is the answer by the European Commission to the great impact on the environment of the millions of cars produced per year when they arrive to its end of live. Every year the end life of vehicles generates more than 9 millions of tones of waste in the community.

In 1997, there was a proposal by the European Commission which aimed to make vehicle dismantling and recycling more environmentally friendly. This proposal included quantified targets for reuse, recycling and recovery of vehicles and their components, pushing producers to manufacture new vehicles with a view on recycling. The proposal was officially adopted by the European Parliament in September 2000 and published in October: this is the 2000/53 EC directive known as the ELV Directive.

In short, the Directive states that the producers must assure that materials and components put on the market do not contain the following heavy metals: lead, mercury, cadmium and hexavalent chromium. The producers must submit to the authorities when requested technical information showing that the materials and components used are in compliance with the regulations.

Regarding chemicals and lubricants, the car producers and component producers request from the complete chain of suppliers written and signed documents stating that the products they are delivering meet the ELV directive.

3.3.   International Material Data System (IMDS)

To answer to these general social requirements, not only in Europe but also in the entire world, the Car manufactures created the International Material Data System (IMDS).

Originally, IMDS was a joint development of AUDI, BMW, DAIMLERCHRYSLER, FORD, OPEL, PORSCHE, VW, VOLVO...and other companies joined this initial community FIAT, NISSAN, TOYOTA, MAZDA, SUZUKI, MITSUBISHI...

In IMDS, all materials used for the car manufacturers are archived and maintained through a centralized automated application database accessible in the net. All the chemical ingredients are tracked across the entire supply chain. The objective is to make possible to meet the obligations placed on car manufacturers and thus on their suppliers by national and international standards, laws and regulations.

IMDS is intended to facilitate the recycling of old cars in future and the companies sustaining the project are getting a detailed overview of the materials used in future old cars and of course IMDS is an answer to help to meet the compliance with national and European Union material legislation (1991/155 EC, 2000/53 EC).

In 2003, there were more than 50.000 entrances and in 2005 probably about 100.000! Regarding chemicals and lubricants, only the direct materials (materials that are part of the final vehicle) are requested to be registered. As an example, the cutting oils used to machine the car engine in the production line are not considered direct materials, so the register is not required; but some greases that are part of some gears, as greases per car life, must be registered.

3.4. REACH

In February 2001 the White Book of Chemicals was published according the indications of the Commission with the title "Strategy for a future chemicals policy". It was the prelude and the base of the future regulations that will be of general application in Europe regarding chemicals and lubricants as a part of them.

In October 2003, a formal proposal of the European Commission of a new regulatory scheme known as REACH was published. This is a plan to change how the chemicals are regulated in the European Union regarding risk assessment. The first reading was made in the European Parliament in 2004 where the proposal suffered some amendments. Probably the Council will adopt the proposal in 2006.

As it is well known in the forum of Chemicals Producers and Lubricant Producers R.E.A.CH. is the acronym of Registration, Evaluation and Authorization (or Rejection) of Chemicals. The acronym defines the key steps of the procedure of all the chemicals prior to be authorized in the Union.

In the Registration all the information of the substance such as physical and chemical properties, toxicity risk and environmental risk will be provided to a Central European Agency. The risk management will take into account not only the producers but also the downstream users. As a first priority, about 30.000 substances produced in volumes up to 1000 Kg per year will be registered. The Evaluation will refer to not only substances but also final chemicals / lubricants. In some cases, expensive tests regarding toxicity, biodegradability, long-term effects and persistency in the media will be necessary and the producers and at the end the users will be the ones involved to support the corresponding huge costs.

The economical impact calculated as direct costs according the Commission is estimated in 2,300 MM Euros!

The whole process is estimated to last 11 years…

4. THE INDUSTRY COMPETITIVENESS

Some developed countries are suffering industrial delocalization, which is an additional factor to the general concerns. For companies, the object of delocalization is to compete to survive in an extraordinarily tough world market where the cost of labor is clearly a competitive factor. Industry has a tendency to change from high cost countries to low cost countries, wreaking turmoil in the countries subject to delocalization.

The developed countries then are facing a hard scenario: delocalization, increasing constraints and costs due to the raw material evolution and shortage, increasing costs associated to the positive facts of harder regulations concerning health, safety and environment, more strict conditions for the safer transport of chemical products and in the lubricants area the management of used oils.

In addition, developed countries must compete with companies in other parts of the world where environment is not given so much priority. The answer is to lead innovation through knowledge management seeking for more differentiated products with greater added value, ideally of a unique nature, going forward in the way of specialization.

4.1. Specialization and Innovation

There are a lot of examples of different origin and nature about innovation of lubricants in terms of specialization regarding technical performance, health, safety and environment.

- New developments to face new materials application- An example may be the SAMMI project. SAMMI means Safe and Economic Machining of Magnesium Castings. The aim of the project was to introduce safe and highly efficient processing of magnesium castings, using an adapted machining process with adapted tools, cooling lubricants and a high-speed cutting (HSC) machining centre with integrated safety devices. This project was sponsored by the EC in 2001 and developed by a consortium of companies and technical centers of R+D. The final aim was to lighter the weight of car vehicles with the final objective to reduce the fuel consumption. Regarding lubricants in this project, new neat cutting oils and soluble fluids for magnesium machining were developed. Now the output of the project is magnesium casting, which is used in the car industry in many small components and in a key part, as is the car gearbox. [3]

- Improving the finishing quality in cold rolling of mild steel. The quality of steel coils after cold rolling is a sensible complex process where the equipment as well as the quality of lubricants are the keys.

There is not a good lubricant emulsion for all the process equipments. This depends of the number of rollers, pressure, the quality of the material to be rolled and the levels of the cold rolled steel requested quality. In fact, there is always a need to adjust the soluble oil to the process equipment or to enhance the collaboration between the equipment manufacture and the lubricant manufacture together with the user. At the end in the majority of the cases the lubricant is a tailor made lubricant or a slight variation of pre-existing lubricant.

The speed of rolling is key in terms of productivity and the levels of roughness and cleaningness after rolling are determined by the most sensible consumers as the car producers for example. A good quality on the surface is a must for the good quality of the painted body car. [4]

- New antifriction coatings with dry film lubricants- Development of colloidal dispersions in water using polymers of high molecular weight. Preferably applied by dipping, when dry they create a tenacious non-slip antifriction film. In the coating of screws, they reduce friction providing higher clamping forces with lower torque moments. In addition, solid film lubricants based on graphite, molybdenum disulfide, fluorated polyethylene… give standing dry lubricating films improving running-in processes and protecting against surface damage. The part is dry lubrication, not wet, making the assembly of parts clean and easy. They are applied on metals, plastics and rubbers. Its interest is so great that the new designs of car the car producers do not imagine in the passenger cabinet parts lubricated in wet, oil or grease… [5]

- Friendly lubricants development. LLINCWA is the acronym for the innovation project Loss Lubricants in Inland and Coastal Water Activities. It was carried out within the frame of the Innovation Program of the EU 5th Framework Program. The objectives of the project were: reduction of diffuse water pollution with lubricants and greases, increased use of non-toxic biodegradable lubricants for the protection of fresh water and the coastal zone. Important technical items were achieved but also it was outlined the need of further governmental initiatives to guarantee a sustainable friendly lubricants use in the aquatic environment. [6]

- Free chlorine derivatives for metalworking, biodegradable esters instead of mineral oils for hydraulics and gear oils, emulsions for metalworking with low Chemical Oxygen Demand and Biological Oxygen Demand after splitting to minimize the waste disposal cost, diethanol amine free products due to carcinogenic effects of nitrosamines and boron free soluble lubricants due to water waste restrictions and new labeling are all some few examples of success stories. They are just showing the way that friendly products are possible and the lubricants producers are prepared for the challenging future. [7]

4.2.   From Lubrication Services to Creating Added Value

Finally, the industrial companies have the aim to concentrate more and more to their core activities outsourcing many of their auxiliary works.

For this reason they are looking from the lubricant suppliers not only the delivery of products but some service activities connected with lubricants.

From Lubricants Monitoring, understood as periodical analysis of the lubricants in service as preventive management practices, skills have helped to develop more complex Lubrication Programs where the lubrication period in all required areas is defined according to a stated plan.

Nowadays, the requirements to be met by lubricant companies have increased to be part of the customers through the development of agreed partnership programs. Not only Lubricant Monitoring and Lubrication Programs are covered, but also the implementation of Lubricants Procuring, fill up and top up of machines and finally the development of created value or additional benefits through the so called Continuous Improvement Programs.

5. CONCLUSION

Perhaps, it may argue that the problems described in this paper are not new. However, the combination of factors is new: it is now required to face an increase of raw materials in addition to the requirement of meering more strict legal regulations (to protect people and environment) together with industrial delocalization is an ever-lasting issue. Nevertheless, what is new at present is the intensity in which these situations are happening. This has never been seen in the past and what is great and unique is that they are happening at the same time.

But as the future creators and leaders say there are not problems but opportunities.

We are forced to move on the way of increased specialization regarding technical performance and friendly solutions and only the best prepared will have its place.

REFERENCES

[1]　ASELUBE Memoria 2004
[2]　LUBE REPORT April 12, 2006
[3]　SAMMI.Project Brite Euram E97-4586. 2001
[4]　A. Mascaró, R. Corripio, F. Alonso, X. Gaillard, C. Silvy-Leligois. J.A. Alvarez, M. Fernández Loria, F. Chicharro: La Revue de Métallurgie-ATS-JSI 2005, pp. 124, 125
[5]　FUCHS LUBRITECH Gmbh March 2006 (www.fuchs-lubritech.com)
[6]　P.van Broekhuizen, D.Theodori, K.Le Blansch, S.Ullmer. Lubrication in Inland and Coastal Water Activities. A.A.Balkema Publishers 2003
[7]　T. Mang, W. Dresel. Lubricants and Lubrication, WILEY-VCH, Weinheim 2001

Session 1
LUBRICATION MANAGEMENT 1

Chair: Ms. Arrate Marcaide

Risk Assessment in the Use of Metalworking Fluids
D. J. NEADLE

The Tribologist as 'Expert Witness'
M. FOX

Oil Analysis as an Improvement Tool for the Behavior of Wind Turbine Gears. Main Problems Detected Through the Condition of the Lubricant
J. TERRADILLOS, M. BILBAO, J. I. CIRIA, A. MALAGA, J. AMEYE

Evaluation of Tribological behaviour in journal bearing using Coast Down Time analysis
R. E. BROWNE, A. K. M. DE SILVA, K. P. RAMACHANDRAN, D. K. HARRISON

Risk Assessment in the Use of Metalworking Fluids

D. J. Neadle

Metalworking Fluids Product Stewardship Group, United Kingdom Lubricants Association, UK

ABSTRACT

The paper provides information on the types of metalworking fluids and conditions encountered during their use. The potential dermal and respiratory hazards are described. Practical guidance on the assessment and control of risks is given.

Keywords: Metalworking fluids, risk assessment, dermal hazards, respiratory hazards.

1. INTRODUCTION

United Kingdom Lubricants Association (UKLA) is the Trade Association representing UK lubricant producers and allied sectors and is committed to promoting high ethical standards and maintaining close contact with regulatory developments. UKLA is also the UK representative to UEIL, the Independent European Trade Association for the sector.

The Metalworking Fluids Product Stewardship Group (MWFPSG) was formed to promote high ethical standards and regulatory compliance relating to health and safety and environmental aspects in the development, manufacture and marketing of metalworking fluids. The MWFPSG consists of representatives of companies which are active in the metalworking fluids field, together with representatives of the Health and Safety Executive and the Environment Agency.

The purpose of this paper is to describe the potential hazards associated with the use of metalworking fluids, particularly regarding the skin and respiratory system, and to offer practical guidance on the assessment and control of risks which could arise therefrom. The paper provides information on the types of metalworking fluids and the conditions encountered in their use because we believe that this knowledge is essential to a meaningful assessment of risk.

Knowledge and skills from many sources contribute to achieving the safe use of metalworking fluids, a point which we believe is well illustrated in this paper.

2. HAZARD AND RISK

There are many ways of highlighting the distinct difference between hazard and risk.

A tiger undoubtedly is hazardous. But when we visit the zoo and observe the beautiful creature from behind high fences or toughened glass, the risk to which we are exposed is very small. On the other hand, if we decide to join the tiger in the enclosure and perhaps behave aggressively towards him or her, the risk of harm is increased immensely. In each case the hazard, the tiger, is the same; however, the risk is changed greatly by the circumstances. Please do not try to verify this example. There are no tigers in the drums of metalworking fluids which we supply, but the risks which could arise do depend upon how the products are used and these risks can be minimised or eliminated by good practice.

3. FUNCTIONS OF METALWORKING FLUIDS

Fluids used in metal removal operations (cutting and grinding) must remove heat and provide lubrication, the required balance between these two functions depends upon the specific operation. The fluid must flush away metallic particles from the cutting zone. Compatibility with the machine tool and the workpiece material is an essential property. The machine tool may rely on the lubricating properties of the metalworking fluid to function correctly. Metalworking fluid must not cause corrosion of the workpiece. Furthermore, the choice of fluid may be influenced by subsequent stages in the production sequence.

Similar requirements apply to metalforming (chipless machining) except that in pressworking and related operations, the needs for heat removal and flushing of metallic particles may be less important.

A metalworking fluid must be formulated to conform with health, safety and environmental regulations and accepted standards of good practice. Additional requirements may be imposed by purchasers, for example suitability for particular disposal procedures.

4. TYPES OF METALWORKING FLUIDS

4.1. Neat oils

Neat oils are used as supplied – they are not diluted in water. These products are available in a wide range of viscosities to suit different applications. There is an increased risk of forming vapours and mists in contact with rapidly rotating machinery when using an oil of very low viscosity. Such very low viscosity neat oils are also potentially more aggressive towards the skin because of their greater penetrating and de-fatting characteristics. These factors should be taken into account when making a risk assessment.

As a generalisation, neat oils are used where required to successfully carry out specific metalworking operations or to facilitate correct functioning of the machine tool. Otherwise, water-mix fluids are normally selected.

Most neat oils consist of a blend of mineral oils (base oils) with additives. Research carried out in the 1960's showed that polycyclic aromatic hydrocarbons (PCAHs) present in less highly-refined base oils had carcinogenic properties and a regulatory limit was set to protect the health of machine operators. Working conditions and general standards of hygiene were also considered to have been very important factors. As a result of this research, reputable manufacturers use only highly-refined base oils, which are of a much higher standard than is specified by regulation.

The additives used in neat oils include natural and synthetic fatty esters, sulphurised hydrocarbons or esters, phosphorus compounds and polymers (to control mist formation).

4.2. Water-mix fluids

There are three main types of water-mix fluids:

- emulsifiable, mineral oil based fluids
- emulsifiable, synthetic fluids
- water-soluble, synthetic fluids

Water-mix fluids are diluted in water prior to use. Generally the working concentration will be in the range 2% to 10%, depending upon the specific fluid and the metalworking operation. Use of the correct mixing procedure is vital – generally the concentrate is added to water with agitation in order to obtain a stable emulsion.

Water quality and cleanliness are key considerations. Water hardness is usually an important factor in fluid selection because metalworking fluids are formulated to give correct performance in a defined range of hardness. Water which is contaminated by bacteria, fungus or chemicals can result in greatly reduced service life, unsatisfactory machining performance and health hazards.

The formulations of water-mix fluids may contain lubricants (including extreme pressure agents), emulsifiers, coupling agents, corrosion inhibitors, defoamers and biocide. There is a wide range of chemistries, depending upon the formulator. Usually the fluid in use is moderately alkaline. The viscosity is consistently low because water is the continuous phase of emulsions.

5. EXPOSURE ROUTES

Skin contact may occur with neat oils and with the concentrates and diluted forms of water-mix fluids. The skin is a complex organ, accounting for approximately one sixth of body mass and varying in thickness between 0.5 and 4.0 mm for different parts of the body. The skin consists of an inner dermis and outer epidermis, with a durable protective layer of keratinised cells. Present in the skin are blood vessels, pressure and pain sensors, hair follicles and oil glands. The characteristics of skin and its tolerance to chemicals vary from person to person. The condition of the skin of an individual can be influenced by many factors.

Although the skin may appear to possess remarkable tolerance to oils and chemicals, contact should be minimised and vigilance maintained. Specialist advice is available for care of the skin (prevention of skin disorders must always be a key objective) and is invaluable in determining the appropriate corrective actions if problems occur.

The lungs include progressively narrower branches of the airways, leading to the alveoli which are tiny air sacs in close contact with blood capillaries to enable gaseous exchange to take place. The respiratory system penetrates deep into the body, and, although it incorporates natural defences against some micro-organisms and particulates, is potentially vulnerable to the vapours, mists and particulates which can be generated in the industrial environment.

6. METALWORKING FLUIDS IN USE

Selection of a metalworking fluid requires knowledge and experience because many factors should be considered, including the type and severity of the process, machine tool design, workpiece material, resistance to microbiological spoilage, ease of disposal and cost.

The characteristics of fresh fluids are altered by service. The changes may be slight or significant and are likely to be progressive unless any necessary corrective actions are taken. The rate of change in fluids depends on their conditions of use. As a generalisation, fluid concentrations usually increase and pH values fall in service. Contaminants may enter both neat oils and water-mix fluids, for example lubricating and hydraulic oils, greases and metals in dissolved or particulate form.

When examined microscopically, metallic particles from cutting and grinding processes are found to be very sharp. They can inflict damage upon the skin especially when embedded in wiping cloths or workwear. The resultant disruption of the skin's outer protective layers facilitates the penetration of oils and chemicals. Damage to the skin produced in this way is progressive and the process of repair may be very slow and problematic.

A Condition Monitoring programme can be very effective in detecting changes in metalworking fluids in service and identifying trends and sudden events. Water-mix fluids in service would typically be tested for concentration, pH value, corrosion resistance and contamination by lubricants, metals and micro-organisms. The tests for neat oils could include viscosity, flash point, infra-red analysis, elemental analysis and particulates. Devising the optimum group of tests, their frequency and sampling methods requires knowledge of the fluid and service conditions. Interpretation of the significance of the test results and identification of trends calls for experience and judgement. A working partnership between the lubricant specialist and user can produce the most successful outcome.

Routine testing for the presence of micro-organisms in water-mix fluids is usually carried out using slides coated with nutrient media. The slides are dipped into the fluid in use and incubated before being examined for growth of colonies in comparison with standards. Determining more specific information about the types of micro-organisms present in a water-mix fluid and their significance may require the special expertise of a micro-biologist.

7. FACTORS INFLUENCING EXPOSURE TO FLUIDS

The machining operation and machine tool design affect exposure to fluids because operations vary in the extent to which they promote splashing and formation of aerosol mists, whilst different machine tools have varying degrees of enclosure and provision for extraction. Fluid characteristics, especially with neat oils, can also affect mist formation. A low viscosity oil used in contact with rapidly rotating machinery in a machine tool without enclosure or extraction, is likely to result in much greater exposure of the operator to splashes and mist than a relatively slow operation carried out with a higher viscosity oil in an enclosed machine fitted with extraction equipment. This is not to suggest that the production engineer can choose to carry out operations slowly or that low viscosity neat oils should never be used. However, the examples highlight the factors which should be taken into account when assessing risk to operators. It is also important to optimise fluid application so as to minimise splashing and mist formation.

Workpiece material may affect exposure because certain metals are potentially hazardous. For example cobalt can be leached into solution in the metalworking fluid in hard metal grinding operations. Special fluids are available to minimise solubilisation of cobalt.

A machine shop with good general ventilation provides a more acceptable and safer environment than a workplace in which mists build up, eventually depositing on walls, ceilings, lighting and electrical conduits.

Appropriate personal protective equipment may be beneficial, for example gloves and eye protection for handling water-mix fluid concentrates during preparation of emulsions. Aprons can be useful to avoid the possibility of splashes on the skin. However, provision of gloves for use in metalworking operations requires careful consideration. Although it must always be an objective to minimise skin contact with fluids, operators often find that gloves are unsatisfactory for many reasons. Special expertise is available to advise upon the subject of skin care and protection taking all factors into account.

8. KEY QUESTIONS

The following questions should be considered:

What is the extent of exposure?

What improvements are required?

How can we achieve the improvement?

How can we maintain the improvement?

8.1. What is the extent of exposure?

Information must be obtained and organised according to a plan to ensure that no important aspects are neglected. The Health and Safety Executive Metalworking Fluids Questionnaire and Metalworking Fluid Guidance Sheet (Engineering Control MW1) provide a structured approach.

Various methodologies are available for risk assessment. Some include the assignment of numerical weightings to help define objectively the greater and lesser risks. Different formats for risk assessment can be used according to the preferences of assessors and procedures of organisations. The important point is that all of the relevant factors should be taken into account.

The Safety Data Sheet is a vital source of information. Check with your supplier to ensure that you have the current issue. The information provided relates primarily to the product as supplied. For water-mix metalworking fluids, this is the concentrate, rather than the mix with water which will be used in the metalworking operation. If you are unsure about the practical implications of the information given in a Safety Data Sheet, ask for clarification. A Product Information Sheet giving further information on the product and its applications may also be available.

In making observations and obtaining measurements to determine the extent of exposure, sources of information and practical assistance include fluid suppliers, occupational health specialists, monitoring equipment suppliers and monitoring service providers. Consult regulatory authorities if you are unsure of required standards for exposure. Health records and results from health surveillance programmes can also provide valuable information, though care must be taken to avoid infringing individual confidentiality.

Document your investigations and conclusions regarding any needs for corrective actions.

The areas in which improvements may be required include: reduction in exposure of the skin and respiratory systems of users to metalworking fluids, improved control of fluid condition and provision of information and training.

8.2.   How can we achieve improvement?

Review the necessity for exposure of the skin and respiratory system of users to metalworking fluids. Consider possible means of reduction both in extent and duration. Evaluate the potential of separation equipment (filters, centrifuges etc.) to periodically or continuously remove metallic particles from the fluids in use.

In the case of water-mix fluids, various designs of skimmers are available to remove tramp oil (ingress of lubricating oils, hydraulic fluids, greases etc.) from the fluids in use. Skimmers should be considered because the tramp oil can cause fluids to deteriorate and may be harmful to the skin of operators.

Assess methods of fluid application and ways of improving enclosure of the metalworking process. Consider fitting extraction equipment. Obtain information about products and services which are suitable for skin care and protection in your process.

Obtain advice from fluid suppliers, equipment manufacturers and occupational health specialists. Develop monitoring and maintenance programmes. Enlist commitment and support from top management in your organisation. Assign responsibility.

8.3.   How can we maintain the improvements?

Regularly review the results from monitoring programmes. Carry out planned checks on equipment function, for example the effectiveness of extraction equipment. Implement an equipment maintenance programme. Record the issue of personal protective equipment and ensure that items are replaced as necessary. Check that personal protective equipment is being used as planned.

Consult regularly with stakeholders, for example at meetings of the Health and Safety Committee where workplace representatives are present. Review health records and the results of health surveillance programmes.

Ensure that employees who handle and use metalworking fluids receive suitable information and training. There are many training resources available, including fluid suppliers, regulatory authorities and occupational health specialists. Carry out refresher training at intervals.

Keep a record of your actions and the improvements achieved.

24

The Tribologist as 'Expert Witness'

M. Fox

Institute of Tribology, School of Mechanical Engineering, University of Leeds, UK

ABSTRACT

The consequences of machine system failure and the apportionment of blame by civil court proceedings are examined, for total costs escalate dramatically by factors of between 3-5 when legal proceedings are followed. Tribologists acting as expert witnesses for plaintiff or defendant have a duty to the court to explain complex technical issues. Initial evidence is often confused and colloquial, the first task is to refine it and establish timelines from which detailed operating logs, service and overhaul reports and damage evidence can be requested. Careful reading of these gives important insights. Two cases of cost claims from mechanical failure using expert tribologists are given, tribological aspects analysed and the use of suitable tests described. The need is strongly emphasized for expert witnesses to stay within their expertise and not to be drawn beyond it by counsel. Statistical treatments of data and results must be explained very carefully. An expert tribology witness must adhere to their duty to the court in helping it understand complex technical issues, maintain tribological truth and explain it in a manner suitable for lay people without simplification becoming misleading.

Keywords: Expert Witness; System Damage; Civil Court Proceedings; Applied Tribology Tests

1. INTRODUCTION

This paper is different from other papers presented here in that they aim to prevent wear, tribological disaster, machinery breakdown and ensuing industrial dislocation. This paper discusses the civil litigation consequences when 'it all goes wrong' from as failure of engines and prime mover mechanical systems causing disablement of entire systems, such as a ship or large scale generator and the associated cost claims and contingent losses. Jost pointed out in his Report nearly forty years ago that the costs of lost activity or production for a machine often substantially exceed the costs of repair [1].

The general approach seeks apportionment of blame, leading to attempted recovery of both direct repair and contingent costs, e.g., loss of charter fees, of the system breakdown. Recourse to civil law by one party usually involves a tribologist to report as an expert witness on the nature of the system wear and an opinion as to its cause. The second party engages its own tribologist to report separately as to cause and responsibility – setting the stage for a civil legal case. Costs escalate dramatically - if mechanical system repair costs are, say £400K, then a successful plaintiff may be awarded civil damage, interest and associated legal costs of the order of £1.2 -£1.6M, a factor of 3-4. The legal process sets in motion a continuous and relentless accumulation of costs, an extraordinary escalation which the tribologist's expert assessment, analysis and witness statement might contain, reduce or stop.

1.1. Peripheral Issues

An expert tribology witness objectively analyses wear and damage in a system; however, their contribution is within a context of subjective managerial, corporate and commercial attitudes. Global corporations give limited local autonomy for national/continental management to resist civil damage claims arising from its products claimed 'lack of fitness for purpose' which allegedly caused premature system failure, e.g., the UK 1979 Sale of Goods Act. However, if civil damage actions continue, relentless increase in contingent costs will exceed corporate local resolution limits and global management intervenes to resolve the claim. Subjective personal, adverse, interactions between principals of the parties involved often significantly prolong cases, which expert witnesses must avoid. Corporate attitudes of 'if we state our liquid products flow uphill, then go to the Supreme Court to disprove it', try to deter claims of whatever validity and only extend civil cases and their expense.

Very much on the other hand, the expert tribology witness presents an individual, professional statement which assesses the problem's tribological aspects. Equally, it is essential that the tribological expert does not give professional opinions outside of their expertise, aspects addressed in the rest of this paper.

2. REFINING THE INITIAL EVIDENCE

Initial damage claim evidence from plaintiff or defendant is usually colloquial and anecdotal. The tribology expert witness's initial task is to review and refine the evidence to examine if, and where, tribology applies, important because the tribology expert might be appointed expecting a wider range of disciplines. This must be resisted strongly – the role of expert witnesses has been questioned, and rightly so, under cross-examination by opposing counsel drawing them to comment on effects and assessments outside of their immediate expertise. Thus, for the hydraulic pump damage case discussed later, it is wrong for the tribology expert witness to be drawn into giving an opinion on the swash plate control aspects of a high power, 180kw, radial piston pump. Whilst the construction and operation of these pumps may well be understood by most technical people, their control aspects must be addressed by a parallel control mechanism expert witness. A fundamental principle for an expert witness is not to stray, or be drawn, outside of their expertise.

Statistical evidence needs careful presentation. Faced with the challenge that lubricant service change intervals of an engine had significant differences for the periods before and during a period of substantial failure, therefore associated with the failures, a Fellow of the Royal Statistical Society analysed the data. He showed that there was no significant difference for the service oil change intervals hours between the two periods of use, also quantifying the nature of 'significance'. This was a very useful and clear judgement made by a statistical expert which established no significant difference in lubricant service change intervals, therefore in this respect the operator had not caused the system failure. Conclusions based on statistical arguments are easy targets for opposing counsel unless presented by statistical experts The alternative for tribological tests is to use established IP/ASTM/ISO statistical significance procedures, e.g., IP 367/96; BS2000 Pt 367 1996; EN ISO 4259; ISO 4259 1992, (partially overlaid).

Initial evidence is usually presented in a chaotic manner and it is important to establish a 'time line' of events as the first objective in analysing data. This is essential in any case but crucial with more than one vessel/vehicle or machine involved. It usually happens that several separate significant changes have taken place over similar time periods, thus a change in lubricant formulation may have occurred in the same time period as mechanical overhauls or replacements, and changes in operational and service patterns, Figure 1.

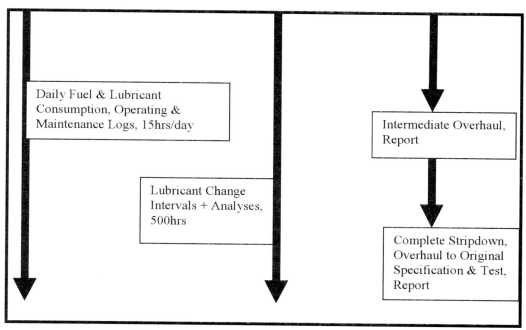

Figure 1. Time Lines for Operational and Wear Data.

Once a time line for a system problem, or separate time lines for parallel vessels, vehicles or machines, are established, then detailed documents can be requested, such as:

- **operating logs**, for patterns of fuel and lubricant service replenishment. Comments written by operators are very informative, knowing their system and its normal response. Perceived power reductions associated and noted with exhaust smoke emissions, with increased lubricant consumption noted later, indicate engine in-bore component deterioration,

- **service reports** and comments made on them. Almost all system operators have a form of condition monitoring and increasingly insurers require it. This usually includes hydraulic and lubricant sample analyses for trend analyses, particularly for wear metals, primarily for iron though other elements have secondary importance after trends are identified for iron. Sample analyses have a high level of accuracy whereas sampling intervals can sometimes be inconsistent, causing variable results. Analytical service laboratories comment on its reports if results exceed limits or increased over a pre-set percentage level. Responsible operators will address issues raised by the analytical results, thus a significantly enhanced wear metal result flagged to the operator suggests an 'early' (reduced time period, 100 hrs instead of, say, 250 hours) sample is submitted for analysis. Often, analytical records show the reduced time period sample indicates that the initial abnormal result was an 'outlier'. However, the same analytical laboratory comment persisting for sample after sample with messages of the ilk of:

'Water content too high, immediate action required to stop contamination/leak into system.'
together with sample particulate analysis consistently indicating a combination of soft cellulosic and hard particulate with high silica levels, indicating grit and dust ingress into the system, then system maintenance appears to be suspect, with third body tribology wear issues for the system,

- **overhaul reports** and comments are particularly useful, showing the components and work required to rebuild the engine or machine back to 'as new/refurbished' standard. For large diesel engines, re-honed cylinder bores are measured for being within specification, the honing process raising the centreline Ra value. If re-worked bores are within specification, then the actual bore wear in previous service use was very low, a good match of engine design and lubricant formulation.

- it is very relevant to read service repair reports that an intake feed valve was not opened after refitting a refurbished pump, causing seizure within 90 minutes, or that the intake feed pipe was fouled by a substantial blockage of cleaning cloths left in the system, causing similar machine failure.

- **evidence of damage** is very important. It is an additional burden to assess a case with no lubricant samples saved, or no reputedly damaged components available for inspection. It is usually the case that samples, lubricant or engine components are not preserved, as their importance to a claim for civil damage is not realised when damage occurs.

3. FAILURE OF HYDRAULIC PUMPS DUE TO AN ALLEGED INAPPROPRIATE FORMULATION OF HYDRAULIC OILS: CLAIM NO: 2004, FOLIO 314, QUEENS BENCH DIVISION, COMMERCIAL DIVISION, 'F.T.EVERARD & SONS LIMITED AND BP MARINE LIMITED' [2].

This case concerned intensively used small tankers transporting products from refineries to distribution European centres. Because of the cargo's flammable nature, ring main hydraulics power fill/discharge pumps and also power other units such as windlasses, cranes and bow thrusters. Up to three hydraulic pumps are driven by auxiliary engines in the engine room, engaged by flexible couplings, the other end of each engine drives alternators for on-board electrical power, each system consists of three in-line rotating elements. Focusing on the individual motive power units, each consists of a linear arrangement of coupled alternator, diesel engine and rotary piston pump on a bed plate.

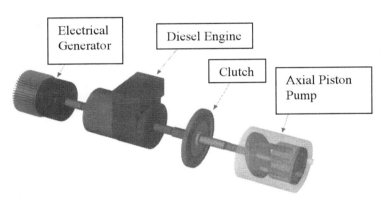

Figure 2. Arrangement of Vessel Hydraulic Pump, Auxiliary and Alternator.

The vessels suffered extensive pump damage which needed replacements and repairs, the cost of each replacement was significant but the loss of charter fees was much greater. From the time line sequences, there were two relevant changes at about this time:

- **first,** the supplier of hydraulic oil **A** from 1979 to 2000 changed its formulation slightly as part of product development. The new formulation, **B**, from 2000 had better performance by the relevant industrial tests. A subsequent complication was a change in industrial commercial collaboration where the hydraulic oil supplier no longer had a lubricant supplier partner, who had merged with another oil company. Hydraulic oil, **C**, formulated in 2001, used additives from a different supplier to be similar to Oil **B**, with the detailed additive compositions withheld, as is normal commercial practice. The initial hydraulic oils **A**, **B** and **C**, derive from a family of automotive lubricants, as is commonly preferred by certain hydraulic OEM's, but were then replaced by another oil, **D** in 2002 with a formulation based upon hydraulic oil practice, as is preferred by another group of OEM's. This latter oil was claimed to reduce damage to the pumps. Central to the plaintiff's claim was that the formulation of oils **B** and **C** were deficient in respect of their performance relative to the original oil and the subsequent oil D. It was also claimed that hydraulic oils **A** and **D** could withstand water contamination better than **B** and **C**. In short, oils **B** and **C** 'were not fit for purpose'.

- but second, the detailed time lines for the vessels show that at the same relevant time as the lubricant formulations were changed, the vessels had their auxiliary engines replaced in a foreign shipyard. Various 'events' noted as this time, such as cleaning cloths found in the hydraulic lines which blocked the input line to a pump and caused it to fail by excessive wear within 90 minutes. A similar event was caused by failure to open the feed flow valve to the pump from the return hydraulic oil return tank which caused pump mechanical failure.

The essential tribological point was if there was a difference between the performance of the four oil formulations. The hydraulic pumps were of rotary axial design, with output and direction of flow controlled by a swashplate, Figure 3. Examining the pump design and its components shows that the basic tribological actions of sliding and rolling apply.

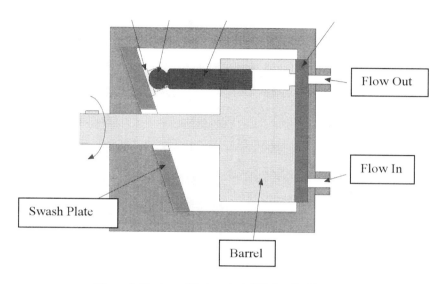

Figure 3. Design of Rotary Axial Hydraulic Piston Pump.

The response was:

(1) to consider manufacturer formulations and their performance specifications with the conclusion that oils B and C should have a superior performance to A and D,

(2) 'Used Oil Analyses' Reports of the vessel's oil samples for the relevant time period showed wear element levels were much lower than expected from comparable hydraulic systems, such as off-road construction vehicles, certainly lower than in i/c engines. But water and particulate levels were considerably higher than expected for hydraulic oils, primarily composed of sand and fibrous materials, indicative of atmospheric dust ingress, and repeatedly reported in the analytical reports.

(3) to commission a reputable laboratory to undertake various comparative tribological tests of the four oil formulations, for sliding and rolling actions. Eight samples were used, A-D both dry and wet with 0.6% water content, the water % content corresponding to the highest level found in the sample analyses:

- the **IP239 Four Ball EP and Wear** tests were chosen for sliding, separate but similar tests which measure different aspects of wear. For IP 239, using the IP 367/96 significance test, there is no significant difference between oils **A-D** (dry) and **A-C** (wet). A variation for **D** 'wet' is probably due to water separation in this oil, which it is designed to do. For the FourBall EP Test (IP239) the Initial seizure load (ISL), Mean Hertz load (MHL) (calculated by the 'Dobson method', IP239 Annex X2.) and Weld load (WL), showed no significant difference between the wet or dry **A-C** formulations. In all six cases, the performance of these oils is statistically superior to that of the wet or dry oil **D**,

- **the FZG test** was used for both dry and wet oils as a severe test of rolling and sliding wear, and specified in the current standard requirements of the hydraulic pump manufacturer, IP 334 procedure, A/8.3/90. A standard reference oil, RL 133/18, gave a failure load at stage 11, confirming satisfactory operation of the apparatus. There was no significant difference between wet and dry oils **A-C** but dry oil **D** gave a poorer result by three stages and 'wet' oil **D** could not be tested as 'steam generation' ejected the sample from the apparatus. The FZG performance of oils **A-C** at levels 10-11 was substantially in excess than the level 5/6 required for the oil in the hydraulic pump by the its manufacturer.

- the **DEFSTAN 91-110/1** single sample test was used as a further severe test for sliding wear but under high frequency reciprocating conditions. It contrasts the Four Ball Wear test which only determines wear when continually rotating in one direction, a difference issue which could used by astute counsel. There was no significant difference between the performance of oils **A** and **B**, and a significant positive improvement for **Oil C**. The performance of the 'wet' oils **A-C** was marginally better than their dry versions.

- the **Water Separation Test, ASTM D-1401**, a single test for dry samples only, addressed the issue of water contamination of the oils and separation, as argued by the plaintiffs. The procedure tests the ability of an oil and water mixture to separate into two layers in a set period of time. The results showed no difference between formulations **A-C**, where water remains suspended for the duration of the test, expected for hydraulic oils derived from lubricating oils where additives solubilise the water. Oil D, with a hydraulic oil-oriented formulation, separates from the added water in the demulsibility test.

The plaintiff's pleadings specifically stated that oils **B** and **C**, supplied and used subsequently to oil **A** had inferior lubricating properties, further, that they were inferior to Oil **D**. The results show that there is no significant difference in tribological and wear performance between the **A**, **B** and **C** oils. The plaintiffs stated that extensive and catastrophic damage occurred to the hydraulic pumps of their vessels. No assessment could be made of the damage claimed because debris samples and damaged components had not been retained. However, from the Used Oil Analysis reports of samples taken over a six year period from vessels using all four oils at different times, that had serious rubbing wear between pump components been taking place, such as might have lead to catastrophic damage of the sort complained of, this would have been preceded and accompanied by substantially enhanced levels of wear elements in the used oil samples. Such wear would have produced enhanced levels of wear elements. Moreover, there was no damage reported to the hydraulic motors of cargo pumps over that time.

On the basis of the tribological, wear and inferential evidence, the firm view taken was that there is no evidence for a causal relationship between the use of the B and C oils in the hydraulic pumps of the vessels and the reported pump damage. Further, there is no evidence that water held in suspension, up to and including 0.6% water by volume, significantly reduces the wear performance or efficiency of oils **A**, **B** or **C**, compared to oil **D**. Oils **B** and **C** are 'fit for purpose', dry or wet at the 0.6% water level. The firm view from the evidence available was that the (quite erratically sampled) analytical results properly identified water contamination early on in the vessels hydraulic systems as fresh water, not seawater. This is an important issue for hydraulic systems where water has deleterious effects. The Lubricant Analysis Service Reports continually urged and advised the vessel's operators to deal with water ingress and particle contamination problems, which they evdently did not heed nor act upon.

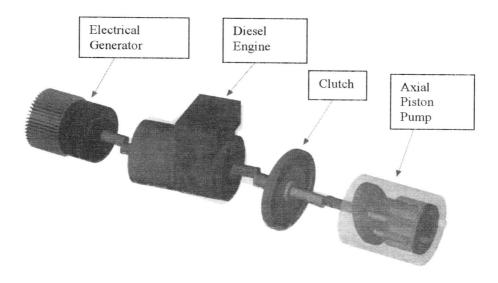

Figure 4. Misalignment of Pump/Engine/Alternator as a Cause of Wear.

However, clearly damage to the hydraulic pumps occurred. The explanation accepted by the court was that the catastrophic pump damage was a combination of mis-alignment of engine/pump/alternator when the engines were replaced in 2000 in a foreign shipyard (no alignment measurements of the system had been made, Figure 4, and also failure to control erratic operation of the swashplate, given as separate evidence by a mechanical/hydraulic control expert witness for the defence.

This case used standard established IP/ASTM tribological tests. Whilst tempting, to introduce a non-standard test, or worse, an ad-hoc test, to resolve an issue is usually disastrous unless there really is no alternative. Any such tests must be extensively referenced, otherwise, they will be demolished by competent counsel under cross examination in court, as advised by their respective expert tribology witness.

4. CASE 2 – EXCESSIVE WEAR/CATASTROPHIC DAMAGE TO VESSEL ENGINES

Background - four engines of two vessels operated very satisfactorily over extended overhaul periods for six years on a certain commercial lubricant formulation. The lubricant supplier then announced another formulation would be supplied which was 'the same but better', an interesting assurance, which was accepted by the vessels operators. Within nine months after introduction of the second oil, all four engines had progressively shown over a period of four months, month by month, either excessive wear as extensive bore polish or component failure in the form of seized and smashed pistons. Each engine was rebuilt by its manufacturer to original specification and rotated back into service, fortunately there was a fifth spare engine. Replacement of the second lubricant by a third, another, brand gave a further six years untroubled service. The suppliers of the second oil disclaimed responsibility, arguing poor seamanship by the operators, excessive time for service oil changes, unauthorised extension of the manufacturers recommended service interval and not using their analytical services for samples, etc. The case was unfortunately compounded by a lack of evidence in the form of used oil samples and damaged engine components, which had not been retained. The major part of the evidence was extensive Used Oil Analyses for wear elements and soot, etc., plus the detailed overhaul reports from the manufacturer, extensive maintenance and ship's logs and documentation contained within twenty large files. Arguments centred upon trends in wear elements, which can be variable and affected by sampling. However, the excessive wear/catastrophic engine problems occurred about 2000 hrs since the change of oil formulation, which gave 4 oil samples of 500hrs duration service interval at most.

When operated on the first lubricant, the manufacturers detailed overhaul reports noted the cleanliness, absence of deposits and freedom of piston ring rotation for the engines, together with small amounts of bore polish. Equally, they commented on the extensive carbonaceous bonded deposits on the piston components and general carbon deposition within the engine for the damaged engines, together with extensive bore polish. The final parameter, 'bore polish', is a difficult topic to discuss, every expert knows what it is, how it is caused and also prevented, but from different, often entrenched, viewpoints. Small amounts of each fresh lubricant were available, far short of the volumes needed for engine tests. Instrumental analysis of these samples showed a much reduced anti-oxidancy reserve for the second oil compared to the first and third lubricants. Electrochemical analyses of these fresh lubricants, RULER™, showed a reduced anti-oxidant additive composition for the second lubricant, supporting the reduction in anti-oxidancy reserve. Whereas the second lubricant had an improved performance, e.g., against bore polish, in the OM 364 A (CEC L-42-A-92) test, the extended service use period appeared to exhaust that improved performance before it was replaced. The pattern of service interval lubricant changes was the same for the three lubricants. It appeared that when the anti-oxidant reserve of the second oil was exhausted, hard carbon and varnish/gum formation resulted giving abrasive bonded deposits which exacerbated bore wear and polish.

But as an example of how evidence may suddenly become available, two used bores, pistons and rings for damaged engines were found in a metallurgy consultant's store close to the court appearance. Examination showed unusual patterns of wear for the bores and pistons. Ring grooves had extensive adhesive deposits and some rings were 'stuck'. The bores showed very unusual excessive wear above the limit of top ring travel for short sections on opposite sides, Figure 5. This excessive wear was matched by polished sections of the piston crown lands. The crown lands were rubbing on the top section of the bores. Examination of the 'stuck' rings showed that they 'tipped' the pistons at Top Dead Centre to contact and wear, the very top section of the bores.

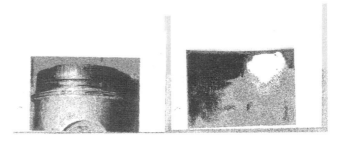

Figure 5. Unusual Wear Patterns in Bores and Pistons.

These photographs show the difficulty of presenting evidence to a court - it is far better to bring along damaged components. Whilst the damaged engine components samples were several years old, two small (10 µml) lubricant samples were obtained, just enough for an Infrared Analysis. Whilst there was good evidence of carbonyl oxidation, this was discounted because oxidation will occur for any oil film on a metal surface over an extended period. However, there was good evidence of nitration caused by a failure to prevent high temperature oxidation of the base oil by nitrogen oxides. This correlated with the soot and varnish/gum formed by oxidative degradation of the base oil, unprotected after a certain period of service for the second lubricant. In this very difficult case the assistance of excellent consulting marine engineering and metallurgy consultants was extremely helpful where areas of expertise overlapped to certain extents and yet expert witnesses could remain within their own disciplines. The shipping company's claim was settled prior to court by an agreed substantial payment without acceptance of liability by the supplier.

5. CONCLUSION

The initial remarks in this paper and the two case studies show how civil claims involving technical issues, particularly tribology, lubrication, wear and system damage can be very confused. They require objective and extensive evidential analysis to cut through to the tribological and other technical issues. Time lines are essential and further information is usually available on request. It is absolutely essential to remember that an 'expert witness' has a duty to the court to aid the understanding of technical issues in a case. There are clear rules, the Civil Practice Rules, and Code of Guidance on Expert Evidence [3] concerning the relationship between an expert witness, their client for whom they appear in support of, and the court. An expert witness must not be drawn out of their area of expertise to give a technical assessment nor be drawn into statements by counsel under cross examination not directly based on their discipline. At all times an expert tribological witness, as for other witnesses, must maintain the tribological truth and explain it in a manner suitable for lay people without that simplification becoming misleading.

REFERENCES

[1]   The Jost Report, UK Department of Education and Science, 'Lubrication (Tribology): Education and Research, HMSO, 1966.

[2]   F.T.Everard and British Petroleum, 2004, Folio 314, Queens Bench Division, Commercial Division, RCoJ, 2005.

[3]   The Civil Procedure Rules (CPR) 'Code of Guidance on Expert Evidence; A Guide for Experts and Those Instructing Them For The Purpose of Court Proceedings'; CPR Rule 35 'Practice Directions – Experts and Assessors, Supplement to Rule 35'. Working Party established by the Head of Civil Justice, December 2001, Lord Chancellors Department. (Similar rules have been developed and apply in other countries).

Oil Analysis as an Improvement Tool for the Behavior of Wind Turbine Gears. Main Problems Detected Through the Condition of the Lubricant

J. Terradillos [1], M. Bilbao [1], J. I. Ciria [1], A. Malaga [1], J. Ameye [2]

[1] Fundación Tekniker, Avda. Otaola, 20, 20600 Eibar, Spain
[2] FLUITEC Interenational, Nieuwbrugstraat 73 B-1830 Machelen Belgium

ABSTRACT

In the present framework of renewable energies, wind power energy has achieved a predominant place as a new driver in the green energies market. Nevertheless, this continuous growth has caused the appearance of many performance and reliability problems, related mainly to bad design and maintenance practices.

The suitable operation of a wind turbine mainly depends on the behavior of the gearbox. These gearboxes have planetary gears, and bearings that require some special attention due to their extreme operating conditions (temperatures, load, etc). In these conditions, lubricant and wear particles analysis is considered as the most efficient predictive/proactive tool to obtain the optimum performance of the wind turbine and its related equipment.

In this paper we will discuss the main related problems with the maintenance of these components through the oil analysis, based on the experiences achieved by the International Wearcheck© Group. The main lubricants issues are micropitting, foam and air inside the oil as well the remaining useful life of the lubricant.

Keywords: Oil analysis, condition monitoring, wind turbine gears

1. GEARBOX OIL SELECTION

Gearbox oil selection and accompanying maintenance practices are one of the main targets that should be obtained so that the system works in optimum conditions during its useful life.

Lubricant selection should be a shared responsibility between the end-user, the wind turbine manufacturer (OEM), the mechanical components manufacturer (bearings, etc.), the oil supplier, the filters supplier, etc.

Wind turbine gearboxes are characterized for their low work speeds and high and alternative loads. Because of that, it's necessary to use oils with extreme pressure additives (EP). The suitable base oils can be mineral or synthetic. The mineral fluids are products that are obtained from petroleum while the synthetic oils are manufactured through synthesis (PAO, Esters or PAG).

The new oil properties of a wind turbine gearbox should be according to the German specification DIN 51517 part 3 and with the following requirements (Table 1):

Table 1. Oil properties requirements of a wind turbine gearbox according to the German specification DIN 51517 part 3

Parameter	Standard	Limits
Viscosity Index	ISO 2909	Min. 90
Oxidation stability	ASTM-D2893-Mod.	Viscosity increase at 121ºC < 6%
Steel corrosion	ISO7120	Negative
Copper corrosion	ISO2160	<1B
Foam	ASTM-D892	75/10; 75/10; 75/10
FZG Scuffing	ISO 14635-1	>=12
Micropitting	FVA nº54	>=10
Filterability	AFNOR NF E48690 5 Microns	Pass
Particles	ISO 4406/99	16/14/11
FE 8	DIN 51819	<30 mgr /80 h
Brugger	DIN 51347	> 50 N/mm2
Air Release at 90ºC	ASTM-D 3427	< 15 minutes
Load wear	ASTM-D 2783	>250 Kg
Wear (1800rpm/20kg/54ºC/60min)		< 0,35 mm
Demulsibility at 82ºC	ASTM-D1401	< 15 Min.

1.1.   Micropitting

Micropitting is a surface damage that is shown in high rolling systems and is characterized by the presence of small holes in the surface showing an inner surface with cracks. First, they appear in the rolling zone of the gears and then progresses towards the root (dedendum) of the gear, the zone where really the gear works more.

Micropitting is not a new phenomenon although it has not received the right attention until now. Nevertheless it is known that it affects to the gear precision and, in many cases it is the first failure mode. Micropitting is a surface fatigue phenomenon that appears with Hertzian contacts, due to the stress of the cyclic contact and the plastic flow of the roughness. As result the formation of microcracks, micropitting and loss of material is found. Micropitting is also called fatigue scoring, flecking, spalling, glazing, frosting grey staining, microspalling, peeling ,...... (Figures 1 and 2)

Figure 1. Gears with micropitting along the rolling zone of a wind turbine gear

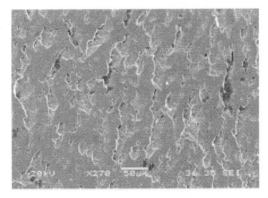

Figure 2. Picture of Micropitting of a wind turbine gear taken with a SEM.

1.1.1.   Elastohydrodynamic lubrication (EHL)

Micropitting appears in an elastohydrodynamic lubrication (EHL) system, where the thickness of the lubricant film is of the same order as the surface roughness, and the load is supported by the surface roughness and the lubricant. Under an elastohydrodynamic lubrication (EHL) regime, the lubricant almost changes in a solid, depending on the type of lubricant.

The film thickness depends on the behaviour of the oil to the shape, viscosity and speed of the contact surface. Higher loads cause an increase of the elastic zone without producing important changes in the geometry. Therefore the film is not affected by the load and elastic properties of the material.

Otherwise, the film thickness is very influenced by the speed of the incoming oil and by its viscosity. Also it depends on the gears temperature but not on the highest specific temperature, usually detected in the central area of the gear.

The central contact area is quite long. Once inside of it, the oil cannot escape because the viscosity is very high, the space and the contact time are very small. In general, the oil that goes through the contact zone is as a solid film with a uniform thickness. In the exit the oil recovers its initial characteristics at atmospheric pressure.

1.1.2.   Operational parameters to control against micropitting

a) Load

Load does not have a strong influence and consequently high loads do not mean that gear micropitting will occur.

b) Speed

Rolling speed is very important and beneficial as the film thickness of the oil increases with velocity. On the other hand, higher sliding speed generates more heat and increases the particles formation.

c) Temperature

Temperature is fundamental for the film thickness and the activation of the lubricant additives. The equilibrium temperature is established between the relation of the heat generated by friction and the heat dissipated by conduction and convention. The temperature of high speed gears can be much higher than the oil temperature supplied to the gears.

The resistance to micropitting decreases when the temperature of the gears increases. Nevertheless, some additives improve its behavior when this temperature increases. This is very important designing laboratory tests to evaluate micropitting.

To prevent micropitting the film thickness should be maximized, the surface roughness reduced and the lubricant properties (avoid additives EP aggressive, clean, low traction coefficient, ..) be optimized.

It has been shown that surface PVD processing of the gears as WC/C OR B-DLC improve the resistance of the gears to abrasion and macropitting in FZG standard tests. If the micro and macro processes are similar then micropitting improves. These coatings produce resistant and hard layers against wear and corrosion of the gears surface. Because of that, a reduction of the friction coefficient is shown. This is an advantage in poor lubrication conditions.

1.1.3.   Micropitting formation process

Initiation: The onset of fatigue cracks begins with the plastic deformation of the surface due to the roughness. Fatigue cracks begin by means of the cyclic contact and tensions by the accumulated plastic deformation.

Propagation: After fatigue cracks have been produced they grow and join. As result, a pit up to 10 microns will start to appear (negligible by the human eye).

The particles that are generated in a micropitting are about 1 micron (or smaller) up to 10 - 20 microns. These particles are difficult to eliminate with filters and act polishing the surface of the gears. It is very common to find polish wear type when a micropitting phenomenon is shown.

Micropitting is a surface damage appearing in high rolling systems and is characterized by the presence of small holes in the surface showing an inner surface with cracks. First, they appear in the rolling zone of the gears and then progresses towards the root (dedendum) of the gear, the zone where really the gear works more.

All gears are susceptible to suffer micropitting, included the external, internal, straight, helicoid, ... Micropitting can appearance in materials with heat treatments, included nitrurated, cemented, quenching, ...

It is not well understood why some oils are more prone to the formation of micropitting than others.

Micropitting causes the loss of the tooth profile, and potentially evolves to macropitting, tooth break, noise and vibrations. It is evident that Micropitting and Macropitting are fatigue processes with the only difference that micropitting is smaller. Metallographic analysis show that the cracks that are produced in micropitting and macropitting have the same morphology but with a very different size.

In many cases micropitting is not destructive for the gear surfaces, even their evolution can be stopped when the tribological conditions of the system are re-established. Sometimes micropitting can be eliminated by means of the polish of the gears during the rolling process. This is referred to a gear system which has produced its cure.

To evaluate the resistance of the new oils to micropitting following test can be applied:

- o   the accelerated gears test, FZG Micropitting test FVA54 I-IV and BGA micropitting test.

1.1.4.   Lubricant effect

The lubricant properties such as base oil, chemistry of the additives and viscosity affect micropitting. Micropitting tests show that the resistance to micropitting varies from some lubricants to others. Some lubricants are able to stop micropitting process once it has begun.

a) Base oils

Under elastohydrodynamic lubrication (EHL) conditions the lubricants solidify due to the high pressure, and the traction on the surface roughness is limited by the break tension of the solidified oil. There are considerable differences between the solidification pressure and the break tension of the different lubricants. Therefore, there are differences in the tractional properties.

PAG and Esters are products that have molecules with flexible ethers bonds and with a lower break tension value than hydrocarbons. Naphtenic oils are relatively rigid, based on compact molecules and they generate high traction, while Paraffin base-oil and PAO have linear and elastics molecules with a low traction coefficient. PAO and very refined oils obtained by non-traditional methods have a lower traction coefficient than oils refined by solvents. Many PAO are mixed with Esters to give a better solubility of the additives. Unfortunately, Esters are very hygroscopic and the resistance to micropitting of the PAO decreases very much.

Micropitting appears with mineral and synthetic oil, too. At high temperatures PAO and PAG have a elastohydrodynamic (EHL) thickness film greater, and therefore they have a greater resistance to micropitting than mineral oils with the same viscosity and additives. When the operating temperature is between 70 and 90° the differences between mineral oils and PAO are very small. However, PAG has a greater film thickness.

b) Additives

Antiscuffing additives are usually necessary but they can be very aggressive chemically and promote the generation of micropitting. Oils without antiscuffing additives have the maximum protection against micropitting.

Experiments have shown different conclusions and they have generated some conflicts on the influence of EP additives in the apparition of micropitting. Some tests show that oils with additives EP Sulfur-phosphorous (S-P) based favour the process of micropitting, while other tests show that these additives increase the resistance to micropitting.

The activation temperature of these additives can be one of the reasons why we see this kind of conflict. If the tests are carried out at different temperatures the behavior is different. This can be explained by the fact that all micropitting tests should be performed at the nearest temperature to the operating temperature. The typical standard test is the FVA 54 that is carried out to 90°C but, nowadays more lubricant-makers are characterizing the oil at 60°C.

1.1.5. Micropitting monitoring methods

There are few methods to control micropitting in gears in use. The main monitoring methods are visual inspections (boroscopy), oil analysis and destructive gear tests.

a) Visual inspections

The visual inspections are a good method of controlling micropitting in gears in use.

Appearance

The appearance is a change of tonality in the gear: matt, greyish, etc. This is a difficult test to be performed correctly.

Where to inspect?

Micropitting begins in the rolling zone of the gears due, mainly to the roughs that remain after the production of the gears. This is the reason why this phenomenon appears at the beginning of the machine life during the first million of cycles of the gears.

Micropitting begins at a surface contact in the edges of the gears where there are crests, waves, peaks, ... It is usually combined with other failure modes as severe adhesive wear (scuffing), macropitting and abrasion.

When the damage caused by micropitting varies from a tooth to another one is mainly due to the different geometry or to the surface rough of the teeth. Two similar gears in different windmill can vary the frequency of micropitting. For example, a couple of gears of 20/45 teeth can have a similar micropitting in each 5 teeth.

b) Oil analysis

Viscosity

Low viscosities result in the film thickness reduction and consequently the propagation of the cracks. Higher viscosities have greater resistance to micropitting as they achieve higher film thickness and therefore fewer tendencies to start the propagation of the cracks. Nevertheless, viscosity should be limited since very high viscosities increases the oil oxidation, loss of energy, greater wastes quantity, etc...

Therefore, viscosity should be calculated with great precision to preserve the components from all type of problems. Oil analysis shall not accept variations of the viscosity above ±10% of the new oil value.

The additives influence can ruin the effect of the viscosity. Therefore, increasing the viscosity will not eliminate micropitting when the base oil contained aggressive additives.

Particles

Solid particles larger than the EHL film can enter between the teeth gears due to the rolling effect. Once they enter they are subject to high pressures. The particles are fragile and they are broken in smaller particles, some are absorbed between the gears and others pass through the contact points.

The hard particles which are larger in size than the thickness will pass through the contact.

The small particles that enter in the contact zone cause bites in the gears and promote the formation of micropitting.

Particles than have not been eliminated in the manufacturing process should be eliminated immediately by the filters. It is very important that the oil is clean when we introduce it in the machine (Table 2).

Table 2. Oil cleanliness ISO code

Lubricant	Clean ISO 4406/99
New oil	16/14/11
Oil from the wind turbine - after manufacturing	17/15/12
Oil from the wind turbine – operating & in-service gearbox	18/16/13

The monitoring of the wear on the gears should be carried out to determine the presence, type, severity and development of the failure mechanism. This can be achieved by measuring the particle size distribution, particles aspect and generation ratio of the wear particles. This can be carried out by means of ferrography and the optical analysis (Lasernet End-C) (see Figure 3).

Particles analysis between 4 and 100 microns has shown to be very useful for detecting the failures mechanisms in a wide range of lubricating systems.

The Lasernet Fines-C instrument determinates the particles silhouette and can be classified in following categories:

> a) Cutting.
>
> b) Fatigue.
>
> c) Sliding.
>
> d) Non metallic.

The instrument will classify the wear particles depending on its silhouette, by the transmitted light used in the instrument. It cannot observe color, texture or other surface attributes. The classification of the silhouettes for the different types of wear is based on neural networks (Figure 3).

When the micropitting phenomenon starts to appear, the generated particles will move to the oil. Consequently, particle analysis of oil represents a very efficient diagnosis tool to evaluate the onset of fatigue processes.

The main particles types related to the fatigue process that appear in the oil are: micro-particles (micropitting), laminar particles, chunks and spheres.

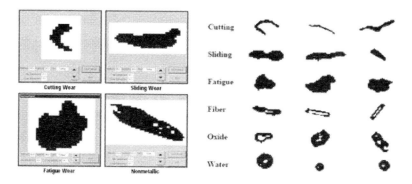

Figure 3. Wear and contamination particle morphology

<u>Micro-particles</u> are generated when the fatigue process begins, but they can not be classified with the eye at the surface of the bearing or gear. These micro-particles enter in the rolling zone and they become in laminar particles that vary their sizes between 10 and 30 microns.

In this first process, the micro-particle generation, little laminar particles and spheres are formed (Figure 4).

Figure 4. Laminar microparticles and little spheres of the fatigue onset

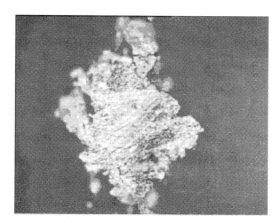

Figure 5. Fatigue laminar particle

These <u>little laminar particles</u> are very similar by its aspect to rubbing and rolling wear particles, but the relationship between large (>10 microns) and small (<10 microns) particles is much higher in the fatigue micro-particles area.

The second process is the generation of laminar fatigue particles which will start to appear when the pitting can be observed at the surface of the bearing or gear. This can be explained as micropitting process has been controlled and consequently has evolved into pitting. The particles have a size between 50 microns and several hundreds microns with a plate surface and an irregular edge/shape (Figure 5).

When the fatigue crack continues to evolve the subsurface will create large particulates, called chunky fatigue particles, with a 45° angle and a length to thickness of 10/1 (Figure 6).

Finally, the <u>spherical particles</u> associated to the fatigue phenomenon are usually appearing next to the large laminar particles and/or chunky particles. They are possibly the best indicator of the fatigue process. The spherical particles appear in other wear phenomena, too. In general, spheres of diameter <5 microns are related to fatigue and spheres of diameter > 5 microns are related to cavitations, sliding, etc phenomena (Figure 7).

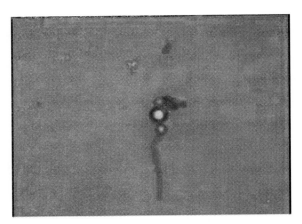

Figure 6. Chunky fatigue particle   Figure 7. Large spherical particle

Water

Many experiments have shown that water accelerates wear and oxidation. Blistering and fragilization phenomena (phenomenon created by the atomic hydrogen that enters between the cracks of the material forming molecules of hydrogen or combining with some metal) can be part a failure process. The maximum content of admissible water in a wind turbine gearoil should not exceed the 200 ppm. The combination of water with fine wear metals (<2 micron), are also a major accelerator of oxidation. Due to their high active surface, these fine wear metals will act as catalysts to accelerate the ongoing oxidation and aging process.

1.2.   Foam and Air Release of the lubricant

Foam formation and retention of air in the oil are two totally undesirable processes in windmill gears. They should be controlled and reduced to achieve optimal operating and working conditions for the wind turbine gear system.

There are many causes of an unacceptable level of foam in windmill gears. Some of them are due to the state of the oil and other to the mechanical nature of the gears. A mechanical problem can be associated with excessive agitation or with too low an oil level. If the foam disappears quickly when the equipment shuts down, the problem may be related to a mechanical problem or the antifoam additives have depleted. According to Jim Fitch in his article "Using oil analysis to monitor the depletion of antifoaming additives" the problems with the foam can be classified as following:

Table 3. Foam related problems

	Air release (ASTMD3427)	Foam stability (ASTMD892)
Mechanical problem	Identical to new oil	Identical to new oil
Air retained problems	Increase regarding due to new oil	Identical to new oil
Additive depleted or ineffective	Increase regarding to new oil	Increase regarding to new oil

To eliminate the foam the following factors should keep in mind:

- ***Filling method***

The filling of the reservoirs is crucial. It is advised to add the oil with a hose immersed in the reservoirs to avoid to introduction of air. When an operator fills a new deposit, the air can remain trapped in the dead zones. Because of that a purge should be done. The suitable procedure is to empty the reservoir with a vacuum pump and to maintain the vacuum during the filling of the reservoir.

- ### *Predictive-Proactive maintenance programs*

The recommended preventive maintenance tasks include the revision of the o-rings, visual inspections, oil level control, control filters,....

Proactive maintenance is a good tool to eliminate the foam through:

- Cleanliness control
- Humidity elimination
- Excellent oil filtration practices
- Immediate Contaminants removal

If in spite of carrying out some good maintenance practices, the foam still persists the air intake should be located and to eliminate it.

- ### *Reservoir design*

The design is usually the most important factor that produces oil foam. The main problems are:

- The return line is over the oil level.
- The reservoir is too small.

The tank should have a capacity between 5 and 10 times the flow of the pump or in sprinkling lubricated systems is recommended 0,4 l/kW.

- The oil level in the reservoir is low
- The mobile parts of the system introduce air.

- ### *Lubricant selection*

There are big differences in the behavior between the different oils. Some of them can accumulate large quantities of retained air but will release it quickly, while others permit the income of small quantities but will have a very slow air release. According to good lubricant manufacturing practices, the lubricant should be highly resistant to the air intake and not retain the bubbles after they have being formed. The oils with the best properties are synthetic fluids and the hydrocracked oils.

The maximum acceptable foam levels for an in-service oil, according to ASTM-D 892, should not be higher than the values in the table 4 below:

Table 4. Maximum acceptable foam levels for in-service oil (ASTM-D 892).

Temperature	Formation (5´ blown)	Stability (10´ stand)
24ºC	100	10
93,5ºC	200	20
24ºC	100	10

The content of retained air should not be over 25% related to the new one, according to ASTM- D3427.

1.3. Remaining Useful Life (RULER Method - ASTM D-6971)

One of the main important issues with the windmill gear oils is applying the correct technical criteria, addressing and monitoring the oil oxidation and degradation, in order to establish the correct oil drain interval. The answer to this question has to be found into the basic characteristic of modern Maintenance Techniques, requiring Root Cause Failure analysis. In order to extend fault free machine life, trending of oxidative health or antioxidants concentration, will be able to look at the root causes of lubricant failures.

By means of laboratory test the onset of oil degradation mechanism can be defined, by measuring the AN (ASTM-D 664), Kinematic viscosity (ASTM-D 445) etc.. The oil change criteria is when the AN of the used oil is above 1 related to the new one. This is a predictive/reactive method and give us a very important information.

Another technical criteria to monitor the oil oxidation, is the Remaining Useful Life of an oil through the control of the antioxidant additives. By monitoring the antioxidants, lubricant operators will detect in advance additive failure and logically avoid oxidation, acid formation, thickening, varnishing, and bearing lubricant starvation.

Organic (weak) acids are produced during oxidation, and they can result in corrosion damage in the long-term. Typically acid concentration is measured by tests like Acid Number (AN). As a second indicator or signal from heavy lubricant degradation exists the viscosity increase, which is a direct result from the polymerization (chain formation) between hydrocarbon (base-oil) chains, enhanced by the oxidation products.

And herein lays the major benefit by monitoring the antioxidant concentration or the Remaining Useful Life (RUL), as users will be able to look forward (rather than backward) by being reactive on changes of parameters like viscosity, acid number (AN) or oxidation by FTIR (FTIR-Ox).

The main drawbacks of techniques like AN, viscosity and FTIR-Ox is their inability to predict the operating time from when the analyzed fluid was sampled until a fluid change will become necessary due to additive depletion, i.e. these techniques like AN, Viscosity, FTIR-Ox can not predict the remaining useful life of a fluids. In addition to that AN-analyses are affected by the operating conditions of the equipment or by the additives, e.g. ZDDP concentration affects AN values.

This is why in contrast to fluid degradation techniques, techniques which routinely monitor the antioxidant concentration are able to look forward, predict the operating time, depending on the operating conditions.

Each trend of antioxidant depletion will be reflecting the characteristic and different operating conditions, enabling operators to look at the root causes for possible abnormal conditions.

As wind turbine gear oils will be degrading through oxidation as a combinational effect between the presence of water (air), metallic contamination, and temperature increase, antioxidants will be consumed.

Modern generation of gear lubricating oils apply different classes of antioxidants, covering aromatic (di) amines, phenols, phenates, carbamates, salicylates, and ZDDP. These antioxidant additives will work synergistically, to optimize the oxidative performances of existing new generation of gear lubricating oils. Hence it will be important to address their total concentration, as a direct measurement of their oxidative health.

This it can be obtained by applying the Voltammetric (RULER) technique (ASTM D-6971), which provides a value of the Remaining Useful Life in few minutes.

The RULER technique belongs to the category of proactive techniques and is used to control the in-service new generation of gear lubricating oils.

The RULER© determines quantitative the Remaining Useful Life of a lubricant by measuring the remaining concentration of antioxidants. The rate of antioxidant depletion vs. time (Antioxidant Depletion Trend) can be monitored and used to predict the right oil change intervals. Besides, it can be used to determine abnormal operating conditions before the base oil is starting to degrade excessively, and the machine fails. Based on several field experiences, as well correlation studies with other oxidative analytical test data, the critical value for a windmill gear lubricating oil appears to correspond with 20% of the initial total antioxidants concentration (or 20% RUL).

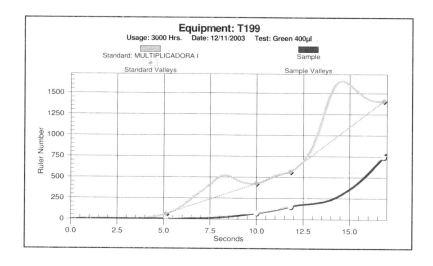

Figure 8. Voltammetric (RULER) test results for an In-service windmill gear oil (PAG)

Table 5. Results for PAG aged oil samples for 3000 hours under laboratory conditions

PAG OIL	NEW	3000 Hours In lab.
Viscosity at 40ºC (cSt)	314.21	348.97
Viscosity at 100ºC (cSt)	54.32	61.35
TAN (mgKOH/g)	0.28	4.12
Ruler (%)	100	11

2. ANALYTICAL PROGRAM AND WIND TURBINE GEAR OILS TYPICAL VALUES

Table 6. Predictive-Proactive maintenance program through oil analysis and recommended limit values

Parameter	Routine	Typical value	Caution value	Alarm value
Viscosity at 40ºC	Normal	New oil	+/-10%	+/-15%
Viscosity at 100ºC	Normal	New oil	+/-10%	+/-15%
AN	Normal	New oil	+0.related to new oil	+1 related to new oil
Viscosity Index	Normal	New oil	+/-10 related to new oil	+/- 15 related to new oil
Water (ASTM D6304)	Normal	<50 ppm	200 ppm	400 ppm
Nitration (FTIR)	Normal	<1 abs/cm	<5 abs/cm	<10 abs/cm
Oxidation (FTIR)	Normal	<1 abs/cm	<5 abs/cm	<10 abs/cm
Particle counter	Normal	17/15/12	19/17/14	20/18/15
PQI	Normal	50	80	>80
Sinicism (ASTMD5185)	Normal	<10 ppm	<20 ppm	>20 ppm
Iron (ASTMD5185)	Normal	<40 ppm	<60 ppm	>60 ppm
Copper (ASTMD5185)	Normal	<10 ppm	<20 ppm	>20 ppm
Chromium (ASTMD5185)	Normal	<10 ppm	<20 ppm	>20 ppm
Lead (ASTMD5185)	Normal	<10 ppm	<20 ppm	>20 ppm
Tin (ASTMD5185)	Normal	<10 ppm	<20 ppm	>20 ppm

Parameter	Routine	Typical value	Caution value	Alarm value
Aluminum (ASTMD5185)	Normal	<10 ppm	<20 ppm	>20 ppm
Nickel (ASTMD5185)	Normal	<10 ppm	<20 ppm	>20 ppm
Additive metals (ASTMD5185)	Normal	>50% related to new oil	<50% related to new oil	<40% related to new oil
Foam	Exceptional	75/10 75/10 75/10	100/10 200/20 100/10	>100/10 >200/20 >100/10
Air release	Exceptional	<15 min.	+20% related to new oil	+25% related to new oil
RULER	Exceptional	>50% related to new oil	>25% related to new oil	<25% related to new oil
Lasernet Fines	Advisable	No particles	Medium	High
Analytical Ferrography	Exceptional	No particles		

3. PRACTICAL CASE STUDIES

Oil Condition Monitoring in the wind turbine industry can have a large impact, certainly if we take into account the growth of wind turbine-generated power in the last 10 years. Many field-operating failures are a direct consequence of gearbox bearing failure, as load factors can reach quite large extreme values..

What are the lubrication applications on a wind turbine?

- Gearbox lubricants -connecting low-speed shaft to high-speed shaft to produce electricity
- Greases on main gearbox and generator
- Hydraulic fluids

Wind turbines can have large reservoirs that can contain up to 150 l of oil for large wind turbines, with oil lifetime approaching 12 months.

With the latest trend of wind turbine parks, proactive measurement of the RUL of the lubricants becomes the new maintenance strategy, rather than the reactive strategy based on measuring acid number or viscosity as main parameter for oxidation.

The main stress factors for wind turbine gearbox oils are:

- temperature – local overheating on the bearing surfaces
- water (mainly from condensates), and
- particle contamination,

These are parameters to be continuously monitored – resulting in high filtration levels and use of vacuum dehydration equipment (to keep the water below a level of approx. 250 ppm).

What is the direct result of oxidation? Formation of deposits, due to oxidation on the bearing surfaces.

Gearbox lubricants have to be seen as oil circulation systems, where large quantities of heat must be removed, and where strong contamination of the oil in service occurs. These oils must possess good water and air separation properties and retain excellent to high oxidation stability over a long period of time.

Type of gearbox lubricants

We can clearly see an evolution from the mineral type of gearbox lubricants, towards synthetic long-life fluids for the larger wind turbines (> 1MW). As these windmills are getting bigger and bigger, but not necessarily the oil reservoir, the lubricant is working at higher temperatures and needs higher oxidative protection.

Mostly these fluids apply mixtures of ashless antioxidants in order to enhance high temperature oxidative protection. Figure 9 below shows a typical graph from a 1,5MW wind gear lubricant, after 36 months of operating time and show high depletion of phenols (AO at 15 seconds), and still having high RUL through antioxidant protection by aromatic amines. Figures 15 and 16 are good examples of difference in RUL or antioxidant depletion based on the same lubricant and antioxidant technology, but reflecting different operating conditions.

Case wind turbine power generation plant: a large wind turbine operator in Europe decided in 2000 to included RUL data as part of their condition based drain program. Before including the RUL the service company received 2 times a year an oil analysis report showing TAN, viscosity, particle counting, water and spectro-analytical analysis for wear metals, for the majority of their gearbox lubricating oils.

As the plant had experienced positive experiences from portable particle counters, and water analyzers (Karl Fisher titration), resulting in optimized lubricant use, the missing link for the wind turbine operator was the information on (remaining) oxidation life. The plant had invested significantly in fine filtration (3 and 6 micron absolute), as well in vent filters to avoid water entering the lubricants reservoir.

Based on the integration of the RULER, as part of the oil monitoring program, the following improvements to the on-site condition-monitoring program were established:

- *Quality control* of all incoming oil batches for RUL estimation

- *Used oil analysis* for all gearbox lubricants (and some cases greases and hydraulic fluids)

- Oil analysis frequency was adapted in function of the RUL% (higher than 50% RUL / every 6 months sampling – for RUL% between 25 – 50 % every 2-4 months – critical limit at 20% RUL).

- Data were correlated with particle counting and water monitoring, and the plant operators were able to trend life of the oil.

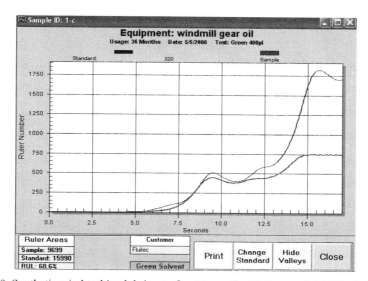

Figure 9. Synthetic wind turbine lubricant after 36 months lifetime on 1.5 MW windturbine

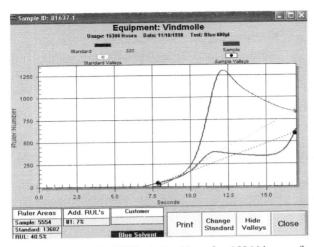
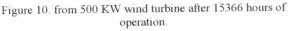

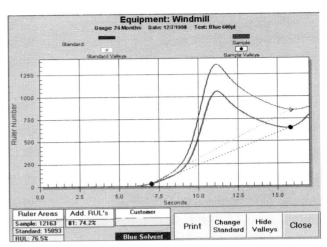

Figure 10. from 500 KW wind turbine after 15366 hours of operation.

Figure 11. 320 cST lubricant from 1 MW Wind turbine after 24 Months been in service.

The savings from this can be significant:

> *Lubricant savings* => on-site oil analysis achieved significant savings in oil life extension – with the higher price for synthetic lubricants
>
> *Maintenance savings* => by detecting proactively potential equipment problems (trend analysis) figures not included, but on-site condition monitoring program allowed to plan maintenance = significant cost reduction – downtime costs. Especially with wind turbines were accessibility can be a problem (off-shore).

For wind turbine gear lubricant the economical contribution to the on-site condition-monitoring program has to be situated on 4 levels:

- Making the right decisions, on the right time, and for the appropriate equipment maximizing oil life without compromising equipment & components.

- Off-shore requirements need proactive information - especially with the new generation oils for offshore, where life time of 3 years is expected.

- Biodegradable lubricants – ashless AO formulation for long-life applications have a high need of RUL monitoring, as oxidative acids

- Greases need also condition monitoring by monitoring the RUL, to enhance maintenance decisions based on oxidative health.

4. CONCLUSIONS

- To prevent micropitting the lubricant film thickness should be maximized, surface roughness reduced and the properties of the lubricant optimized by avoiding aggressive EP additives, maintaining fluid cleanliness during its useful life, and using lubricants with low traction coefficient.
- Once the correct lubricant is selected, the lubricant must be kept clean and dry at a desired temperature.
- Correct lubricant selection will extend the useful life of the machine components as well the lubricant itself. The selection of the lubricant is critical, and should result from a consensus decision between the machine manufacturer (OEM), and suppliers of turbine components, filters, lubricant and additives.
- The main problems generated in the lubricant (micropitting, foam/air release, lubricant degradation & oxidation) can be controlled through oil analysis, as part of best

predictive/proactive maintenance practices that guarantee an optimum performance of the wind turbine gear.

- Studying the particles in the oil can determine the severity of wear of windmill gears. A good routine analytical program should include more than conventional analysis by including the physical-chemical characterization, contaminant analysis, the metals content, and the evaluation of the particles, to obtain optimum performance of the oil analysis program.
- The recommended oil analysis frequency is every 6 months. It is very important to maintain this frequency in order to establish well defined (fail or acceptance) criteria as part of modern predictive maintenance strategies leading to an optimized (and economical) drain oil interval.
- The right selection of the sampling ports is a critical factor in order to study trend results and undertake particles analysis of the lubricating oil.
- Finally, it is very important for the maintenance staff to be trained correctly to carry out in situ inspections when taking oil samples.

REFERENCES

[1] "Full Synthetic Industrial Gear Oil Performance Report-Lubrizol Technical Report 5085-Turbines". *Lubrizol*, February 2004.

[2] "Lubrizol Technical Report 5048-Gear Oils". *Lubrizol*, February 2004.

[3] "Foam, the whole truth-up to now", *News from the C.C: Jensen Group*, nº2, March 2003.

[4] Verbruggen TW. "Wind Turbine Operation & Maintenance based on Condition Monitoring". Final Report, April 2003.

[5] Kempkes D., Aceites ecológicos para multiplicadoras. *Energética*, July/August 2003.

[6] Ding J. "Determining Fatigue Wear Using Wear Particle Analysis Tools". Practicing Oil Analysis, September/October 2003.

[7] Errichello R., Muller J., "Limpieza del aceite en cajas de engranajes de turbinas de viento", http://ccjensen.com/, 2002

[8] AGMA/AWEA 6006-AXX 6/05. "Standard for Design and Specification of Gearboxes for Wind Turbine Generator Systems", 2002.

[9] "Recommendation to Comply with the requirements in the Technical Criteria for the Danish Approval Scheme for Wind Turbines", *The Danish Energy Agency*, February 2002.

[10] "Informe Técnico. Cepsa Aerogear", *CEPSA Lubricantes S.A.*, February 2002.

[11] Walsh D., "Gear lube Test Slate Selection", *Practicing Oil Analysis*, March/April 2002

[12] Errichello R., Muller J., "Oil Cleanliness in Wind Turbine Gearboxes", *Machinery Lubrication*, July/August 2002, pp. 34-40

[13] Barr D., "Modern Wind Turbines: A Lubrication Challenge", *Machinery Lubrication*, September/October, 2002

[14] Errichello, R., "Selecting and Applying Lubricants to Avoid Micropitting on Gear Teeth", *Practicing Oil Analysis*, November/December, 2002.

[15] Errichello R., Muller J., "How to analyse Gear Failures", *Practicing Oil Analysis*, January/February, 2001

[16] Dempsey, P.J., "Gear Damage Detection Using Oil Debris Analysis", *NASA/TM-2001-210936*, September 2001

[17] Duncanson M., "Controlling Oil Aeration and Foam", *Practicing Oil Analysis*, November/December 2001, pp. 44-49

[18] Gold P.W., el al., "Expertise: Air Bubbles in Lubricating Oil", *IME*, October 2001

[19] Erricholli, R., "Friction, Lubrication and Wear of Gears. Friction and Wear of Components", pp. 535-545

[20] "Industrial Gear Oils. Presentation Chevron/Texaco Global Lubricants"

Evaluation of Tribological behaviour in journal bearing using Coast Down Time analysis

R. E. Browne [1], A. K. M. De Silva [2], K. P. Ramachandran [1], D. K. Harrison [2]

[1] Department of Mechanical & Industrial Engineering, Caledonian College of Engineering, PO Box No 2322, CPO Seeb, PC 111, Sultanate of Oman.
[2] School of Engineering Science and Design, Glasgow Caledonian University, City Campus, Cowcaddens Road, Glasgow G4 0BA.

ABSTRACT

The tribological behaviour could be effectively monitored through CDT (Coast Down Time) analysis. The CDT monitoring has been conducted on a horizontal rotor system with a full journal bearing for different lubricants under different pressures. When the power supply is cut off to any rotor system, the entire momentum gained through the sustained operation will dissipate and the system will come to halt. The time elapsed between the power cut-off and the system to halt is defined as CDT (Coast Down Time). The characteristic plots drawn between RPM and CDT resemble the Stribeck Curve which attributes the potential benefit of using CDT as a useful parameter for condition monitoring. The performance is compared with steady state vibration analysis in order to emphasize the potential benefit of using CDT as a useful diagnostic parameter for condition monitoring.

Keywords: Coast down time, Coast down time phenomenon, vibration, tribology, condition–based maintenance, diagnostic parameter, deceleration.

1. INTRODUCTION

In order to maximize the life of the rotating machineries condition based maintenance has been accepted and has been found more effective and cost- efficient. Most modern industries practice a condition monitoring programme which integrates vibration analysis and oil analysis. By measuring and analyzing the vibration of rotating machinery, it is possible to determine the severity of the defect hence the machine's failure could be predicted [1]. Vibration signature analysis offers information on the progress of machine degradation and incipient failures. It also serves as a base line reference signature for future comparative diagnosis [2]. Continuous oil and wear analysis can provide early information on wear modes and condition of the machinery. Tribo monitoring is found to be more efficient and reliable technique for any rotating machinery which is supported between bearings [3]. The performance of the journal bearing is very much dependent upon the functional characteristics of lubrication related to basic properties like viscosity, density, operating speed and thermal effects [4, 5]. The main purpose of the maintenance programme is to achieve optimum bearing life. Failure free running of any rotor system depends on the maintenance programme adopted on bearings. It is important to evaluate the performance of the bearing by efficient techniques and methods which support proper diagnosis and assessment of mechanical degradation, lubricant performance and lubricant deterioration for a journal bearing [6]. In order to increase equipment availability, the most reliable and efficient method of condition monitoring needs to be adopted for fault detection and failure prediction.

When the power supply to any rotor system is cut off, the system will begin to loose its momentum gained during the sustained operation and come to a permanent stop. The behaviour of a rotating system after the power is cut off is known as coast down time phenomenon (CDP). The exact time that is elapsed between the power cut-off and the system coming to a permanent stop is known as coast down time (CDT) [7, 8]. CDT has been found as an indicative parameter for the tribological behaviour and could be used as an effective diagnostic parameter for monitoring the performance of the lubricant [9]. In this paper the effects of bearing lubrication under different operating pressures for different lubricants have been experimentally analysed using CDT as a diagnostic parameter.

2. EXPERIMENTAL SET-UP

The experimental set-up shown in the Figure 1 has been used for this investigation. A rotor weighing 800 grams is fixed at the centre of 10 mm shaft, which is supported between an anti-friction bearing at the motor end and journal bearing at the non drive end. A preload frame consisting of a ball bearing supported by three radial springs under tension to minimize the effect of oil whirl / whip has been used between the rotor and drive end support but closer to rotor. Lubricant under investigation is circulated through the journal bearing by means of a gear pump. The drive to the rotor is generated by a variable speed AC motor. Instrumentation with built in RS -232 interfaces, having an update time of 195 milliseconds is used to record CDT. A Bal Pac 1200 vibration data collector along with velocity probe are used for measuring the steady state vibration. Data collector measures the vibration amplitudes and automatically plots the vibration spectrum over a range of frequencies.

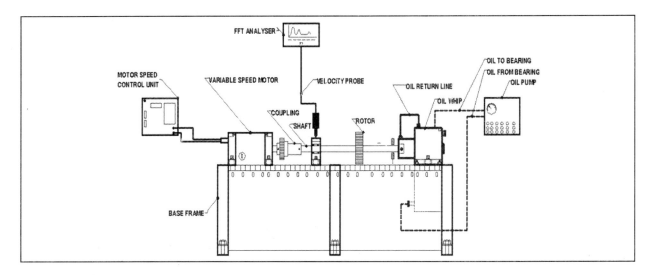

Figure 1. Experimental Set-up

The critical speed of the rotor system was computed to be 6000rpm. Three different oils (SAE 40, SAE 90 and SAE 140) have been used for the experiments. Experiments were conducted for different cut-off speeds selected in such a way that the lubricant behaviour during deceleration could be studied. Different cut-off speeds (1000 rpm, 2000 rpm, 3000 rpm, 4000 rpm and 5000 rpm) were selected to run the rotor system and allowed to attain the sufficient momentum with the selected lubricant under investigation with an operating oil pressure for a considerable amount of time. Three oil pressures 80kPa, 100 kPa and 120 kPa were selected for investigation. During sustained operation of the rotor system, vibration data have been obtained on both the drive end and non drive end (journal bearing end) in vertical and horizontal axes. At the desired cut-off speed, by tripping the power supply to the motor the speed change on the rotor was recorded using the instrumentation during the deceleration period till the rotor system reached to a complete stop.

2.1. SPECIFICATION OF JOURNAL BEARING

Length of the journal = 25.4 mm

Diameter of the journal = 25.06 mm

Diameter of the journal bearing = 25.38mm

Clearance of the bearing = 0.3mm

3. RESULT AND DISCUSSION

The CDT in milliseconds for different lubricants (SAE 40, SAE 90 and SAE 140), at different oil pressures (80kPa, 100kPa and 120kPa) and for different cut-off speeds (1000 rpm,200rpm,300rpm,4000rpm and 5000rpm) were obtained. The steady state vibration of the rotor system was recorded at different locations (motor end and journal end on both vertical and horizontal axes) with the corresponding CDT values which are given in the Table 1-3.

Table 1. CDT and Vibration Data -80kPa.

Axes at which vibration readings taken	Cut-off Speed in RPM	SAE 40					SAE 90					SAE 140				
		Time	Displacement		Velocity		Time	Displacement		Velocity		Time	Displacement		Velocity	
		CDT Sec	JE mm	ME mm	JE mm/s	ME mm/s	CDT Sec	JE mm	ME mm	JE mm/s	ME mm/s	CDT Sec	JE mm	ME mm	JE mm/s	ME mm/s
Vertical	1000	1.56	0.0011	0.0013	0.283	0.243	1.56	0.0000	0.0000	0.0312	0.0212	1.365	0.0013	0.0013	0.228	0.247
Horizontal			0.0013	0.0013	0.278	0.278		0.0002	0.0006	0.0271	0.0211		0.0015	0.0012	0.289	0.269
Vertical	2000	2.535	0.0011	0.0034	0.321	0.381	2.73	0.0000	0.0001	0.0042	0.104	2.535	0.0009	0.0014	0.255	0.262
Horizontal			0.0024	0.0015	0.345	0.352		0.0002	0.0001	0.0573	0.0087		0.0012	0.0011	0.245	0.240
Vertical	3000	3.315	0.0048	0.0017	0.649	0.367	3.9	0.0024	0.0012	0.510	0.456	3.51	0.0052	0.0017	0.752	0.414
Horizontal			0.0011	0.0026	0.255	0.468		0.0004	0.0020	0.463	0.505		0.0014	0.0036	0.275	0.550
Vertical	4000	4.686	0.0017	0.0046	0.419	0.538	4.686	0.0003	0.0044	0.2 13	0.406	4.485	0.0018	0.0011	0.402	0.310
Horizontal			0.0033	0.0022	0.493	0.536		0.0011	0.0016	0.260	0.531		0.0015	0.0019	0.386	0.387
Vertical	5000	6.24	0.0032	0.0041	0.443	0.646	6.240	0.0030	0.0035	0.329	0.523	5.655	0.0029	0.0047	0.564	0.627
Horizontal			0.0032	0.0029	0.469	0.496		0.0028	0.0016	0.360	0.563		0.0032	0.0019	0.550	0.501

JE- Journal End: ME- Motor End: CDT – Coast Down Time.

Table 2. CDT and Vibration Data -100kPa..

Axes at which vibration readings taken	Cut-Off Speed in RPM	SAE 40					SAE 90					SAE 140				
		Time	Displacement		Velocity		Time	Displacement		Velocity		Time	Displacement		Velocity	
		CDT Sec	JE mm	ME mm	JE mm/s	ME mm/s	CDT Sec	JE mm	ME mm	JE mm/s	ME mm/s	CDT Sec	JE mm	ME mm	JE mm/s	ME mm/s
Vertical	1000	1.56	0.0012	0.0012	0.309	0.289	1.365	0.0000	0.0001	0.0324	0.0228	1.17	0.0011	0.0013	0.321	0.314
Horizontal			0.0014	0.0013	0.307	0.280		0.0002	0.0005	0.0303	0.0222		0.0013	0.0014	0.307	0.308
Vertical	2000	2.34	0.0012	0.0013	0.336	0.346	2.535	0.0000	0.0001	0.0114	0.0751	2.34	0.0012	0.0016	0.311	0.301
Horizontal			0.0014	0.0012	0.304	0.328		0.0004	0.0005	0.0841	0.0122		0.0014	0.0012	0.275	0.287
Vertical	3000	3.315	0.0045	0.0017	0.621	0.388	3.315	0.0031	0.0013	0.527	0.250	3.12	0.0052	0.0019	0.712	0.435
Horizontal			0.0014	0.0037	0.263	0.409		0.0008	0.0022	0.481	0.518		0.0013	0.0032	0.306	0.537
Vertical	4000	4.485	0.0013	0.0011	0.372	0.333	4.290	0.0013	0.0050	0.258	0.537	4.095	0.0017	0.0012	0.392	0.330
Horizontal			0.0017	0.0017	0.403	0.447		0.0012	0.0017	0.274	0.555		0.0019	0.0019	0.395	0.450
Vertical	5000	5.265	0.0019	0.0021	0.479	0.472	5.46	0.0032	0.0037	0.324	0.531	5.07	0.0026	0.0033	0.482	0.522
Horizontal			0.0022	0.0019	0.497	0.503		0.0030	0.0018	0.453	0.589		0.0025	0.0017	0.479	0.459

JE- Journal End: ME- Motor End: CDT – Coast Down Time.

Table 3. CDT and Vibration Data -120kPa..

Axes at which vibration readings taken	Cut-off Speed in RPM	SAE 40					SAE 90					SAE 140				
		Time	Displacement		Velocity		Time	Displacement		Velocity		Time	Displacement		Velocity	
		CDT Sec	JE mm	ME mm	JE mm/s	ME mm/s	CDT Sec	JE mm	ME mm	JE mm/s	ME mm/s	CDT Sec	JE mm	ME mm	JE mm/s	ME mm/s
Vertical	1000	1.56	0.0014	0.0012	0.313	0.290	1.56	0.0002	0.0003	0.0395	0.0232	1.17	0.0012	0.0012	0.362	0.346
Horizontal			0.0015	0.0013	0.288	0.299		0.0005	0.0008	0.0316	0.0236		0.0014	0.0015	0.333	0.350
Vertical	2000	2.535	0.0013	0.0016	0.314	0.305	2.34	0.0001	0.0013	0.0238	0.126	2.34	0.0012	0.0016	0.321	0.300
Horizontal			0.0015	0.0013	0.283	0.277		0.0005	0.0009	0.0863	0.0306		0.0015	0.0013	0.272	0.277
Vertical	3000	3.51	0.0042	0.0023	0.715	0.405	3.51	0.0038	0.0014	0.536	0.330	3.12	0.0053	0.0016	0.728	0.426
Horizontal			0.0014	0.0035	0.301	0.562		0.0011	0.0027	0.511	0.697		0.0013	0.0030	0.269	0.550
Vertical	4000	4.485	0.0013	0.0011	0.344	0.280	4.290	0.0016	0.0059	0.335	0.548	3.9	0.0018	0.0012	0.423	0.420
Horizontal			0.0017	0.0019	0.387	0.449		0.0015	0.0022	0.337	0.560		0.0019	0.0020	0.466	0.536
Vertical	5000	5.265	0.0017	0.0014	0.401	0.352	4.875	0.0038	0.0039	0.354	0.568	5.07	0.0024	0.0032	0.475	0.507
Horizontal			0.0018	0.0016	0.473	0.449		0.0034	0.0019	0.465	0.628		0.0022	0.0017	0.491	0.485

JE- Journal End: ME- Motor End: CDT – Coast Down Time.

Data from the above tables indicate that the SAE 90 oil performance at 80KPa has shown a higher CDT value with less steady state vibration. Figure 2 illustrates the typical CDT curve for journal bearing. The frictional resistance of lubricant with any rotating system has been clearly represented by three different lubrication regimes. It is observed that the CDT curve has two transition regimes. One transition regime is found between the boundary lubrication regime and elastohydrodynamic lubrication regime and the other transition regime is found between elastohydrodynamic lubrication regime and hydrodynamic lubrication regime which are represented by concave and convex curves respectively. The typical CDT curve resembles the Stribeck curve. The profiles of CDT for different lubricants at different cut-off speeds for different lubricant pressures are given in the Figures 3-7.

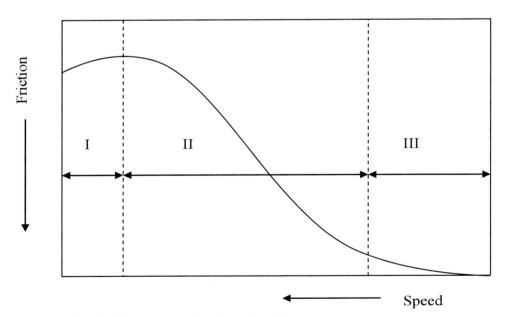

I   Hydrodynamic Lubrication Zone
II   Elastohydrodynamic or Mixed Lubrication Zone
III   Boundry Lubrication Zone

Figure 2. Typical CDT curve for journal bearing

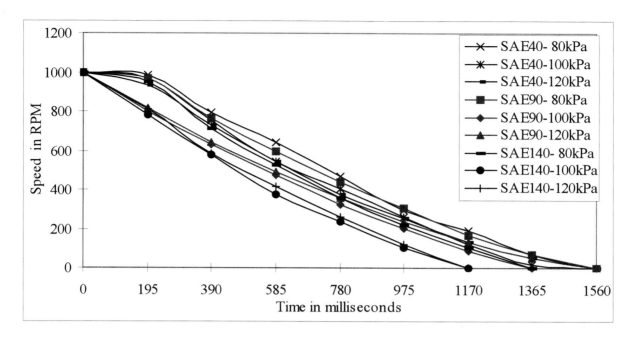

Figure 3. CDT curve at 1000 rpm cut-off speed

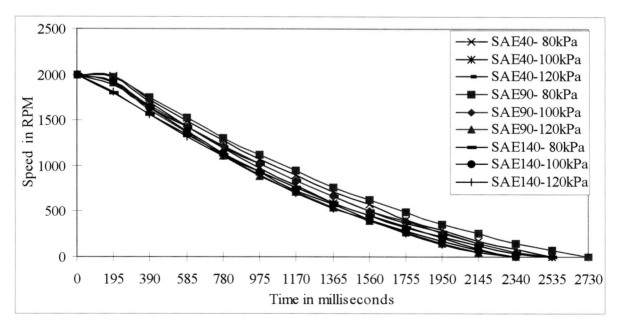

Figure 4. CDT curve at 2000 rpm cut-off speed

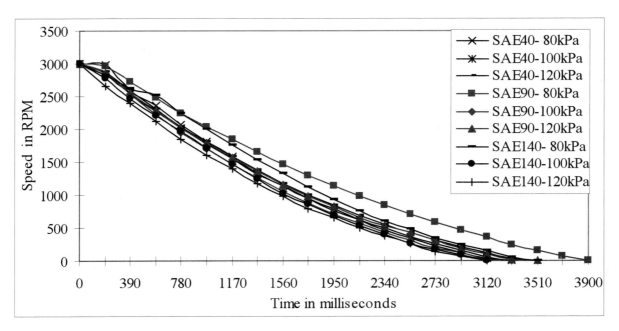

Figure 5. CDT curve at 3000 rpm cut-off speed

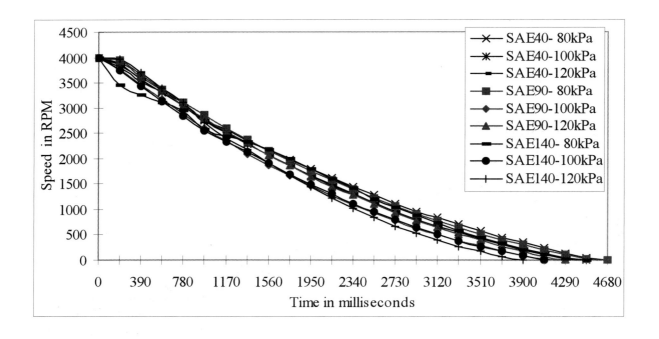

Figure 6. CDT curve at 4000 rpm cut-off speed

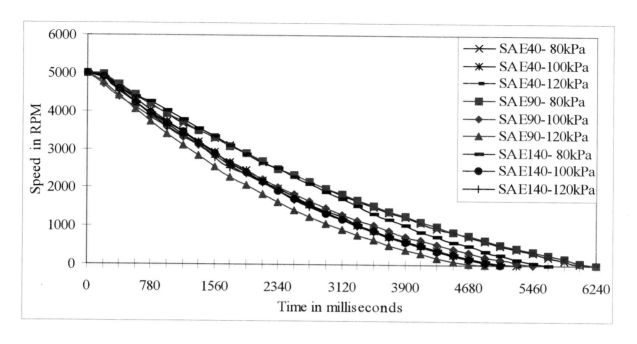

Figure 7. CDT curve at 5000 rpm cut-off speed

Figure 3 shows the CDT plots at the cut-off speed 1000 rpm for three different lubricants (SAE 40, SAE 90 and SAE 140) at three different operating oil pressures (80kPa, 100kPa and 120kPa). Lubricants under investigation are basically good oils and the values of CDT indicating their true tribological character. SAE 90 at 80kPa exhibiting a typical performance which is expected from a good lubricant as shown in Figure 2. The generic profile of the coast down behavior represents the frictional characteristics as described by a Raimondi & Boyd design curve for a journal bearing [10].The viscosity and bulk properties of the lubricant contribute to the tribological behaviour and profile of CDT. Higher operating oil pressure at lower cut-off speed has been found to affect the oil film thickness inside the journal clearance due to a reduced hydrodynamic effect, which causes significant deviation to the CDT profiles.

Figure 4 depicts the CDT at cut -off speed 200 rpm. As the cut –off speed increases the CDT value also increases. It is evident that the bulk properties of the good oil makes the CDT more concave shaped before reaching zero speed. A higher CDT value has been observed for SAE 90 oil at 80 kPa and also the CDT curves for other oils at all investigated pressures are found to be lower than the SAE 90.

Figure 5 exhibits the CDT at cut-off speed 3000 rpm. The CDT profile of the SAE 140 oil at 80 kPa has shown a typical profile in the transition regime between hydrodynamic lubrication zone and elastohydrodynamic lubrication zone. The frictional resistance inside the oil film during the referred transition regime could be the reason for this deviation from the typical CDT profile. SAE 90 oil at 80 kPa has shown higher CDT and all other CDT profiles have been found lower than the CDT profile of SAE 90. The higher vibration at this cut-off speed is attributed to the presence of resonance due to motor supply line input.

Figure 6 portrays the CDT at a cut-off speed of 4000 rpm. Characteristics which were noted for SAE 140 oil at 80 kPa at a cut-off speed of 3000 rpm, have been found once again at 4000 rpm, nearer to the transition zone between hydrodynamic and elastohydrodynamic lubrication regimes. The CDT profile of SAE 40 oil at 80 kPa has been found to be a little higher than that of SAE 90 oil at 80 kPa.

Figure 7 shows the CDT at cut-off speed 5000 rpm. The CDT profiles for SAE 90 oil at 80 kPa and at 120 kPa have extreme characters for the rotor under investigation, and are found to be one at upper and the other at lower end profiles respectively. The SAE 90 oil at 80 kPa has higher CDT value that follows typical frictional character as expected. The CDT characteristics for SAE 90 oil at 120 kPa deviates from the typical CDT profile with a more predominant concave nature in the mixed lubrication region. This may be attributed to the changes in tribological behaviour due to the high oil pressure causing prominence in the frictional resistance of oil film. The CDT plots of the other oils for all oil pressures are found to be aligned in between the CDT profiles of SAE 90 oil at 80 kPa and at 120 kPa. CDT profiles at this cut-off speed emphasises that each profile has potential characteristics to reveal the qualities of the lubrication.

4. CONCLUSION

The profile of CDT is the result of tribological behaviour and rotor inertia. Tribological behavior varies with the changes in the bulk properties of the lubricants. As the cut-off speed increases the CDT also increases. In general SAE 90 oil at 80 kPa is exhibiting better performance. The higher steady state vibration amplitudes and the variation in the CDT profile for both SAE 40 and SAE140 oils, at all investigated pressures, indicate that SAE 90 oil at 80kPa is the best suited lubricant for this rotor system under investigation. This confirms the author's earlier findings [9].

Higher operating pressure changes the oil film characters inside the journal bearing and the corresponding CDT profile becomes an indicative parameter. The CDT decreases with the increase of oil pressure. The CDT of the SAE 90 oil at 80 kPa is found to be the optimum CDT profile for the rotor system under investigation. CDT of SAE 90 oil at 120 kPa is showing more prominence to fluid frictional resistance characteristics of the oil film in the mixed lubrication region. SAE 40 and SAE 140 oils at all pressures have shown more vibration and less CDT and hence found not suitable for this rotor system. Critical analysis on the pattern of the CDT profile will provide useful information to distinctly interpret the tribological behaviour of lubricants. CDT follows a defined pattern based on the bulk properties of the lubricants with respect to cut-off speeds. Any deviation in the bulk properties will have an effect on the tribological behavior of a lubricant and hence CDT becomes a vital indicative parameter not only for tribological behaviour but also for condition based monitoring system.

Though both vibration and oil analyses are useful to predict the failure progression, at times they would mislead the diagnosis with inappropriate interpretation of data. In order to enhance the diagnosis methods along with vibration analysis, oil analysis CDT could be used as diagnostic tool for condition monitoring.

ACKNOWLEDGEMENTS

Authors are grateful to their colleagues Mr. Ragavesh, Mr.A. Vallavaraj and Mr. Antony of Caledonian College of Engineering, Oman for helping to set up the instrumentation for recording the CDT.

REFERENCES

[1]   Amarnath.M., Shrinidhi.R., Ramachnadra.A., Kanadagal.S.B., July 2004 "Prediction of defects in antifriction bearings using vibration signal analysis", Institution of engineers (India) Mechanical journal ,85, pp 88-92.

[2]   Ramachandran.K.P., 2004, "Vibration signature analysis for machine health monitoring and fault diagnosis", Caledonian Journal of Engineering, 1. pp 26-39.

[3]   Ran Barron. 1996 *"Engineering Condition Monitoring Practices, Methods and Application"*, Longman,UK.

[4]   Ramachandran.K.P., and Ramakrishna.A., 1996, "Lubrication scheduling in   manufacturing industries and its optimisation", Transaction of Industrial product finder, pp 244 -248.

[5]   Santhana Krishnan.G., Prabhu.B.S., Rao. B.V.A., 1983, "An investigation of tribological   effects on coast down phenomenon in horizontal machinery", Journal of wear, 91,pp 25-31.

[6]   Ramachandran.K.P., Ramakrishna.A., 1996, "Oil analysis for failure prevention of plant machinery", National seminar on failure analysis, HIMER, Madras, pp88-93.

[7]   Craig.R.J., 1976, "Application of coast down monitoring techniques for vertical shaft motors", DTNSRDC Rep, 76,13.

[8]   Daugherty.T.L., Craig. R.J., January 1976 "Coast down time as a mechanical condition indicator", DTNSRDC Rep, 4547.

[9]   Edwin Browne. R., De Silva.A.K.M., Ramachandran.K.P., Harrison.D.K., Sharif.M.EL, 2005 "An evaluation of bearing lubrication and the selection of lubricants using CDT analysis as a condition monitoring parameter". Regional conference in Recent trends in Maintenance Management, Sultanate of Oman, Paper no 4, pp 25-29.

[10] Joseph. S Shighley and Charles R Mischke, 1976 *Hand book of Machine design*, McGraw Hill.

Session 2
LUBRICATION TECHNOLOGY 1

Chair: Prof. R. Derek Arnell

Lubrication of Linear Ball Guides in semiconductor processing equipment. Special requirements, coatings and lubricants.
F. BREMER

Proactive Management and Control of the Performance Characteristics of Hydrodynamic Bearings
J. K. MARTIN

Studies on Microtopography of Oil-Film for Piston Rings
M. SOEJIMA, Y. WAKURI, T. HAMATAKE, T. KITAHARA

An Experimental study on the influence of different surface topographies on mechanical seal performance
J. VIŽINTIN, A. VEZJAK

Lubrication of Linear Ball Guides in semiconductor processing equipment. Special requirements, coatings and lubricants.

F. Bremer

Philips Applied Technologies, Eindhoven, The Netherlands, f.bremer@philips.com

ABSTRACT

In semiconductor equipment, contamination as result of outgassing of construction elements and lubricants can be very critical. This paper describes the consequences of replacing an air-bearing system by a lubricated linear ball bearing system. A lot of tests are carried out to collect information on which can be decided to change from bearing system. The different type of tests and their results are discussed.

In general there is a great risk of contamination from the environment as result of using lubricated linear ball guides in semiconductor equipment. Besides, the lifetime of the linear ball guides can be insufficient. In the case of using linear ball guides with a chrome coating on the rail and bearing blocks, flaking of that coating will occur. The use of coatings or other materials in linear ball guides always must be tested.

Keywords: Semi-conductor industry, linear ball guides, lubrication, lithographic process, outgassing, contamination.

1. INTRODUCTION

In industrial semiconductor processing, positioning of the wafer-stage in the X- and Y-directions is extremely critical and, in the high accuracy system in question, a two-step positioning system is used. In the present equipment the first (coarse) positioning step, feedback loop-controlled Lorenz motors are used and the bearing system consists of air bearings. The second (fine) positioning step is accomplished using very precise actuators. This report describes changing the air bearing system by a bearing system consisting of three linear ball bearings. Certain requirements of this new application are new and more demanding than in traditional semiconductor applications. Examples are out-gassing of materials and lubricants because of possible contamination issues, contamination due to particle generation, and lifetime issues as a result of small amplitude oscillations.

2. LUBRICATION SELECTION

The base for the linear ball guide lubricant choice was a compromise between three factors. There is a strong relation between them. See the schematic presentation in figure 1.

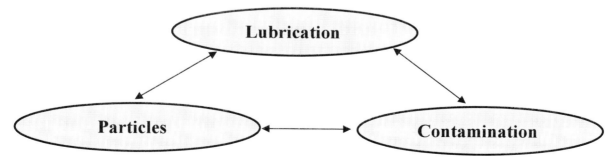

Figure 1. Schematic presentation of the compromise for the lubrication choice.

The lubricant has to lubricate the linear ball guides for a period of 5 to 10 years. This without contamination of the environment e.g. lenses and wafers. Also other guide parts like rubber seals and plastic end-caps can result in contamination. Last but not least particle generation of the guides must be as less as possible. Particles are critical for reducing the yield. Critical elements in the lubricant for contamination are S (sulphur), F (fluorine), Si (silicon) and Cl (chlorine). There are selected 9 lubricants with a low percentage of these elements. The present of the amount of these elements is checked by XRF analysis (X-ray fluorescence spectrometry). See paragraph 3.1.1.

3. TEST AND ANALYSIS RESULTS

3.1. Contamination

Lubricants can contaminate the environments e.g. lenses and wafers in semiconductor equipment. To collect information about this risk some analytical tests have been carried out. The selected lubricants are checked on the basis of some critical elements. Gas chemical composition analysis tells more about the outgassing of the different lubricants.

3.1.1. Lubricant chemical composition analysis

All the samples were measured using an X-ray fluorescence (XRF) spectrometer, equipped with a Rh X-ray tube. Table 1 shows the results of the XRF survey analysis for various greases. The relative errors in the reported concentrations (wt. %) are 5 % for S, 10 % for P and Cl and 20 % for Si, respectively.

Table 1. Overview of element analysis of greases.

Grease number	Supplier	S (wt. %)	P (wt. %)	Si (wt. %)	Cl (wt. %)
1	A	< 0.003	< 0.003	< 0.01	< 0.003
2	A	0.21	< 0.003	< 0.01	0.003
3	B	0.003	< 0.003	< 0.01	< 0.003
4	B	0.006	0.10	0.01	0.006
5	C	< 0.003	< 0.003	< 0.01	< 0.003
6	C	< 0.003	< 0.003	≈ 0.01	0.012
7	C	< 0.003	< 0.003	< 0.01	< 0.003
8	C	0.35	< 0.003	< 0.01	< 0.003
9	C	0.27	< 0.003	≈ 0.01	< 0.003

Sulphur, phosphorus and silicon could not de detected (using the present analytical procedure) in the greases 1, 5 and 6. The high level of sulphur in the greases 8 and 9 can be critical. This was only a first screening. Only elemental compositions of the greases have been determined. Outgassing characteristics should be determined to find out the real risk for contamination. On the basis of some tribological tests three greases 1, 6 and 9 were subjected to the outgassing tests.

3.1.2. Gas chemical composition analysis

Three greases survived the first screening and were subjected to the outgassing tests. Table 2 shows some of their most important properties.

Table 2. The three selected greases for the outgassing tests.

Product name	Supplier	Base oil	Thickener	Additives	v in mm^2/s @ 40 °C
1	C	PAO	Diurea	yes	100
6	A	PFPE	PTFE	no	25
9	C	Mineral+PAO	Calcium	yes	30

The total outgassing rates were measured using thermogravimetric analysis (TGA). To this end, a 10 micron lubricant layer was applied to a glass blade using a doctor blade. The outgassing rate data at 22 and 30 °are compiled. In addition to these outgassing analyses, the total amounts (ng) of condensable organics were collected. The results are shown in table 3.

Table 3. Overview of outgassing results using TGA and the concentration of condensables.

Grease number	T in °C	Outgassing rate (μg / $cm^2 hr$)	Outgassing rate (molecules / cm^2/s)	TOC concentration in WS (ppb)	Concentration condensables in WS (ppb)
1	22	0.062	1.04×10^{11}	0.015	
1	30	0.086	1.44×10^{11}	0.021	0.031
6	22	0.21	3.45×10^{11}	0.05	
6	30	0.53	8.86×10^{11}	0.13	0.10
9	22	0.085	1.38×10^{11}	0.020	
9	30	0.115	1.94×10^{11}	0.028	0.022

The calculated concentrations of contamination from the measured outgassing rates never exceed the specifications.

3.2. The Lifetime of linear ball guides

The lifetime of linear ball guides is an important item. Three failure mechanisms determine the lifetime:

1. Wear
2. Tribo corrosion
3. Fatigue

Wear should not occur as a failure mechanism. In this respect the boundary lubrication properties of the lubricant are very important. These properties are tested with a pin-on-disk test (paragraph 3.2.1). A tribo corrosion test was performed to check if small repeated movements reduce the lifetime (paragraph 3.2.2).

The corrosion resistance of the race-ways is important during assembly, transportation and operations. Yet the use of corrosion resistant race-ways should not reduce lifetime. Therefore the quality of the hard chrome on the rail was tested (paragraph 3.2.3). Normally the lifetime is limited by the fatigue in the race-ways of the linear ball guide. The resistance of a linear ball guide to fatigue is expressed in the dynamic load rate number C. This dynamic load rate of the linear ball guide is checked (paragraph 3.2.4).

3.2.1. Test boundary lubrication properties of lubricant.

Wear should not occur as a failure mechanism of a linear ball guide. In this respect the boundary lubrication properties of the lubricant is very important. These properties are tested in a pin-on-disk test.

The wear-factor is normative for the boundary lubrication properties of the lubricants. In the pin-on-disk test, the wear that occurred using grease 8 was used as the reference. Wear occurring while using other lubricants should be comparable or less than the reference.

A standard pin-on-disk (cq. ball-on-disk) is used for the experiments. See also figure 2.

 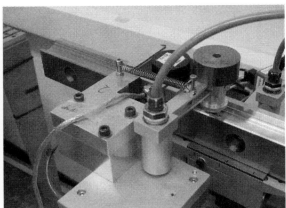

(a)   (b)

Figure 2. Layout of pin-on-disk (a) and the ball-on-race-way (b) test.

The test conditions were:

Normal load	: $F_n = 4.6$ N
Speed	: $v = 1$ m/s
Hertzian contact pressure	: $p_0 = 704$ N/mm^2
Environment	: atmospheric conditions (humid air, room temperature)
Ball	: $\varnothing$ 12 mm, bearing steel AISI 52100
Disk	: tool steel , hardened, diameter 100 mm
Surface roughness disk	: $R_a = 0.05 - 0.10$ μm
Test duration	: $t = 24$ hours

The lubricant was applied to the disk with an EDF 800 dosing system. The amount of lubricant was approximately 1 gram, equally divided over the running track. Before application of the lubricant, the ball and disks were cleaned by IPA.

With the lubricant in consideration two tests were performed, respectively on a diameter of 80 and 90 mm running track.

The coefficient of friction and the wear factor are determined as normative for the boundary lubrication properties. Test result of grease 8 was already available. The test results of the different lubricants are compared. See the graphs in figure 3.

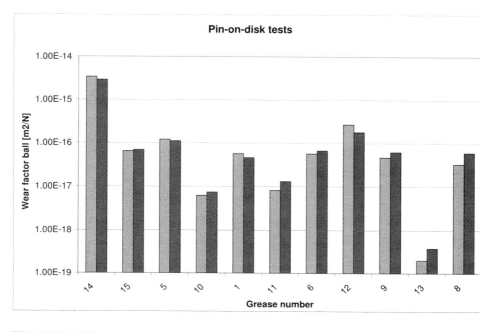

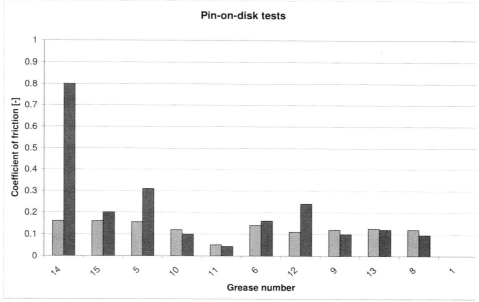

Figure 3. The wear and coefficient of friction as function of the lubricant.

On base of this results the lubricants 1, 6 and 9 were chosen for further investigations e.g. outgassing tests.

3.2.2. Tribo corrosion test

As result of standing still in a servo controlled system, small movements of the linear ball guides could occur. Representative small movements are a 0.5 mm at 3 Hz and 0.03 mm at 1 Hz. If these small movements are continuously repeated, tribo-corrosion could occur in the contact areas of the linear ball guides. Tribo-corrosion will reduce the lifetime of the linear ball guides dramatically. The goal of this test was to establish if tribo-corrosion occurs due to the small movements. Figure 4 shows the test set-up used.

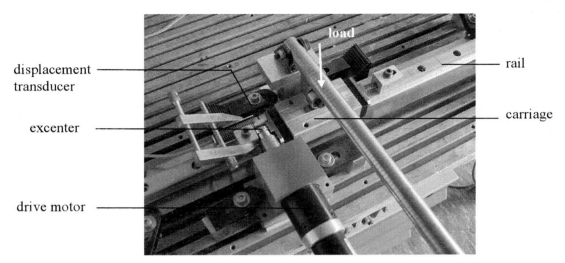

Figure 4. The set-up for tribo-corrosion test. lubricant.

The change on tribo-corrosion was checked on a number of linear ball guides. The guides in test 1, 2 and 3 were lubricated with grease 8 and in test 4 grease 9 is used. The load was 1000 N in all the tests. This was approximately 5 % of the dynamic load rate C. Most of the tests shows tribo-corrosion before the end of the test. The maximum test duration was 24 hours. The results are collected in table 4.

Table 4. Overview of results of the tribo-corrosion tests.

No.	Supplier	Material		Stroke [μm]	Freq. [Hz]	Degradation		Stopped	
		Roller	Rail			Time [hrs]	Strokes [-]	Time [hrs]	Strokes [-]
1.1	X	100Cr6	steel	450	3	14.5	156,600	15.25	164,700
1.2	X	100Cr6	steel	45	1	13.33	48,000	13.33	48,000
2.1	X	stainless steel	chrome	450	3	6	64,800	22.66	244,800
2.2	X	stainless steel	chrome	45	1	4	14,400	18	64,818
3.1	Y	100Cr6	chrome	450	3	-	-	24	259,200
3.2	Y	100Cr6	chrome	45	1	-	-	24	86,400
4.1	Y	ceramic	chrome	450	3	17	183,600	22	237,600
4.2	Y	ceramic	chrome	45	1	-	-	24	86,400
4.3	Y	ceramic	chrome	45	1	-	-	24	86,400
4.4	Y	ceramic	chrome	450	3	20	216,000	24	259,200

The column degradation shows the first time that a deviation of the perfect moving profile (sinusoidal form) was determined. This is done by measuring the movement by an inductive displacement transducer. Figure 5 shows some typical wear spots on the rail and the balls of wear as result of tribo-corrosion.

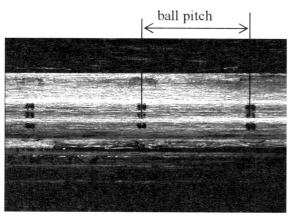
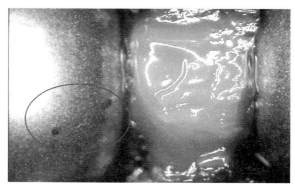

Figure 5. Tribo-corrosion determined in the race-way on the rail and on ball.

The linear ball guides from supplier Y lubricated with the greases 8 and 9 give a good protection against tribo-corrosion.

3.2.3. Test wear hard chrome coating

The corrosion resistance of the race-ways is important during assembly, transportation and operations. Yet the use of corrosion resistant race-ways should not reduce lifetime. Therefore the quality of the hard chrome race-ways is tested on two points:

- adhesion of hard chrome coating to the substrate material and
- the resistance of the coating against wear.

During testing, the cohesion of hard chrome coating to the b must be preserved.

Wear of hard chrome coated race-ways must be less than the wear of a race-ways 100Cr6 without coating (reference).

A ball (Ø 12 mm) slides to and from along the race-ways without lubricant. Wear will occur to surface of race-ways. The amount of wear is normative for the material quality of the surface.

This test are executed with the following pieces of race-ways:

1. Guide 15, race-ways 100Cr6, no coating (reference) from supplier X
2. Guide 15, race-ways 100Cr6 with a hard chrome coating from supplier X
3. Guide 45, race-ways 100Cr6, no coating (reference) from supplier Y
4. Guide 45, race-ways 100Cr6 with a hard chrome coating from supplier Y

The test conditions were:

Stroke	: s = 25 mm
Frequency	: f = 3 Hz
Normal load	: F_n = 4 N
Average speed	: v = 0.15 m/s
Hertzian contact pressure	: p_0 = 366 N/mm^2
Environment	: atmospheric conditions (humid air, room temperature)
Surface roughness disk	: R_a = 0.05 – 0.10 μm
Total sliding distance	: s = 540 m

Photo b in figure 1 shows the ball-on-rail test set-up.

The hard chrome layers of both suppliers improve the wear resistance of the rail. A combination of a ceramic ball (Si_3N_4) against a chrome layer results in less wear than a steel ball against a chrome layer.

3.2.4. Dynamic load rate test of linear ball guides.

The resistance of a linear ball guide to fatigue is expressed in the dynamic load rate C. The dynamic load rate is specified by the supplier assuming the race-ways and balls are made of 100Cr6 and a good lubricant is used. Yet in practice C found during the test could be significantly different from what the supplier claimed it to be due to another lubricant and/or other materials like coatings on the race-ways. The goal of the test was to verify the dynamic load rate C specified by the supplier for the linear ball guides in combination with the used lubricant.

To perform the test within 3 months the external load was increased whereas the total distance traveled will be reduced. The test results were used to conduct Weibull statistics. Therefore 8 carriages of every type linear ball guide undergo the test period.

In total 16 linear ball guides with 2 carriages each were tested in 4 tubes. Two drive units (Hauser) were used to move the 32 carriages. In between 2 carriages a pre-tension spring is placed to apply the external force. A rigid body connected the two carriages of a guide on one rail (see figure 6).

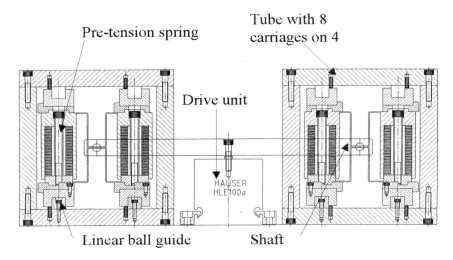

Figure 6. Cross section of layout dynamic load rate test.

The following linear ball guides are tested:

In every tube one type of linear ball guide was tested. Table 5 shows the four tested types.

Table 5. The four tested linear ball guide types.

Supplier	Material ball	Coating race-ways	Lubricant with grease
X	100Cr6	No	9
X	hardened stainless steel	hard chrome	9
Y	100Cr6	hard chrome	9
Y	Ceramic	hard chrome	9

Some linear ball guide properties and the test conditions are collected in table 6.

Table 6. The test-conditions of the lifetime test.

Test parameter	Supplier X	Supplier Y
Rail width in mm	25	25
C in kN specified by supplier	27	23
Test duration in weeks	16	16
External force in N	5,500	5,500
Sliding distance s in km	7,850	7,850
Acceleration a in m/s^2	15	15
V_{max} in m/s	1.5	1.5
Stroke s in mm (half cycle)	430	430
Environment	Test room	Test room
Temperature in °C	15-25	15-25
Humidity in %RH	40-80	40-80
Lubricant (grease nr. . .)	9	9
Re-lubrication interval	2 wk	2 wk

During the test the linear ball guides were checked at least 3 times a week. The rolling resistance was measured each time the linear ball guides were re-lubricated. The radial stiffness was measured at the begin and at the end of the test. None of the four tested linear ball guides reached the specified L_{10} lifetime of 9,500,000 cycles. The best result is reached by the standard guide of supplier X followed by the guide with steel balls and a chrome coating on the rail and the guide blocks from supplier Y.

The specified L_{10} lifetime (R = 90 %) is 9,500,000 cycles. None of the guide types reached that lifetime. See also table 7.

Table 7. The characteristic life η, the shape factor β and the L_{10} lifetime (R = 90 %) at a confidence level C = 80%.

Supplier	Construction	Characteristic life η in number of cycles	Shape factor β	Number of cycles at R = 90 % and C = 80 %
X	Standard steel version	11,105,000	7.70	4,800,000
X	Chrome coating on rail and blocks / stainless steel balls	6,213,600	2.80	700,000
Y	Chrome coating on rail and blocks / 100Cr6 balls	11,005,000	4.80	4,300,000
Y	Chrome coating on rail and blocks / ceramic balls	6,285,000	5.47	2,000,000

Most of the guides of supplier X fail as result of cage breakage, flaking of the chrome coating and / or fatigue. In most cases, it is a combination of these failures mechanisms. The cage is a critical component in the construction of the guides of supplier X. Supplier X mentioned that the life of their guides with a chrome coating should be the same or longer than the life of standard guides. In our tests the life is shorter as result of flaking off the chrome coating. It is known that the pre-load in the linear ball guides with chrome coating was relative high. Maybe this is the explanation for the very short lifetime of this type of guide.

The guides of supplier Y mainly fail as result of flaking of the chrome coating. See figure 7.

Figure 7. Failures of a guide from supplier X (a) and a guide from supplier Y (b).

The lifetime of the guide with ceramic balls from supplier Y is less that the life of the their guides with steel balls. At the last one the pre-load in the guide be realized by measuring the clearance between the rail and the guide block and filling the guide block with oversized balls. In the case of guides with ceramic balls the diameter of the ceramic balls is known. The clearance between the rail and the guide block be measured and than the rail be grinned on the right dimensions for realizing the specified pre-load. This way of working is much more critical and should result in a greater spread in the pre-load. There may be expected that in our case the pre-load in the guides with ceramic balls from supplier Y was relative high.

Lubrication

Re-lubrication of the guides from supplier X was not possible with the prescribed amount. Most of the 1.8 gram came out of the guide block between the steel part and the end-cap and belong the grease nipple. There for this guides have been re-lubricated with an amount of 1.2 gram instead of 1.8 gram.

All of the guides gives pollution of the environment. Grease came out of the guide blocks and collected on the rail at the ends of the stroke. Besides there occurs drops on the guide blocks which can fall down. In the beginning these effects are stronger at the guides of supplier X. Later on contamination of the guides from supplier Y was determined. The amount of contamination is the result of the guide block construction and the present of a cage.

4. CONCLUSIONS

On base of some analytical and tribological tests the grease 9 seems to be the best choice for using in linear ball guides for semiconductor equipment.

None of the four tested linear ball guides reached the specified L_{10} lifetime of 9,500,000 cycles. The best result is reached by the standard guide of supplier X followed by the guide with steel balls and a chrome coating on the rail and the guide blocks from supplier Y.

Not standard linear ball guides are much more critical for reaching a specified lifetime. There occur other failure mechanisms. The lifetime of not standard linear ball guides always must be tested.

There occurs flaking of the chrome coating of both suppliers. This is the result of fatigue of the coating and the difference in hardness between the substrate material and the coating. So the use of a chrome coating in linear ball guides seems to be very critical.

All the guide types result in contamination of the environment. This can be critical in semiconductor equipment.

Proactive Management and Control of the Performance Characteristics of Hydrodynamic Bearings

J. K. Martin

Lubrication Research Group, Department of Environmental and Mechanical Engineering, The Open University, Milton Keynes, MK7 6AA, UK

ABSTRACT

New forms of adjustable fluid film hydrodynamic bearings have shown great potential for controlling the position of rotational centres, irrespective of loading, and suppressing vibration orbits arising from low load instabilities. First tested on a simulated machine tool rotor and spindle system, the principle has also been demonstrated in a large marine gearbox test rig. In both cases the bearing adjustment feature was used to maintain and displace in a pro-active manner the centre of rotation irrespective of loads and changes of load, and to suppress instabilities and vibrations provoked by running at low loads. These and other characteristics could be of significant benefit in a range of fluid film bearing applications when coupled with appropriate management and control systems.

Keywords: Lubrication Management, Adjustable Hydrodynamic Bearing

1. INTRODUCTION

Fluid film bearings are widely used where rotating parts are supported. The fluid film completely separates the running surfaces by sustaining a suitably high enough pressure. There are mainly two types – the externally pressurised "hydrostatic" bearing and the self pressurised "hydrodynamic" bearing. In particular, hydrodynamic bearings by generating their own very high lubricant film pressures can carry large loads and provide significant stiffness and damping. They can be of radially and axially supporting forms. The radial type most commonly comprises a shaft or journal rotating within a stationary bearing housing. Less common is the inverse arrangement of a rotor on a stationary journal. The axial form is the thrust bearing where the rotating member bears on thrust faces, reacting axial loads. The clearance space between the two bearing surfaces is small, for a journal bearing typically 0.1 % of the journal diameter, and this clearance space is occupied by the lubricant film which provides the hydrodynamic lubrication, stiffness and damping.

Hydrodynamic lubrication is a self-sustaining fluid film separation of the two bearing surfaces. Loads are carried by pressures within the lubricant film generated independently of the supply pressure, the latter is merely to ensure adequate supply of lubricant to the bearing. The lubricant, usually oil, must have significant viscosity, there must also be relative tangential motion of the two bearing surfaces, and the oil film shape must at some part be convergent. The magnitude of this convergence is very small, for example less than $0.1°$, but its effect is most significant. In a conventional journal bearing arrangement the convergence is achieved by an eccentricity between the centres of the stationary and rotating members. This is produced by the loads acting, the more load - the greater eccentricity - the greater the convergence and higher film pressures to provide the reaction and hence carry the load. This feature in a journal bearing manifests itself as high stiffness in the radial direction, and the rate of change of load and eccentricity are reacted by significant damping, also in the radial direction. Figure 1 shows a cross section of such a pressure field, with the clearance and eccentricity both greatly exaggerated for illustration.

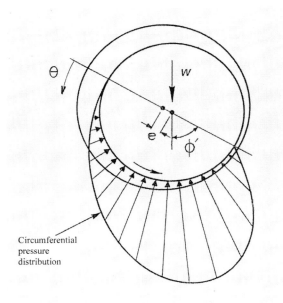

Figure 1. Conventional journal bearing scheme

For this type of bearing there is a drawback. In the absence of loading there will be no eccentricity and no pressure field. This in turn leads to an unstable condition where the rotating member is only lightly supported and its centre of rotation can itself rotate or vibrate in the presence of any small nearby disturbing forces. There are thus two main issues of concern in an operating hydrodynamic bearing: 1) that load carrying capacity involves the eccentricity required to produce the pressure fields, and 2) that in the absence of load there is no eccentricity, no pressure field and low radial stiffness and damping. The ideal arrangement would be to have the load capacity whilst maintaining a zero eccentricity for all loads, and significant stiffness and damping available at zero and light loads. Recent developments have led to this combination being achieved and demonstrated.

2. PREVIOUS DEVELOPMENTS IN HYDRODYNAMIC BEARINGS

There have been many developments in hydrodynamic bearings intended to improve performance in terms of stiffness, damping, load capacity etc. as shown in Fig. 2, again with clearances and profiles greatly exaggerated (and one picture incorrectly orientated!). For example it is possible to "build in" a converging oil film shape in the stationary member. This has the effect of reducing the eccentricity that would be required otherwise to provide a converging shape. This imposed convergence can be by special machining of the bearing surface or by machining and assembling the bearing in two halves to provide an offset. Another successful idea was the use of bearing pads which were pivoted and allowed to adopt, within limits, any angle of convergence to suit different loading conditions. These tilting bearings are generally known as tilting pad bearings of the Michell type in the UK, or pivoted shoe bearings of the Kingsbury type in the USA.

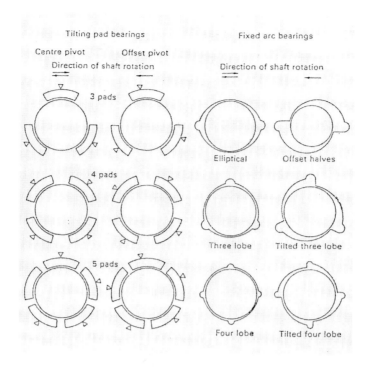

Figure 2. Variable profile journal bearings
(Reproduced by permission of the Council of the Institution of Mechanical Engineers)

In China the Shanghai Machine Tool works introduced a contoured multiple wedge hybrid bearing with clearances about 40 % of current designs, with consequent improvements in accuracy, stiffness and stability [1]. All of these developments have been to varying degrees successful in improving operating performance compared with the conventional forms. Like the conventional arrangement, however, they are still reactive to the loading conditions. The degree of eccentricity and hence pressure field forces are generated in response to the prevailing operating conditions. The novel adjustable bearing system goes one stage further, however, and permits the proactive adjustment of the eccentricity, whatever the load.

3. ADJUSTABLE HYDRODYNAMIC BEARING – A PROPOSED GRINDING ROTOR

An adjustable bearing concept was devised initially to improve the precision of grinding machine bearings, in particular for a proposed design which combined hydrostatic and hydrodynamic segments. This design was unusual in that a rotor assembly contained the bearing surface and rotated on a stationary journal. The rotor simulated a belt driven grinding wheel assembly. The journal diameter was 70 mm and the hydrodynamic segments comprised two bearings in parallel. Each hydrodynamic bearing in turn comprised 4 separate pads, each pad incorporating a means of adjustment. By such means the individual pad tilt angle could be varied independently from zero to a maximum, i.e. from flush with the journal surface through to contact with the bearing surface.

Each pad was supplied with mineral oil to ISO VG 32 and could develop its own pressure field and to a small degree was conformable. A theoretical analysis resulted in an expanded form of the original Reynolds' equation [2] from which a comprehensive computer model was developed [3]. After extensive theoretical modelling and studies [4], a practical system was designed in which each pad tilt angle could be adjusted continuously (i.e. infinitely variably) in a proactive manner during operation, irrespective of the load and operating conditions.

The principle of adjustment involved the bearing pad being supported by a tapered pin near the trailing end and rigidly at the leading end. The pin in turn was located by a thread and when turned could translate along an axis parallel to the longitudinal axis of the journal. In so doing the pad tilt angle could be varied whilst still supporting a given load. A special test rig was manufactured in which the relative rotor radial position and thereby its centre of rotation could be determined by non-contacting inductive transducers. The bearing clearly demonstrated characteristics predicted by the theoretical model, in all cases whilst it continued in operation. This included the ability to move the position of the centre of rotation in any lateral or radial direction. It was a simple matter to reset the centre of rotation to an initial position whenever the load magnitude or direction, or both, were altered.

It was also possible to initiate and maintain zero eccentricity condition under various radial loads, and changes in load. Radial stiffness was high all directions and conditions, with loads applied in any direction, and itself variable by means of the adjustment system. Figure 3 shows the test rotor. Figure 4 shows the adjusted radial positions of the centre of rotation of the rotor, adjusted during operation in 4 approximately orthogonal directions from an equilibrium position for a given load and speed combination. The movement was equivalent to a change in eccentricity ratio of 0.6 to 0.7 in each case and was both repeatable and predictable

Figure 3. Bearing test rotor

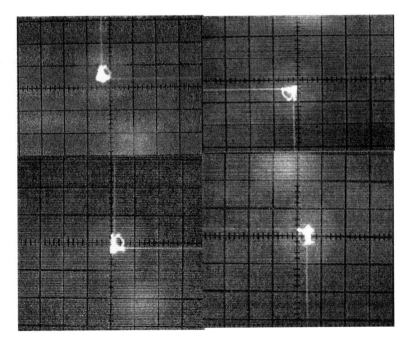

Figure 4. Rotor centre repositioning in any direction

4. ADUSTABLE HYDRODYNAMIC BEARING – A MARINE GEARBOX APPLICATION

Further work was conducted on a military ship gearbox test rig installation, [5]. This was a conventional orientation, i.e. rotating shaft within a stationary bearing housing. An adjustable bearing assembly was designed and manufactured to fit within the same packaging space and constraints as the hydrodynamic bearing normally used. The shaft contained the pinion of a double helical gear set and was supported by two bearings. One of these bearings was substituted for an adjustable bearing assembly. Figure 5 shows the installation of the adjustable bearing assembly prior to testing. The journal diameter was 190 mm, operating speed 1500 rev. min^{-1} and the oil was a mineral oil for steam turbine gear applications, supplied through the standard supply pipes and at the normal pressure.

Figure 5. Adjustable bearing being installed

The adjustable test bearing comprised 4 separate bearing pads each supported by 2 tapered pins which on being turned could adjust the pad radial position and/or tilt angle. A schematic view is shown in Fig. 6. The shaft was driven directly by an electric motor and the load on the test bearing could be set in response to changing the output resistance load of an AC alternator coupled to the main gear through a speed-increasing gearbox. The relative radial position of the journal and thereby its centre of rotation was again determined using inductive transducers.

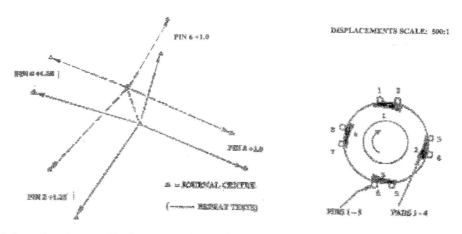

Figure 6. Journal centre repositioning approx. 0.1 mm in any direction (left). Scheme for adjustable bearing pads (right).

All tests were conducted with the rig warmed up and the journal running at its normal speed. Pad adjustments were carried out in situ during operation for various load settings. For low net radial loads, journal orbits could be provoked and maintained. It was believed they were driven by small variations in radial load due to the gear teeth meshing, possible unbalances in pinion and shaft masses and influences of a shaft coupling. Once a journal orbit was established, orbit reduction was quickly achieved by imparting equal adjustments to each pad's trailing pin (Nos. 2,4,6,8), leaving the leading pins (Nos. 1,3,5,7) set at zero. Equal pad adjustments of tilt angle of up to 0.18 $^\circ$ were set for all 4 pads. This had the effect of quickly suppressing the journal orbit in the time it took to make the adjustments (manually in just a few seconds). The orbit could be equally quickly "reinstated" by reversing the adjustments. These experiments were repeated many times on different occasions, all with the same result. Figure 7 shows a typical orbit suppression result. In this case the unsuppressed orbit was approximately 0.13 mm diameter, the orbit with the pad adjustments invoked was reduced nearly 80% to 0.03 mm diameter.

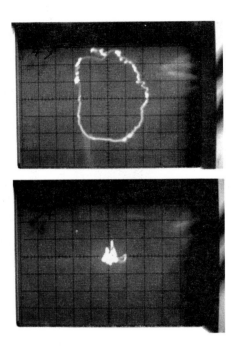

Figure 7. Journal orbit suppression – mean diameter reduced from 0.13 mm to 0.03 mm

The effect of asymmetric adjustments was also tested. For given load conditions pad adjustments were all set first at zero. Then each pad was adjusted singly in turn to tilt angle 0.174°, with all other pads set at zero, and the effect on journal centre position noted. The effect was very similar to that observed with the rotor bearing. It was a simple matter to move the centre of rotation in any of 4 orthogonal directions by single adjustments to the appropriate pad. Figure 6 illustrates the magnitudes and directions of tests given for one set of loading conditions, repeated a few days apart. The average journal centre adjusted radial displacement was just over 0.1 mm, equivalent to a shift in eccentricity ratio of 40 % - in any direction and for the same constant load and speed. As with the adjustable rotor bearing it was also a simple matter to reinstate a given orbit centre position if the load was changed and the centre of rotation position altered as a consequence.

For all tests the adjustments were carried out whilst the bearing continued to operate at a constant speed, supporting a given load with no ill effects. Indeed in all cases the overall oil temperature rise was less than that observed with the conventional bearing for the same conditions. Individual pad oil exit temperatures also provided a useful secondary indication of the loading conditions on the pad. The pad oil temperatures increased with the severity of loading on the pad.

5. POTENTIAL USE IN AN AUTOMATED MANAGEMENT AND CONTROL CONTEXT

Tests and development so far have been conducted using prototype bearing designs and test rigs after comprehensive theoretical models enabled studies to optimise design features and predict performance characteristics. With 4 pad bearings, having symmetry in 4 quadrants, it was a simple matter to predict and implement particular adjustments to suit given conditions. For example to suppress a vibration orbit and/or to move the position of the centre of rotation in a desired direction was a straight forward procedure free of any complex cross - coupling effects.

Adjustments were implemented by manual means but in terms of logic circuitry design, instrumentation and adjustment systems, the various technologies are already available to consider automatic management and control. For example the basic instrumentation used for experimental work is shown in Fig. 8. This comprises pairs of inductive proximity transducers and thermocouples with amplifiers, processing units and displays. This was all that was needed to monitor and measure the shaft relative position, the shape and size of journal orbits, the temperatures of oil inlet, outlet and exit from each pad. The inductive transducers themselves are reliable and not affected by the presence of any oil in the gap between their ends and the shaft and are already widely used in industrial applications. Thermocouples are also of course standard items.

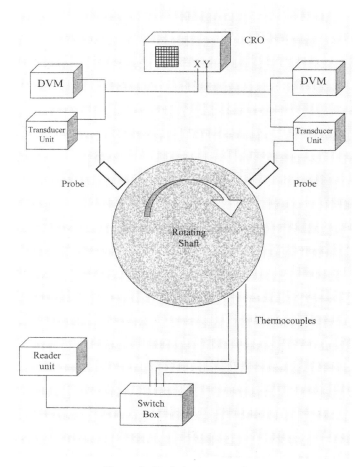

Figure 8. Basic instrumentation

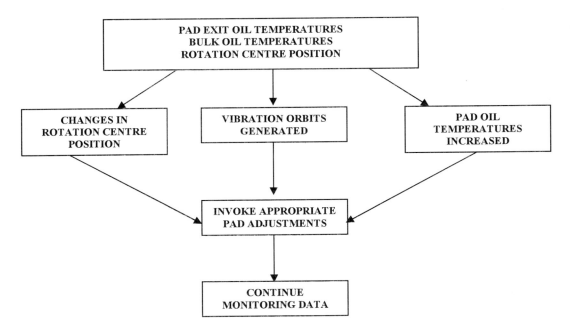

Figure 9. Control system scheme

For an automated control and monitoring function the output signals representing journal position, vibration and pad oil temperatures are all low voltages. These can be linearised and amplified in order to drive either electrical or hydraulic servo systems to apply individual adjustments. Figure 9 gives an overall view. Each adjustment pin could be connected via a threaded and worm drive arrangement providing 2 levels of gear reduction and non-reverse to balance and transmit any conceivable pad loading. All mechanical parts are relatively simple and can be made with conventional materials and machine tools. This system would provide means to maximise bearing operational accuracies by virtue of a) precision control of rotating centres, b) suppression of vibration instabilities generated in conditions of light loading and c) reduced temperature change effects. Such characteristics may have benefit for example in the remote condition monitoring of machinery and plant [6].

6. CONCLUSIONS

Two completely different forms of hydrodynamic bearing have been designed and manufactured to include a similar novel infinitely variable means of pad position and tilt adjustment. In both cases the adjustment features were contained within the stationary member, and within the packaging space of a conventional bearing. Both have been tested for a variety of operating conditions.

Both novel bearings demonstrated the ability to reposition the rotating member's centre of rotation whilst in operation, in any direction, in a repeatable and predictable manner, for a range of loads with differing initial adjustment conditions (e.g. full adjustments or zero adjustments).

Both novel bearings demonstrated the ability to maintain the position of the rotating member's centre of rotation, including zero eccentricity, for a range of loads and changes in load.

The size of rotating centre orbits could be repeatedly reduced by up to 80% for any of the test load conditions, including that of zero radial load. Such reductions were repeatable and reversible, responding directly to the mode and direction of adjustment whilst the bearings continued in operation.

The novel bearings produced oil temperature rises which were consistently lower than those for comparable conventional bearings using the same oil supply system and pressure. Examination of all bearings subsequent to testing showed negligible wear or damage. The individual pad oil exit temperature provided a simple and reliable secondary means to monitor the loading conditions on a particular pad.

The characteristics demonstrated indicate a number of potential benefits and improvements available in the design and operation of fluid film bearings, using conventional materials and manufacturing techniques.

ACKNOWLEDGEMENTS

The author gratefully acknowledges the support of the former UK Defence Evaluation and Research Agency, the Ships Support Agency, Cranfield University, the Open University, BTG International and Dr D. W. Parkins.

REFERENCES

[1]   Zhen-Qian, D. and Fu-Yan, J. "Dynastat Bearing – a new hydrodynamic and hydrostatic bearing. Report, Shanghai Machine Tool Works, (1985).

[2]   Martin, J.K. "Extended Expansion of the Reynolds Equation." *Proceedings of the Institution of Mechanical Engineers,* Vol. 216 Part J Engineering Tribology: 49-51 (2002).

[3]   Martin, J.K., "A Mathematical Model and Numerical Solution Technique for a Novel Adjustable Hydrodynamic Bearing." *Int. J. Numer. Meth. Fluids* 30: 845 864 (1999).

[4]   Martin, J.K., and Parkins, D.W., "Theoretical Studies of a Continuously Adjustable Hydrodynamic Fluid Film Bearing." *Trans. ASME, Jnl of Tribology,* Vol. 124: 203 - 211, (2002).

[5]   Martin, J.K., and Parkins, D.W., "Testing of a Large Adjustable Hydrodynamic Journal Bearing."*STLE Trib. Trans.,* Vol. 44-4: 559-566, (2001).

[6]   Qu, L., He, Z., and Zhang, Y., (Eds.) "IMS2003" *Proceedings of the International Conference on Intelligent Maintenance Systems,* Xi'an, China, ISBN 7-81099-014-4, 943-950, (2003).

Studies on Microtopography of Oil-Film for Piston Rings

Mitsuhiro Soejima [1], Yutaro Wakuri [2], Toshiro Hamatake [3], Tatsumi Kitahara [4]

[1] Kyushu Sangyo University, Fukuoka, 813-8503, Japan. (soejima@ip.kyusan-u.ac.jp)
[2] Emeritus Professor, Kyushu University, Japan
[3] Oita University, Oita, Japan
[4] Kyushu University, Fukuoka, Japan

ABSTRACT

The microtopography of oil-film due to piston rings on the surface of cylinder liner is closely related to the friction, wear and oil consumption in internal combustion engines. The cyclic change of oil-film behavior for a piston ring pack was theoretically predicted under the starved lubrication condition with the interaction between piston rings, where cyclic changes of minimum oil-film thickness and effective oil-film pressure built-up region with crank angle were obtained.

The experiments to examine the oil-film behavior for the ring pack were conducted with a reciprocating ring and liner contact model test rig, where cyclic changes of minimum oil-film thickness were firstly measured for the ring pack with two or three cylindrically circular faced ring model specimens sliding on an optically flat metal plate. Also, cyclic changes of effective oil-film pressure built-up region were secondly observed by using a cylindrically circular faced transparent glass slider and photographing the oil-film behavior between sliding surfaces with a camera. Then, the oil-film cavity flow characteristics were clarified from dynamic changes of the effective oil-film pressure built-up region, the sliding and squeeze velocities and the number of oil stream or air meniscus in the diverging flow-out side of slider width so that the microtopography of oil-film due to the top compression ring on the surface of cylinder liner during the downward power stroke of piston could be empirically estimated to investigate influences of the oil-film thickness on the oil consumption and others.

Keywords: Internal Combustion Engine, Oil Consumption, Oil-Film Formation, Piston Ring Pack, Measurement, Oil-Film Thickness, Visualization, Cavity Flow, Reciprocating Ring/Liner Test Rig, Sliding Velocity, Squeeze Velocity, Oil Stream Number

1. INTRODUCTION

The internal combustion engines have serious issues to keep the global environment sustainable by reducing the exhaust gas of carbon dioxide, nitrogen oxides and other toxic substances. Various challenges of technologies have been tried to improve the fuel economy from both aspects of the combustion and the tribology. Recently, regarding the deterioration in performances of the diesel particulate filter and the de-NOx catalyses in the exhaust gas after-treatment system, the reduction of the sulphide ash, phosphorus and sulphur contents in engine oils, as the low-SAPS oils, have been required for the future of engine oil regulation on base oils and oil additives. On the other hand, the consumption of engine oil should be reduced as much as possible because the lowering of oil viscosity has been promoted to reduce the friction loss so that the changes in oil-film thickness, volatility and other oil properties influence the oil consumption through the passes of the piston system and the valve stem guide.

The thickness of oil-film formed on the surface of cylinder liner has been supposed to relate to not only the lubrication of piston system but the consumption of lubricating oil in internal combustion engines. One of the reasons for the oil consumption is the difference of oil-film thickness of the top compression piston ring between upward strokes and downward strokes of piston [1, 2]. As another reason, the evaporation of the oil on the surface of cylinder and piston has been pointed out [3-7]. The evaporation depends on the volatility and the temperature of oil. The temperature of oil-film surface is instantaneously risen by the combustion gas in the cylinder and the temperature rise becomes large as the oil-film becomes thick [5].

The oil-film thickness on the cylinder surface depends on the interaction of piston rings under the piston ring pack [8, 9]. It also changes with the condition of oil supply to the piston system. The thickness under the starved lubrication is quite different from the one under the fully flooded lubrication [10]. On the other hand, concerning the hydrodynamic lubrication between piston ring and cylinder liner, it has been considered that the oil-film pressure equation, Reynolds equation, should be applied as a one-dimensionally viscous flow like an infinite width bearing [1, 11]. However, it has never been made obvious whether the oil-film thickness and pressure built-up region are governed as the one-dimensional flow when lubricated with the oil deposed on the cylinder surface [12-14].

In the present study, firstly the oil-film behavior for the piston ring pack was theoretically predicted to examine cyclic changes of minimum oil-film thickness and effective oil-film pressure built-up region with crank angle. Secondly, the oil-film thickness was experimentally measured with a reciprocating ring and liner contact model test rig to examine the cyclic changes of minimum oil-film thickness for the ring pack where two or three cylindrically circular faced ring model specimens were slided as a pack on a flat plate. Thirdly, the oil-film behavior was observed with the same test rig by using a transparent glass slider to examine the cyclic change of effective oil-film pressure built-up region. Lastly, relationships among the effective oil-film pressure built-up region, the sliding and squeeze velocities, the contact load and the number of oil-film crest on the flat surface were examined to clarify the two-dimensional oil-film cavity flow characteristics governing the micro topograghy of oil-film on the liner surface.

Symbols

a : Parabolic curve profile factor of the ring
B : Half width of the ring
h : Oil-film thickness
h_0 : Minimum oil-film thickness
h_i : Oil-film thickness at the inlet boundary
h_o : Oil-film thickness at the outlet boundary
H : Bulge height of ring, aB^2
n : Number of cavity per unit length
N : Rotational speed
p : Oil-film pressure
p_1 : Gas pressure in the combustion chamber
p_2 : Gas pressure at the second land of piston
P_e : Contact pressure due to ring tension

q : Oil flow rate, Rate of oil-feeding
t : Time
u : Oil velocity in the sliding direction
U : Sliding velocity of the ring
V : Squeeze velocity of the ring
W : Load per unit length of the slider
x, y, z : Coordinates
x_i : Inlet boundary position of the oil-film
x_o : Outlet boundary position of the oil-film
X : Position in the piston stroke
θ : Crank angle
μ : Oil viscosity

2. PREDICTION OF OIL-FILM BEHAVIOR FOR PISTON RING PACK

The cyclic change of oil-film behavior for a piston ring pack was theoretically predicted under the starved lubrication condition taking account of the oil flow continuity interacting between piston rings as follows.

2.1. Basic Equations

The hydrodynamic lubrication model for piston rings is shown in Fig.1. The oil-film thickness is expressed as below, where the profile of ring sliding faces is assumed to be a parabola with a profile factor a.

$$h = h_0 + a x^2$$

Reynolds equation governing the hydrodynamic lubrication for piston rings reciprocating on the liner surface is the same as for dynamically loaded bearings.

$$\frac{\partial}{\partial x}(h^3 \frac{\partial p}{\partial x}) + \frac{\partial}{\partial z}(h^3 \frac{\partial p}{\partial z}) = 6\mu U \frac{\partial h}{\partial x} + 12\mu V$$

In here, the equation is assumed to be the one-dimensional because the contact between ring and liner is circumferential symmetry.

$$\frac{\partial}{\partial x}(h^3 \frac{\partial p}{\partial x}) = 6\mu U \frac{\partial h}{\partial x} + 12\mu V$$

Reynolds boundary condition is applied for the oil-film pressure in the diverging oil flow region of the outlet side of ring width [15]. Then, any influence of the oil streams forming the air meniscus is neglected not only in the diverging oil flow region but in the converging oil flow region of the inlet side.

The lubrication of an oil ring for the ring pack is assumed to be fully flooded and the oil flow continuity among rings illustrated in Fig.2 is taken into account. As shown, the oil flow rate at the inlet boundary $x = x_i$ depends on the amount of oil left on the liner by the preceding ring, where the oil flow rate at the outlet boundary varies according to the Reynolds boundary condition, $x = x_o : p = p_o, \ dp/dx = 0$.

The force balance equation is assumed as below, where the friction between the ring and the ring groove of piston is neglected.

$$\int_{-B}^{B} p \, dx = 2B(P_e + p_g)$$

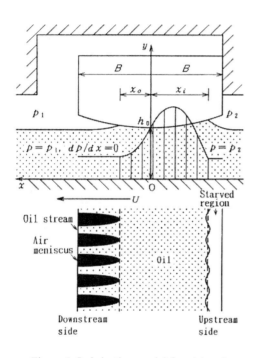

Figure 1. Lubrication model for piston rings

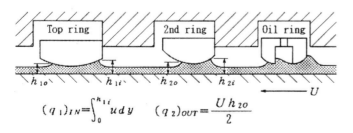

$$(q_1)_{IN} = \int_0^{h_{1i}} u \, dy \qquad (q_2)_{OUT} = \frac{U h_{2o}}{2}$$

Figure 2. Oil flow continuity for a piston ring pack

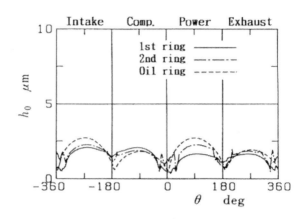

(a) Minimum oil-film thickness for the compression rings and the oil ring

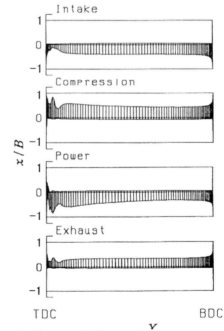

(b) Changes of effective oil-film pressure built-up region with the piston displacement for the top ring

Figure 3. Cyclic behaviors of oil-film with crank angle under the starved lubrication [8]

2.2.   Calculations and Results

The above theory was applied to predict the cyclic change of oil-film behavior for a piston ring pack of a four-stroke cycle diesel engine. The piston rings are arranged in the order of a top compression ring, a second compression ring and an oil control ring [8]. The top ring has a symmetric barrelled face and the second ring has a composite profile of tapered and barrelled faces. The oil ring has two lands shaped as a pair of non-symmetrically half barrel faces. The gas pressures around rings were the one in the combustion chamber at the engine operation of 43kW / 2400 rpm and the inter-ring gas pressure predicted by the C. English's estimation method [8].

The cyclic changes of minimum oil-film thickness and effective oil-film pressure built-up region with crank angle is shown in Fig.3. When the oil starvation is considered for the ring pack, the minimum oil-film thickness of the top and second rings is much reduced over a whole cycle to be similar to that of the oil ring. It is obvious that the oil-film thickness in the ring pack is subject to the ring forming the thinnest oil-film of all rings.

Also as shown, the effective oil-film pressure built-up region changes cyclically with the piston displacement for the top ring. The region becomes extremely narrow and distributes only in the vicinity of the ring width centre over all of the piston strokes.

3.   EXPERIMENT METHOD AND RESULTS

The experiments to examine the oil-film behavior for the ring pack were conducted with a reciprocating ring and liner contact model test rig illustrated in Fig.4 and Fig.9.

3.1.   Measurement of Oil-Film Thickness for Ring Pack Model

As shown in Fig.4, Fig.5 and Fig.6, two or three ring model slider specimens are individually supported

with long suspension rods and arranged as a pack contacting with a cylinder liner model plate in the test rig. The sliding surfaces of ring specimens are ground and polished with a special finisher so that they have cylindrically circular faces [10]. The sliders have a width of 6.6mm and a length of 60mm. The ratio of the bulge height H of circular face to the width $2B$ is approximately as large as that of piston rings worn in real engines ($H/2B \fallingdotseq 0.001$-$0.003$) [5,9,11]. The surface of flat plate is precisely polished to be less than 0.25 micron in optical flatness. It is reciprocated at a stroke of 240mm by the crank mechanism. The material of these model specimens is a hardened SNCM steel.

The load of the circular faced slider is individually set by the pressure of compressed air in the load device. The lubricating oil is supplied from a hole at the centre of flat plate. The test oil is spindle oil or turbine oil with the viscosity low at the room temperature. They were supplied at comparatively large rates of oil-feeding. The minimum oil-film thickness between the ring specimen and the flat plate is measured with an eddy current type displacement sensor installed on the slider.

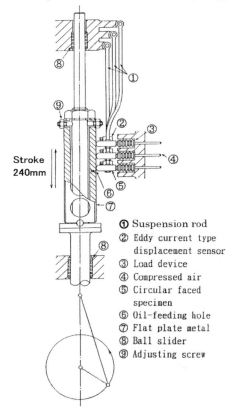

Stroke
240mm

① Suspension rod
② Eddy current type
   displacement sensor
③ Load device
④ Compressed air
⑤ Circular faced
   specimen
⑥ Oil-feeding hole
⑦ Flat plate metal
⑧ Ball slider
⑨ Adjusting screw

Figure 4. Reciprocating test rig for circular faced specimens sliding on the flat metal plate

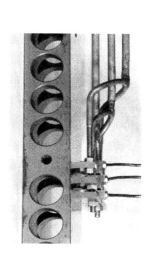
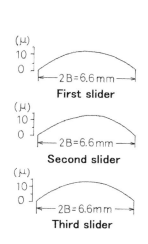
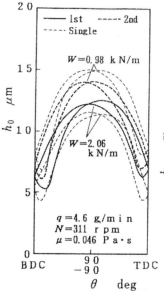
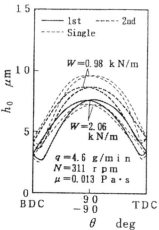

Figure 5. Outer view and arrangement of test specimens

Figure 6. Profiles of cylindrically circular faced slider specimens

Figure7. Changes of minimum oil-film thickness with crank angle for two piston rings pack model with two slider specimens

3.1.1. Two rings pack

Cyclic changes of minimum oil-film thickness measured for the ring pack with two sliders are shown in Fig.7. The load of the first slider is 124N and that of the second one is 59N. Fine dotted lines are the values measured under the single slider condition. As shown, the oil-film thickness of the first slider is a little smaller but that of the second one is a little larger than the respective thickness under the single slider condition. Namely, each oil-film thickness under this pack changes so as to lessen the difference of those between the sliders.

3.1.2. Three rings pack

Cyclic changes of minimum oil-film thickness measured for the ring pack with three sliders are shown in Fig.8. The load of the first and second sliders is 124N and that of the third one is 59N. As shown, the oil-film thickness of the second slider is a little larger but those of the first and third ones are a little smaller than the respective thickness under the single slider condition. The oil retained among the sliders is supposed to act on the increase of oil-film thickness for the second slider. Thus the interaction of the oil-film flow among the sliders reciprocating under the pack condition is too complicated to estimate the influence on the oil-film thickness so easily.

3.2. Measurement of Oil-Film Thickness and Observation of Oil-Flow between Ring and Liner Specimens

Cyclic changes of the minimum oil-film thickness and the effective oil-film pressure built-up region were also measured and observed by using a cylindrically circular faced transparent glass slider and photographing the oil-film behavior between sliding contact surfaces with a camera as shown in Fig.9, Fig.10, Table 1, Fig.11 and Fig.12. These experiments were conducted under the test conditions with the load of 1.5kN/m to 12.7kN/m, the oil viscosity of 0.01Pas to 0.39Pas and the rotational speed of 114rpm to 333rpm.

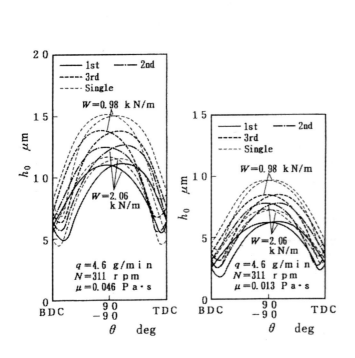

Figure 8. Changes of minimum oil-film thickness with crank angle for three piston rings pack model with three slider specimens

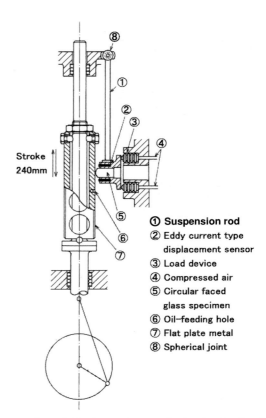

① Suspension rod
② Eddy current type displacement sensor
③ Load device
④ Compressed air
⑤ Circular faced glass specimen
⑥ Oil–feeding hole
⑦ Flat plate metal
⑧ Spherical joint

Figure 9. Reciprocating test rig for circular faced glass specimens sliding on flat plate

In every photograph shown in Fig,11, the oil flows from the upside to the downside. The airation and rapture of oil-film in the diverging flow region of the half slider width initially occur at the crank angle around 22.5deg to 37.5deg. There are many streams of oil cavity with air meniscuses not only in the oil flow-out side but in the oil flow-in side under the starved lubrication at the small rate of oil-feeding such as the cases of C and D, while both the oil-film thickness and the effective oil-film pressure built-up region obviously become small as the rate of oil-feeding decreases exponentially as shown in Fig.12.

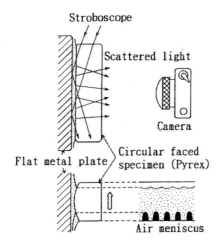

Figure 10. Observation of oil-flow

Table 1. Test specimens and conditions

		A	B	C	D
q	cm³/cycle	0.2	0.0002	0.14	0.002
$2B$	mm	6.5	6.5	19.5	19.5
H	µm	11	11	21	21
W	kN/m	2.35	2.35	3.92	3.92
μ	Pa·s	0.032	0.032	0.093	0.093
N	rpm	114	114	114	114

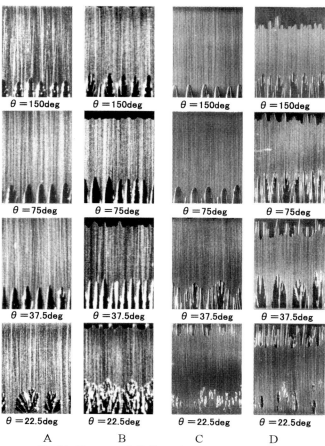

Fig.11 Changes of oil-flow view with crank angle

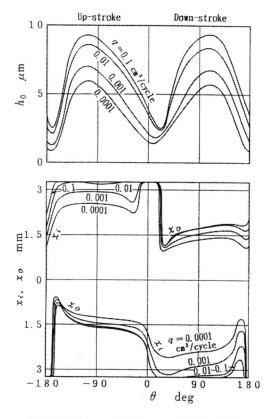

(a) $2B=6.5$ mm, $H=11\,\mu$m, $W=3.24$ kN/m
$\mu=0.031$ Pa s, $N=224$ rpm

3.3.   Oil-Film Cavity Flow Characteristics for Piston Ring

Furthermore, the oil-film cavity flow characteristics were clarified from dynamic changes of the effective oil-film pressure built-up region, the sliding and squeeze velocities and the number of oil stream or air meniscus in the diverging flow-out side of slider width as shown in Fig.13, Fig.14 and Fig.15, where the variables for Reynolds equation are expressed with non-dimensional ones as follows.

$$X=\frac{x}{B}\sqrt{\frac{2H}{h_0}}\qquad Z=\frac{z}{B}\sqrt{\frac{2H}{h_0}}$$

$$H^*=\frac{h}{h_0}=1+\frac{X^2}{2}\qquad P=\frac{p}{\mu UB}\sqrt{2Hh_0}$$

$$V^*=\frac{V}{U}\frac{B}{\sqrt{2h_0H}}$$

Then non-dimensional expression for Reynolds equation is

$$\frac{\partial}{\partial X}(H^{*3}\frac{\partial P}{\partial X})+\frac{\partial}{\partial Z}(H^{*3}\frac{\partial P}{\partial Z})=6\frac{\partial H^*}{\partial X}+12V^*$$

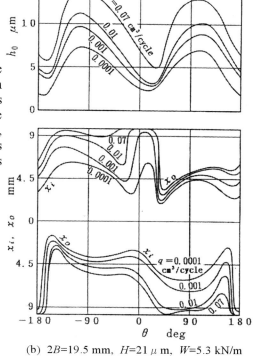

(b) $2B=19.5$ mm, $H=21\,\mu$m, $W=5.3$ kN/m
$\mu=0.016$ Pa s, $N=224$ rpm

Figure 12. Changes of minimum oil-film thickness h_0 and inlet and outlet boundaries, x_i and x_o

Also the load per unit length of slider is expressed as below.

$$w = n \int_0^{\frac{1}{n}} \int_{x_o}^{x_i} p\, dx\, dz$$

Therefore, concerning the measured values for the inlet position of oil-film corresponding to the oil-film pressure built-up boundary, the outlet position of oil-film corresponding to the occurrence of oil-film rapture and cavity in the diverging flow region, the number of cavity flow per unit length and the load per unit length, the non-dimensional variables are expressed as follows.

$$X_i = \frac{x_i}{B}\sqrt{\frac{2H}{h_0}} \qquad X_o = \frac{x_o}{B}\sqrt{\frac{2H}{h_0}}$$

$$n^* = nB\sqrt{\frac{h_0}{2H}} \qquad W^* = \frac{w}{\mu U}\frac{2h_0 H}{B^2}$$

Where, the non-dimensional variable for the load carried by the oil-film pressure is expressed as below.

$$W^* = n^* \int_0^{\frac{1}{n^*}} \int_{X_o}^{X_i} P\, dX\, dZ$$

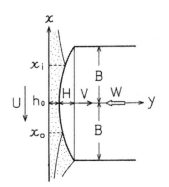

Figure 13. Symbols for oil-starved cavity flow

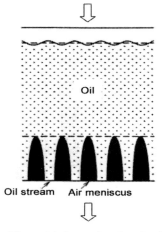

Figure 14. Starved and cavity flow

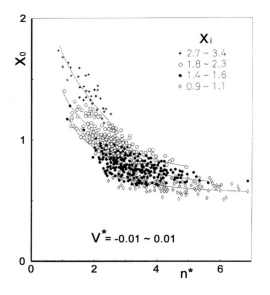

(a) Non-dimensional relationship of cavity number n^* to inlet and outlet boundaries, X_i and X_o for a constant squeeze velocity V^*

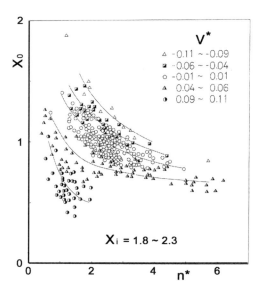

(b) Relationship of cavity number n^* to squeeze velocities V^* and outlet boundaries X_o for a constant inlet boundary X_i

Figure 15-1. Oil-film cavity flow characteristics for the sliding contact between piston ring and cylinder

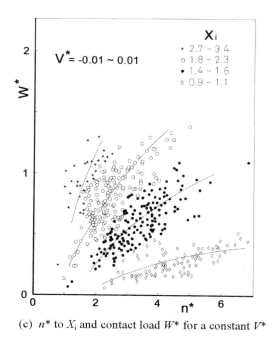

(c) n^* to X_i and contact load W^* for a constant V^*

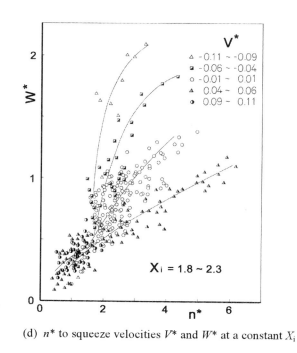

(d) n^* to squeeze velocities V^* and W^* at a constant X_i

Figure 15-2. Oil-film cavity flow characteristics for the sliding contact between piston ring and cylinder

Regarding the oil-film cavity flow between the slider and the flat under the reciprocation, some characteristics are made obvious in Fig.15. For every value of parameters, Xi and V*, as n* increases, W* becomes large but Xo becomes small. And both W* and Xo increase with Xi. Further, as the influence of squeeze velocity, both the value of W* and its varying rate with n* decrease as V* becomes large, and also the product of Xo and n* tends to decrease as V* decreases to become zero or minus. Thus the influence of V* is intensive and characteristical as much as those of other parameters.

According to these characteristics of oil-film behavior, the microtopography of oil-film on the surface of cylinder liner after the slide of top compression ring during the power stroke of piston can be empirically estimated. And then, it will be possible to investigate the influence of the microtopography of oil-film on the tribology of ring and liner, especially on the oil consumption from the aspect of oil volatility considering that the instantaneous temperature rise of the oil-film surface heated by combustion gas is made large as the oil-film becomes thick.

4. CONCLUSIONS

As study results the following conclusions have been made obvious from the theoretical and experimental examinations on the oil-film behaviors of piston rings interacted under the piston ring pack. Particularly, the cyclic changes of the minimum oil-film thickness and the oil-film extent with crank angle have been measured and observed for the cylindrically circular faced slider reciprocating on the flat under the starved lubrication so that the empirical relationships among the oil-film extent, the sliding and squeeze velocities, the contact load and the number of the fingered oil stream were examined to clarify the two-dimensional oil-film cavity flow characteristics governing the micro topography of oil-film on the liner surface.

(1) The oil-film thickness of top compression rings becomes thinner under the ring pack condition than that under the fully flooded lubrication. Also the oil-film extent in the ring width becomes narrower. The interaction of oil-film flow among the top, second and/or third rings reciprocating under the pack condition is too complicated to estimate the oil-film flow and oil-film thickness so easily.

(2) For every inlet side boundary of oil-film extent Xi and squeeze velocity V*, as the number of cavity flow n* increases, the load carrying capacity W* becomes large but the outlet side boundary of oil-film extent Xo becomes small. And, both W* and Xo increase with Xi. Further, both the value of W* and its varying rate with n* decrease as the squeeze velocity V* becomes large, and also the product of Xo and n* increases as V* decreases.

REFERENCES

[1]   Wakuri, Y., Tsuge, et al., A study on the oil loss past a series of piston rings, Bulletin of the Japan Soc. Mech. Engrs, 1970, Vol.13, No.55, pp.150-163.

[2]   Ma, M., Sherrington, I., Smith, E. H. and Grice, N., Development of a detailed model for piston-ring lubrication in IC engine with circular and non-circular cylinder bores, Tribology International, 1997, Vol.30, No.11, pp.779-788.

[3]   Kawamoto, J., Yamamoto, M., Ito, Y. and Hanaoka, M., Study of the mechanism of engine oil consumption ; Part 1, Junkatsu, 1977, Vol.22, No.11, pp.705-712.

[4]   Furuhama, S., Hiruma, M. and Yoshida, H., An increase of engine oil consumption at high temperature of piston and cylinder, SAE Paper 810976, 1981.

[5]   Wakuri, Y. and Soejima, M, On the mechanism of lubricating oil consumption in engines, Pre-print of the Japan Soc. Mech. Engrs, 1990, No.908-1, pp.14-15.

[6]   Yilmaz, E., Tian, T., Wong, V. W. and Heywood, J. B., An experimental and theoretical study of the contribution of oil evaporation to oil consumption, SAE 2002-01-2684.

[7]   Liu, L., Tian, T. and Yilmaz, E., Modeling oil evaporation from the engine cylinder liner with consideration of the transport of oil species along the liner, Proc. of the 3rd WTC, 2005, Paper No.63984, pp.1-2.

[8]   Wakuri, Y., Hamatake, T., Soejima, M. and Kitahara, T., Piston ring friction in internal combustion engines, Tribology International, 1992, Vol.25, No.5, pp.299-308.

[9]   Wakuri, Y., Hamatake, T., Soejima, M. and Kitahara, T., Studies on tribology between cylinder liner and piston ring in marine diesel engine ; Past 30 years, Proc. of the 24th CIMAC, 2004, Paper No.46, pp.1-16.

[10] Wakuri, Y., Ono, S., Soejima, M. and Taniguchi, T., Oil-film Behavior of a circular faced slider in the reciprocating motion, Proc. of JSLE-ASLE Int. Lubrication Conf. Tokyo, 1975, pp.419-427.

[11] Wakuri, Y., Soejima, M. and Taniguchi, T., On the oil-film behavior of piston rings, Bulletin of the Japan Soc. Mech. Engrs, 1978, Vol.21, No.152, pp.295-302.

[12] Wakuri, Y., Hamatake, T., Soejima, M. and Kitahara, T., Lubrication of piston ring pack, Trans. of the Japan Soc. Mech. Engrs, 1993, Vol.59, No.561, pp.1504-1511.

[13] Kim, S., Azetsu, A., Yamauchi, M. and Someya, T., Dynamic behavior of oil film between piston ring and cylinder liner, Int. Journal of the Japan Soc. Mech. Engrs, Sec.C, 1995, Vol.38, No.4, pp.783-789.

[14] Dellis, P. and Arcoumanis, C., Cavitation development in the lubricant film of a reciprocating piston-ring assembly, Proc. Instn Mech. Engrs, 2004, Vol.218, Part J, pp.157-171.

[15] Wakuri, Y., Ono, S., Soejima, M. and Masuda, K., Oil-film behavior of reciprocating slider with circular profile, Bulletin of the Japan Soc. Mech. Engrs, 1981, Vol.24, No.194, pp.1462-1469.

An experimental study on the influence of different surface topographies on mechanical seal performance

J. Vižintin, A. Vezjak

University of Ljubljana, Center for Tribology and Technical Diagnostics, Slovenia

ABSTRACT

Many factors influence the performance of mechanical seals, but hardly one besides material selection is as vital as the surface roughness of sealing rings. Characterization of sealing surfaces is usually presented by roughness parameters such as average roughness Ra. Although this parameter gives some rough information about the surface, it is usually insufficient. Thus, from the tribological point of view, other parameters such as core-roughness depth, reduced-peak height and reduced-valley depth are used. Thanks to the development of modern devices for surface characterization, 3D topography and extrapolation of 2D roughness parameters become useful tools for many engineers in the field.

Two types of PV tests were performed: one with varying speed and one with varying net sealing pressure. Parameters such as temperature and displacement of the seal seat, fluid temperature, friction torque, and normal load on the sealing contact, shaft speed and leakage rate were monitored on-line. Commercially available self-mated alumina was tested in tap water. Different roughness and topographical characteristics of the sealing ring were obtained by plane grinding, fine grinding and polishing. Sealing surfaces were characterized by 3D stylus profilometry and by analyzing various roughness parameters before and after the tests. Lubrication regimes were identified by Stribeck type curves.

Results indicate that surface roughness directly influences the lubrication regime in the sealing gap, which is of a self-maintaining nature. During the tests, surface roughness and topography due to wear changed and therefore influenced tribological performance of the seal. This was shown by friction coefficient and performance limit.

Keywords: Seals, Mechanical seals, Lubrication regime, Roughness

1. INTRODUCTION

The increased emphasis on economy and energy conservation is forcing seal manufacturers and end users towards optimization of existing sealing systems. The area of surface engineering or optimization of contact surfaces is especially promising in this regard.

It is well-known that surface roughness plays an important role in deciding the tribological behavior of mechanical components, such as bearings and seals, operating under full film and mixed (or partial) lubrication conditions. Surface roughness not only interacts with the hydrodynamics of the fluid film but it also leads to very high local contact pressures near the asperity tip regions and small real contact area which is only a fraction of the nominal contact area (1-3).

In seals, surface roughness of the mating surfaces directly affects the leak rate and is probably the most critical parameter in determining the effect of hydrodynamic lubrication. In general, it is considered that the surface characteristic of seal faces in the form of waviness has the most important role in hydrodynamic-ally stabilizing the sealing interface. However, it is virtually impossible to provide full film hydrodynamic lubrication in some applications, no matter how much waviness is used, if the surface roughness is too large. (4-6) In presented paper, the influence of different surface rough-nesses on lubrication behavior of mechanical seal is presented. Lubrication in the seal was analyzed with Stribeck curves.

2.　EXPERIMENTAL SETUP AND PROCEDURE

2.1.　Test rig

Experiments were performed on a test system of our own design, shown on Figure 1.

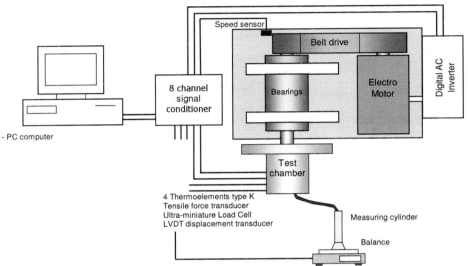

Figure 1. Test system with chamber.

The central part of the system is a test chamber, Figure 2. The test chamber was designed in such a way that it provides simulation of conditions analogous to those found in real systems and, on the other hand, enables easy assembly of a testing seal and seal rings and accessibility for measuring probes.

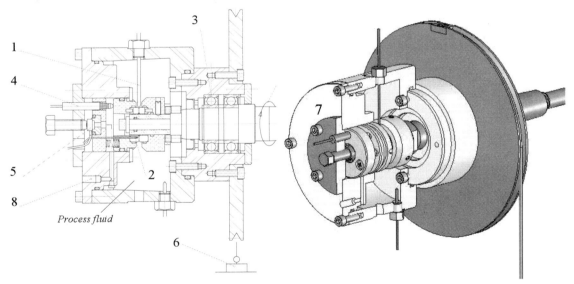

Figure 2. The test chamber with transducers and probes.

Since the operation of a mechanical seal is by itself a very complex tribo-dynamical process, it is very important that during the tests the quality acquisition of a sufficient amount of parameters is provided. Therefore, the test chamber was equipped with different probes and transducers by which the following data were obtained: the fluid temperature near the sealing interface (1), the near-face temperature of the primary seal ring (2), the bearing temperature (3), the displacement of the primary seal ring (4), the net closing force (5), frictional torque (6), shaft speed (7) and leakage (8).

2.2.   Materials

The tribological studies were conducted on self-mated commercially available 96% grade alumina in the form of seal rings, with a face mean diameter 26 mm and a face width 4 mm. Some properties of this alumina are given in Table 1. Although self-mated alumina is not a standard material combination used in mechanical seal applications, it was used due to its well-defined transition from mild to severe wear mechanism indicating material failure, and is therefore suitable for studying performance under different lubricating conditions.

Table 1. Properties of commercial 96% alumina

Property		Unit	Value
Density	ρ	g/cm^3	3.72
Hardness	H	HV$_{500}$	1750
Young's modulus	G	GPa	300
Flexural strength		MPa	350
Fracture toughness	K$_{Ic}$	MPa.m$^{1/2}$	3.5 - 5
Thermal shock		Wm^{-1}K^{-1}	6.3
Poisson's ratio	ν	-	0.22
Grain size	d	μm	3 – 8

2.3.   Specimen preparation

The as-delivered rings were systematically ground and polished to three major groups of surface roughness, namely plane ground (PG), fine ground (FG) and polished/lapped (P/L). All specimens were prepared in the laboratory with MD-System grinding discs (Struers, Denmark). The procedures for obtaining different surface roughness, as well as achieved average Ra values are, given in Table 2.

Table 2. Specimen preparation

Abb.	Method	Procedure				Ra
		1.phase	2.phase	3.phase	4.phase	[μm]
R	Raw	As-delivered				1.50
PG	Plane ground	Piano* 120				0.64
FG	FG1-#220	Piano 120	SiC paper-mesh 220			0.30
	FG2-9μm	Piano 120	Allegro* + 9μm			0.29
P/L	Polished	Piano 120	Allegro + 9μm	Plan* + 6μm		0.13
	Lapped	Piano 120	Allegro + 9μm	Plan + 6μm	Dur* + 3μm	0.08

*-Trademarks of Struers Company, Denmark

2.4.   Surface characterization

Surface roughness of each specimen (ring) was measured by stylus profilometry using a skid diamond stylus probe with a 5μm tip radius. The cut-off length of the filter was 0.25 mm and the traversing length 1.5 mm. Topography measurements were analyzed using specialized software (Hommel Map Expert).

Three measurements of topography of the size of 1.5 by 1.5 mm were taken on each ring before and after the test. Each measurement consisted of 50 roughness profiles as shown in Figure 3.

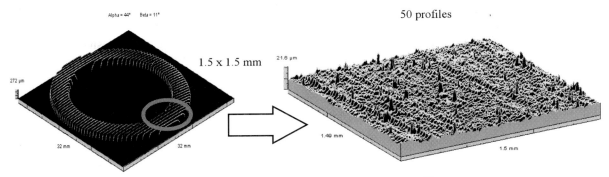

Figure 3. Topography map of 50 roughness profiles.

Beside surface roughness, waviness of the surface at the circumference, due to its direct influence on hydrodynamic effects, is a very important parameter. Initially, no intentional waviness was introduced to the surface; therefore, any waviness present was random, resulting from the previous grinding/polishing process. Only initial waviness before the test was measured. The measurements were performed on a 3D-CNC measuring system with accuracy within 0.1 μm. The measurements were presented in diagrams in the form as shown on Figure 4.

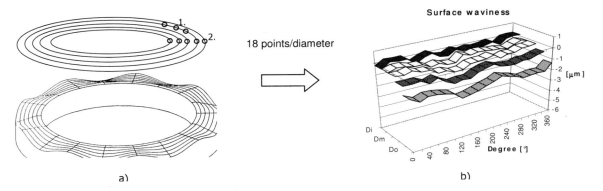

Figure 4. Waviness measurement.

Waviness with an amplitude about 1μm and with two waves was sometimes observed on plane ground (PG) surfaces. Waviness was more rarely observed on fine ground (FG) and polished surfaces (P/L). Table 3 shows the average values of wave amplitude for different surfaces.

Table 3: Waviness amplitude range

Surface	Amplitude [μm]
PG	1-1.25
FG	~1
P/L	0.75-1

2.5.   Test procedure

Lubrication in mechanical seals is usually studied by constructing Stribeck-type curves with the assumption that the governing lubricating mechanism would be hydrodynamic. In order to construct such a curve at least one of the parameters included in the hydrodynamic coefficient (viscosity, velocity or pressure) should varied. Similarly, a performance limit study, where the total load (pressure, velocity) applied on the seal contact should be brought up to the point of material failure, also requires variation of at least one of these parameters. To obtain both, namely the Stribeck curve and performance limit data, through a properly selected testing procedure would be the optimal solution to restrictions given by the capability of the testing system.

With this in mind, two types of stepped (PV) tests were devised. First, where the nominal pressure was constant and velocity varied (Figure 5a), and the other where velocity was constant and nominal pressure varied (Figure 5b).

In this way, a wide range of different lubricating and contact conditions was obtained within a single test, which substantially reduced testing times and the number of tests needed.

All tests were performed in pressure-less tap water as a process fluid. In order to simulate as arduous conditions as possible at given operating conditions, no additional cooling of the fluid was provided. Test conditions are summarized in Table 4.

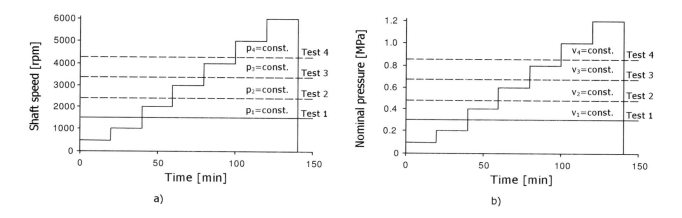

Figure 5: The PV-test procedure; a) p=const.; v-stepped, b) v=const.; p-stepped

Table 4. Test conditions

Test fluid:	Tap water (pH~7)
Fluid temperature:	35-90° C (without cooling)
Net face pressure:	0-2.0 MPa
Shaft speed:	0-6200 rpm (0-10m/s)
Mean face diameter:	~26 mm

3. RESULTS AND DISCUSSION

3.1.   f-G plots

The most common way of identifying the lubrication regime in a seal is to determine the friction coefficient (f) vs. duty parameter (G) plot, which is a Stribeck-type curve known in thrust bearings. The duty parameter G is defined by:

$$G = \frac{\eta\, vb}{F_N}, \tag{1}$$

where η is the dynamic viscosity of the sealing fluid, v is the sliding velocity on the mean face diameter, b is the face width and F_N is the net closing force. The f-G plots presented in the following section were classified into two groups, according to the test type from which they were obtained.

3.2.   Load study tests

Figure 6 shows how the f-G plot was constructed in tests performed at constant speed and increasing load during the test. Generally, the test started with the lowest load (60N or 0.2 MPa) resulting in low contact severity and favourable lubricating conditions, most probably with some sort of hydrodynamic load support. With increasing load the friction coefficient decreased. With increasing load asperity contact the load support also increased. When the envelope of minimum friction coefficient data attained its minimum value, it was considered that the transition from fluid (i.e. hydrodynamic) to mixed lubrication regime had occurred . The load was further increased until the friction coefficient abruptly increased indicating the wear transition, i.e. the performance limit was attained and the test was stopped.

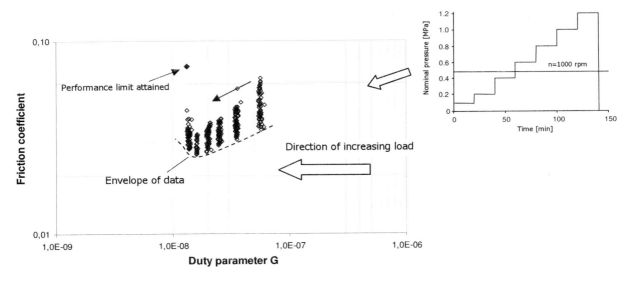

Figure 6. f-G plot in a load study test.

Figure 7 shows a set of f-G plots constructed at different speeds for all three surfaces. In general, in all cases the characteristic minimum point of the f-G curve was observed. Beyond the speed of 2000 rpm f-G plots with a minimum point, which represents the lubrication regime transition, could not obtained for PG surfaces, while beyond 3500 rpm for none of the surfaces. The transition point shifts with increasing speed to higher G values for all cases. Similarly, the friction coefficient of transition points with decreases increasing speed.

A drop in the highest transition friction coefficient from 0.029 at 500 rpm to 0.012 at 2000 rpm was observed for P/L surfaces (Fig. 7a). For FG surfaces the transition friction coefficient drop for the same conditions was the lowest, namely from 0.029 to 0.021 (Figure 7b). It is interesting that PG surfaces exhibited the lowest transition friction coefficient and lowest G transition value at lower speeds, as shown on Figure 7c.

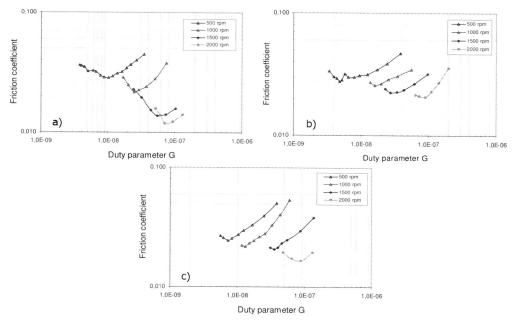

Figure 7. f-G plots for different speeds and surfaces in a load study:
a) polished (P/L); b) fine ground (FG) and; c) plane ground (PG)

3.3.   Speed study tests

Figure 8 shows the f-G plot construction in tests performed at constant nominal load and increasing shaft speed.

Generally, the severity of the contact was the worst at the beginning of test, starting with the lowest speed (500 rpm or 0.7 m/s). During the test, increasing speed enhanced hydrodynamic effects and therefore the load-carrying capacity of the fluid film. Consequently, the portion of asperity contacts reduced, which resulted in a lower friction coefficient, as shown in Fig. 9. When the envelope of friction coefficient data attained the minimum point, it was considered that the transition from mixed to hydrodynamic lubrication regime had occurred.

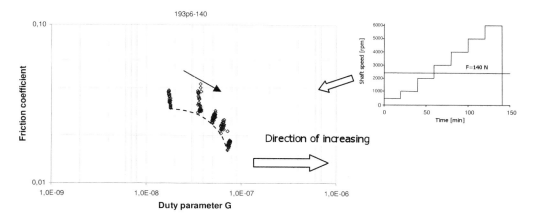

Figure 8. f-G plot in a speed study test.

This case in tests occurred only at 60 N (0.2 MPa) regardless of which surfaces being were used, as shown on Fig. 9. The transition friction coefficient assumed for all three cases had practically the same value of 0.028.

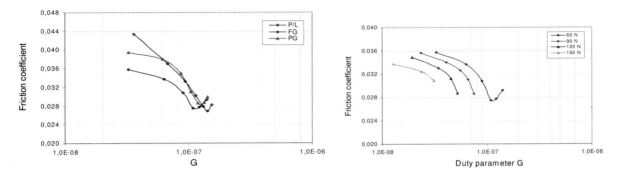

Figure 9. Regime transition in a speed study and f-G plots for different loads in a speed study with no transition point.

However, when the combined preset load and increased speed during the test were too high, they caused a wear transition before the transition from mixed to hydrodynamic lubrication could actually occurred. Therefore, for loads over 60 N only the left side of the f-G curve was constructed, as shown for the FG surfaces on Figure 9.

4. REGIME TRANSITION

A common characteristic observed for most f-G plots is that the transition from a hydrodynamic to a mixed lubrication regime occurs at different G values. In general, the reason for this phenomenon could be in different seal design, material combination and surface characteristics, but the influence of none is fully understood. The same seal-design and material combination were used throughout the tests; thus, the influence of the latter two factors was eliminated.

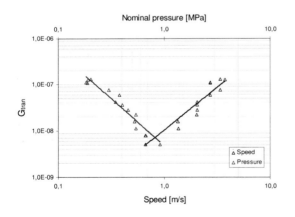

Figure 10. Correlation between speed, load and G in regime transition

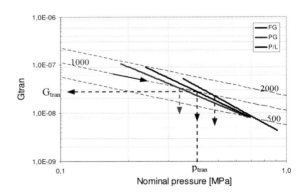

Figure 11. Regime transition as a function roughness

Figure 10 shows the G transition value as a function of speed and load (pressure) for FG surfaces. It can be seen that the transition from an ML to an HL regime is proportional to speed and inversely proportional to the nominal pressure. Such an empirically obtained chart is very useful in practice, since it can relatively precisely define the optimal working point of a seal.

The transition G values at the same operating conditions varied between different surfaces, as shown in Figure 11. This is a chart obtained from load study tests. The chart can be interpreted as follows. For example, at a given speed of 1000 rpm one starts at low pressure and follows the dashed line in the direction of increasing pressure (load) as indicated by the black arrow. The first intersect is the PG transition line indicating that a transition from a hydrodynamic to a mixed lubrication regime occurred and by which the transition pressure and G value are defined. Similarly, the transition pressure and G values for the P/L and FG surfaces are obtained, respectively.

A lower transition G value at a given speed indicates that a higher normal load is needed for the transition from a fluid to a mixed lubricating regime. According to hydrodynamic theory, this indicates a thicker fluid film which has a higher load-carrying capacity. Such surfaces, in our case the FG surfaces, have a higher capability to generate hydrodynamic load support. Hydrodynamic effects are higher at higher speeds, and therefore differences in the G transition value between different surfaces will here be larger, and the opposite at lower speeds where differences in G value diminish, as shown in Figure 11.

5. CONCLUSION

In general, f-G plots in a load study test exhibited a friction decrease with increasing load until the minimum point of the plots was attained, which represented the transition from a hydrodynamic to a mixed lubrication regime. Further load increase increased the contact load support and thus the friction coefficient. When the load reached a critical level for the wear transition of alumina, the performance limit was attained. Similarly, in speed study tests the friction coefficient decreased with increasing speed until the minimum of the f-G curve was attained. This time the minimum point represented the transition from a mixed to a hydrodynamic lubrication regime. However, the regime transition in these tests was achieved only at the lowest load of 60 N, because for all higher loads the condition for the wear transition of alumina was achieved before hydrodynamic lift-up could actually occur.

The transition G value varied with operating conditions, namely, with increasing speed the value increased, associated with a friction coefficient decrease, and similarly, with increasing load the transition G value decreased, associated with friction coefficient increase.

The influence of roughness on the regime transition was negligible at lower speeds. At higher speeds, fine ground surfaces exhibited the highest hydrodynamic load support of all surfaces, resulting in the lowest transition G value.

Polished surfaces exhibited the largest transition-friction coefficient drop from 0.029 at 500 rpm to 0.012 at 2000 rpm. The correlation functions between speed, load and the transition G value were obtained for all surfaces.

REFERENCES

[1]   Kumar P., Jain S.C., Ray S., Study of surface roughness effects in elastohydrodynamic lubrication of rolling line contacts using a deterministic model, Tribology International, 34, (2001), 713-722.
[2]   Majumdar A., Bhushan B., Characterization and modeling of surface roughness and contact mechanics, Chapter 4 in Handbook of micro/nano tribology, Bhushan B. (Ed.), CRC press, 1999, 187-247.
[3]   Zahouani H., Assoul M., Vargiolu R., Mathia T., The morphological tree transform of surface motifs. Incidence in tribology, International Journal Of Machine Tools & Manufacture, 41, (2001), 1961-1979.
[4]   Lebeck A.O., Principles and Design of Mechanical Face Seals, John Wiley & Sons, Inc., New York, (1991), 371, 404-472.
[5]   Muller H.K, Nau B.S., Fluid sealing technology, Marcel Dekker, Inc., New York, (1998), 235.
[6]   http://www.advpro.com/rings/rings4.htm
[7]   Kalin M., Vižintin J., "Rolling bearings and lubricants testing machine CTD-ML1", Journal of Mechanical Engineering, 45, 5-6 (1997), 239-247.

Session 3
LUBRICANTS & ADDITIVES 1

Chair: Prof. Joze Vižintin

Biodegradable Lubricants for a Sustainable Lifetime
H. BOCK, A. MARCAIDE, J. BARRIGA, E. ARANZABE,
O. AREITIOAURTENA, J. SEABRA

Room-Temperature Ionic Liquids: Green Solvents as Lubricants
A. E. JIMÉNEZ, M. D. BERMÚDEZ, G. MARTÍNEZ-NICOLÁS

Biolubricants for Heavy Duty Engine Oil
A. ARANZABE, A. IGARTUA, X. FERNÁNDEZ, B. FERNÁNDEZ,
O. AREITIOAURTENA, R. LUTHER, C. H. SEYFERT,
L. URDANGARÍN, P. ARRIBALZAGA, M. BERG, H. SCHULTHEIß,
M. WOYDT

Biodegradable Lubricants for a Sustainable Lifetime

H. Bock [1], A. Marcaide [2], J. Barriga [2], E. Aranzabe [2], O. Areitioaurtena [2], J. Seabra [3]

[1] ROWE Mineralölwerk GmbH, Borkensteiner Mühle, 7, 67308 Bubenheim, Germany
[2] Fundación Tekniker, Avda. Otaola, 20, 20600 Eibar, Spain
[3] Instituto de Engenharia Mecânica e Gestão Industrial, Rua do Barroco, 174, 4465-591 Porto, Portugal

ABSTRACT

The growing importance of environmental awareness has led to new demands for lubricants based on biodegradable materials. Besides that, the European Ecolabel for Lubricants has been published in the Official Journal (26th April 2005). The product group "lubricants" comprises hydraulic oils, greases, chainsaw oils, two-stroke oils, concrete release agents and other total loss lubricants, for use by consumers and professional users. To apply the European Eco-label the products have to meet requirements for performance, show limited toxicity to aquatic organisms, have high biodegradability and low potential for bioaccumulation and contain a certain percentage of renewable sources.

In this project equivalent bio-oils to their reference mineral oils have been developed for different application purposes. The bio-oil formulations requirements and the technical requirements have been considered as the main criteria for the development of bio-oils. Mixtures of base oils have been studied in order to achieve the main targets: technical performance, renewability and compatibility between them. Also adequate biodegradable and not ecotoxically harmful additives without generating any compatibility problems have been incorporated.

A comparative study of lubricants during use has been carried out in order to know whether they still accomplish its original specifications or not.

Keywords: European Ecolabel for lubricants, Technical Performance, Toxicity, Biodegradability, Renewability.

1. INTRODUCTION

The increasing awareness of environmental aspects has led the industry to become more sustainable and to adopt the use of environmentally friendly products. The market of biolubricants is still in a development stage and it's a priority to formulate high performance biodegradable lubricants in Europe.

According to the background document for the European Eco-label to lubricants [1], Several European countries regulations and policies exist in favour of biolubricants. In Germany, Austria and Switzerland, it is forbidden to use mineral oil based lubricants around inland waterways and in forest areas. In Italy there is a tax for mineral oils. In Portugal there is a regulation that mandates the use of biolubricant twostroke engine oils in outboard boat engines. In Belgium, it is required to use a biolubricant in all operations taking place near non-navigable waters. In the Netherlands there is an action programme in favour of biolubricants since 1996.

The vegetable oils are non-toxic and have low volatility, even more, vegetable oils pose no work-place hazards and are really biodegradable [2]. The polar ester groups which are present in the vegetable-based lubricants, are able to adhere to metal surfaces, and therefore, possess a good boundary lubrication properties. In addition, vegetable oils have high solubility power for polar contaminants and additive molecules [3].

On the other hand, vegetable oils have poor oxidation stability [4,5], so that they are highly susceptible to radical attack and consequently undergo oxidative degradation to form polar oxy-compounds [3]. Lubricants based on renewable resources, such as vegetables-based ones, have the challenge to maintain their environmentally friendliness and to attain an improved behaviour. To meet the increasing demands for stability during various tribochemical processes, the oils structure has to withstand extremes of temperature variations, shear degradation and maintain excellent boundary lubricating properties by strong chemical and physical adsorption on the metal surface in contact [6].

Latest studies to develop lubricants using vegetables oils include chemical modification of vegetable oils [3,6]. On the other hand, the use of additives allows to increase the overall performance of an oil and to improve its physical properties, but they also may raise the cost of lubricants and, in some cases, may even be harmful, as in the case of antioxidant lubricants commonly composed by phenolic and amine molecules [7,8].

Besides the technical behaviour, the industry thinks that the most important restriction for biolubricants is that they are 1,5 to 5 times more expensive than the conventional ones [2].

Until now, biodegradability has been the criteria to define if a lubricant could be named as biolubricant, however, in the future the renewability will be considered. The use of renewable materials benefits the environment by reducing greenhouse gases and the use of natural resources; improves the economic competitiveness of industry through the development of new markets and produces social benefits by stimulating rural communities. That meets the three pillars of sustainability because it will save fossil resources and because the uses of renewable raw materials in industry directly contributes to sustainable development, which recently was endorsed by heads of States and governments at their submit in Gothenburg as one of the Community's main political aims for the future [9].

2. EUROPEAN ECOLABEL FOR LUBRICANTS

The final criteria of European Eco-label for lubricants have been published in the Official Journal of 5 May 2005. It comprises hydraulic oils, greases, chainsaw oils, two stroke oils, concrete release agents and other total loss lubricants, for use by consumers and professional users.

The criteria are designed to reflect the philosophy of the new EU regulatory framework for chemicals (REACH - Registration, Evaluation and Authorization of Chemicals) and are in line with the Dangerous Substances Directive and Dangerous Preparations Directive.

The main criteria that have been included in this eco-label are the following:

Any R-phrases indicating environment and/or human health problems according to the classification, packaging and labelling of Dangerous Preparations Directive.

Aquatic toxicity requirements for the different lubricant subgroups (OECD 201, 202 &203). These criteria shall be provided for each constituent substance in the product by test method (OECD 201, 202, 203).

Biodegradability requirements for the different subgroups. The biodegradability shall be determined for each constituent substance in the product separately by test methods (OECD 301 A-F). The product shall not contain substances that are both non-biodegradable and bioaccumulative.

Renewable material requirements for the different subgroups. The formulated product shall have a carbon content derived from renewable raw materials.

3. DEVELOPMENT OF THE BIO-OIL

In order to develop an adequate biodegradable oil versus a mineral oil based Fuchs product Renolin MP 68 (ISO VG 68 / MP=Multi-purpose) which is currently in use for roller bearing purposes at FERSA, ROWE started some trials with higher saturated, renewable esters based biodegradable fluids.

The economical background has been to generate a relatively "universal" purpose oil for different applications on account of stock rationalization reasons and in order to minimize the incorrect first-fill service as well.

The classification of the mineral oil and its equivalent bio-oil has been studied: Renolin MP 68 fulfills the DIN 51 517/3 (CLP) and the automotive gear oil standard GL 4. Therefore, the important criteria requirements of FZG test rig (DIN 51 354/2) min.12 load stage under the stringent conditions A/16.6/120 and the Four ball (ASTM-D 2783) min. 250 kg have been kept.

The table 1 shows us the technical data of the biolubricants.

A good air release is necessary to avoid cavitation and resulting scuffing / pitting on the gear's surfaces. A bad yellow metal compatibility would lead to higher wear and possible gear damage and a bad seal compatibility to higher oil losses and in the last step finally to broken gears because of this oil loss.

The new developed bio-oil version A6 (BE2) consists of renewable esters plus less than 5% additive amount accordingly to the limits for biodegradable oils. The predominant parts of this additive package are special S-/P-compounds plus lower amounts of additional antioxidants, anti-wear and corrosion inhibitors.

If we compare MP 68 with A6 due to their kinematic viscosities we recognize that their viscosities at 100°C (v100) are more or less within the same range, although their v40 are entirely different. This results from the high Viscosity Index (VI) of higher than 150 of A6 whereas MP 68 only shows a VI of ~98. This offers the possibility to formulate the recipe with a lower ISO VG class: A6 is an ISO VG 46 oil on the upper limit with the result of improved heat transfer and less foaming characteristics under the same application conditions but with more or less identical film thickness at 100°C. A6's shear stability and deep temperature behaviour (pour point) are excellent.

The ageing property of A6 is quite good if we compare it with other commercially available biodegradable oils of the same viscosity grade. That is the fact of a well-balanced anti-oxidants/ basic ester system

The copper and brass compatibility are tested versus ASTM-D 130 at 3h/100°C without significant metal discolourations.

No corrosion occurred following the specific corrosion inhouse test RRSt 14O5 (plus 20% tap water 24h/100°C).

The extreme pressure behaviour of A6 is not as high as MP 68, because we focused on its "universal" application character as hydraulic and gear oil. For instance the FZG of 10 (under same severe conditions written above for MP 68) is fair. Hence it is not recommended for automotive applications, but for rolling contacts in gears is sufficient.

Table 1. Technical data of the bio-oil A6 (BE2) vs. Renolin MP 68

	BIO-bearing oil	**Norm**	**DIN 51 517/3**	**Mineral oil**
	ISO VG ...			**68**
	Product names		**CLP** ISO VG 46 / 68	**Renolin P 68**
Phys.-Chem. Data	v40 (mm²/s)		41.4-50.6 / 61.2-74.8	65.7
	v100 (mm²/s)		-	8.5
	VI		-	98
	P.P.(°C) max.		-15 / -15	-27
	Flp. (°C), COC min.		175 / 185	>210
	d15 (g/cm³)		-	0.890
	TAN (mgKOH/g)		-	-
AW / EP	Four ball EP weld load (kg) LWI (kg)	ASTM D 2783	-	250
	FZG, damage load A10/8.3/90 and A20/16.6/90	DIN 51 354/2	min. 12	>12 / min. 12
Corrosion	Cu-corrosion 3h@100°C	ASTM D 130	max. 2 (SEB)	< 2
	Steel corrosion method **A**-dest. water	ASTM D 665 A	pass	pass
	Corrosion vs. steel RRSt 14O5 tap water 24h@100°C	Inhouse test: 20 ml water in 130 ml oil	-	pass
Demulsibility	Demulsibility @82°C (min.)	DIN 51 599 ASTM D 1401	max. 30 (SEB)	10
	Demulsibility 10 ml oil in 150 ml water	Inhouse method 1 min. @54°C	-	Good (no emulsion phase)

(SEB): Stahl Eisen Blatt (german test methods)

The bio-oil A6 (BE2) has no foaming tendency and shows good air release behaviour even under severe conditions. Also the tested demulsibility at 54°C was acceptable.

The seal compatibility of A6 in relation to MP 68 is critical when tested against typical NBR-seals. Normally esters tend to shrink or swell such NBR (rubber) sealings depending on their chemical structures. Therefore Viton is recommended to avoid these problems of damaging sealings and resulting oil leakages etc..

In general esters show better friction coefficients than equiviscous mineral oils, but depending on their chemical structures of worse yellow metal and seal compatibilities. To minimize or even overcome such problems, special alloys and Viton sealings are recommended.

The biodegradability has been determined for each constituent in the bio-oil separately (base oils and additives used in the formulation) by OECD 301F test. Besides that, the toxicity has been evaluated by OECD 201 and 202 tests. All of them are ready biodegradable and non-toxic. On the contrary, the mineral oil was not biodegradable.

4. COMPARATIVE STUDY OF LUBRICANTS DURING USE

A new oxidation method has been developed and used instead of ASTM D 943, widely used to evaluate the oxidation stability of inhibited steam-turbine oils in the presence of oxygen, water, and copper and iron metals at 95°C and ASTM D 2274, to measure the inherent stability of middle distillate petroleum fuels under specified oxidizing conditions at 95°C. The oxidation conditions were the following: 1.5 l of lubricant in a bath reactor at 140°C with stirring, air flux and without presence of water and catalyst. This oxidation process has allowed us to compare the bio-oil versus the mineral oil degradation mechanism in the same oxidation conditions.

In the case of mineral oil, the warning level was reached at 182 h of oxidation and the danger limit was reached at 288 h of oxidation. The biodegradable oil was submitted to an oxidation process during 2214 h in order to study the whole degradation process.

5. RESULTS

As shown the table 2, the viscosity, density, %Solids and Acid Number increase with the time due to the oxidation.

Table 2. Study of lubricants during use.

	A.N.	RULER	Viscosity at 40°C	Density	Water separation-Oil	Water separation-Water	Water separation-Emulsion	% Solids
Mineral-0il	0.47	---	68.11	0.889	40	37	3	0.64
Mineral oil-24	0.47	---	73.15	0.888	40	40	0	0.75
Mineral oil-48	0.86	---	77.92	0.889	36	22	22	0.79
Mineral oil-72	0.98	---	79.72	0.890	30	14	36	0.80
Mineral oil-96	1.06	---	82.66	0.891	22	13	45	0.82
Mineral oil-182	1.09	---	89.48	0.893	29	24	27	1.65
Mineral oil-216	1.12	---	91.32	0.894	37	25	18	1.94
Mineral oil-288	2.40	---	129.14	0.902	47	23	10	2.07
Biolubricant	0.47	100	49.98	0.952	40	40	0	0.68
Biolubricant-24	0.42	95.6	49.20	0.952	40	30	10	0.68
Biolubricant-48	0.45	95.2	49.23	0.953	35	15	30	0.68
Biolubricant-72	0.51	94.8	49.50	0.952	31	26	23	0.70
Biolubricant-96	0.55	94.6	49.36	0.952	40	40	0	0.71
Biolubricant-168	0.68	94.0	48.94	0.953	40	40	0	0.71
Biolubricant-216	0.74	93.4	49.10	0.954	40	40	0	0.74
Biolubricant-366	1.15	40.6	49.20	0.955	40	40	0	0.85
Biolubricant-432	2.32	16.1.1	49.22	0.956	40	40	0	0.97
Biolubricant-504	3.04	16.0-	49.43	0.956	40	40	0	0.98
Biolubricant-1020	4.81	15.0	46.15	0.956	40	40	0	0.98
Biolubricnat-1350	6.56	0	46.63	0.958	40	40	0	1.20
Biolubricant-1974	16.08	0	53.48	0.965	2	0	78	2.56
Biolubricant-2142	18.04	0	62.01	0.970	2	0	78	6.0

The chemical process involved in oxidation process has been monitored by FTIR in the zone I (3520-3220 cm^{-1}) hydroxyl groups, zone II (1850-1612 cm^{-1}) carbonyl groups and zone III (1175-1135 cm^{-1}) C-O groups. The emulsification capacity increases slightly in the first stage of the oxidation but in the latest stages of it decreases due to the polymerization. The Ruler Test has not been carried out as the mineral oil has no antioxidant additives. Taking into account the AN, % Solids and Viscosity evolution, the mineral oil has reached the warning level at 182h of oxidation and the danger limit at 288 h.

In the case of the biolubricants, there aren't limits established for the AN, and Viscosity. The table 1 shows two strong changes in the Viscosity, Acid Number and Ruler at 432 h and 1350h of oxidation. The monitoring by FTIR has been carried out in three zones wider that in the case of mineral oil: zone I (3725-2900 cm^{-1}), zone II (1850-1550 cm^{-1}) and zone III (1400-1000 cm^{-1}) due to the complex nature of the oxygenated compounds which are formed.

In the table3 there is a summary of the results of friction (COF) and wear obtained during the tribological tests.

Table 3.Results of friction and wear.

Oil	COF Mean	Mean Wear Scar (μm)
Bio Oil A6	0.09	756
Bio oil A6 oxidized for 216 hours	0.09	787
Bio oil A6 oxidized 432 hours	0.10	902
Bio Oil A6 oxidized for 504 hours	0.10	884
Bio Oil A6 oxidized for 1974 hours	0.10	947
Bio Oil A6 oxidized for 2214 hours	0.10	862

It can be observed that there is no difference in the coefficient of friction: new of aged oils present a friction around 0.09-0.10. Regarding wear there is a slight variation but again there are not conclusive data.

In order to extract more information from the tribological data friction plots and wear scars have to be examined in detail (see next graphs):

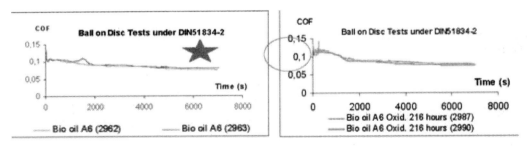

Bio oil A6 Bio oil A6 Oxidized 216 hours

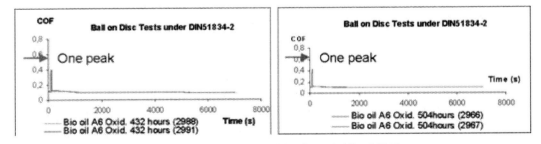

Bio oil A6 Oxidized 432 hours Bio oil A6 Oxidized 504 hours

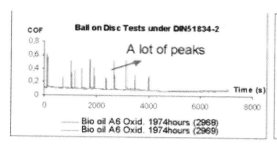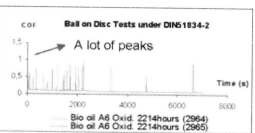

Bio oil A6 Oxidized 1974 hours Bio oil A6 Oxidized 2214 hours

Microwelding in the tribological test is indicated by an increase in the friction coefficient greater than 0.2 over the steady state. We can appreciate that, whereas the average coefficient of friction is not affected, the number of microwelding peaks increase with the oxidation time.

6. CONCLUSIONS

The oxidation mechanism for biolubricants are different from the mineral oils. This fact has been checked by means of emulsionability and solids content measurements.

A new oxidation method must be standardized for the evaluation of the oxidation stability of biolubricants as the available standardized methods are for mineral oils.

The % solids has been selected as the main parameter to control the oxidation level in biolubricants. Other techniques which allow to control the oxidation degree are the FTIR and Ruler. Those techniques must be correlated with traditional lubricant monitoring parameters as AN, Viscosity, considering wider zones in the case of FTIR.

In the standard wear tests there are not clear differences in average friction or scar sizes when new or oxidized bio-oils are tested. However, looking in more detail the friction plots reveals that microwelding peaks appear when aged lubricants are tested. Even more, there is a direct relationship in between aging hours and friction peaks. These peaks are resulted of an unstable behaviour caused by the oxidation.

ACKNOWLEDGEMENTS

This work is being developed in the framework of the BIOMON European project (Project contract N° COOP-CT 2004-508208).

REFERENCES

[1]   D. Theodori (2004), "Development of criteria for the award of European Eco-label to lubricants".

[2]   N.S. Battersby (1998), Chemosphere 24, 1998-2000, "A correlation between the biodegradability of oil products in the CEC L-33-T-82 and modified strum test tests".

[3]   A. Adhvaryu (2005), Industrial Crops and Products, 21, 113-119, "Synthesis of novel alkoxylated triacylglycerols and their lubricant base oil properties".

[4]   A. Adhvaryu (2000), Thermochimica Acta, 364, 87-97 "Oxidation kinetics studies of oils derived from unmodified and genetically modified vegetables using pressurized differential scanning calorimetry and nuclear magnetic resonance spectroscopy".

[5]   N.J. Fox et al. (2001), Lubrication Engineering, 57, 14-20, "Sealed Capsule Differential Scanning Calorimetry-An Effective Method for Screening the oxidation Stability of vegetable oil formulations".

[6]   A. Adhvaryu (2004), Wear, 257, 359-367, "Tribological studies of thermally and Chemically modified vegetable oils use as environmentally friendly lubricants".

[7]   J. Ameye and R.Kaufman (2001), Turbine lubrication in the 21st century ASTM STP 1407, "Antioxidant analysis for monitoring remaining useful life of turbine fluids".

[8]   (2001) "About Performance Additives and Fluids" Great Lakes Chemical Corporation (http://www.e1.greatlakes.com/webapp/jsp/paf_about.jsp).

[9]   R. Ferret (2005), Proceedings of 4th International conference on Business and Sustainable Performance, Aalborg-Denmark, "Health and Environmental benefits substituting conventional mineral sources by vegetal ones in the production of dielectrics fluids through a Life Cycle Assessment".

Room-Temperature Ionic Liquids: Green Solvents as Lubricants

A. E. Jiménez, M. D. Bermúdez, G. Martínez-Nicolás

Grupo de Ciencia de Materiales. Dpto. Ingeniería de Materiales y Fabricación. Universidad Politécnica de Cartagena. Campus de la Muralla del Mar. 30203-Cartagena (Spain)
e-mail: anaeva.jimenez@upct.es; mdolores.bermudez@upct.es; gines.martinez@upct.es

ABSTRACT

Room-temperature imidazolium ionic liquids have been used as lubricants of aluminium-steel contacts. Their tribological performance has been studied both as neat lubricants and as oil additives and compared with that of a mineral naphtenic-paraffinic oil and with that of the synthetic ester propylene glycol dioleate. Friction values and wear rates under variable conditions are discussed in terms of thermal stability, viscosity, molecular structure and reactivity of the lubricants.

Keywords: Lubricants and Additives, Lubricant Testing.

1. INTRODUCTION

The rapid expansion of the use of aluminium alloys in sectors such as aircraft, automobile and precision machinery industries, makes it necessary to develop the tribological study of these materials.

It is estimated that synthetic lubricants represent around 10% of the global lubricating oil production. Of particular interest are environmentally friendly ester derivatives of natural fatty dicarboxylic acids [1].

Some esters have been reported as effective aluminium-steel lubricants and have been used in rolling processes [2]. However, some of these synthetic lubricants increase aluminium wear. On the other hand, conventional antiwear additives, which were developed for mineral oils, cannot be applied to low viscous esters.

Low viscous lubricating fluids are expected to exhibit low friction under hydrodynamic lubrication. However, their tribological properties under boundary conditions are usually unsatisfactory [3]. Therefore, effective antiwear additives and friction modifiers are necessary.

Esters are inherently polar molecules. Previous results suggest that polar additives are effective in polar oils. Some organic salts have been shown [4] to reduce wear in polar esters, but they promote corrosive reactions and their thermal stability was too low for practical purposes. Therefore, a precise study of molecular structure and its relation to tribological properties has to be taken into account when developing new base oils or additives.

Ionic liquids (ILs) are salts with a melting point lower than room temperature and are called green solvents because they are non-volatile, non-flammable and have high thermal and chemical stabilities. In the case of imidazolium ionic liquids, their properties can be tailored by varying the alkyl side chains attached to the nitrogen atoms and the anion species [5, 6, 7].

We have previously shown [6, 7] the lubricating ability of a series of ionic liquids in aluminium-steel contacts both as neat lubricants and as mineral oil additives.

In the present work we will compare the tribological properties of imidazolium ionic liquids with that of a mineral oil (MO) and a synthetic oil, propylene glycol dioleate (PGDO) when used as lubricants of Al2011-AISI52110 in pin-on-disk contacts. The results are discussed in terms of tribochemical processes and of the thermal stability, molecular structure, polarity and viscosity values of the lubricants.

2. RESULTS AND DISCUSSION

2.1. Thermal stability of the neat lubricants.

From the point of view of practical application, one of the relevant characteristics of the lubricants is their thermal stability.

Table 1 shows the weight loss variation with increasing temperature obtained by thermogravimetric analysis for the two base oils and for two ionic liquids (L102 = 1-ethyl, 3-methylimidazolium tetrafluoroborate and L106 = 1-hexyl, 3-methylimidazolium tetrafluoroborate).

Table 1. Thermal properties of the neat lubricants

Lubricant	Temperature (°C)	Weight loss (%)
Mineral oil (MO)	149.9	2.7
	304.2	78.5
	351.0	98.3
Synthetic oil (PGDO)	150.0	14.2
	314.4	78.5
	357.7	96.6
Ionic liquid (L102)	149.6	0.05
	423.2	93.0
	459.6	96.1
Ionic liquid (L106)	149.5	1.3
	398.6	91.2
	431.1	95.9

As can be seen, the synthetic ester PGDO shows the lowest thermal stability, with a 14% weight loss at 150°C. At this temperature, the weight loss for the other three oils is much lower, the order of stability being L102 >L106 >MO >PGDO. Complete decomposition takes place around 350°C for both PGDO and MO oils, however this decomposition temperature increases to 459 and 431°C for the ILs L102 and L106, respectively.

2.2. Friction coefficients and tribochemical processes.

The higher thermal stability of ionic liquids is one of the factors that account for their good lubricating ability at high temperature. Figure 1 shows friction records with time for Al2011 disks sliding against AISI52100 pins lubricated with MO, PGDO and L106 at 100°C. Both the mineral MO and synthetic PGDO oils show similar high friction values (mean value of 0.19 for the MO and the PGDO), while L106 gives a mean friction value of 0.11. However, after an initial low friction, an increase is observed, to recover a lower friction coefficient from mid test to the end.

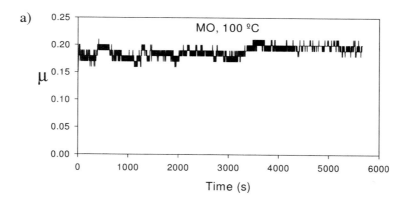

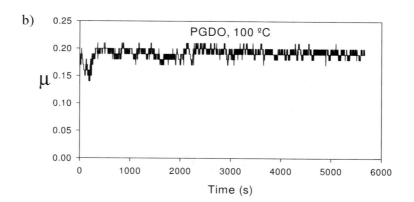

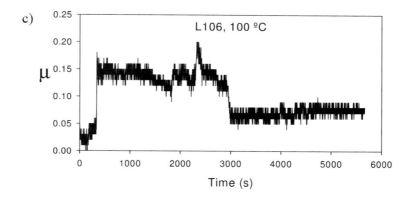

Figure 1. Friction records for MO, PGDO and L106 at 100 °C, 0.15 ms^{-1}, 2.45 N.

Also relevant is the fact that at 200°C, temperature at which the mineral and synthetic oils show thermal decomposition, the ionic liquid L106 (Figure 2) is still a better lubricant than the base oils at 100°C. In this case, a similar behaviour to that described at 100°C is also observed, but the maximum friction reaches higher values at 200°C.

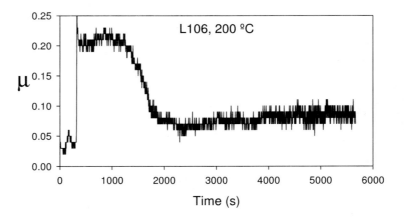

Figure 2. Friction records for L106 at 200 °C, 0.15 ms^{-1}, 2.45 N.

These friction increments at high temperature are related to tribochemical changes at the aluminium-steel contact due to tribocorrosion reactions with the lubricant. Figure 3 shows SEM micrographs and EDS spectra and Figure 4 shows elemental maps of wear debris particles from Al disc after the lubrication test with L106 at 200°C.

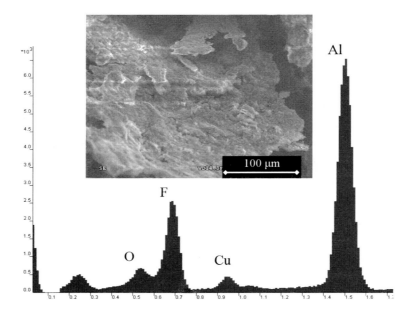

Figure 3. Micrograph and EDS spectrum of wear debris after lubrication with L106 at 200 °C.

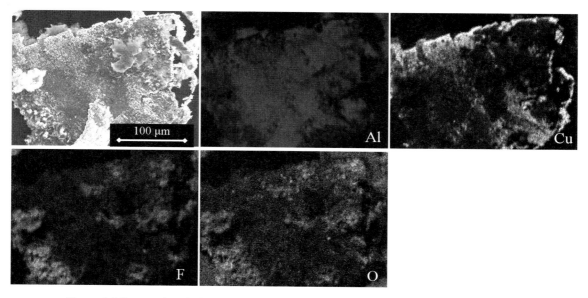

Figure 4. Micrograph and elemental map of wear debris after lubrication with L106 at 200 °C.

Wear debris particles contain the main alloy elements aluminium and copper. Together with aluminium oxide, the tribochemical reaction of L106 with Al at 200°C produces aluminium fluoride.

2.3. Wear rates as a function of the properties of base oils and additives.

Aluminium atoms on the moist surface combine with oxygen to form an oxide layer [2]. Synthetic lubricants such as alcohols, carboxylic acids and esters strongly bind to hydrophilic substrates through hydrogen bonds [5]. This could reduce friction, but if many of these molecules contact the Al surface, they react to form compounds which are less protective than the oxide layer. In this way, synthetic lubricants could give higher wear values than mineral oils.

The good lubricating ability of ILs has been attributed to the polarity of their molecules and their ability to form ordered adsorbed layers.

C. Wakai et al. [8] have determined the polarity of 1-alkyl-3-methylimidazolium salts, from dielectric constant ($\in$) measurements. The results classify ILs as moderately polar fluids, with $\in$ values between 8.8 and 15.2.

These polarity values are of the same order as those obtained for alcohols of intermediate chain length such as n-pentanol ($\in$ =15.1) and n-octanol ($\in$ =8.89).

Alkyl chain length and anion nature influence the polarity of the molecules. Thus, for the same BF_4^- anion (see Table 2), polarity decreases with increasing chain length (L102 >L106). But it also depends markedly on the anion. The anion polarity sequence being: trifluoromethylsulfonate $(CF_3SO_3)^-$ > tetrafluoroborate (BF_4^-) ≈ hexafluorophosphate (PF_6^-).

Table 2. *N*-alkyl-3-methylimidazolium ionic liquids used in Al2011-AISI52100 lubrication.

IL	Imidazolium cation	R_1	R_2	Anion
L102			C_2H_5	BF_4^-
L106			C_6H_{13}	
L-T102		CH_3	C_2H_5	$(CF_3SO_3)^-$
L-P106			C_6H_{13}	PF_6^-

Wear rates have been determined for aluminium 2011 disks sliding against AISI 52100 steel pins lubricated with the mineral and synthetic oils modified by a 1wt.% addition of the four ILs shown in Table 2.

The antiwear properties of the four IL additives with respect to the two base oils is illustrated in Figure 5, as a function of base oil viscosity and additive polarity.

The Wear Index [3] has been calculated as follows:

$$Wear\ Index = \frac{\left(Wear\ rate\ of\ oil + 1\%\ additive\right) - \left(Wear\ rate\ of\ base\ oil\right)}{\left(Wear\ rate\ of\ base\ oil\right)}$$

Thus, neat base oils have a wear index of 0, while a negative wear index means that the additives improve the antiwear properties of the base oils.

In the first place, it is important to notice that, in all cases, MO+1%IL gives lower wear rates than the corresponding PGDO+1%IL mixtures, probably due to the lower viscosity of PGDO.

Although all additives improve the mineral oil (MO) performance, antiwear properties are higher for those ILs with the highest polarity (L102 and L-T102).

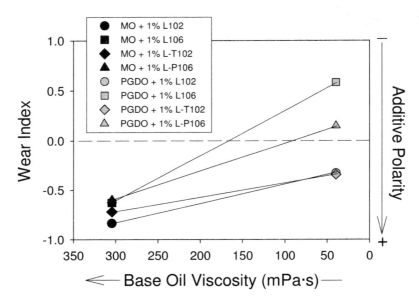

Figure 5. Wear Index for the ionic liquids L102, L106, L-T102 y L-P106 used as 1 wt% additives in the mineral and synthetic oil (25 °C, 0.15 ms^{-1}, 2,45 N).

Again, in the case of the synthetic oil, the wear reduction capacity of the additives is in agreement with increasing molecular polarity. The less polar L106 and L-P106 additives increase aluminium wear rate with respect to PGDO due to their low miscibility with the synthetic ester.

ACKNOWLEDGEMENTS

We wish to thank the financial support of the Fundación Séneca de la Región de Murcia (00447-PI-04), the Spanish Ministry of Education and the EU FEDER program (MAT2005-00067).

REFERENCES

[1] Gryglewicz S, Stankiewicz M, Oko FA, Surawska I. Esters of dicarboxylic acids as additives for lubricating oils. Tribology International 2006; 39(6):560-564.

[2] Igari S, Mori S, Takikawa Y. Effects of molecular structure of aliphatic diols and polyalkylene glycol as lubricants on the wear of aluminum. Wear 2000; 244(1-2):180-184.

[3] Minami I, Hirao K, Memita M, Mori S. Investigation of anti-wear additives for low viscous synthetic esters: Hydroxyalkyl phosphonates. Tribology International In Press, Corrected Proof, doi: 10.1016/j.triboint.2005.11.012.

[4] Minami I, Mori S. Antiwear additives for ester oils. Journal of Synthetic Lubrication 2005; 22(2):105-121.

[5] Zhang P, Xue Q, Du Z, Zhang Z. The tribological behaviors of ordered system ultrathin films. Wear 2003; 254(10):959-964.

[6] Jimenez AE, Bermudez MD, Iglesias P, Carrion FJ, Martinez-Nicolas G. 1-N-alkyl -3-methylimidazolium ionic liquids as neat lubricants and lubricant additives in steel-aluminium contacts. Wear In Press, Corrected Proof, doi: 10.1016/j.wear.2005.04.016.

[7] Jimenez AE, Bermudez MD, Carrion FJ, Martinez-Nicolas G. Room temperature ionic liquids as lubricant additives in steel-aluminium contacts: Influence of sliding velocity, normal load and temperature. Wear In Press, Corrected Proof, doi: 10.1016/j.wear.2005.11.004.

[8] Wakai C, Oleinikova A, Ott M, Weingartner H. How polar are ionic liquids? Determination of the static dielectric constant of an imidazolium-based ionic liquid by microwave dielectric spectroscopy. Journal of Physical Chemistry B 2005; 109(36):17028-17030.

Biolubricants for Heavy Duty Engine Oil

A. Aranzabe [1], A. Igartua [1], X. Fernández [1], B. Fernández [1], O. Areitioaurtena [1], R. Luther [2], C. H. Seyfert [2], L. Urdangarín [3], P. Arribalzaga [3], M. Berg [4], H. Schultheiß [4], M. Woydt [5]

[1] Fundación Tekniker, Eibar, Spain
[2] FUCHS, Germany
[3] Guascor, Vitoria, Spain
[4] IAV, Germany
[5] BAM, Germany

ABSTRACT

In this paper a study of the biodegradability and the tribological properties has been realised for engine oils. Finally, the real simulation tests have also been performed. The biodegradable oils have improved friction behaviour and antiwear properties that make then suitable to be applied to engine oil.

1. INTRODUCTION

Replacing mineral oils with biodegradable products is one of the ways to reduce adverse effects on the ecosystem caused by the use of lubricants. It concerns, in particular, a group of lubricants that, as a result of inevitable or uncontrolled leakages, can penetrate the environment (e.g. heavy duty engines).

The use of ester oils for engine lubricants, as substitutes for mineral oils, can result in different kinds of environmental compatibility:

❑   Rapid biodegradability and lower toxicity.
❑   Lower fuel consumption due to improved tribological properties: The polarity of ester oils offers excellent lubricity in boundary friction conditions, combined with a very high natural Viscosity Index
❑   Favourable influence on exhaust gas emissions due to lower evaporation losses in combination with adapted additivation: increase of lifetime of after-treatment systems.

The new ester-based engine oils have to be formulated with carefully selected additives to minimise the overall ecological impact. The biggest challenge is the reduction of substances with negative effects on the lifetime of exhaust gas after-treatment systems. Today, these substances are responsible for wear protection and engine cleanliness. The use of innovative chemistry has allowed the formulation of oils that combine today's performance with tomorrow's requirements for environmental impact reduction.

2. EXPERIMENTAL DETAILS

GUASCOR's main interest is the reduction of fuel consumption and therefore CO_2-emissions in heavy duty Diesel engines. Besides, increased oil life and reduction of particle and hydrocarbon emissions are of big interest. To meet these targets, three main issues have been addressed in the development of a new oil candidate. First of all, the viscosity at operating conditions has been significantly reduced to achieve improved fuel efficiency. A major reduction of volatility and sulphur content is supposed to reduce the particle and hydrocarbon emissions. This is achieved by using new additive technology and a suitable ester-based fluid. A summary of the physical data of the candidate fluids developed by Fuchs is given in Table 1.

Figure 1 illustrates the difference between today's reference oil and the new HDDO *ehd-22*. There is a strong reduction in metal-organic content (displayed as S-ash) to less than half of today's value. As a consequence, the total base number TBN is reduced, too. However, by using new additive technology, the deposit formation in the panel coker test is better than in the original oil. Besides, the reduction of sulphur content in land fuels will lead to lower demands in basicity, since less SO_2 will be produced. Thus, the lower TBN seems feasible.

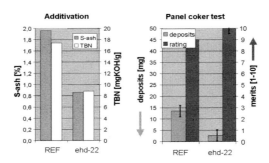

Figure 1. Comparison of detergent-additivation and resulting deposits in panel coker test

Table 1. Physical and chemical data of specification and candidate oils ehd-25, ehd-26, ehd27, ehd28, ehd29, ehd30 and ehd-31

			HDDO-Ref.	Ehd-25	Ehd-26	Ehd-27	Ehd-28	Ehd-29	Ehd-30	Ehd-31
	SAE grade		15W40	10W30	10W30	XW40	XW40	XW40	XW40	0W20
Viscosity	Kin. Viscosity @40℃	[mm²/s]	108	57	57	81.2	79.5	72.1	75.9	41.8
	Kin. Viscosity @100℃	[mm²/s]	14.4	9.3	9.4	13.5	13.2	14	14.4	8.6
	CCS@ -20℃		6300							
	CCS@ -25℃	[mPas]		4700	4800			2300		
	CCS@ -35℃	[mPas]						4300		4600
	HTHS@ 150℃	[mPas]	4.2	3	3.1					2.9
Shear stability (Bosch)			n.d.	Yes	Yes					-
Pour point		[℃]	<-25	<-48	<-48					-45
Elements	P	[mg/kg]	1135	590	600					570
	S	[%wt]	1.2	1400ppm	1580ppm					2300ppm
	Zn	[mg/kg]	1230	Free	Free					Free
Sulphated ash		[%wt]	1.95	0.8	0.8					0.5
TBN		[mgKOH/g]	17.2	7.3	7.8					8.7
Noack evaporation loss		[%wt]	11.5	7	7					6
Fuel efficiency potential acc. To M111-FE (CEC-L54) engine test		[%]	-	-	-					3.9
Biodegradability OECD 301F		[%]		71	64		74			74
Toxicity OECD 201, 202		[mg/l]		>100	>100		>100			>100

The activity from BAM has been related to the blending and characterization of the poliglycol lubricants. Their thermophysical determination, HTHS measurements, pressure resistance, heat capacity, and conductivity.have been measured (See Table 1).

Table 2. Properties of polyglycol-based lubricant tested

Lubricant	ICOT Life TAN or $A\eta_{40℃}$+100%	η_{40}(mm²/s)	OECD301F (%)	Aquatic toxicity algae daphnia fish OECD (mg/l)	
				201	202
PPG32-2+3.2% Phopani	96h	40	79	519	733

PAG water soluble and PPG oil soluble have been considered. A new biolubricant designed PPG32-2+3.2 sample has been selected for the comparison.

Oxidative evaporation losses of polypropyleneglycols have been evaluated. The resistance against oxidation was evaluated using the French ICOT (iron catalysed oxidation test) test, which is standardized in GFC Lu T 02. 96 h in the ICOT test corresponds to a potential of drain of up to 30.000 km.

The data in Table 2 underline the bionotox-properties of the custom made polygylcol base oils, but also the antiverse effect of the proprieraty additive package regarding the bionotox-properties.

3. BIODEGRADABILITY AND TOXICITY TESTS

Biodegradability and toxicity tests are performed in order to assess the biodegradability and toxicity of the new lubricants.

Table 3. Result of EHD25, EHD26, EHD28, EHD31 and PPG32-2 with 3.2% Phopani samples. Fully formulated motor oils.

Day	Ehd-25	Ehd-26	Ehd-28	Ehd-31	PPG-32
0	0	0	0	0	0
7	39.4	35.79	16.7	37.34	12.3
14	58.16	49.7	36	52.81	44.4
21	70.36	56.66	54.84	59.02	75.4
28	71.29	63.62	73.91	74.13	79.3

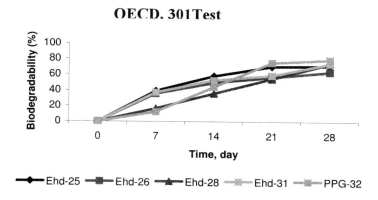

Figure 2. Result of EHD25, EHD26, EHD28, EHD31 and PPG32-2 with 3.2% Phopani samples. Fully formulated motor oils.

Ecotoxicity results developed with Test OECD 202 "Daphnia Magna" and Test OECD 201, Algal Growth Inhibition (The 24h EC_{50} Acute Immobilisation) show that all new lubricants developed are classified like "Not Harmful" to aquatic organisms with EC_{50}>100 mg/l.

4. TRIBOLOGICAL TESTS

Tribological tests were performed to simulate different engine applications, such as *piston ring, stem valve guide and journal bearing simulations.*

Piston Ring Simulation Tests in SRV Tribometer:

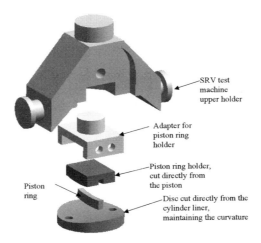

Figure 3. Piston Ring Simulation configuration

To study these new oils we have chosen the **PL72 piston ring** from Tarabusi (CIE Automotive Group). Also we had compared these new lubricants with the Reference Oil M4000. The first tests conditions were (Extreme Pressure conditions): time: 41 minutes, load: 50/2000N (increasing the load by 100N every 2 minutes using the slow ramp until the limit load of the apparatus is attained, or failure occurs. Failure is indicated by a rise in coefficient of friction of greater than 0.35 oversteady state or stoppage in the oscillating of the test machine), frequency: 50Hz, stroke: 3mm, temperature: 200°C. As a result, the new bio lubricants EHD25, EHD26, EHD27, EHD28, EHD29 and EHD30 presented higher resistance to the load than the reference oil. These new oils support the highest friction load at which no failure occurs, 2000N. The new oil EHD31 and PPG32-2 3.2% have similar extreme pressure properties to the reference oil.

Table 4. Piston Ring Simulation. Extreme Pressure Conditions Tests Results.

Oils	Extreme Pressure Conditions		
	Time at which test is terminated (minutes)	The highest friction load at which no failure occurs (N)	Type of failure*
Reference M4000	31	1500	Stroke<0,3 mm
EHD25	41	2000	No failure
EHD26	41	2000	No failure
EHD27	41	2000	No failure
EHD28	41	2000	No failure
EHD29	41	2000	No failure
EHD30	41	2000	No failure
EHD31	28	1400	Stroke<0,3 mm
PPG32-2 3.2%	33	1500	Stroke<0,3 mm

*The failure is considered when the first micro-welding appears.

The second tests conditions are (Wear conditions): time: 90 minutes, load: 50/300N, frequency: 50Hz, stroke: 3mm, temperature: 200° C. Therefore, the new bio lubricant EHD28 has slightly better friction and wear behaviour than the reference oil but the difference is not very significant.

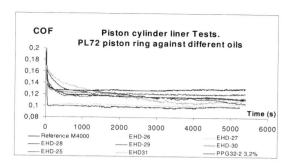 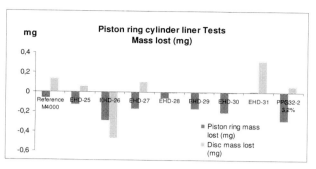

Figure 4. Piston Ring Simulation. Wear Conditions Tests Results

Stem valve-guide Simulation Tests in SRV Tribometer:

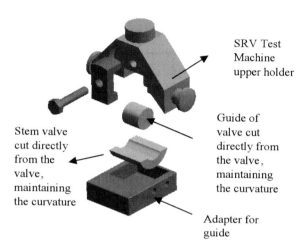

Figure 5. Stem valve-guide simulation configuration

To study these new oils we have chosen two different guide materials, designated **PL108 and PLS120.** Also we have compared these new lubricants with the Reference Oil M4000. The tests conditions are (Wear conditions): time: 1 hour, load: 135/135N, frequency: 50Hz, stroke: 2mm, temperature: 200ºC. As a result, the new bio lubricants EHD25, EHD26 and EHD28 have better friction behaviour than the reference oil with the two guide materials tested. The new oil EHD31 and PPG32-2 3.2% have similar friction behaviour to the reference oil with the two guide materials tested. However, the difference between different bio oils is not very high.

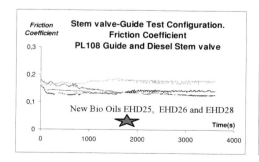 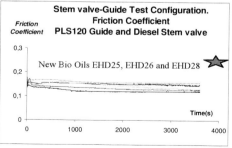

Figure 6. Stem Valve-Guide Simulation. Wear Conditions Tests Results

Journal Bearing Simulation Tests" in a SRV Tribometer: The sample used as a bearing is cut directly from the real bearing maintaining the curvature. The bush material is 42CrV4 and the sample is a roller with a diameter of 16mm. The contact represented is a line and the movement oscillatory. In these tests the fluctuations of the friction coefficient were high. The Guascor materials (**sputterlayer coating and reference materials**) have similar friction and wear behaviour with all of the oils tested. We can only see a slightly lower mass loss of the sputtered layer bearing with the bio oils EHD26 and EHD25.

To study these new oils we have also chosen two different IAV reference materials, designated **AlSn6 and CuPb22Sn and a new developed coating, TiCN/DLC**. Also we have compared these new lubricants with the Reference Oil M4000. The tests conditions are (Wear conditions): time: 30 minutes, load: 50/250N, frequency: 10Hz, stroke: 1mm, temperature: 90ºC. The TiCN/DLC material has the best friction behaviour with all of the oils tested. We can also say that the difference between TiCN/DLC material and the two reference IAV materials is relevant. With reference to to wear or mass lost we can say that the bush mass lost is very low. So we have only considered the bearing mass lost to study different oils and materials. The TiCN/DLC material presents the lowest mass lost of the bearing with all of oils tested. Finally, we can also say that the bio oils EHD25, EHD31 and PPG32-2 3.2% have a good friction and wear behaviour. According to this test it seems that the coating TiCN/DLC could be a good alternative for the reference materials, AlSn6 and CuPb22Sn.

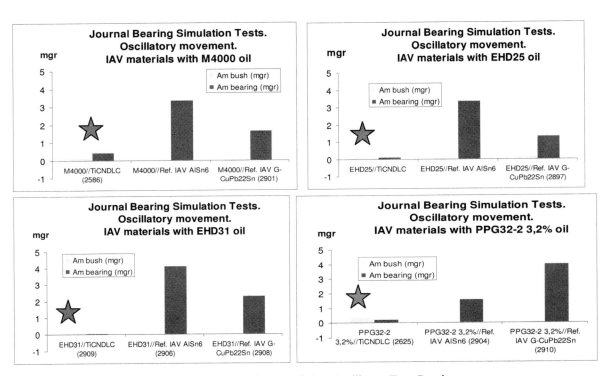

Figure 7. Journal Bearing Simulation. Oscillatory Tests Results

Journal bearing Simulation (Wettability Tests) A commercial goniometer (Surftens UNIVERSAL) has been used to do the wettability measurements. This device uses an optical method to measure the contact angle (θ), the so-called *Sessile Drop method*. A droplet of a liquid is dispensed on a solid surface with the help of a syringe. The drop is iluminated with diffuse light in order to obtain an image of the drop with sharp border. The image is recorded with a camera and the angle between the baseline of the drop and the tangent at the droplet boundary is measured by special software. It is also possible to to apply this method on curved samples. In this way, it is possible to estimate wetting properties of a localized region on a solid surface.

All the possible combinations between 3 flat samples (**2 reference materials and the developed coating TiCN/DLC**) and 3 lubricants (2 new bio oils and the reference M4000) have been tested. All the possible combinations between 2 curved samples (bearings) and 3 lubricants have also been tested. As a result, TiCNDLC and EHD25 bio oil have been found to have the best wettability behaviour.

Journal bearing Simulation (Thrust washer test in Unidirectional tribometer):

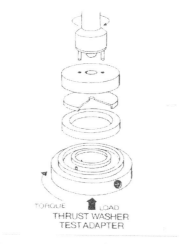

Figure 8. Thrust washer configuration

To study this new oil we have chosen an uncoated ring (50CrV4 material) which was tested against another disc which is a typical sheet steel of bearing coated with **CuPb22Sn** (reference disc). Also we have compared these new lubricants (EHD25 and PPG32-2 3.2%) with the Reference oil M4000. The tests conditions are: Pressure 1 MPa (648Nw), Initial temperature: ambient (15-25°), Speed 1750rpm (4,25m/s). It has been found that the new bio lubricant EHD25 has better friction, wear and increment of temperature behaviour than the reference M4000.

To study these new oils we have also chosen the uncoated ring (50CrV4 material) which was tested against another disc which is a typical sheet steel of bearing coated with **TiCNDLC** (new developed coating). Also we have compared these new lubricants (EHD25 and PPG32-2 3.2%) with the Reference oil M4000. The tests conditions are: Pressure 0.5 MPa (324Nw), Initial temperature: ambient (15-25°), Speed 1750rpm (4,25m/s). The new bio lubricants EHD25 and PPG32-2 3.2% have been found to have better friction and increment of temperature behaviour than the reference M4000. Refered to mass lost, the new bio oil PPG32-2 3.2% has the lowest mass lost.

Finally, with the reference disc CuPb22Sn the new bio oil EHD25 has the best friction, wear and increment temperature behaviour. And with the new developed coating TiCNDLC, the bio oil PPG32-2 3.2% has the best friction, wear and increment temperature behaviour.

The pressure applied on the reference material disc CuPb22Sn was 1MPa, but that applied on the new developed coating TiCNDLC was 0.5Mpa. We had tried to apply 1Mpa on TiCNDLC discs but the new coating could not support this pressure.

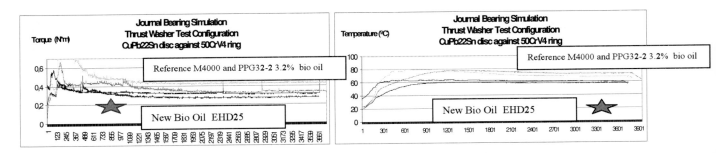

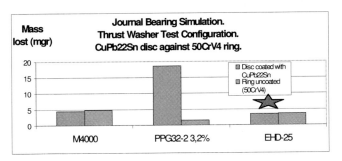

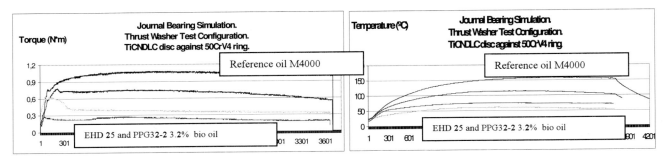

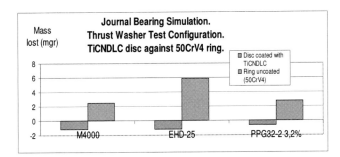

Figure 9. Journal Bearing Simulation. Thrust Washer Tests Results

5. ENGINE TESTS

IAV Engine Tests: Figure 10 shows a view of the analysed test bearings examined on the friction bearing test bench for the study of the two different materials **(reference AlSn20 and new deleloped coating TiCN/DLC).**

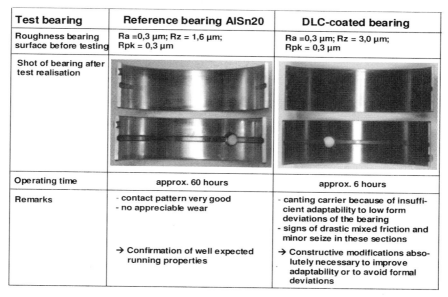

Test bearing	Reference bearing AlSn20	DLC-coated bearing
Roughness bearing surface before testing	Ra =0,3 µm; Rz = 1,6 µm; Rpk = 0,3 µm	Ra =0,3 µm; Rz = 3,0 µm; Rpk = 0,3 µm
Shot of bearing after test realisation		
Operating time	approx. 60 hours	approx. 6 hours
Remarks	- contact pattern very good - no appreciable wear → Confirmation of well expected running properties	- canting carrier because of insufficient adaptability to low form deviations of the bearing - signs of drastic mixed friction and minor seize in these sections → Constructive modifications absolutely necessary to improve adaptability or to avoid formal deviations

Figure 10. Comparison of different test bearings (Reference AlSn20 and TiCN-DLC coated bearings)

❑   Reference bearing shows good to satisfactory measuring results and a good contact pattern after completion of the tests.

❑   With the DLC-coated bearing, the test was terminated because of high friction at a low applied load. This was caused by insufficient bearing adaptability to low form deviations of the bearing. Unfortunately, the results with the new coatings of the bearing shells are not good at present. Constructive modifications are absolutely necessary to improve the adaptability or to avoid form deviations. As we have seen in the tribological tests, it seems that the coating does not support the load of the application.

Also IAV compared these new lubricants (EHD25, EHD31 and PPG32) with the Reference oil in an engine test. Especially with the lubricants PPG32 and EHD31 the engine friction can clearly be reduced. The maximum friction reduction reached with oils PPG32 and EHD31 is up to 5%. This potential means a theoretical reduction of fuel consumption for the investigated engine of approximately 2%.

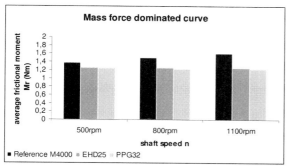

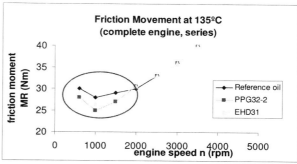

Figure 11. Comparison of different oils in engine tests by IAV

Guascor Engine Tests: This test was performed with reference materials and lubricants EHD25 (low friction) and EHD31 (low fuel consumption), in order to check that these new lubricant concepts bring environmental advantages for engines in two ways:

❑ Firstly, a friction reduction in the engine will reduce the fuel quantity needed to get the same amount of energy, and lower fuel consumption means less pollution and less CO2 emissions.

❑ Another source of contamination, is the oil layer that covers the liner, this layer is needed to reduce friction between the liner and the piston rings and to avoid seizure. Part of this oil is burnt during the expansion stroke where combustion is still in process, this contributes to pollution in the form of smoke, hydrocarbons, particles.

Fuel Consumption:

The reference oil presented higher fuel consumption than the rest of the oils only at low speed and low load. However, we consider that, under these operating conditions, the fuel economy benefits due to the engine oil are relatively small and difficult to measure.

Cycle D2-E2: At 1200rpm and lower load, the fuel consumption is reduced with HD31 in relation to M4000.
At 1800rpm and any load, no differences are found for the different oils.

Cycle E3: Similar fuel consumption relationships are found between the oil at high load and some reduction has found at lower load.

Cycle C1: Similar fuel consumption is found between oils.

Emissions and Smoke:

The emissions were similar for the different oils:

- CO, NOx, Smoke similar.
- SO2, slightly higher due to the fuel influence.
- THC was for EHD 31 lower than reference oil.

The different behaviour between heavy duty and passenger cars is explained as follows.

▪ Firstly, heavy duty diesel engines operate more hydrodynamically than passenger car engines: This is because the proportion of valve train losses is far higher in a typical passenger car compared to a heavy duty diesel engine. Since it is the valve train which is the main boundary lubricated component in an engine, it is clear that friction modifiers will be effective in reducing passenger car engine friction losses, but will not be so effective in diesel engines.

▪ The second major difference between passenger car engines and heavy duty diesel engines is in the typical operating conditions. Passenger car engines are typically used under low load, low speed conditions, where engine friction comprises a major part of the total power loss of the vehicle. Therefore, by reducing engine friction by the use of a fuel economy lubricant, one would expect to see reasonable fuel consumption savings.

Heavy duty diesel engines are operated for significant periods under medium and high load conditions. Under these operating conditions, fuel economy benefits due to the engine oil are relatively small and difficult to measure.

Conclusions of comparative results in performance test operating under all conditions.

-
- Fuel consumption   HD 25=HD31 = MOTOROIL 4000
- CO   HD 25=HD31 = MOTOROIL 4000
- NOx   HD 25=HD31 = MOTOROIL 4000
- SO2   HD 25=HD31 > MOTOROIL 4000 (Fuel influence)
- SMOKE   HD 25=HD31 = MOTOROIL 4000
- THC   HD 25=HD31 < MOTOROIL 4000

The EHD31 oil brings benefits in fuel consumption at low load and speed but not at high speed and high load.

HD31<MOTOROIL 4000 low speed, low load
HD31=MOTOROIL 4000 high speed, high load

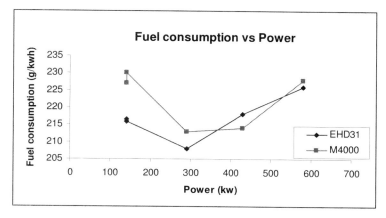

Figure 12. Engine Test carried out with cycle E3: 1800, 1638, 1440, 1134rpm

6. CONCLUSIONS

The new biolubricants for heavy duty engine oil, EHD25, EHD26, EHD28 and EHD31 are biodegradable according to OECD 301F and according to OECD 202, Daphnia Magna Toxicity Test and OECD 201 Algal Growth Inhibition Test, they also are "Not harmful" to aquatic organisms.

Tribological tests show a good friction and anti wear behaviour in three different simulations of engine components tested (piston ring, stem valve guide and journal bearing simulation).

Table 6. Tribological Test Summary

Tribological Tests Summary	
Piston Ring Simulation Test	
Extreme pressure Tests	**EHD25**, EHD26, EHD27, EHD28, EHD29 and EHD30
Wear Tests	EHD28
Stem valve Guide Simulation	**EHD25**, EHD26 and EHD28
Journal Bearing Tests	
Journal Bearing Simulation Tests" in a SRV Tribometer:	**TiCN/DLC** and **EHD25**, EHD31 and PPG32-2 3.2%
Journal bearing Simulation (Wettability Tests)	**TiCN/DLC+EHD25**
"Thrust washer Tests" in a Falex HP Tribometer:	CuPb22Sn + **EHD25** TiCNDLC+ PPG32-3.2%

The bio oil EHD25 is selected because it presents the best friction, wear, extreme pressure and wettability properties in the tests performed.

In the bearing component test performed by IAV the behaviour of the (TiCN/DLC) coating was poor. Despite the facts that its friction properties and wettability are very good, it does not support enough the load. With the lubricants PPG32 and EHD31 the engine friction can be reduced clearly. The maximum friction reduction reached with oils PPG32 and EHD31 amounts up to 5%. This potentially means a theoretical reduction of fuel consumption for the investigated engine of approximately 2%.

Finally, in the Guascor engine tests, it can be mentioned that EHD25 and EHD31 lubricants have slightly lower total hydrocarbon emissions. For the rest, similar values have been found. A reduction of fuel consume has been observed for the EHD31 oil at low load and speed, but this is not the typical working condition of the heavy duty engines.

The great advantage of the EHD25 and EHD31 oil is that it has a minimum content of sulphur, phosphorous (SAP) and is also biodegradable and non toxic. Therefore, this lubricant is very compatible with after treatment systems.

ACKNOWLEDGEMENTS

The authors express their gratitude to the European Union for the financial support given to this work through the GROWTH Project N°. GRD2-2001-50119, Contract N° G3RD-CT-2002-00796-EREBIO, "EREBIO - Emission reduction from engines and transmissions substituting harmful additives in biolubricants by triboreactive materials" and also to the partners.

REFERENCES

[1]   Rakopoulos CD, Antonopoulos KA, Rakopoulos DC "Multi-zone modeling of Diesel fuel spray development with vegetable oil, bio-diesel or Diesel fuels". Energy conversion and Management 47 (11-12): 1550-1573 Jul2006.

[2]   Ramadhas AS, Muraleedharan C, Jayaraj S "Performance and emission evaluation of a diesel engine fueled with methyl esters of rubber seed oil" Renewable Energy 30 (12): 1789-1800 Oct 2005.

[3]   Miura M "Trends in environmentally friendly diesel engine oils" Journal of Japanese Society of Tribologists 49 (10): 793-798 2004.

[4]   Ulusoy Y, Tekin Y, Centinkaya M, et al. "The engine tests of biodiesel from used frying oil" Energy sources 26 (10): 927-932 aug 2004.

[5]   Megahed OA, Abdallah RI, Nabil D "Rappeseed oil esters as diesel engine fuel" Energy Sources 26 (2): 119-126 Feb 2004.

[6]   Tanabe H "Recent trends in marine engine oils" Journal of Japanese society of tribologist 48 (6): 442-446 2003.

[7]   Hashimoto T "Trends in engine technology for heavy duty commercial vehicles and requirements for engine oils" Journal of Japanese society of tribologist 48 (4) 278-282 2003.

[8]   Chen CI, Hsu SM "A chemical kinetics model to predict lubricant performance in a diesel engine" Tribology letteres 14 (2): 83-90 Feb 2003.

[9]   Gamble RJ, Priest M, Taylor CM "Detailed analysis of oil transport in the piston assembly of a gasoline engine" Tribology letters 14 (2): 147-156 Feb 2003.

Session 4
LUBRICANT TESTING 1

Chair:　　　Dr. Trevor Sperring

On-line visible sensor to monitor the quality state of lubricants

A. ARANZABE, A. ARNAIZ, J. TERRRADILLOS, F. GINDELE,
J. BELLEW, P. WEISSMAN, A. ANITUA, A. AGDAR

Infrared Sensor System for On-Line Oil Analysis

F. GINDELE, M. HOLZKI, U. SCHWAB, J. BELLEW, A. ARANZABE,
A. ARNAIZ

Oil Quality Sensors

S. GREENFIELD, R. KAUFMAN

On-line visible sensor to monitor the quality state of lubricants

A. Aranzabe[1], A. Arnaiz[1], J. Terrradillos[1], F. Gindele[2], J. Bellew[3], P. Weissman[4], A. Anitua[5], A. Agdar[6]

[1] Fundación Tekniker, Spain
[2] Institut für Mikrotechnik Mainz (IMM), Germany
[3] Martechnnic GmbH, Germany
[4] Wearcheck GmbH, Germany
[5] Compresores Betico, Spain
[6] Universidad de Sunderland, UK

PAPER NOT AVAILABLE

Infrared Sensor System for On-Line Oil Analysis

F. Gindele [1], M. Holzki [1], U. Schwab [1], J. Bellew [2], A. Aranzabe [3], A. Arnaiz [3]

[1] Institut für Mikrotechnik Mainz GmbH, Carl Zeiss Str. 18-20, 55129 Mainz, Germany
[2] Martechnic GmbH, Adlerhorst 4, 22459 Hamburg, Germany
[3] Fundación Tekniker, Avda. Otaola, 20, 20600 Eibar, Spain

ABSTRACT

A new generation of IR sensors providing real-time oil analysis is under development that will comprehensively assess lubrication oil quality and provide an integrated management solution for end users. The IR sensor system is based on the analysis of the optical properties of oil in the infrared spectral range between 2.9μm to 8.5μm. Contaminations by water and soot as well as degradation processes like oxidation can be measured on-line by the sensor. A total acid number (TAN) number and water concentration up to 3mgKOH/g and 1500ppm are detectable, respectively. The parameters are combined and compared with an expert platform based on about 450 samples to result in an oil quality status displayed by a three point scale. The sensor system represents a new approach to measure the oil quality on-line. Consequently, the availability of such a sensor system for on-line monitoring of lubrication oils is expected to impact current maintenance practices essentially.

Keywords: Infrared, sensor system, on-line analysis, water, oxidation

1. INTRODUCTION

The analysis of lubrication oil is well established in the laboratory. The condition and contamination of oil is measured by various methods: Common analysis techniques are Fourier-Transform infrared FT-IR spectroscopy applied to measure contaminations like oxidation and sulfation by-products, nitration, phosphate based antiwear additives, soot, fuels and glycol, inductively coupled plasma (ICP) spectrometry to analyse the wear particles and debris, titration methods to quantify the water concentration and TAN to mention a few of examples. This analysis results in a thorough information about the oil and engine condition. The final decision about e.g. a required change of oil or the prediction of possible damage of the engine underlies the evaluation and recommendation of the oil experts. However laboratory analysis is performed in fixed maintenance intervals and can not afford the in time information needed to encounter an unforeseen critical situation of engine operation. Therefore on-line analysis of the oil condition is required by a compact sensor system.

Although optical analysis enables the monitoring of a broad range of oil contaminations, most on-line system are based on other principles. Particularly for monitoring water in oil several methods and systems have been developed: oil is heated up to vaporize water and measuring the condensed water droplets by electrical impulses [1], the dielectric constant of the oil is monitored by the increase of a capacitance with increasing water concentration [2], the influence of the dielectric constant on the frequency of an oscillator circuit is used [3] or the absorption of water molecules by a thin film polymer coating is measured by the change of capacitance [4]. In another example the change of the optical absorption in the infrared spectral range by water concentration is measured [5].

To monitor the overall condition of the oil on-line great progress was achieved by the miniaturisation of capacitive sensors in different configurations to measure the dielectric constant and to relate that quantity to the quality of oil [6], [7]. However a main restriction of this method is the influence on the dielectric constant of the oil not only by water but metallic particles, soot, additives or oxidation by-products in different degrees. Hence, as a sum parameter is monitored by the dielectric constant the contribution of individual contaminations is not possible to be separated. Miniaturised sensors for monitoring the oil quality on-line by other methods are not available. However a sensor system addressing this idea of optical detection of oil quality is proposed by Foster-Miller [8].

The progress in optic and optoelectronic technologies enables to apply optical measurement methods for the detection of individual parameters known from laboratory analysis for on-line sensors. The development of a sensor for monitoring the crucial contaminations in oil and to derive an overall parameter for the oil condition is the subject of this contribution. The paper first gives a short summary of the optical properties of oil. The sensor concept and design is described followed by the experimental characterization of the sensor. Finally the sensor results for used oil samples are evaluated by a comparison to laboratory analysis.

2. OPTICAL PROPERTIES OF OIL

The study of the optical properties of oil mainly concentrates onto the Mid Infrared (MIR) spectral range. One exception is the use of the color for monitoring the degradation process in lubrication oil. Thereby the visible spectrum is analysed resulting in an overall parameter for the degradation, called color number [9]. Contrary to the visible spectrum the MIR provides characteristic optical information about individual contaminations and processes inside the oil. The measured absorption is caused by vibrational modes of the molecules. In combination with methodologies for signal analysis a powerful indicator for the oil condition is given by that. Most of the optical analysis can be performed by spectroscopy with e.g. FT-IR equipment. An overview of the main important features in the MIR spectrum of fresh oil is given in Figure 1.

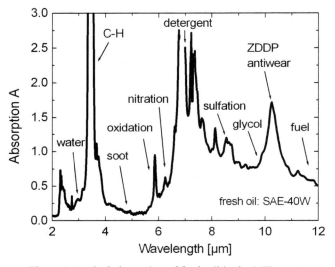

Figure 1. Optical absorption of fresh oil in the MIR spectrum.

The absorption of the C-H bonding, detergents like $CaCO_3$ and the phosphate based antiwear ZDDP are well pronounced. Features important for the detection of possible contaminations are the absorption of oxidative by-products, nitration and sulfation as well as the absorption of water, soot, glycol and fuel. In this paper we concentrate onto contaminations and relevant spectral information that are of importance for lubrication oil for compressors. For a more detailed overview of the optical properties of oil we refer to ASTM E2412-04 [11].

3. SENSOR DEVELOPMENT

First the term quality has to be defined for lubrications oils for compressors and second the sensor has to be designed as a mobile system that operates on-line. Both items are discussed in the following.

3.1.   Sensor Concept

The term oil quality has to be transformed into a set of relevant parameters to be measured by the sensor. In laboratory about 30 parameters are typically analysed. To identify a strongly reduced number of parameters measurable with the sensor, the correlation between the complete laboratory analysis and the optical information was investigated for ~450 used oil samples coming from various engines and operation conditions. The results of 27 individual parameters are compared with the information gained by optical absorption spectra of the oil samples in Figure 2. For 6 parameters the correlation of optical information and the laboratory analysis is about 80%. Thereof the contamination by water and oxidative by-products (band 6 and 2, 4, respectively in Figure 2) are of main importance for any machine failure during operation. This is emphasised by the fact that for more than 75% of analysed used oil samples classified to "change oil" by the laboratory experts, one of both parameters is strongly increased compared to fresh oil.

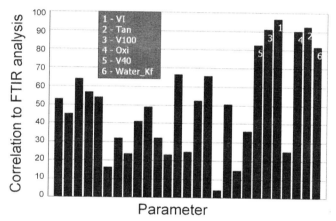

Figure 2. Correlation between optical analysis (FT-IR) and the individual parameters analysed in the laboratory.

Figure 3 illustrates the change of the absorption for fresh oil artificially contaminated with water and degradated. The spectra are normalised to the reference value labelled by soot around λ~4.5-5μm. That wavelength range is not influenced by other contaminations and is used as reference value, typically. Water shows a characteristic absorption caused by the stretching mode of the hydrogen bonded O-H (hydroxyl) group. The broad absorption band is in the wavelength range of λ~2.85-3.15μm, whereas the environment of the water molecules gives rise to line broadening and shifts in the centre wavelength. The absorption increases with water concentration detectable from well below 50ppm up to 1% and more. The second pronounced feature, the degradation is monitored by the oxidative by-products containing a carbonyl group (C=O). The absorption is shown between λ~5.6-6μm increasing with the degradation of the oil. A concentration range of TAN 0.1 to 4mgKOH/g is well measurable by the optical absorption. Sulfation by-products like SO_2 and SO_3 are measured by their vibrational modes at λ~8.5-9μm. They are formed by the oxidation of sulphur indicating the change in the total base number (TBN) and decreasing additive concentration.

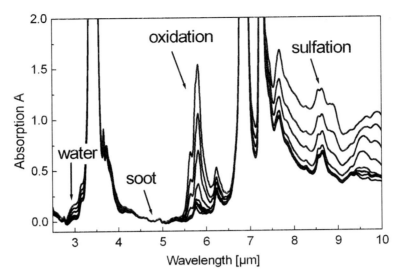

Figure 3. Absorption spectra for artificial contaminated and degradated oil.

Based on those results, three individual spectral information`s, meaning three wavelength bands have to be detected by the sensor system in minimum: water contamination, oxidative by-products and a reference value. Additional a fourth spectral band is used to monitor early stages of degradation by a change of sulfation by-products.

The change of the absorption by the individual contaminations has to be monitored separately in the concentration range of below 50 up to 1500ppm for water and 0-3 mgKOH/g for the oxidation by-products. The measurement has to be performed on-line in a flow-through configuration. All the components like signal sources, optical components, detectors and flow-through cell have to be mounted in a single unit including the electronic for signal amplification and the interface to a control unit.

The optical design is the central task to fulfil the requirements by a compact system. We concentrate in the following on this subject. The choice of components is driven by the addressed wavelength range and the cost requirements and is not subject of this paper.

3.2. Sensor Design and set up

To measure the four selected wavelength bands different signal sources are used that are controlled individually. The signals of the four signal channels are detected by one detector element. As well only one flow-through cell is used for the sensor. The optical design of the sensor is symmetric for the beam path of the four wavelength bands from the signal source to the detector. The design of the sensor is illustrated in Figure 4. A sequential ray tracing simulation is shown for one signal path measuring one contamination parameter of oil. The signal form the signal source is collimated first by the parabolic shaped mirror. The numerical aperture NA is equal 0.2. The signal is guided to the second mirror and focussed through the flow-through cell onto the detector. Both mirrors are gold coated showing a reflection of R>0.95 for the detected spectral range. As window material of the flow-through cell ZnSe is applied whereas one window has been replaced by a ZnSe lens to reduce the focussing point of the beam compared to the case without lens. The spot size at the place of the detector is around 2mm in diameter for each signal path. The cell thickness has been chosen to 700μm to cover the above mentioned concentration range.

For spectral selection each signal path has been combined with a filter element. The different filters are transmittive for the wavelength bands discussed in the previous chapter.

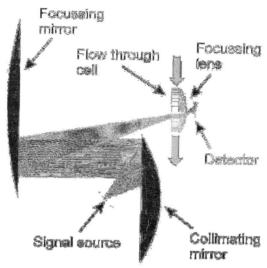

Figure 4. Optical design for one detection channel of the sensor system. Ray-tracing simulation.

Figure 5 illustrates the case when all beam paths are switched on. Due to the symmetrical design a comparable signal intensity is guided to the detector for each detection channel. The geometrical properties are the same for each channel except the wavelength.

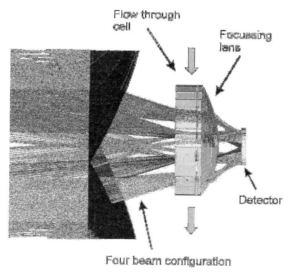

Figure 5. Optical design: Four detection channels of the sensor system are switched on. Ray-tracing simulation.

Based on this optical design the sensor has been set up. Figure 6a) shows the focussing and collimating mirror already assembled with parts of the sensor housing. Figure 6b) shows the complete demonstrator of the sensor including the optical, mechanical and optoelectronical components. The interface of the sensor to the engine is performed by a 3mm tube connection in a by-pass configuration. To control the signal sources and the read out of the detector a RS232 interface is used.

Figure 6. a) Optical mirrors for beam focussing and collimation. b) Sensor demonstrator including all optical, mechanical and optoelectronic components.

4. EXPERIMENTAL TESTING

For testing and characterisation of the sensor, mineral (Betico Turbo 200) and synthetic (Betico Rotosint) oil samples were used from different compressor machines, locations and operation times. To characterise the full measurement range of the sensor, the artificial contaminated samples were taken first. Used oil samples were measured in the classification experiments discussed below. Contamination of soot was not present for this application whereas the so called soot band is only used as reference band. Any major change in the sulfation by-product concentration was not detected and is not considered in the following.

4.1. Water in oil contamination

The sample preparation is important for the correct analysis of the water concentration by optical methods. Samples that are bottled and shipped have to be homogenised before the measurement to assure that a concentration gradient of water inside the bottle is avoided. Especially for higher water concentrations where the water is not dissolved completely and a water-in-oil emulsion is forming up the homogenous mixing is crucial for a correct measurement results. To classify the sensor performance and to avoid uncertainties by the sample condition FT-IR measurements were performed parallel to the sensor tests with a first set of samples. Both results are compared to each other. The absorption measured with the sensor A_S is related to the one measured with FT-IR lab equipment A_{FTIR} in Figure 7a). The linear dependence is well shown with a standard deviation of $sd=0.006$. The difference in the absolute value of both measurements is due to the different width of the wavelength range.

To compare the sensor results with the absolute values of water concentration a second set of oils have been analysed by the Karl-Fischer titration method (Figure 7b)). The general linear increase of the absorption with increasing water concentration is well approved for the considered concentration range. According to the optical absorption of the first set of samples and referencing it to Karl-Fischer the water concentration of the tested samples goes up to $c_w=1500$ppm. For that concentration range a resolution of below ±45ppm is possible.

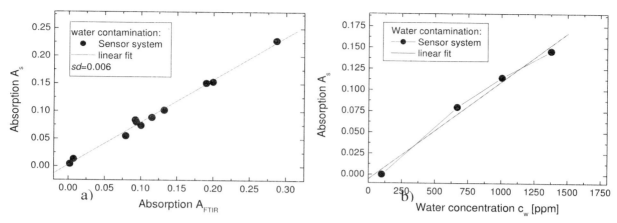

Figure 7. a) Water contamination: Comparison between the measured absorption by the sensor to the absorption measured with FT-IR. b) Absorption as a function of the absolute value of the water concentration measured with the sensor. Karl- Fischer titration method was used as reference method.

4.2. Oxidative by-products in oil

Artificially degraded oil samples have been analysed with the sensor and FT-IR equipment again. Figure 8a) shows the measured dependence between the absorption A_S and A_{FTIR} for different degradated oils. The linear relation is well established with sd=0.04. The degree of oxidation is measured by a titration method neutralising the acid and is used as an independent reference method. Figure 8b) shows A_S related to the TAN value. The sensor signal increases linear with the TAN value up to 1.5mgKOH/g followed by a slower increase than linearity for higher TAN values. The outlier (marked with an arrow) at a TAN value of ~2.5mgKOH/g was probably caused by wrong sample handling. The detectable concentration range for this set up is up to ~3mgKOH/g with a concentration resolution of well below 0.3mgKOH/g.

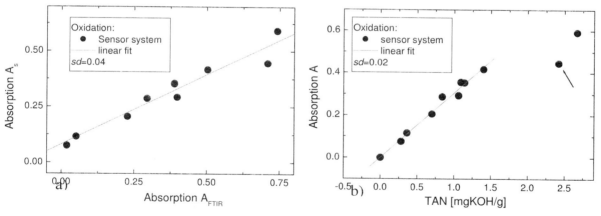

Figure 8. Oxidation: a) Absorption caused by oxidative by-products measured with the sensor A_S and the FT-IR system A_{FTIR}. b) A_S as a function of the TAN value measured with a reference method.

5. RESULTS AND DISCUSSION

The final classification model has been derived by the use of neural network techniques [10]. 450 samples of used oil are taken to build up a calibration platform with the complete information from the laboratory oil analysis. 91% of the samples show a TAN value below 0.5mgKOH/g and 85% a water concentration below 150ppm. The operation time was above 2000h for 24% of the samples. More detailed information about the sensor calibration and date handling is given in Ref.[11].

The outcome of the sensor analysis has to be displayed in a clear and easy-to-handle way for the end-user. The processing of the sensor signals results in a single number describing the oil quality (quality number). A three point scale differencing the operation conditions: normal, monitor and caution is defined by the quality number. The value of the quality number is <0.45 for normal operation, between 0.45 and 0.65 for monitoring and between 0.65 and 1 for caution level. The limit values of each level of classification have been determined by the experts in oil analysis and compressors. The quality number includes a weighting factor for the parameters. More detailed information like the concentration of the individual contaminations can be provided by the software when required.

23 used oil samples were classified to compare the sensor results based on the four measurement parameters to the expert evaluation based on lab analysis. Figure 9 summarizes the results. For both cases the achieved quality number is scaled to the three level of classification. The listed values are predicted by the developed classification model. The difference of both evaluations for the quality number and the derived classification is shown in the last column. An accuracy above 85% is obtained for the classification. For some oil samples the quality number of both analysis strongly differs, see samples with the ID 11 and 12. The high value of the quality number in the expert evaluation may be caused by an unusual contamination like metal particles that is not mapped by the sensor or the use of a different oil not specified. It has to be mentioned that 8% of the oil samples shows an unusual high concentration of metal wear particles and 5% are mixed with an undefined oil by the user. Those cases are not detectable for the sensor system and cause some differences in the comparison of the results. Up to now the sensor was operated at a test rig and at a compressor for several months.

ID	Expert evaluation		Sensor result		Difference	
	Quality number	Classification	Quality number	Classification	Quality number	Classification
1	0,176	0	0,18	0	0,00	0
2	0,182	0	0,25	0	-0,07	0
3	0,268	0	0,45	1	-0,18	-1
4	0,264	0	0,39	0	-0,13	0
5	0,298	0	0,46	1	-0,16	-1
6	0,35	0	0,37	0	-0,02	0
7	0,36	0	0,4	0	-0,04	0
8	0,456	1	0,49	1	-0,03	0
9	0,509	1	0,51	1	0,00	0
10	0,657	2	0,58	1	0,08	1
11	1,16	2	0,66	2	0,50	0
12	1,115	2	0,71	2	0,41	0
13	0,178	0	0,21	0	-0,03	0
14	0,178	0	0,17	0	0,01	0
15	0,182	0	0,07	0	0,11	0
16	0,178	0	0,16	0	0,02	0
17	0,181	0	0,16	0	0,02	0
18	0,261	0	0,19	0	0,07	0
19	0,552	1	0,45	1	0,10	0
20	0,176	0	0,25	0	-0,07	0
21	0,178	0	0,25	0	-0,07	0
22	0,364	0	0,4	0	-0,04	0
23	0,372	0	0,38	0	-0,01	0

Figure 9. Sensor testing: Comparison between expert evaluation and sensor analysis results.

In conclusion about 85% of oil samples used in compressors at different sites could be classified well. By optimizing the classification limits and eliminating the unusual contaminations not accessible by the sensor the correlation of the expert evaluation and the sensor results could be increased up to 95%. Considering the novelty of the method the results are very promising.

REFERENCES

[1]   Instrument Continously Monitors Water in Oil Concentration, Practicing Oil Analysis, July 2004.
[2]   H2Oil Analyzer System, Honeywell Inc., www.honeywell.com; WS07X series, www.pall.com;
[3]   R. B. Schüller, B. Engebretsen and M. Halleraker, Measurement of Water Concentration in Oil/Water Dispersions by a Single-electrode Capacitance Probe. IMTC 2003, Vail, CO, USA, p. 635-639
[4]   Vaisala HUMICAP, Vaisala News 163/2003, p. 16 or www.vaisala.com
[5]   Kytola instruments, www.kytola.com
[6]   E. Iron, K. Land, T. Gürtler, M. Klein, Oil-Quality Prediction and Oil-Level Detection with the Temic QLT-Sensor Leads to Variable Maintenance Intervals, Society of Automotive Engineers, Inc, 1997, 970847
[7]   D. Wüllner, Hella KG Hueck & Co, Multi-functional Microsensor for Oil Condition Monitoring Systems, AMAA proceedings, 2003, p. 315.
[8]   Foster-Miller Inc., www.Foster-Miller.com
[9]   DIN ISO 2049
[10]   Adgar, A., Schwarz, M.H. & MacIntyre J. (2004) Automated On-line Oil Analysis using a Microsensor and Neural Networks. Natural Computing Applications Forum, University of Sunderland, UK, Jun 9-10, 2004.
[11]   I. Aranburu, A. Arnaiz, A. Adgar, M. Schwarz, E. Gilabert. On line oil aging monitoring & predictive maintenance." Computers in Industry, (2005), in press.

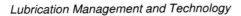

Oil Quality Sensors

S. Greenfield [1], R. Kauffman [2]

[1] European Business Development Manager, Eaton Aerospace Engineered Sensors UK.
[2] Research Chemist, University of Dayton Research Institute, USA

ABSTRACT

Modern Gas Turbines both flying and stationary are under increasing pressure to be cleaner and generally more efficient to meet future "Green" regulations. Subsequent generations of Gas Turbines are increasingly less polluting than even 5 years ago in terms of the publicly aware NOx emissions, as well as less publicised emissions. The traditional, normal, practice of consuming and regularly replenishing the lubricating oil is now no longer acceptable.

Whilst this is good for the environment the lubricating oil has a harder and longer working life, depleting the lubricant of critical additives that aid lubricity and acid control. Therefore a need has arisen to determine the health of the lubricating oil on-line to protect the asset, off-line analysis is currently considered too difficult a logistical task to manage effectively for a large airline fleet since the oil condition can degrade rapidly.

The paper will explore the technologies available today and those being developed to produce an effective, affordable on-line oil quality sensor.

1. INTRODUCTION

Lubricating bearings and gears is vital to sustaining the working life of plant and equipment, as the sophistication and stresses increase in machines the lubricant to protect the asset is also increasing in complexity, even the modern motor car now requires a fully synthetic oil.

The lubricating oil chemistry required to maintain a reasonable working life must, as a minimum, contain a good anti- oxidant and anti- wear additive package. It is the condition of the additives that dictate when an oil should be changed or in an ideal world have fresh additives added to restore the performance.

There are several sensors available today working on viscosity measurement to indicate the presence of fuel dilution and catastrophic breakdown of the oil, however in the experience gained within the Eaton engineering laboratories, evaluating several technologies the conclusion is that, in the case of Gas Turbine lubricants, Viscosity measurement is a good complimentary technology for base oil, but not a key indicator of the critical additive package depletion.

As a generalisation the most useful indicator of oil quality is the state of the anti oxidant package, as the anti oxidant depletes the acidity of the oil increases and is measured by the parameter of TAN (Total Acid Number).

In modern lubricating systems there are three main drivers resulting in the high requirements of the lubricant's protection against oxidation:

- Extended lubricant life time
- Higher equipment load factors and operating temperatures
- Increased uptime of equipment

To meet these performance requirements, lubricant suppliers are continuously improving the base-oil quality, whilst the additive manufacturers improve the type of antioxidants, the net result is a modern high performance lubricant as the result of both developments.

What is oxidation?

It is the chemical reaction of a lubricant at elevated temperatures between the dissolved atmospheric oxygen and the base-oil.

What is the role of antioxidants?

Chemical compounds added to the lubricant to retard the oxidation to the base oil and help prevent the lubricant degradation. The lack of antioxidants allows, reactive oxidation compounds (known better as C-radicals) to form and as their levels increase, result in excessive base-oil degradation (the secondary degradation mechanism).

Varnish, sludge and lacquer formation are typical phenomena of this secondary degradation, contaminating filters, level gauges and oil jets. Modern maintenance strategies rely on the accurate detection of the antioxidants, to monitor the lubricant's general health. Existing standards addresses the voltammetric test method (Linear Sweep Voltammetry), and advanced variations to this technique form the basis of this paper.

2. R.U.L.E.R. ®

2.1. Remaining Usable Life Evaluation Rig

Ruler is an established off line technique developed by UDRI [1] and has proven useful for many years, it is now available from Fluitech in Belgium and is aligned with COBRA®, (Complete Oil Breakdown Analyser), another useful diagnostic tool in the chemists arsenal. However, an on-line low cost system is demanded by the operators of capital equipment, with an easy to interpret interface and results.

3. S.E.C.T. ®

3.1. Single Electrode Conductivity Technique

S. E. C. T. was developed by Dr Robert Kauffman, Distinguished Research Chemist, University of Dayton Research Institute, USA. [2].

3.2. Practical application of S.E.C.T.

The application of SECT to a modern fighter aircraft gas turbine engine [3] currently in development, utilising synthetic MIL-L-23699 Generation II pentaerythritol ester type basestock oil. (Generation II oils use amine type antioxidant systems with higher temperature capabilities than the traditional secondary aromatic amines used in Generation I oils).

The objective is to provide an on-line indication of oil condition to maximise the lubricant life whilst offering the best protection to the asset.

The remainder of this paper is an abbreviated report on critical seeded fault testing to determine the effectiveness of the technology in a real on engine environment. Prior to the seeded fault tests base line determination of the lubricating oil characteristics were determined in the laboratory, this encompassed both liquid oil and oil vapours to establish and classify anomalies such as the addition of incorrect fluids to the reservoir, contamination by fuels and coolants and the effect of oil stressing.

Off line techniques were used (RULER® and COBRA®) to distinguish between two typical oil degradation mechanisms, SECT increasing due to anti oxidant depletion versus SECT reading increasing by hot spots / oil fire (without antioxidant depletion).

The algorithms were simply the rate of change, sudden changes are attributed to hot spots, (or contamination by other fluids), whilst anti oxidant depletion is usually a gradual change over an extended period.

4. ENGINE TEST STAND SECT SENSOR EVALUATIONS

The following information was provided by Dr Kauffman

4.1. Accelerated Oxidation Seeded Fault Test

Once the SECT sensors were evaluated and optimised using laboratory testing, four sensors were packaged for testing on the engine test stand. Minor modifications were made to engine components selected to be monitored by the sensors. Connectors containing the sensing wires were attached to fittings incorporated into an oil return line (2 sensors) and brazed onto the exterior surfaces of the bearing compartment and breather tube. The connectors supplied a liquid tight, electronically isolated seal around the wires while providing the desired gap width of the wire pair submerged in liquid lubricant or exposed to lubricant vapour. Additionally, approx 15 Metres of cable was added between the SECT electronic circuit board/sensor wires and the power supply to allow the power supply to be located in the control room.

To initiate the engine stand test, seven engine runs (Runs 1 – 7) were made under normal lubricant operating conditions [seeded fault was a bearing race with indents].

Then five more engine runs (Runs 8 – 12) were made with the oil cooler by-pass valve closed up to 80% resulting in increased oil temperatures and accelerated oxidation. The oil in the monitored return line reached a temperature of 232°C when the engine speed reached 9900 rpm during the accelerated oxidation seeded fault. At the end of each engine run [approximately 90 minutes simulating take-off, flight with different engine speeds (with afterburners) then landing], oil samples were obtained for on-site oil analyses. The on-site analytical techniques used in this study were the RULER™ (percent remaining antioxidant), the COBRA (oil degradation), and ASTM Method D-974 TAN (build up of organic acids from oil oxidation) measurements.

4.2. Liquid SECT Sensor Evaluation

For the first evaluation of the on-line monitoring capabilities of the four SECT sensors, the liquid SECT readings taken at 8600 rpm and the on-site oil condition measurements of the oil samples obtained at the end of each engine run were plotted versus the engine run number. The results show that the oil was stable for engine runs 1 - 3 due to the high oil make-up rate between engine runs, i.e., the RULER™ readings were ≈100% remaining antioxidant and the COBRA, TAN and SECT sensor measurements were constant. During runs 3 – 7, the oil additions were minimized allowing the antioxidants to deplete at an accelerated rate due to the minimized antioxidant replenishments. By the end of engine run 7, the percent remaining antioxidant levels of the oils decreased to approximately 70% of the original concentration while the SECT, COBRA and TAN measurements remained constant indicating that the oil was still stable but had reduced oxidation protection. The capability to detect rapid antioxidant depletion allows the RULER™ to detect accelerated oil oxidation prior to the on-line SECT sensors and off-line COBRA and TAN condition monitoring techniques.

For the accelerated oxidation seeded fault (runs 8 - 12), the antioxidant levels decreased to 20% remaining antioxidant (RULER™) and the readouts of the liquid SECT sensors increased at a rapid rate for engine runs 8 and 9. The rate of increase for the liquid SECT sensor outputs slowed after engine run 10 similar to the liquid SECT outputs during the laboratory oxidation test. The COBRA and TAN measurements begin to increase after engine run 10 indicating the oil was beginning to oxidize. The results also show that the two liquid SECT sensors had similar results illustrating the reproducibility of the SECT sensors' oxidation detection capabilities even though their wire pairs had different sensitivities to oxidation (different wire lengths due to location restraints).

Therefore, the results demonstrate that the liquid SECT sensors detected accelerated oil degradation during the seeded fault test, one engine run prior to the on-site COBRA and TAN analytical tests.

4.3.   Vapour SECT Sensor Evaluation

In addition to the liquid SECT sensor readings, the continuous readouts of the vapour SECT sensor were recorded every 10 seconds for the accelerated oxidation seeded fault test (engine runs 8 – 12).   The recorded vapour SECT readings were plotted versus engine time for each engine run.   Engine time was added arbitrarily between runs to separate the vapour SECT sensor readings into specific engine runs. The breather air temperature varied between 93 up to 193°C as the engine speed varied between 4400 rpm up to 9800 rpm, respectively, during each engine run.

The readouts of the vapour SECT sensor are constant during engine runs 7 – 10.   At the ends of engine runs 9 and 10, the vapour SECT sensor readings rise sharply indicating the accumulation of degradation products onto the sensor's wires as the breather tube air temperature decreases.   At the beginning of engine run 11, the vapour SECT sensor spiked and then decreased with increasing run time.   Inspection of the vapour sensor after run 11 found that the degradation vapours had thinned the oil film between the sensors' wires resulting in the loss of the oil drop.   A new drop of oil was added to the sensor wires.   As in engine runs 9 and 10, the readouts of the oil replenished vapour SECT sensor increased rapidly at the end of run 12 (condensation of degradation products) as the breather air temperature decreased.

Visual inspection of the breather tube after engine run 12 detected the presence of coke on the inner walls of the breather tube.   Consequently, the oil degradation detected by the vapour SECT sensor may be due to degradation products from the bulk oil or due to the degradation products from the further oxidation of the oil (reduced antioxidant concentration) condensing on the hot walls of the breather tube. Regardless of the source of the oil degradation products, a vapour SECT sensor could be used to detect oil oxidation in the breather air of the engine.   Since the oil degradation products concentrate in the breather tube, the vapour SECT sensor would have the added advantage of being less oil type dependent than the liquid SECT sensors.   Small changes in the sensor designs such as the addition of Teflon mesh (tested in the engine companies oil analysis laboratory) to maintain the oil drop/accumulated degradation products would ensure the performance of the vapour SECT sensor in degradation rich vapour environments. Placing sensors at different positions along the inside of the breather tube at selected surface temperatures would allow degradation vapours produced from the bulk oil and produced inside the breather tube to be monitored separately.

4.4.   Effects of Engine Speed and Temperature on Oxidation Detection by Liquid SECT Sensors.

 To determine the effects of engine speed and oil temperature on the oxidation detection capabilities of the liquid SECT sensors, the readouts of the liquid SECT sensors at three different engine speeds (4400, 8600 and 9900 rpm) were plotted versus engine run number.   The ranges of the oil temperature readings during the five engine runs were 126 - 154°C for 4400 rpm, 182 - 216°C for 8600 rpm and 216 - 229°C for 9900 rpm.

The results indicate that during engine run 8, the engine speed/temperature had minimal effect on the readouts of the liquid SECT sensors.   However, the readings for the liquid SECT sensors at the different engine speeds/temperatures diverged as the oil degraded during engine runs 9 - 12.   The SECT readings increased the fastest at 9900 rpm and the slowest at 4400 rpm, respectively.   Since the sensitivities of the SECT sensors to degradation increase with temperature, the SECT sensors at engine temperature would be expected to be more sensitive to oil oxidation than the room temperature measurements (COBRA).

Consequently, two methods can be used to detect oil oxidation with the liquid SECT sensors.

The first method is to record the SECT sensor reading at a preset engine speed/temperature range.

The second method is to record the difference between the readouts of the SECT sensor at two preset engine speeds.   The second method would make the SECT oxidation detection capabilities independent of oil type, i.e., Generation II oil has higher original SECT reading than Generation I oil but rate of increase due to oxidation is similar.   Therefore, increases in the absolute value and/or increases in the differences of the SECT sensor readings with temperature could be used to detect accelerated oil oxidation directly on-line. These results also indicate that the SECT readings would have been even more sensitive to accelerated oxidation if the 9900 rpm readings had been used instead of the 8600 rpm readings.

4.5.   Effects of Engine Speed and Temperature on Oxidation Detection by Vapour SECT Sensor.

Since the vapour SECT readings increase at the ends of engine runs 9, 10 and 12 as the breather tube air temperatures decrease, the vapour SECT readings for a single engine run were plotted to better study the relationships between engine speed/breather tube air temperature and the vapour SECT readings. The readings of the vapour SECT sensor and breather tube air temperature were plotted at 3 to 10 second intervals versus the engine run time for engine run 8. The breather air temperature varied between 93 and 193°C as the engine speed varied between 4400 and 9800 rpm, respectively.

In contrast to the liquid SECT sensors, the vapour SECT sensor reading was inversely proportional to the engine speed/breather tube air temperature. The vapour SECT sensor output increased with air temperature up to 149 - 160°C and then decreased as the air temperature increased from 160 to 193°C. The vapour SECT sensor then showed the reverse trend as the breather air cooled. These results are in complete agreement with the vapour SECT sensor reading increases at the ends of engine runs 9, 10 and 12 i.e., the vapour sensor readouts increased at the end of the engine run as the breather tube air cooled. It is speculated that the degradation products/oil vapours condense on the sensor wires at air temperatures below 160°C causing the sensor readouts to increase and evaporate from the sensor wires at air temperatures above 171°C causing the sensor readouts to decrease.

4.6.   Fire and Contamination Seeded Fault Tests

Of the planned seeded fault tests to initiate a bearing compartment fire and to introduce liquid contaminants into the engine stand lubrication system, only the fuel dilution test was accomplished. The spark plug installed into the bearing compartment failed to ignite the oil (the readouts for the SECT sensor in the bearing compartment also did not change, i.e., did not detect oil degradation due to fire/hot spot) under a wide range of oil: air ratios. Due to their expected detrimental effects on oil-wetted components and the excellent laboratory results, commercial hydraulic fluid, motor oil and antifreeze were not injected into the engine oil system to ensure the other mechanical seeded faults could be performed prior to engine failure.

To test the capabilities of the liquid and vapour SECT sensors to detect fuel dilution (fuel leaks through breach in separating walls of the oil cooler), injections with Jet A fuel were made into the oil system using a modification of a selected oil return line. Although several fuel injections were made (designed to obtain a 1-2% fuel dilution), the liquid SECT readings remained constant in agreement with the laboratory results. As expected, the readings of the vapour sensor in the breather tube showed a slight (less than 10%) decrease with the fuel injections.

5.   CONCLUSIONS

The test results presented herein and in Figure 1, indicate that the SECT sensors, regardless of location, detected the oxidative degradation of the stressed oils during the laboratory tests and the seeded fault engine test in agreement with the off-line viscosity, COBRA and TAN techniques. The engine results also indicate that the liquid SECT sensor outputs should be recorded at two or more selected engine speeds to minimize the effects of oil formulation on the sensors' oxidation detection capabilities. In contrast to the liquid SECT sensors, the engine results indicate that the vapour SECT readings should be made only at low engine speeds (cooler breather tube air) to improve detection of oil oxidation.

The laboratory results indicated that the vapour and liquid SECT sensors could detect oil fires within seconds of the fire initiation and addition of contaminant fluids above 1% within minutes of fluid addition. The laboratory and engine tests indicated that only the vapour sensor had potential for detecting fuel leaks and the sensor's detection potential was dependent on identifying an optimum location in the engine's breather tube.

Due to the success of the laboratory and engine test results, the SECT sensors techniques were selected as the oil condition monitoring sensors for the engine being developed for the new aircraft program.

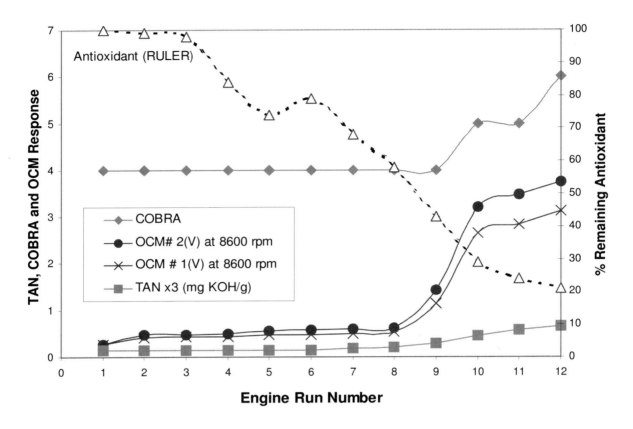

Figure 1. Plots of the %Remaining Antioxidant (RULER™), COBRA, Total Acid Number (TAN) and Two Liquid (Supply Line) OCM Sensor Measurements Versus Engine Run Time for Engine Test. Accelerated Oxidation Seeded Fault Engine Test During Engine Runs 8–12.

ACKNOWLEDGEMENTS

The authors would like to thank Larry Sqrow and Doug Wolf of the University of Dayton Research Institute for constructing the sensor prototypes used in this study and the development team of the engine company for overseeing the seeded fault engine tests.

REFERENCES

[1] Kauffman R, Remaining useful life measurement of Diesel, Hydraulic oils and Grease using Voltametric methods, UDRI May 1994.
[2] Kauffman R, Conference proceedings, JSF – JOAP 2002
[3] Kauffman R, Conference proceedings, JSF - STLE 2002

Session 5
LUBRICANTS & ADDITIVES 2

Chair: Dr. Ramón Gallifa

Lubricating micromechanisms: computational and experimental analysis of OTS
J. BARRIGA, B. FERNÁNDEZ, B. COTO

Solid Lubricants for Space Applications: State of the Art
F. VELASCO, N. FLEISCHER

Alkylated Naphthalenes as High Performance Synthetic Fluids
M. J. HOURANI, R. A. ABRAMSHE, J. G. LIANG, E. T. HESSELL

Lubricating micromechanisms: computational and experimental analysis of OTS

J. Barriga, B. Fernández, B. Coto

Fundación Tekniker, Avda. Otaola, 20, 20600 Eibar, Spain

ABSTRACT

Self-assembled monolayers (SAMs) have become a field of great interest for researchers due to their multiple applications as boundary lubricants. The studies about the structure and characterization of SAMs coatings adsorbed in surfaces are the basis to reach a deeper knowledge of SAMs properties and applications. Computational molecular dynamics (MD) simulations allow us to see what is happening at the atomic level. We have studied the optimal packing structure of Octadecyltrichlorosilane (OTS) SAMs chemisorbed on a silicon substrate. In order to determine and characterize the optimal packing structure of the OTS-SiO_2 system, we have performed molecular dynamics (MD) simulations and found that results obtained in terms of number of molecules per surface unit are in agreement with those reported in literature using other experimental characterization techniques ($\sim 1OTS/22\text{Å}^2$). We have prepared OTS layers on silicon substrates and experimental characterization of the boundary lubrication layer was performed. Measuring the contact angle with water and hexadecane the surface energy was calculated. Microtribological tests were performed to analyse the friction properties of OTS showing a reduction in coefficient of friction from 0.20 to 0.11.

Keywords: MEMS, microtribology, Molecular Dynamics, OTS, silicon.

1. INTRODUCTION

Single-crystal silicon is the most widely used substrate material for MEMS and Microsystems due to different reasons: its mechanical stability, high Young's modulus and melting point, low thermal expansion coefficient,... Furthermore, there is a greater flexibility in design and manufacture with silicon than with other substrate materials and there are different treatments and fabrication processes for silicon substrates well established and documented.

The large surface-area-to-volume ratios of surface and bulk microsystems produce sometimes failures in micromachines. Adhesion, stiction and the production of wear debris are the most common processes that cause the loss of efficiency when there are parts in contact and in relative sliding motion. It has long been known that the application of monomolecular organic layers, particularly those with long hydrocarbon chains, work as boundary lubricants, having an important effect on the macroscopic tribological properties of the substrate upon which the film is attached.

Taking into account all these points, SAMs of OTS attached to a surface of silicon (oxidized) constitutes an interesting system: silicon is many times used in MEMS and OTS acts as a lubricant. Capillary forces play a dominant role in low energy coatings like the OTS. The adsorption of water gives rise to capillary forces which results in a significant increase in the friction force. The introduction of low energy surfaces such as SAMs reduces this adsorption of water, thereby reducing the friction force.

Molecular dynamics (MD) simulations is an interesting tool to study this kind of systems because it allows us to see what is happening at the atomic level avoiding the problem of their sensitivity to reaction conditions. There are some contributions reported in the field of tribology and in SAMs characterization using MD simulations, but OTS has never been studied from this point of view. We have studied the optimal packing structure of Octadecyltrichlorosilane (OTS) SAMs chemisorbed on a SiO_2 (100) surface on an oxidized silicon substrate. In order to determine and characterize the optimal packing structure of the OTS-SiO_2 system, we have performed molecular dynamics (MD) simulations and found that results obtained are in the range of those reported in literature using other experimental characterization techniques. The method used is similar to that used in other MD characterization studies of SAM molecules and additives, and is based on an energetic study of different packing configurations

2. EXPERIMENTAL ANALYSIS

2.1. Sample preparation

The samples studied have been Si(100) with a native film of oxide and Si(100) in which SAMs of OTS have been attached in vapor phase. The Si wafers were cut in small squares of about 1cm x 1cm.

Si(100) wafers (Cemat Silicon) were cleaned with piranha solution during 15 minutes and then rinsed with water deionized (H_2O DI) in order to eliminate any impurity on the substrate. Piranha is a mixture of 3:1 (v/v) 98%H_2SO_4 and 30%H_2O_2. There have been cases in which a spontaneous explosion has occurred when it has entered into contact with organic material so this kind of agent has to be treated very carefully.

The preparation of the OTS (Aldrich, ≥90 %) samples was a more delicate matter. All the process of formation was carried out in a clean room (22 °C and 47% RH). After cleaning the wafers, the following step must be the oxidation of the surface of the wafer so that SAMs of OTS can attach to the surface of Si(100). The oxidation is achieved rinsing the squares during 10 minutes firstly in H_2O DI and then in H_2O_2 and finally in H_2O DI again for 5 minutes. Silicon wafers and OTS precursors were introduced in a vacuum chamber as showed in Figure 1. Three different deposition times were taken into account in the deposition process: 15, 30 and 60 minutes.

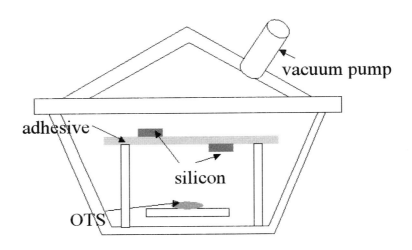

Figure 1. Vapor phase deposition process.

2.2 Contact Angle Measurements

Contact angles are parameters of interest in systems where the interface is important, as for example, the surface wettability, surface or interfacial energy in the solid, the analysis of the surface in different materials where the problem of the adhesion exists, all those present in the micro/nanotribological phenomena.

Through contact angles it is possible to know how much hydrophilic/hydrophobic is a surface when a liquid is in direct contact with it. Contact angle is a quantitative measurement of the wetting of a solid by a liquid. It is defined geometrically as the angle formed by a liquid at the three phase boundary where a liquid, gas and solid intersect in a point. This value depends on the superficial energy of the substrate just as superficial tension of the liquid. If the contact angle is greater than 90°, the surface is said to be hydrophobic and if it is less than 90°, hydrophilic.

For determining the superficial energy of a substrate a method can be used based on the Owens-Wendt theory:

$$1 + \cos\theta = \frac{2}{\gamma_L}\left[\sqrt{\gamma_S^d \gamma_L^d} + \sqrt{\gamma_S^h \gamma_L^h}\right] \qquad (1)$$

where θ is the contact angle, γ_L is the liquid surface tension and γ_S is the solid surface tension, or free energy. The addition of d and p in the subscripts refer to the "dispersion" and "polar" components of each.

When a polar solvent, as, for example, water, is used as test liquid, the contact angle is mainly a measurement of the polarity of the surface, i.e., the grade of hydrophobia/hydrophilia of the surface. On the other hand, if the liquid tested is a non polar one, as for example n-hexadecane, contact angle shows the attractive forces to the surface owing to the van der Waals forces. When contact angle of a liquid is used to calculate the surface energy of a substrate there are several details that must be taken into account in order to ensure the correct application of eq. (1). The substrate has to be atomically flat and chemically homogeneous.

Contact angles were determined putting a small drop of the liquid on the surface of the solid substrate. Then, the drop was illuminated with diffuse light in order to get a clearer image in the edges of the drop. The image of the drop was taken with a CCD and processed by a computer to calculate contact angle. Two liquid were used, deionized water (Tekniker, 0.4 µS/cm, $\gamma_L^d = 21.8$ mN/m, $\gamma_L^h = 51.0$ mN/m) and n-hexadecane (Merk, 226.45 g/mol, 0.773 g/mL (20°C), $\gamma_L^d = 26.8$ mN/m, $\gamma_L^h = 0.2$ mN/m) and they were tested on OTS/Si(100) and Si(100). Each contact angle has been obtained from the average of a set of five measurements.

Table 1: Contact angles measured on Si(100) and Si(100) covered with OTS and their surface energy.

Sample	Contact angles (°)		Surface Energy (mN/m)		
	H₂O DI	n-hexadecane	γ_S^d	γ_S^h	γ_S
Si(100)	14	11	20.8	49.9	70.7
OTS/SI(100)	94	30	22.3	2.7	25.0

Table 1 shows the contact angles of H2O DI and n-hexadecane produced on Si(100) and OTS/Si(100) substrates and the surface energy results following equation (1). While contact angles of both liquids are related to an hydrophilic behavior when the substrate of Si(100) is not treated, contact angles measured on the system OTS/Si(100) are characteristic of a hydrophobic one. Also the total surface energy calculated for the OTS/Si(100) sample shows a lower value than the bare silicon.

2.3. Microtribology

In this work we have used a CSM microtribometer in linear reciprocating mode to study the friction properties of the samples. The range of load that can be applied is in the range of milinewtons and the mode of operation of this device is very simple. A known load is applied through a cantilever which has a small ball of 2 mm of diameter attached to its edge. The ball slides on the surface and the coefficient of friction (COF) is determined during the test from the deflexions that the cantilever suffers.

A glass cantilever was used (Kx= 54 N/m; Kz= 233 N/m). Testing conditions were selected in order to obtain proper friction plots versus time. Sliding speed was 100 µm/s and the stroke was 100 µm. Load was varied between 0.5 and 2.5 mN. In Figure 2 is represented the friction force vs. the normal force analysing four different systems: silicon and silicon with OTS (3 different deposition times).

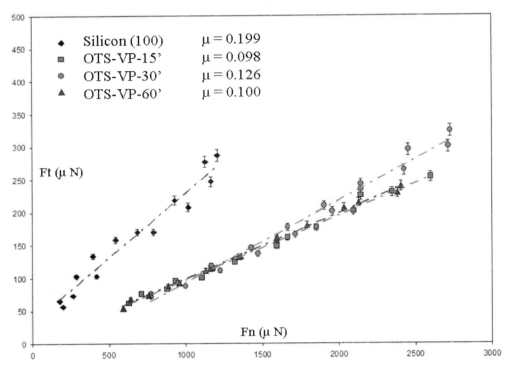

Figure 2: Friction vs. Normal force.

It can be seen that friction behavior is linear with normal force in this range of testing conditions. It is clear from the graph that OTS has an influence reducing friction from 0.2 (silicon) to ~0.11 (silicon+OTS). It seems that there is no influence of the deposition time in the performance of the OTS layer.

3. COMPUTATIONAL APPROACH: MOLECULAR DYNAMICS

3.1. Methodology and first approach

All the studies were performed using MS Modeling 3.1 commercial software from Accelrys Inc. The COMPASS forcefield was employed in the simulations. Molecular substitution, substitution pattern, and molecular orientation were the main factors we have taken into account to perform our minimizations. Molecular substitution is the percentage of hydroxilated atoms in the surface that will be replaced with OTS molecules for an optimal packing structure when the reaction occurs. Substitution pattern tell us the location of atoms substituted. Molecular orientation takes into account the different orientations that OTS molecules can take in the surface. We found that in the case of our study the influence of molecular orientation is negligible. We have performed the minimizations exploring these factors to obtain optimal packing structure.

Molecular packing energies were determined by subtracting surface and OTS energy contributions so we obtain the packing energy per OTS molecules as shown in equation (2):

$$E_{packing} = (E_{SiO2-OTS} - E_{surface} - N \times E_{OTS})/N \quad (2)$$

Where N is the number of OTS molecules attached to the surface.

In a first approach we have studied small systems to avoid too large computational times. 20%, 25%, 33%, 50%, 66%, 75% and 100% substitution percentages were examined for different substitutions patterns and orientations. We found that orientation has a negligible effect on the minimizations: OTS molecules arrange almost vertically because of their length and their close packing. Crosslinking is a factor that also restricts molecular orientation. We found that 20%, 25% and 33% are substitutions that show lower packing energies. Moreover variations between different patterns for these systems are small while for the rest of the systems different patterns showed more dispersion on packing energies.

Once we have found the results for small systems we extend the computational cells to 3x2, 3x3, 4x3, 5x3. This allowed us to explore 20%, 25% and 33% substitution percentages for a wider variety of substitution patterns. Several different substitution patterns were examined for each molecular substitution. The structures that yielded the minimum packing energies were chosen to study characterization variables.

System tilt angles, molecular tilt angles, film thickness and gauche defects were examined for 20%, 25%, 33% minimum packing energy systems. System tilt angle is the one between surface normal and the vector from the first to the last carbon atom in the chain. Molecular tilt angle is an average value of the angles between surface normal and the vectors that join two middle points of two adjacent C-C bonds. Film thickness is measured from the topmost carbon atom in the chain to the surface (taking into account head polar group), on the surface normal direction. Gauche defects are determined analyzing torsional angles. A gauche defect is defined as a torsional angle that differs by more than $+10°$ from the all-trans conformation ($+180°$). Gauche factor is the fraction of the number of gauche defects over the total number of torsion angles in molecular chains.

3.2. Results, validation and stability

Measurements of characterization variables were taken for 20%, 25% and 33% minimum packing energy systems. Results compared with those from experimental techniques are summarized in Table 2.

We found that our data are in good agreement with those reported in experimental measurements: Allara et al. have reported a $10°$ tilt angles, and Vallant et al. reported $7°$ tilt angles. Film thickness are reported to be between 2.0 and 2.9 nm, but most of references point to a value between 2.2 and 2.35 nm. The results obtained for the density of OTS molecules per unit area agree better with those reported in literature in the case of 33% substitution (see Table 2 and Figure 3).

Table 2: Packing energies, characterization variables and comparison with experimental (bibliographical) data.

Molecular substitution	20%	25%	33%	Experimental
Packing energy (kcal/mol)	-177.77	-170.24	-157.01	
Film thickness (Å)	22.54	22.53	22.51	22-23.5
System tilt (°)	10.76	5.94	7.02	7-12
molecular tilt (°)	12.36	9.06	11.03	
Gauche factor (%)	5.21	4.16	2.08	
Molecules/unit area (molecule/Å²)	1/36.86	1/29.49	1/22.12	1/22

Once we have the structures for 20%, 25%, and 33% packing, we run 10 ps (10^{-11} s) molecular dynamics simulations employing the NVT ensemble to study film stability and how characterization variables change with temperature. Andersen method was chosen as thermostat to control temperature during simulations. 1 fs time steps were used. We have performed computational simulations ranging form 100 K to 600 K, and we found that films are stable up to 500 K when monolayer bonds begin to break.

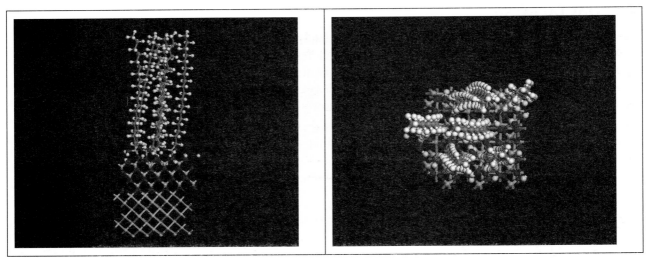

Figure 3: From and top view of conformational structure for 33% packing of OTS on Si(100).

Film thickness was found to be stable around 2.25 nm up to 400K when thickness begins to drop until bonds begin to break (Figure 4). The 33% molecular substitution is the one that shows more thickness stability with temperature as it is almost constant up to 450 K. Gauche factor is found to grow as temperature, it reaches stability in the range from 200 K to ambient temperature, and then rises again. Our results are again in good agreement with those found in literature that report stable OTS monolayers up to 475-500 K. 33% substitution was found to be the packing that showed more stability in terms of film thickness and gauche defects. This result together with the fact that the density of OTS per unit area agrees with the commonly accepted data of $1OTS/22Å^2$ points to 33% substitution as the optimal packing structure for an OTS monolayer.

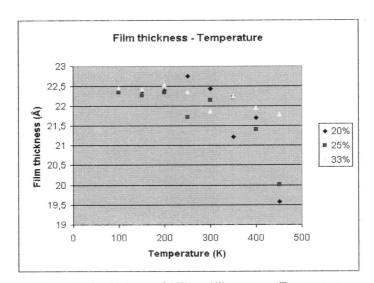

Figure 4: Film thickness of OTS on Silicon versus Temperature.

The good agreement obtained with the experiments also validates the COMPASS forcefield for the study of $OTS-SiO_2$ systems, and it could be used in a future work to analyze, by means of MD computational simulations, the tribological behavior of the optimal structures found in this work.

4. CONCLUSIONS

An experimental approach has been followed to study the tribological behavior of OTS. Besides, a computational methodology was developed to analyse the system. These conclusions can be extracted:

- ➢ OTS coatings are hydrophobic.
- ➢ Deposition time (15'-60') seems to have no influence in the quality of the coating.
- ➢ Friction is reduced from 0.20 (Si-Si) to 0.11 (Si-OTS).
- ➢ Computational results (energetic balance) show that there is 1 molecule of OTS / 2.2 nm^2 and the film thickness is 2.3 nm.
- ➢ Molecular Dynamics simulations show that OTS films are stable up to 500K.
- ➢ Computational results agree with experimental data.

ACKNOWLEDGMENTS

Authors would like to thank the Basque Government for financial support of this work through SAIOTEK programme.

REFERENCES

[1] R. Maboudian, W. R. Ashurst, C. Carraro, Tribology Letters, 12, 95–100, 2002.
[2] I. Ahmed, G. Bregliozzi, H. Haefke, P.A. Steinmann, 1st Vienna Conference on Micro- and Nano-Technology, 299-304, March 2005.
[3] L. Lin, Y.T. Cheng, C.J. Chiu, Microsystem Technologies 4 (1998).
[4] N. S. Tambe, B. Bhushan, Nanotechnology 15 (2004) 1561–1570.
[5] S. A. Miller, B. McDonald, J. Malone, P. I. Oden, Proceedings of the Symposium TRIMIS 2003.
[6] I. S. Forbes, J. Wilson, Thin Solid Films 420 –421 (2002) 508–514.
[7] B. Bhushan, S. Sundararajan, Acta mater., Vol 46, No 11, pp. 3793-3804, 1998.
[8] S. Park, K. D.Costa, G. A. Ateshian, Journal of Biomechanics, J. Biomechanics 37 (2004) 1679–1687.
[9] [. I. Kim, M. Graupe, O. Oloba, T. Koini, S. Imaduddin, T. R. Lee, S. S. Perry, Langmuir 1999, 15, 3179-3185.
[10] U. Landman, W. D. Luedtke, J. Gao, Langmuir 1996, 12, 4514-4528.
[11] S. Sundararajan, B. Bhushan, J. Appl. Phys., Vol. 88, No. 8, 15 October 2000.
[12] A. Noy, C.D. Frisbie, L.F. Rozsnyai, M.S. Wrighton, C.M. Lieber,J. Am. Chem. Soc. 117 (1995) 7943–7951.
[13] Huiwen Liu, S. Imad-Uddin Ahmed, Matthias Scherge, Thin Solid Films 381 2001 135-142.
[14] W. Hild, G. Hungenbach, S.I.-U. Ahmed, M. Scherge, J. A. Schaefer, Proceedings of the Symposium TRIMIS 2003.
[15] MS Modeling 3.0, Accelrys Inc., San Diego, CA, 2003.
[16] Vallant,T.; Kattner, J.; Mayer, U.; Hoffmann, H.; Langmuir 15 (1999).
[17] Allara, D.L.; Parikh, A.N.; Rondelez, Langmuir 11 1995.
[18] Britt, D.W. ; Hlady, H.; J. Coll. Inter. Sci. 178, 775 (1996).
[19] Peters, R.D. ; Nealey, P.F. ; Crain, J.N.; Himpsel, F.J.; Langmuir 18 (2002).
[20] Tidswell, I.M.; Ocko, B.M:; Pershan, P.S.; Phys. Rev. B 41, 1111 (1990).
[21] Maboudian, R.; Ashurst, W.R.; Carraro,C.; IEEE Trans. Dev. Mat. Rel. Vol3 NO 4 (2003).
[22] Kim, B.H; Chung T.D.; Oh, C.H.; Chun K. Journal of microelectromechanical systems. Vol 10, No 1 (2001).

Solid Lubricants for Space Applications: State of the Art

F. Velasco [1], N. Fleischer [2]

[1] Jost Institute for Tribotechnology, University of Central Lancashire, United Kingdom
[2] NanoMaterials Ltd., Israel (Subsidiary of ApNano Materials Inc., USA)

ABSTRACT

The environment of space offers extreme conditions for the lubrication of components on sliding and rolling mechanisms. These include the presence of an ultrahigh vacuum, a wide operating temperature range, an absence of gravity, radiation, and lack of moisture. Solid lubricants have been increasingly used as an alternative to traditional liquid lubricants since they can provide solutions to these space environmental conditions.

This paper reviews the lubrication of components operating in space by providing an overview of space environmental conditions, an explanation of some typical engineering applications of lubricants and a summary on the use of solid lubricants. A review on state of the art materials is provided, in particular Diamond-Like Carbon (DLC) and the nano-technology inorganic fullerene-like nanospheres based on transition metal dichalcogenides.

Inorganic Fullerene-like (IF) nano-sized particles (commercialized under the trademark NanoLub® by ApNano Materials), has the structure of multi-walled (i.e., onion-like) spherical particles that can also be synthesized in the form of nano-tubes. The material is available in several grades as an advanced solid state lubricant for coatings, and as an additive for enhancing the wear and friction properties of oils and greases. It reduces friction and wear significantly better than other conventional solid lubricants, especially under extreme conditions such as high loads.

Keywords: solid lubricants, space engineering, nanomateirals, Diamond-Like Carbon (DLC), NanoLub®, Inorganic Fullerene (IF), nano-particles, nano-lubricants, nano-spheres, nano-technology.

1. INTRODUCTION

Lubrication is a subject of tribology, which has also been referred in recent years as triboscience and tribotechnology. The term "Tribology" was first introduced and defined in 1966 by Prof. H. Peter Jost, in a report set up by the British Department of Education and Science. Tribology was defined as "The science and technology of interacting surfaces in relative motion, and of associated subjects and practices" [1]. Tribotechnology may be defined as the engineering discipline dealing with the technical and economical management of friction, lubrication and wear through scientifically based measures.

Space tribotechnology has developed as experience has been gained with satellites, orbital missions, and devices for planetary exploration. Many failures and successes have been achieved since the first artificial earth satellite (Sputnik 1) was placed in orbit in 1957 by the former Soviet Union. Some examples of failures and breakdowns due to lubrication related problems since the beginning of space exploration are listed below [2,3]:

- The spaceship Vostok (1960): Failure of the IR vertical generator mechanisms due to the enhanced friction and welding of contact surfaces.
- The manual craft Soyuz-1 (1967): Explosion and burn down of the spaceship due to excessive friction in the parachute system.
- The scanning platform Voyager-2 (1981): Failure of the platform due to the wearing out of the lubricant in the gear drives.

- The spacecraft Galileo (1991): Failure to deploy its high-gain antenna fully due to excessive friction between the pins and sockets due to the loss of dry lubricant on some of the antenna's ribs.

In the last decade, tribological systems have increasingly become the limiting factor in spacecraft reliability and performance [4] due to the long life of missions and the non-maintainable condition of lubricated contacts. Materials such as Diamond-Like Carbon (described in this paper) have recently shown promising tribological performance for applications in space sliding and rolling components. However, recent research has led to the discovery of a new class of inorganic structures termed Inorganic Fullerene (IF)-like nano-particles and nano-tubes [5], which show excellent low friction behaviour under the ultra-high vacuum conditions present in space [6].

Inorganic Fullerene nano-particles have a similar geometry to the hollow C60 carbon fullerenes but, in contrast, are inorganic compounds such as WS2 and MoS2 with a spherical multi-walled structure. These nano-particles, due to their size, shape, chemistry and structure, have unique properties making them attractive for many commercial applications. Efforts have been made to increase the production of IF, resulting in the establishment of a high-tech company, ApNano Materials, that is commercialising this novel material under the trade name NanoLub®, as reviewed in this paper.

2. LUBRICATION OF SPACE MECHANISMS

2.1. Operational factors

Moving devices in outer space are required to offer extreme reliability and precision in a wide range of environments, at the same time as costs must be reduced through the minimisation of mass and power consumption. There are a number of factors to consider during the Engineering Design Process (EDP) of space mechanisms, which will affect the behaviour of lubricants; these have been summarised below from a number of sources [7-13].

Table 1. Common operational factors in space systems and associated consequences

FACTOR	CONSEQUENCE
Weightlessness or gravity absent	Difficulties when supplying the oil to where it is needed
Low temperatures: down to -181 °C	May increase the viscosity of fluids lubricants, limiting their free flow
Ultra High Vacuum: $P \sim 10^{-13}$ torr	Evaporation of lubricants which may form a vapour around the spacecraft and contaminate optical and mechanical surfaces
High temperatures: up to 111 °C (1000 °C re-entry)	
Lack of Oxygen	Absence of surfaces oxide films, and consequent increase of the friction coefficients in metal-to-metal non-lubricated contacts.
Radiation	Ionisation of materials and excitation of electrons to high-energy states, which can lead to degradation of a lubricant
Micrometeorites and space debris	Direct impacts on spacecraft external surfaces which can hasten starvation of contact areas.
Launch and landing stages	Exposition of all components to high vibration and impact loads
Assembly, test and storage phases	Exposition of components to humid air
Inaccessibility to space systems	Difficult or impossible maintenance

2.2. Engineering applications

Typical engineering applications where lubricants are used in spacecraft include rolling bearings, linear bearings, ball bushes, gears, screws (ball, plain and roller), threaded fasteners, slip-rings, electrical sliding contacts, separating surfaces and impacting surfaces. From this wide range of applications, a focus is made in this paper on rolling bearings, since it is one of the most common components subject to space tribology research.

Rolling bearings are typically used to produce angular rotation of satellite components. Generally, rolling bearings are classified into two groups depending on the direction of load: radial bearings (radial load) and thrust bearings (axial load). The rolling element is in most cases a ball (ball bearings) or a roller (roller bearings).

The components on a rolling bearing are generally an inner ring, an outer ring, a set of rolling elements, and a cage to keep the rolling elements separated while in operation. Table 2 below shows typical materials used for the most common parts in rolling bearings used in space [10]:

Table 2. Base materials and lubricants commonly applied to bearing components operating in space [10]

BEARING PART	MATERIAL
Outer and inner rings	- SAE 52100 steel - AISI 440C steel - AISI M50 steel Rings will often be lubricated and/or a solid coating applied to the races
Rolling elements	- AISI 440C steel coated with Titanium Carbide (TiC) coating - Tungsten Carbide (WC) ceramic, which may be coated with Titanium Carbide (TiC) or Titanium Nitride (TiN). - Other un-coated ceramics such as Silicon Nitride (Si3N4), Silicon Carbide (SiC), Aluminia (Al2O3), Zirconia (ZrO2)
Cage	- For fluid lubricated applications: Brass, polyacetal, phenolic, porous polymide, soft stainless steel (AISI 410), reinforced PTFE - For dry applications: Leaded bronze and PTFE base materials (Rulon, Salox, Duroix 5813 or Bartemp)

3. SOLID LUBRICANTS

3.1. Definition and classification of solid lubricants

A solid lubricant is a material used to provide protection on the contact between surfaces, which may be used in any of the following ways: as an additive in greases or fluid lubricants (dispersions), as a lubricant composite film (metal and plastic based), for impregnating sintered metal parts, or more commonly, as a solid lubricant coating.

Solid lubricants typically used in space applications may be classified in the following categories [10]:

- Lamellar solids: graphite, molybdenum disulphide (MoS_2), tungsten disulphide (WS_2), etc.
- Soft metal solids: lead, gold, silver, etc.
- Polymers: polytetrafluoroethylene (PTFE), polyamides, polyethylene, etc.
- Oxides: Lead oxide (PbO), antimony oxide (Sb_2O_3), silicon dioxide (SiO2), etc.

Solid lubricant coatings are generally obtained by any of the following methods:

- Vacuum deposited coatings: solid coatings are deposited in a vacuum (or low-pressure plasma) environment. Common processes are Physical Vapour deposition (CVD) and Chemical Vapour Deposition (CVD). CVD processes typically used to produce coatings for space applications include Ion-plating and Sputtering.
- Burnished coatings: a thing film of lubricant powders is applied to a metal surface by a rubbing process, producing a highly polished surface
- Resin-bonded coatings: lubricant powders are dispersed in a binding resin to form coatings. These are then applied onto the substrate by spraying, brushing or dipping.
- Plasma-sprayed coatings: lubricant powders are injected into a very high temperature plasma flame. The powder is heated rapidly and impacts on the substrate surface, where it rapidly cools forming a coating.

- Arc discharge: solid particles are deposited by ablating a compressed solid powder target by an arc discharge in the presence of localized high-pressure nitrogen. The arc is ignited (at 75A and 22V) in the localized region of high-pressure nitrogen.
- Co-deposition via electro-less metal coating or galvanic metal coating from plating solutions containing suspended particles.

3.2.   Advantages of solid lubricants

Table 3 illustrates the advantages and disadvantages of using solid lubricants [4-14]. As shown, dry lubrication is capable of offering solutions for many of the environmental factors present in space (which were previously listed in Section 0)

Table 3. Advantages and disadvantages of solid lubricants

ADVANTAGES	DISADVANTAGES
- Negligible vapour pressure, which will prevent contamination of optical devices due to lubricant evaporation - Wide temperature operating range - Electrically conductive, which makes them suitable for a number or electromechanical applications (such as use in slip-rings or motor brushes) - Negligible surface migration, which will allows the design of lighter and simpler lubrication solutions, reducing energy costs as seals and lubrication distributions systems are not required. - Good boundary lubrication and electrical conductivity. - Accelerated life testing possible, since wear rate is not generally dependent on running speed. - High resistance to deterioration in storage - Low contact adhesion, which will prevent adhesion/cold welding in release mechanisms.	- Endurance life depends on operating conditions (atmosphere, sliding speed, load, contact geometry and etcetera) - Finite life - Generation of wear debris, which will create frictional and torque noise and may affect clearances - Reapplication is difficult or impossible - Low thermal conductivity which will impede heat dissipation between lubricated components

3.3.   Testing of solid lubricants

As described in the ESTL Space Tribology Handbook [10], there are mainly three levels of testing:

- Tribometer level testing (e.g. pure sliding or pin-on-disk tests): allows the measurement of friction coefficient and wear rates in bulk materials, solid coatings and fluid lubricants.
- Component level testing: a test rig represents the real operation of components (e.g. rolling bearings). Typical parameters measured for bearings are torque and life.
- Mechanism level testing: the component is tested in the mechanisms where this is intended to operate, and parameters such as noise, contact resistance, reaction torque, etc. are measured.

Tribometer level testing is essential to produce comparative data between materials at relatively low cost and short time, as no real component is required at this stage. Scientific research in space lubrication often produces tribological data from tribometer tests to draw conclusions on the suitability of specific products.

Solid lubricant testing requires an understanding of the Theory of Thin Films. This theory is well described in various sources which may be consulted for reference [10,15].

4. STATE OF THE ART LUBRICANTS

This section provides a description of state of the art solid lubricants for space applications. The materials described are Diamond-Like Carbon (DLC) and IF.

4.1.   Diamond-like carbon (DLC)

Diamond-Like Carbon (DLC) is a category of solid lubricants which has been under study since the early 1990s. However, the application of modern deposition techniques has recently resulted in the production of improved formulations of this material.

DLC may be defined as "the group of meta-stable amorphous carbon materials whose network consists of a mixture of sp^3 and sp^2 hybridised carbon atoms, and contains variable amounts of hydrogen" [16]. DLC films are produced by a wide variety of physical vapour deposition (PVD) and chemical vapour deposition (CVD) techniques. Some of the typical properties of this material include high wear resistance, low friction coefficient, chemical inertness, infrared transparency and high electrical resistivity [17].

Currently, there are number of terrestrial applications of DLC, including microelectronic surfaces and devices, magnetic storage media, abrasion-resistant optical products, implant components in medical applications (e.g. hip and nee joints), treatment of plastic packaging materials, razor blades (Gillette MACH3®), etc.

The literature available on DLC film research shows that the measurements of sliding friction coefficients (μ) fall in the range of 0.003 to 0.6, which represents a wide range of friction behaviour. Wear rates are less often investigated and recorded in non-standard units which make the comparison between results difficult. However, it is known that DLC films can be produced with wear rates as low as 10^{-8} $mm^3N^{-1}m^{-1}$.

In ambient humid air with relative humidity in the range 20% to 60%, the friction coefficient generally ranges between 0.05 and 0.3, with wear rates that are strongly dependent on the nature of the film [18]. Non-hydrogenated coatings (commonly ta-C) generally exhibit lower friction ($\mu < 0.3$) than hydrogenated coatings (commonly a-CH). Both coating types appear to be affected by the amount of humidity in a different manner. Thus, in ta-C films friction decreases with increasing humidity [19], while in a-CH films friction increases with humidity [20].

In inert environments, including dry nitrogen and vacuum, friction coefficients can reach either ultra-low values ($\mu < 0.01$ or less) or high values ($\mu > 0.5$) [21,22]. The hydrogen content of the films can control this fluctuating friction behaviour. According to previous investigations [23], hydrogen concentrations lower than 34 atomic % systematically lead to high friction, while hydrogen concentrations greater than 40 atomic % lead to ultra-low friction.

Case Study: DLC as a possible alternative to currently used MoS2 in space

Recent investigations on Diamond-Like Carbon [24], has shown that specific formulations of highly-hydrogenated DLC coatings (~ 50 at. % hydrogen) may offer an alternative to currently used solid lubricants in space mechanisms. The coatings were deposited using high-density Inductively Coupled Plasma (ICP) process, which is based on Plasma Assisted Chemical Vapour Deposition (PACVD) technique.

Sliding ball-on-disc tests of DLC coated AISI 52100 steel specimens were conducted against uncoated AISI 52100 balls. Results have shown a steady-state friction coefficients around 0.27 in air (50% RH) for a live exceeding the 100,000 disc cycles, and extremely low friction coefficients around 0.013 in vacuum ($P < 5 \times 10^{-6}$ mbar) for a life equivalent to 66,000 disc cycles.

These results are shown in Figure 1 below, where a comparison is made with results obtained under similar testing conditions for Molybdenum Disulphide (MoS$_2$) [25], the most currently used solid lubricant in space. It appears from this investigation [24] that DLC coatings may show higher friction coefficients in air than MoS$_2$, however does not exceed the limit of 0.3 generally attributed to the steel against steel contact. The friction performance in vacuum is lower and more stable for DLC (see Figure 1a). As shown in Figure 1b, the life of DLC coatings in air appears to be five times higher than for MoS$_2$, although the life performance in air does not improved.

Post test examination of samples tested in air and vacuum, showed that the coating has been worn through to the underlying steel in several locations within the wear track. The ball wear spot showed areas with high percentage of Carbon, which is presumably material transferred from the DLC coating. This factor is relevant because the transfer of material from the coated disc to the surface of the uncoated ball may have provided protection against friction.

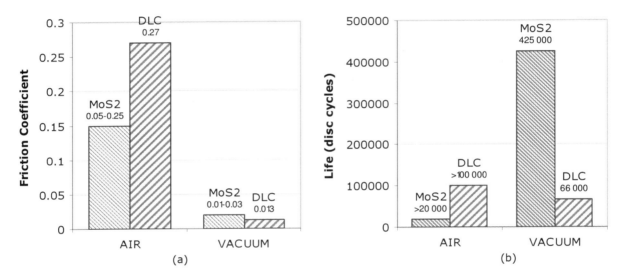

Figure 1. Comparison of (a) steady-state friction and (b) life between MoS2 and DLC tested under similar pure sliding conditions (disc & ball material AISI 52100, only disc is coated; load 5N; speed 200rpm; ball diameter 7.14 mm; vacuum pressure <5310^{-4} Pa; track radius 9.6mm). Sources [24,25]

4.2. Inorganic Fullerene-like materials: A new class of Nano-structures

In 1992 [5] the Nano-materials Synthesis Group at the Weizmann Institute of Science (Israel) discovered a new class of inorganic nano-structures. The group found that certain inorganic compounds, specifically naturally layered materials of transition metal dichalcogenides such as WS2, MoS2, TiS2 and NbS2 that normally occur as large flat platelets, can be synthesized into much smaller nano-spheres (see Figure 2) and nano-tubes (see Figure 3). These were named inorganic fullerene-like (IF) nano-structures.

As shown in Figure 2, each particle consists of a number of progressively smaller concentric forms, sometimes twenty or more, nested one within the other. The nested structure of these particles has been compared to that of an onion. The diameter of the nano-particles is on the order of 100 nm. These nano-particles, due to their size, shape, chemistry and structure, have special properties that are not possible with conventional sized materials of the same composition making them attractive for many commercial applications.

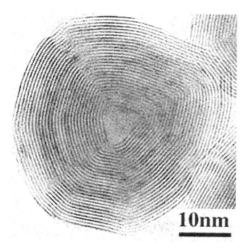

Figure 2. IF nano-sphere

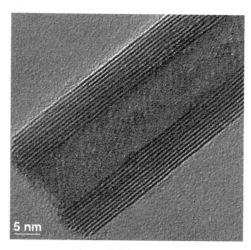

Figure 3. IF nano-tube

The accomplishment of the Weizmann group was identifying the particular conditions for inducing certain inorganic compounds to curve and close into multi-walled nano-particles. Before this discovery it was thought that fullerenes could only be made with carbon atoms.

Comprehensive biocompatibility tests at certified laboratories according to protocols by the Organisation for Economic Co-operation and Development (OECD) have clearly shown that the IF-WS$_2$ nano-particles are non-toxic and safe in acute oral administration to rats, dermal sensitisation tests, and acute inhalation evaluations in rats. This makes them suitable for 'green' lubrication products.

IF nano-particles are being developed into advanced coatings to reduce friction and improve wear resistance of many applications. In particular, they can be used in medical devices such as orthodontic arch wires and artificial joints as well as catheters, needles, and other mechanical items that are inserted into the human body. A new generation of coatings and surface engineering solutions based on the use of IF nano-particles significantly reduce friction and extends operational life. This conserves energy, reduces pollution, and saves money.

Coatings based on IF nano-particles can be prepared by various innovative deposition methods and techniques that enables accurate control of the incorporation of the IF nano-particles, their adhesion to surfaces, their physical properties such as thickness, hardness, and tribological characteristics.

Stability under vacuum

Evaluation of IF's outgassing properties was done in accordance with the ASTM E595 standard test method at the Soreq Nuclear Research Center, Israel. This test measures the Total Mass Loss (TML) and the Collected Volatile Condensed Material (CVCM) of 100-300 mg samples heated under vacuum to 125°C for 4 hours. The criteria of TML<1% and CVCM<0.1% are used for certification of materials for space applications. The results (see Table 4 below) showed that the total mass loss and volatile mass loss of IF-WS2 under these conditions was several times lower than the specified target values.

Table 4. Outgassing under simulated space conditions

ITEM	TARGET	NanoLub®
Total Mass Loss	Less than 1%	0.4%
Volatile Matter Loss	Less than 0.1%	0.02%

<u>Case Study I: Reducing Friction by Incorporating IF into electro-less nickel-phosphorous coatings</u>

Recent investigations [26] have demonstrated that the friction force of stainless steel wires coated with IF-WS$_2$ nano-particles embedded in annealed electro-less nickel phosphorous coatings showed up to a 54% reduction in friction compared to non-coated wires.

Tribological tests using a ball-on-flat configuration performed by Prof. Lev Rapoport of the Holon Institute of Technology (Israel) showed that the IF electro-less nickel coating has a friction coefficient that is five times lower than that for uncoated wire (see Figure 4 below).

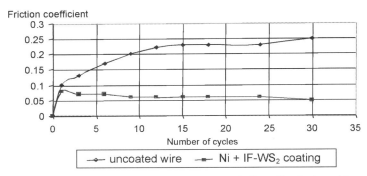

Figure 4. Friction tests performed using a ball-on-flat device with a sliding velocity of 0.2mm/s and a normal load of 50g (ca. 1.5 GPa).

A method for incorporating the nano-particles into a coating is by composite electro-less deposition. Within the variety of metals in use, the most common nickel-phosphorous (Ni-P) films have proven their supremacy in corrosion and wear resistance. Figure 5 shows an image of a Ni-P coating with embedded nano-particles, deposited on a steel substrate.

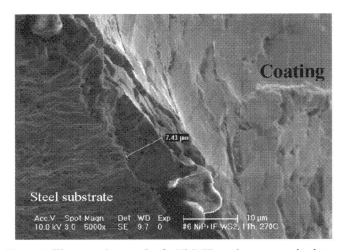

Figure 5. Electron micrograph of a Ni-P-IF coating on a steel substrate

<u>Case Study II: Improving the Wear Resistance of Ceramic Moving Parts</u>

Ceramic materials are increasingly being considered in various extreme tribological applications because of their outstanding mechanical and physical properties, such as strength, hardness, and chemical inertness. The low toughness of this class of materials has raised interest in understanding the relationship between wear and fracture responses and material microstructure. The role of micro-structural features is contradictory. Tensile strength and hardness of alumina often decrease with increasing grain size while fracture toughness of alumina, increases with increasing grain size because various toughening mechanisms such as grain bridging and crack deflections are activated. Therefore, to gain an understanding of wear-fracture properties interaction, investigating the role of fracture processes at the micro-structural scale during controlled wear tests is required. Wear and wear transitions are the major concerns regarding the tribological application of ceramic materials. Cracking and material loss were the main damage mechanisms in wear or fretting of ceramics materials under continuous contact pressure and moving surfaces.

Dry powders of IF nano-particles are excellent as dry film lubricants and have been used successfully to reduce the wear of ceramic/ceramic couples under sliding contact conditions. Coatings can be prepared by a burnishing procedure as described below. The nano-particles apparently reduce the local concentration of the shearing force at the point of contact and can maintain the coefficient of friction at a desired value for optimal working conditions.

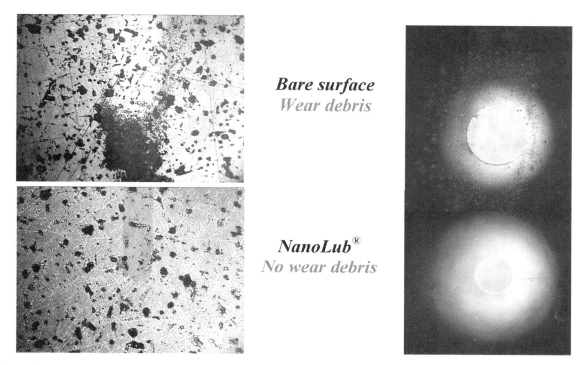

Bare surface
Wear debris

NanoLub®
No wear debris

Figure 6. Direct ceramic/ceramic contact: (upper left) – wear track on an alumina flat with accumulated debris at end of stroke limit caused by the sliding of a silicon nitride rod with hemispherical tip, diameter 2 mm, at a maximum contact pressure of about 2 GPa and reciprocating sliding velocity of 0.2 mm/s; (upper right) – surface of the silicon nitride hemisphere after friction tests. Coated ceramic contact: (lower left) – wear track on an alumina flat that was burnished with a coating of tungsten disulfide IF nano-spheres. The wear track is significantly narrower than the control bare surface and no debris hill is observed at the end of the track; (lower right) – the surface of the silicon nitride hemisphere after friction tests on the IF coated surface. The tip is significantly less worn than the control as noted by a much smaller flattened area.

Burnished coatings

In work conducted by Prof. Lev Rapoport of the Holon Institute of Technology (Israel) IF-WS2 solid lubricant particles were burnished on the surface of steel disks using plastic deformation of the surface layers [27]. A pin-on-disk instrument was re-equipped in order to burnish the surfaces of the disks. In order to optimize the parameters of burnishing, the velocity and loads were varied. The solid lubricant films were coated under three sliding velocities – 200, 400 and 600 rpm. Three loads of 250, 500 and 1,000 grams were used in this test. After the burnishing, the durability of solid lubricant film was determined via analysis of curves of friction force vs. time. A jump in the friction force testifying to the damage of the solid lubricant film which was chosen as the parameter of durability. Based on these results, the best parameters of burnishing were determined. These are a sliding velocity of 200 rev/min and load of 200 grams.

The roughness and surface morphology of burnished films were analyzed. The roughness profile of the IF film is shown in Figure 7; the roughness profile for the as received disks is given in Figure 8. The photo micrographs of the smooth surface obtained for thin IF films at two different magnifications are shown in Figure 9.

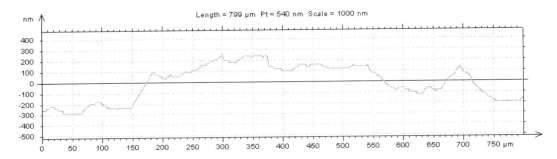

Figure 7. Typical roughness profile of IF-WS$_2$ on the surface of the original disk, R$_a$ = 48 nm

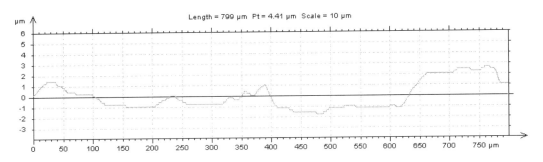

Figure 8. Typical roughness profile of original disks, R$_a$ = 13.2 µm

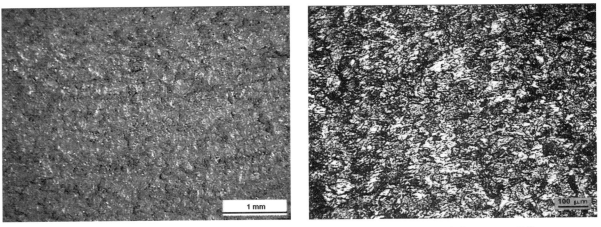

Figure 9. Typical microscopy image of IF-WS2 film burnished on the surface of steel discs at two different magnifications, R$_a$ = 48 nm

5. CONCLUSION

Solid lubricants show the ability to reduce wear in situations where fluid lubricants are either impractical or inadequate, such as miniature devices, maintenance-free operations, high-load applications or severe environmental conditions (high vacuum, radiation, etc.).

Metal Dichalcogenides MX_2 (where M is, for instance, Mo or W, and X is S or Se) are widely used as solid lubricants; in particular MoS_2 and WS_2 are commonly used in space applications. These materials in their conventional layered structure (2H phase) have a layered structure with weak (van der Waals) inter-layer forces that allow easy, low-strength shearing for lubrication action. Other materials currently under review, such as Diamond-Like Carbon (DLC), have shown promising tribological performance for application in space. These compositions also present layered structures and commonly require the application of interlayer to improve adhesion of the coating to the steel substrate.

One of the mayor drawbacks associated to layered structures is the chemical reactivity of layer edges, which may cause slow decomposition. The relative large size of the layered platelets prevents the protective material from entering the pores of metal and ceramic parts and thus these tend to accumulate on the surface and stick to the components causing the movements to 'stick-and-slip'. These factors ultimately diminish their lubricating ability causing components to grind against each other and wear down. Thus, there is a need for finding improved solutions to traditional layered solid lubricants.

Within the past few years, new inorganic fullerene-like (IF) nano-particles of MX_2 with structures similar to those of nested carbon fullerenes and nano-tubes have been synthesized in bulk quantities exclusively by ApNano Materials. These compounds in their fullerene-like nano-sphere structure act as extremely effective solid lubricants in a variety of applications: recent research have shown that $IF-WS_2$ outperforms the layered 2H form of these compounds in every respect (friction, wear and lifetime of the lubricant) under varied test conditions [27] and especially at high loads and long operating times [28,29]. The outstanding performance of $IF-WS_2$ may be attributed to its chemical inertness, nano-size and the hollow cage structure, which imparts elasticity and allows the particles to roll rather than to slide.

REFERENCES

[1] Jost HP. "Lubrication, Education and Research – A report on the Present Position and Industry's Needs". Her Majesty's Stationery Office, London; 1966.

[2] Drozdov YN. "The Main Problems of Space Tribology". WTC II. Proceedings of the II World Tribology Congress; 2001 Sep 3-7; Vienna, Austria.

[3] Miyoshi K. "Aerospace mechanisms and tribology technology". Tribology International 32 (1999) 673-685.

[4] Jones WR and Jansen MJ. "Space Tribology". Technical Memorandum NASA/TM-2000-209924; National Aeronautics and Space Administration (NASA), US; 2000.

[5] Tenne R, Margulis L, Genut M and Hodes G. "Polyheddral and cylindrical structures of tungsten disulphide". Nature 360 (1992) 444-445.

[6] Cizaire L, Vacher B, Le Mogne T, Martina JM, Rapport L, Margoline A and Tenne R. "Mechanisms of ultra-low friction by hollow inorganic fullerene-like MoS2 nanoparticles". Surface and Coatings Technology 160 (2002) 282–287.

[7] Sanders JH, Cutler JN, Miller JA and Zabinski JS. "In Vacuuo Tribological Investigations of Metal, Ceramic and Hybrid Interfaces for High-Speed Spacecraft Bearing Applications". Tribology International 32 (2000) 649-659.

[8] Fusaro RL and Khonsari MM. "Liquid Lubrication for Space Applications". Technical Memorandum NASA/TM-105198; National Aeronautics and Space Administration (NASA), USA; 1992.

[9] Fusaro RL. "Lubrication of Space Systems". Technical Memorandum NASA/TM-106392; National Aeronautics and Space Administration (NASA), US; 1994.

[10] Roberts EW, editor. "Space Tribology Handbook" 3rd edition (2002). ESTL, AEA Technology, UK.

[11] Zaretsky EV. "Liquid lubrication in Space". Tribology International 23-2 (1990) 75-93.

[12] Yuga I, Chevichelova TM, Yu. M. Simeonova and T. G. Nazarsky. "Application of a New Antifriction Material at Tribological Junctions of Space Research Equipment". WTC II. Proceedings of the II World Tribology Congress; 2001 Sep 3-7; Vienna, Austria.

[13] Donnet C, Fontaine J, Le Mogne T, Belin M, Héau C, Terrat JP, Vaux F and Pont G, "Diamond-like carbon-based functionally gradient coatings for space Tribology". Surface Coating Technology 120/121 (1999) 548-885.

[14] "Engineering and Design - Lubricants and Hydraulic Fluids". Engineer Manual EM 1110-2-1424; Department of the Army, US Army Corps of Engineers, Washington DC, US; 1999.

[15] Quinn TFJ. "The Application of Modern Physical Techniques to Tribology ". Butterworth & Co (Publishers) Ltd, London, UK; 1971.

[16]　Velasco F. "Evaluation of diamond-like carbon films for lubrication in space". Thesis Collection 621/VEL; University of Central Lancashire, Preston, UK; 2003.

[17]　Grill A. "Diamond-Like Carbon: State of the Art". Diamond and Related Materials 8 (1999) 428-434.

[18]　Erdemir A and Donnet C. "Tribology of Diamond, Diamond-Like Carbon and Related Films". Modern Tribology Handbook Vol. 2 (2001) 871-908, B. Bhusham, ed. CRC Press LLC.

[19]　Voevodin AA, Phelps AW, Zabinski JS and Donley MS. "Friction-Induced Phase Transformation of Pulsed-Laser-Deposited Diamond-Like Carbon". Diamond and Related Materials 5 (1996) 1264-1269.

[20]　Franks J, Enke K and Richardt A. "Diamond-Like Carbon - Properties and Applications". Metastable and Nanocrystalline Materials November (1990) 695-700.

[21]　Erdemir A, Eryilmaz OL and Fenske G. "Synthesis of Diamondlike Carbon Films with Superlow Friction and Wear Properties". Journal of Vacuum Science Technology 18 (2000) 1987-1992.

[22]　Erdemir A, Eryilmaz OL, Nilufer IB and Fenske G. "Effect of Source Gas Chemistry on Tribological Performance of Diamondlike Carbon Films". Diamond and Related Materials 9 (2000) 1987-1992.

[23]　Donnet C and Grill A. "Friction Control of Diamond-Like Carbon Coatings". Surface Coating Technology 94/95 (1997) 456-462.

[24]　Vanhulsel A, Velasco F, Jacobs R, Roberts EW, Sherrington I, Anderson MJ and Gaillard L. "Development of Highly Hydrogenated DLC Coatings for Solid Lubrication in Space". 11th ESMATS. Proceedings for the 11th European Mechanisms and Tribology Symposium. 2005 Sep 21-23; Lucerne, Switzerland.

[25]　Vercammen K, Meneve J, Dekempeneer E, Smeets J, Roberts EW and Eiden MJ. "Study of RF PACVD diamond-like carbon coatings for space mechanism applications". Surface and Coatings Technology 120-121 (1999) 612-617.

[26]　Katz A, Redlich M, Rapoport L, Wagner HD and Tenne R. "Self-lubricating coatings containing fullerene-like WS2 nanoparticles for orthodontic wires and other possible medical applications". Tribology Letters 2006 (to be published).

[27]　Rapoport L, Bilik Yu, Feldman Y, Homyonfer M, Cohen SR and Tenne R. "Hollow nanoparticles of WS2 as potential solid-state lubricants." Nature 387 (1997) 791-793.

[28]　Greenberg R., Halperin G., Etsion I and Tenne R. "The effect of WS2 nanoparticles on friction reduction in various lubrication regimes". Tribology Letters 17-2 (2004) 179-186.

[29]　Joly-Pottuza L., Dassenoy F., Belin M., Vacher B., Martin J. M. and Fleischer N. "Ultralow-friction and wear properties of IF-WS2 under boundary lubrication". Tribology Letters 18-4 (2005) 477-485.

Alkylated Naphthalenes as High Performance Synthetic Fluids

M. J. Hourani, R. A. Abramshe, J. G. Lianh, E. T. Hessell

King Industries Inc, USA

PAPER NOT AVAILABLE

Session 6
LUBRICATION TECHNOLOGY 2

Chair: Prof. Edward H. Smith

Thermoelastohydrodynamic Lubrication Analysis of Modification Helical Gears
W. LI, Y. LIU, W. XIAO, C. WANG, C. CHEN

Influences on the Lubrication of Piston-Rings in Large Two Stroke diesel Engines and the Impact of MARPOL VI
I. SHERRINGTON, D. SHORTEN

Filtration of Oil and Related Benefits
C. J. THOMSEN

Thermoelastohydrodynamic Lubrication Analysis
of Modification Helical Gears

Li Wei, Liu Yanjun, Xiao Wangqiang, Wang Chunyan, Chen Chenwen

Mechanical Engineering School, University of Science and Technology Beijing, 100083 Beijing, China

ABSTRACT

An involute helical cylinder gear is one of the most important elements widely used in mechanical devices. In order to improve the overall performance of the total devices, how to analyze the lubrication characteristics of the helical gear in the practical working condition is very important. This paper introduces a physical model used for analyzing the EHL of helical gears, deduces the initial slot equation in the meshing gear surface, presents an ordinary method of analyzing thermoelastohydrodynamic lubrication of helical gears with modified teeth, describes the methods and basic rules for deciding both the unit line load up and down limits and rigid center oil-film thickness before and behind modifying teeth, obtains the numerical solutions of EHL before and behind modifying teeth along the contacting line and meshing line, and compares the results of non-modified teeth with one of the modified teeth. Finally, some effective measures for improving lubrication characteristic in helical gears are demonstrated simultaneously.

Keywords: Modification Helical Gear, Thermoelastohydrodynamic Lubrication, Oil-Film Thickness.

1. INTRODUCTION

The existence of elastohydrodynamic lubrication is first found from the gears, for example, some large ships sailed over ocean for a long time, and the processing trace on its' transmission gear tooth surface was still kept very well as before, which reminded people of great interests in gear lubrication. The study on the theory of the gear lubrication state is the process of studying multi-subjects theory including more factors on the basis of the theory of EHL.

Martin [1] wrote a paper of Lubrication in Gears, which presented a good outset for the study of the EHL in gears in 1916. On the assumption that contact loadings were constant and the influence of nonsteady effect was ignored in the process of whole meshing circulation, Dowson and Higgson [2] studied the change of the film thickness using present theory when involute gear tooth contacted in 1966. Gu [3] expanded their analysis method that was used in calculation about whole meshing circulation and built a thermal EHL model in 1973. In 1981 Sato and Taknashi [4] solved the problem of gear lubrication using theory of full thermal EHL, but the instantaneous influence was not considered. And in the same year Vilmossimon [5] discussed load capacity and efficiency of spur gears and analyzed the effects of viscosity, the minimum film thickness, the entrainment velocity , the meshing position , the temperature of oil supply, the environment temperature and body temperature on the load capacity and transmission efficiency. In his calculation, he thought oil must be formed in the area that was shaped between the meshing gear tooth surfaces on a meshing point. In general, people think the oil is only formed in the area of some Hertz contact width on the contact point, while the calculation region that is used in the literature [5] is bigger than that range, so the calculation seems to be wrong and the result is not satisfied. Wang and Cheng [6] applied Vichard theory to solve the EHL problem of involute spur gear whose tooth number ratio is 1 to 2 and resolved the calculation of central film thickness later. On the assumption that load was invariable, isothermal and full-film and $\partial u / \partial x$ was considered, Lin and Medley [7] studied non-stationary elastohydrodynamic lubrication of involute spur gear by analyzing problems in inlet region on the basis of Grubin assumption in 1984. Wang and Yang [8] made a transient EHL analysis of an involute spur gear and a complete numerical solution is obtained by using simplified multigrid method.

We could find by the representation as above, people have done some study on the steady EHL and non-steady EHL of involute spur gears and make some achievements, while the investigation on the EHL of helical gear is very difficult, because geometry parameter and movement parameter of every point on contact line at every moment are different. Studying the EHL problem of involute helical gear is highly necessary.

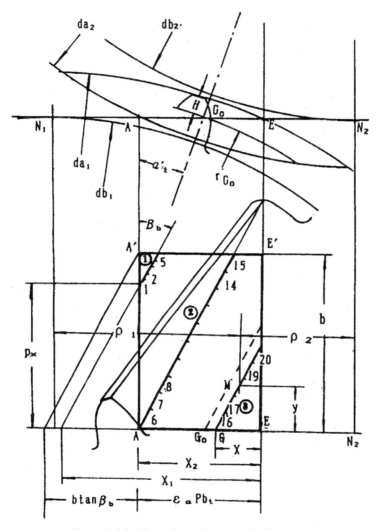

Figure 1. Meshing schematic chart of helical gears

2. CALCULATION OF VARIABLE CURVATURE AND VARIABLE VELOCITY ON INSTANTANEOUS CONTACT LINE OF HELICAL GEAR

Fig.1 shows that the intersection point of instantaneous contact line and an obtuse angle end surface on tooth surface of helical gear is G and the length $\overline{GE}$ between point G and E is used to show the position of contact line. To assume X as the length $\overline{GE}$, while the length X is close to zero, contact line that is on tooth tip of the obtuse angle end surface and the length is close to zero, it is the place where a drive wheel finishes to mesh or a follower wheel begins to mesh. When the length X is close to ($\varepsilon_\alpha P_{bt} + b \tan \beta_b$), the contact line that is on tooth root of an acute angle end surface and the length is also close to zero. It is the place where a drive wheel begins to mesh or a follower wheel finishes to mesh. The position of one point M on contact line is expressed by axial distance Y between an obtuse angle end surface and that point.

To assume that there are three pairs of gear tooth that mesh and three contact lines at one time, the point M is on the contact line l_3, the curvature radius ρ_1, ρ_2 of the tooth profiles' end-surface and the colligation curvature radius ρ_{red} on this point is written as

$$\rho_1(x,y,t) = \frac{m_n \cdot z_1}{\cos\beta} \cos[\arctan(\tan\alpha_n/\cos\beta)] \cdot \tan\left(\beta_1 + i\Delta t(x) \cdot \frac{\pi n_1}{30}\right) - y\tan\beta_b$$

$$\rho_2(x,y,t) = \frac{m_n \cdot z_2}{\cos\beta} \cos[\arctan(\tan\alpha_n/\cos\beta)] \cdot \tan\left(\alpha_{a2} - i\Delta t(x) \cdot \frac{\pi n_1 z_1}{30 z_2}\right) + y\tan\beta_b$$

$$\Delta t(x) = 60 \times \cos\beta / (m_n \cdot i \cdot \pi n_1 z_1 \cos\alpha_t)$$

$$\rho_{red}(x,y,t) = \frac{\rho_1(x,y,t) \cdot \rho_2(x,y,t)}{\rho_1(x,y,t) + \rho_2(x,y,t)} \cdot \frac{1}{\cos\beta_b}$$

Where

$$\beta_1 = \arctan\left[\tan\alpha_t + \frac{z_2}{z_1}(\tan\alpha_t - \tan\alpha_{a2})\right]$$

α_{a2} is the pressure angle of addendum circle of follower wheel; α_t is the end-surface pressure angle; n_1 is rotational speed of drive wheel.

In the contact area, two tooth profiles' entrainment velocity u on point M should be calculated by the end-surface velocity u_1, u_2. The formulation is given as following

$$u_1(x,y,t) = (2\pi n_1/60) \cdot \rho_1(x,y,t)$$
$$u_2(x,y,t) = (2\pi n_2/60) \cdot \rho_2(x,y,t)$$

Instantaneous entrainment velocity is given as

$$u(x,y,t) = \frac{1}{2}[u_1(x,y,t) + u_2(x,y,t)]$$

Instantaneous sliding velocity is given as

$$u_s(x,y,t) = u_1(x,y,t) - u_2(x,y,t)$$

3. NUMERICAL CALCULATION OF ELASTOHYDRODYNAMIC LUBRICATION FOR STANDARD HELICAL GEARS

Determination of rigid-body central film thickness and upper-lower Limit of line load before modification is as following:

(1) To calculate the total load W_{all} and contact line total length L_{all}.

(2) To calculate the average unit-line load. That is $\overline{W} = W_{all}/L_{all}$.

(3) the average unit-line load were put into the every small segment to calculate corresponding dimensionless load $W = \overline{W}/E' \cdot R$ and then call the subprograms of the EHL calculation in every small segment to calculate corresponding rigid-body central film thickness h_{oi} (i=1,...,20) on every segment; where $h_{oo1} = \min\{h_{o1},...,h_{o20}\}$, $h_{oo2} = \max\{h_{o1},...,h_{o20}\}$. h_{oo1} and h_{oo2} are the upper and lower limit of rigid-body central film thickness h_{oo} respectively.

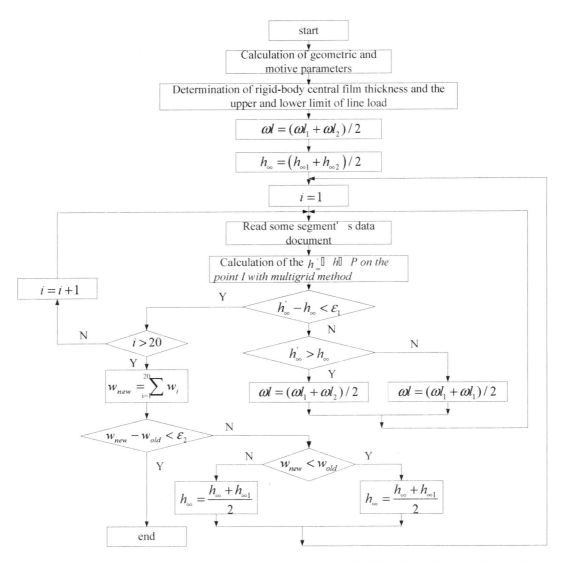

Figure 2. The computational procedure of the numerical calculation of the EHL of helical gear before modification

(4) To calculate the maximum of $h_{o1},...,h_{o20}$ and when the minimum of rigid-body central film thickness is taken from $h_{o1},...,h_{o20}$, that unit-line load is the maximum line load. And put it to wl_2. Then calculate the minimum of $h_{o1},...,h_{o20}$ and when the maximum of rigid-body central film thickness is taken from $h_{o1},...,h_{o20}$, that unit-line load is the minimum line load. And put it to wl_1. where wl_1 and wl_2 are the upper and lower limit of wl respectively.

After the upper and lower limit of h_{oo},wl is confirmed, we can use dichotomy method to adjust h_{oo},wl again and again to satisfy   (a) $|h_{oo}-h_{oi}|\le\varepsilon_1$ (i=1,2,...,20); (b) $\left|W_{all}-\sum_{i=1}^{20}W_i\right|\le\varepsilon_2$;The computational procedure is illustrated in Fig.2.

Because the parameters on every contact line are different, to unify and compare that ,c p_0 and c b_0 are introduced to be dimensionless reference to the contact pressure and contact width ,whose value is the maximum Hertz pressure and contact width on node C respectively when total loads are average distributed on contact line.

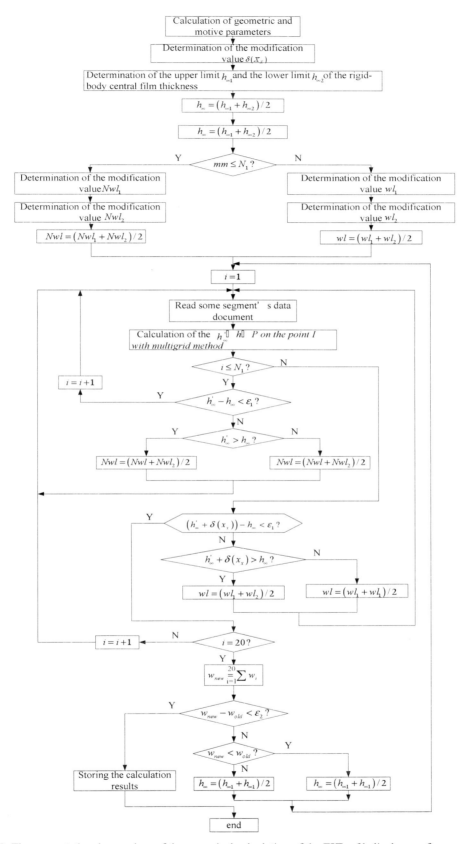

Figure 3. The computational procedure of the numerical calculation of the EHL of helical gear after modification

4. NUMERICAL CALCULATION OF ELASTOHYDRODYNAMIC LUBRICATION FOR MODIFIED HELICAL GEARS

The determination of rigid-body central film thickness and the upper and lower limit of line load after modification is as following: The rigid-body central film thickness and the upper and lower limit of unit line load should be re-determined in the calculation of the EHL after modification, but the result before modification will be used to determine the reasonable $h_{oo1}, h_{oo2}, wl_1, wl_2$ and to reduce the search range of dichotomy method and the CPU working time, otherwise the calculation becomes larger and the iterative speed becomes slower and even divergent.

Now the method is described briefly as follows which determines the upper or lower limit of stiffness central oil film thickness and unit line load after modification.

(1) The determination of $h_{\infty 1}$. To distribute evenly all loads into contact line that is not modified,

compute the stiffness central oil film thickness of every segment , and the minimum of oil film thickness is $h_{\infty 1}$. While the amount of modification is very small, $h_{\infty 1}$ can be determined directly by

$$h_{\infty 1} = h_{\infty 2} - \delta(x_z).$$

(2) The determination of $h_{\infty 2}$. $h_{\infty 2}$ is the real rigid central oil film thickness before modification in the

same working conditions.

(3) To determine the upper or lower limit of unit line load in non-modification region. (a) wl_1: the

minimum unit line load is determined by calculation in the region before modification. (b) wl_2: the segment's rigid central oil film thickness in the process of determination $h_{\infty 1}$ which holds the maximum

oil film thickness is $h_{\infty 2}$, while the corresponding unit line load is wl_2.

(4) To determine the upper or lower limit of unit line load. (a) wl_1 is the corresponding minimum unit

line load for every segment in modification region when rigid central oil film thickness is $h_{\infty 2} + \delta(x_z)$. (b) wl_2 is the corresponding maximum unit line load for every segment after modification when rigid central oil film thickness is $h_{\infty 1} + \delta(x_z)$.

According to the theory, the method and steps as mentioned above, the relevant FORTRAN programs were developed and the computation procedure is showed in Fig.3.

5. RESULTS AND DISCUSSION

Taking a pair of helical gears used in gearbox as an example, we analyzed its lubrication performance and obtained the minimum film thickness, the center film-thickness, the unit line load, and the maximum pressure along the contact lines. Before modification, for the gear transmission whose speed ratio is bigger than 1, the minimum film-thickness and the central film-thickness increase gradually along the contact line from tooth root to tooth tip of smaller gear and the changing trend of the maximum pressure is opposite to the film-thickness, and the changing trend of the unit line load is basically same with the film-thickness. It is not difficult to analyze that: the gear makes pure rolling at the pitch point and the entrainment velocity of two gears is equality, because the rotation speed of big gear is smaller than small one, the increased or decreased velocity of big gear is smaller than small gear at some distance that is deviated from the pitch point along the contact line and the colligation curvature radius can increase gradually from tooth root to tooth tip along the contact line. When the speed ratio is bigger than 1, the meshing point of gear tooth that is near the midpoint of theoretical meshing line is the maximum colligation curvature point, so the colligation curvature radius also increases gradually. The increase of entrainment velocity along the contact line and the colligation curvature radius makes the increase of the minimum film thickness and the central film thickness, and the increase of colligation curvature radius causes that the line load distributes in wider contact area to reduce the maximum pressure. When helical gears that transmission speed ratio is bigger than 1 meshes at a moment, we can get the minimum value of the central film thickness and the minimum film thickness, the maximum value of the pressure at tooth root of small gear and the maximum value of the central film thickness, the minimum film thickness, the unit line load, and the minimum value of the maximum pressure at the tooth tip. Though the calculation example is calculated at one meshing moment, it isn't difficult to illuminate that the result is still correct at other meshing moment and have only a little difference in numerical value. In the calculation example, the variable ratio of the minimum film-thickness $h_{\min}$, the central film thickness h_c, the maximum pressure and the unit line load wl along the contact line is 3.1%, 2.89%, 10.4% and 13.7% respectively. Therefore, in the four characteristics value as above, the variable ratio of the unit line load is the biggest; the variable ratios of the minimum film thickness and the central film thickness are the smallest, while the variable ratio of the maximum compressive stress is middle among them.

There is quite a difference between the EHL state of helical gears before modification and after modification. Under the same working conditions, central film thickness and maximum film thickness of gear tooth on modified contact line in the meshing area after modification keep unchangeable in comparison with that before modification. The line load and maximum Hertz contact pressure reduce in evidence and the width in the contact area becomes narrower, while the line load and maximum Hertz contact pressure on contact line in the non-modified area make it the exact opposite. The central film thickness and maximum film thickness on the contact line of non-modified area changes very little compared with it before modification, and the line load and oil film pressure on the contact line also increases little compared with it before modification, because there are longer contact line in modified area, big film thickness and short contact line in non-modified area, therefore, though the line load and maximum contact pressure change greatly on the contact line in modified area, under the same working condition the calculation example reduces by 62.5% and 5.4%, while the line load and maximum pressure in non-modified area change little and increase by 8.21% and 2.77% not to have bad effect on the EHL on the whole. Therefore, there is some improving function to the lubrication performance by modifying helical gear. If gears are modified greater, the line load and central oil film pressure on the contact line in modified area increase greater, so we should modify helical gears carefully.

The reason that the real oil film of every node on contact line after modification keeps not to change is that the effect that the load exerts on the rigid central film thickness counteracts the effect that the load exerts on the elastic deformation. The real film thickness includes the rigid central film thickness and the elastic deformation, when the rigid central film thickness becomes larger, the unit line load and the elastic deformation reduce, and vice versa.

6. CONCLUSIONS

The method presented in this paper is very useful to analyze the lubrication performance of modification helical gears. The following conclusions can be attained in accordance with the results:

(1) In this paper, the EHL calculation of helical gears is discussed, and the problem can't be solved with existing methods, so a new universal numerical solution is necessary. To calculate the EHL characteristics of helical gears before and after tooth modification along the direction of the contact line and the meshing line using the domain dichotomy method. This method's basic idea and solution principle can be divided into two big loops. Firstly, adjust constantly the supposed load in order to meet the equivalence of every segment rigid central oil film thickness. Secondly, modulate constantly rigid central oil film thickness so that the sum of every segment load along the direction of the contact line is equal to the sum of the external load.

(2) To provide the basic method and calculation process which might determine the rigid central oil film thickness before modification and the upper or lower limit of the line load. Whether the method and calculation process is correct or not will affects directly the time of the whole calculation process and the success of numerical solution. The rigid central oil film thickness after modification and the upper or lower limit of unit line load require to be determined, however, the calculation result before modification is needed to determine reasonable $h_{\infty 1}, h_{\infty 2}, h_{\infty 3}, wl_1$ and wl_2, then the search range of dichotomy method is narrowed and the time using CPU can be reduced.

(3) Before modification, for gear transmission with transmission speed ratio that is bigger than 1, the central oil film thickness, the minimum oil film thickness and the unit line load increase gradually along the direction of contact line from the tooth root to the tooth tip of small gear, while the maximum contact stress reduces gradually. The variable ratio of the minimum oil film thickness, the maximum pressure and the unit line load is 3.1%, 10.4% and 13.7% respectively. After modification, the contact stress and the unit line load located in the tooth root of driving wheel or the tooth tip of driven wheel (modification region) reduce distinctly, while the central oil film thickness and the maximum oil film thickness change a little in comparison with that before modification. In non-modification region, the contact stress and the unit line load on every point located on the contact line increase a little than that before modification, however, the oil film thickness on these points is thicker, so the EHL performance of helical gears improves obviously after modification.

ACKNOWLEDGEMENT

The authors express their deep gratitude to the National Natural Science Foundation of China (No.50575021) for the financial support of this research project.

REFERENCES

[1]   Martin, H. M., Lubrication of Gear Teeth, Engineering, Lond., 102, 1916, p. 199.
[2]   Dowson D, Higginson G.R., Elastohydrodynamic lubrication, the fundamentals of roller and gear lubrication. Oxford: Pergamon; 1966.
[3]   Gu. A, Elastohydrodynamic Lubrication of Involute Gears. Trans ASME, J. Eng. For Ind, Vol. 95, No.4, 1973, p. 1164-1170.
[4]   Sato, M. , Takanashi, S, On the Thero-Elastohydrodynamic Lubrication of the Involute Gear, JSME Conference, Tokyo, Japan, 1981, p. 307-312.
[5]   Vilmos Simmon, Load Capacity and Efficiency of Spur Gear in Regard to Thermo- EHD Lubrication, International Symposium on Gearing & Power Transmissions, Tokyo, Japan, 1981, p. 299-306.
[6]   K. L. Wang and H. S. Cheng., A Numerical Solution to the Dynamic Load, Film Thickness and Surface Temperature in Spur Gear, Part   : Analysis, Part   : Results, J. Mach. Des, Vol.103, 1981, p. 177-184
[7]   Z. G. Lin and J. B. Medley, Transient Elastohydrodynamic Lubrication of Involute Spur Gears Under Isothermal Conditions, Wear, Vol.95, 1984, p. 143-163.
[8]   Wang Y. Li H. Tong, J. Yang P., Transient Thermoelastohydrodynamic Lubrication Analysis of An Involute Spur Gear, Tribology International, Vol.37, 2004, p. 773-782

Influences on the Lubrication of Piston-Rings in Large Two Stroke diesel Engines and the Impact of MARPOL VI

I. Sherrington [1], D. Shorten [2]

[1] Jost Institute for Tribotechnology, University of Central Lancashire, Preston PR1 2HE, UK
[2] Lloyd's Register EMEA, 71 Fenchurch Street, London EC3M 4BS, UK

ABSTRACT

This paper begins by highlighting the economic and environmental impact of the lubricant loss associated with the operation of piston-rings in large two stroke diesel engines. The paper focuses of the use of these engines for marine propulsion, but they are also used as stationary power generation systems. In both applications there is a need to reduce lubricant loss to improve economic viability and to reduce environmental impact in sensitive environmental habitats. The need to reduce environmental impact is highlighted by new marine pollution regulations (MARPOL, Part VI), issued in 2005 to control emissions from ship engines in specific areas of sea and which have now begun to drive new approaches to two stroke ship engine design.

Lubrication of the piston-ring to liner contact is a critical element in the operation of marine diesel engines. There are some common problems associated with these engines and the paper summarises these along with the methods used to try to reduce them. This discussion is accompanied by a review of the design and operating factors which influence the operating film thickness in an engine, demonstrating that determination of the optimum supply rate is a non-trivial problem.

New emissions regulations will affect ship engine design significantly and alternative engine design approaches, proposed to allow MARPOL VI standards to be met, are briefly reviewed in this paper. These approaches are broadly based on cleaning emissions by scrubbing exhaust gases and/or by reducing SO_x in the fuel. In support of these changes the automatic control of lubricant supply to piston rings is also discussed. The rate of lubricant loss from piston-ring to liner contacts is primarily dependent on the rate of delivery which is conventionally determined by parameters such as engine load and speed. The rate of delivery is to some extent a semi-subjective decision taken by an onboard engineer and the balance to be achieved is a difficult one as the influences are complex. The rate should be sufficient to minimise wear by ensuring a complete hydrodynamic film and deliver an appropriate quantity of anti-corrosion additives without being excessive and contributing to needless loss. Inevitably the tendency, even under normal operating conditions will be to err on the side of caution and over lubricate. An automatic method for the delivery of lubricant to piston-rings has the potential to optimise lubricant flow rate for given operating conditions and can provide new and flexible ways of delivering anti-corrosion additives. A system is this type is outlined and some of its potential advantages are discussed.

Keywords: Marine Lubrication, Piston –ring lubrication, oil film thickness, MARPOL VI.

1. INTRODUCTION

Large two stroke marine engines have a total loss lubrication system which lubricates the piston assembly as it reciprocates in the cylinder. Due to the number of ships in service and their engine size, lubricant loss from these systems, when taken globally, represents a significant economic cost and makes a considerable contribution to environmental pollution. Recently, new marine pollution regulations (MARPOL Annex.VI) were issued to begin to control the emissions from ship engines operating in specific regions. These developments, taken with an increasing awareness of rising economic costs and environmental issues, have forced both engine designers and ship operators to consider what technologies can be adopted to meet new demands. This paper considers the influences in piston-ring lubrication as well as the technologies currently and potentially available to control emissions from ship engines.

1.1.   Piston-ring lubrication in large two stroke diesel engines

Large two stroke diesel engines usually run at up to about 250 rpm. The diameter of their cylinders may be in excess of 1m and power output can reach up to around 100,000 kW. They are unusual engines in that cylinder lubrication is separated from that of the remainder of the engine which allows the formulation of the lubricant and other aspects of the lubrication system to be treated independently from that of the rest of the engine. Lubricant is supplied to the cylinder by means of lubricant injectors and lubricating quills placed at points in the liner at intervals around its circumference and along its axis. Mechanical injectors deliver lubricant at varying rates, normally around 0.9 g (kW h)-1 to 1.2 g (kW h)-1 [1]. The rate is normally controlled by changing the volume injected on each stroke. However, recently developed electronic systems also achieve this by changing the interval between injection. i.e., by injection on one stroke followed by several strokes without injection before the next application [2].

1.2.   Piston-ring lubricant consumption – a global perspective

Figure 1 illustrates the size distribution of low speed engines in vessels classed with Lloyd's Register. (Representing about 20% of the global fleet.) It can be seen that the distribution of size is weighted towards a larger number of smaller units.

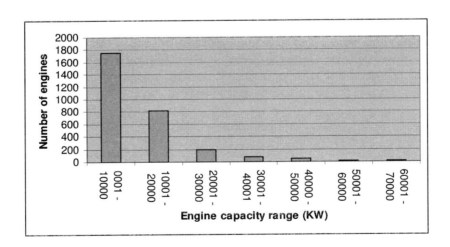

Figure 1 Size distribution of two stroke low speed marine engines in vessels classed with Lloyd's Register.
(Where engine capacity is known.)

Figure 2 translates this information to illustrate the consumption of cylinder lubrication oil by engine size, assuming that all engines operate at a dose rate of 1 g (kW h)$^{-1}$ and have 300 days of duty per year. It can be seen there is a peak in consumption around the 10,000 kW to 20,000 kW engine size range.

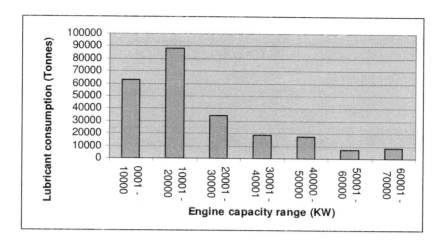

Figure 2 Estimate of annual cylinder lubricant consumption for two stroke low speed marine engines in vessels classed with Lloyd's Register. (Where engine capacity is known.)

Data used to generate figure 2 allows the global annual consumption of lubricant from the cylinder components for low revving two stroke marine engines to be estimated at 1.18m tonnes. An accurate figure is very difficult to calculate due to the number of variables at play. However, assuming that the distribution of size for the global fleet is reflected in the ships classed with Lloyd's register and a cylinder oil lubricant cost of between £800 and £1200 per tonne, this data suggests that the annual economic cost of lubricant consumption by the global fleet is between £944m and £1416m annually. Based upon a 25 year life, this means that the lifetime cost for cylinder oil for a typical vessel at today's prices, is about £2 million. This is a significant amount and therefore, it is desirable to reduce both the economic and the environmental impact of lubricant consumption on this scale. This paper considers the issue of piston-ring lubrication with a view to attempting to understand what steps could be taken to achieve a meaningful reduction.

1.3. Gas emissions

Gas emission from ship engines, is also an issue. Sulphur emissions from exhausts have been estimated at 4.5 to 6.5 million tons per year representing about 4 percent of total global sulphur emissions [3]. In some areas where shipping is concentrated emissions create significant environmental problems. Areas of this type include the English Channel, the South China Sea and the Strait of Malacca. Furthermore, Nitrogen oxide emissions from ships contribute about 5 million tons per year, which is about 7 percent of total global emissions. [3]

2. TRIBOLOGICAL / CORROSION PROBLEMS AT THE PISTON-RING LINER INTERFACE

One of the main challenges in marine engine lubrication is that marine (bunker) fuels are of fairly low quality and generally have a fairly "high" sulphur content which leads to the formation of sulphuric acid during the combustion process. This tendency to form acidic residues promotes corrosion of the soft matrix elements in the iron of the cylinder liner which releases the harder (cementite) particles from the liner surface, leaving a damaged liner [4]. Additionally, the released particles may themselves promote further wear through abrasion.

To counteract the influence of acids formed in the combustion process, lubricants for the cylinder are normally formulated with basic, i.e., alkaline, additives. However, it remains a considerable technical challenge to ensure that these additives are distributed in the right quantity around the cylinder surface to counteract corrosive wear effectively. Sometimes the additives can fail to reach all parts of the cylinder liner and remain effective only in an area just below the lubricant injectors. This can lead to a characteristic uneven wear pattern in which an area near to the injector remains in good condition, but areas further away suffer corrosive wear after a period of operation [5]. It should be noted, however, that wear/corrosion is not always considered to be detrimental. A controlled degree of corrosion is considered by some to be helpful in preventing blow-by and maintaining an effective surface for lubrication to take place [6, 7]. However uncontrolled and excessive corrosion must not be allowed to occur.

Low levels of the basic additives can lead to corrosion, but high levels can also cause problems. An excess of lubricant additives can lead to hard calcium based deposits on piston crowns and in ring grooves which may contact the liner and lead to "scuffing" failure.

In addition to these relatively straightforward problems the condition of the lubricant around the piston-rings in large marine diesel engines deteriorates over time as it resides on the surface of the liner in the high temperature environment of the combustion chamber. This influence is becoming increasingly significant in practice with year on year demands from consumers for higher power, lower oil consumption, reduced servicing and lower qualities of fuel and lubricant, etc. These requirements arise alongside new emerging needs to meet environmental protection criteria which seem to be leading to even greater complexity as some vessels will be effectively forced to operate with a mixture of fuel types depending on their geographical location.

2.1. Piston rings – principle of operation

Piston-rings in internal combustion engines are designed to operate mainly in the hydrodynamic (full fluid film) regime to minimise ring to liner contact. This is achieved by arranging a convergent geometry between the ring and liner in the direction of motion so that the ring inlet becomes pressurised as it advances over the oil film on the liner surface ahead of it. The resulting force lifts the ring away from the liner until a dynamic balance is formed between forces due to hydrodynamic action and forces arising due to the pressure acting in the opposite direction as a consequence of combustion chamber gases and ring elasticity. This principle is illustrated in figure 3.

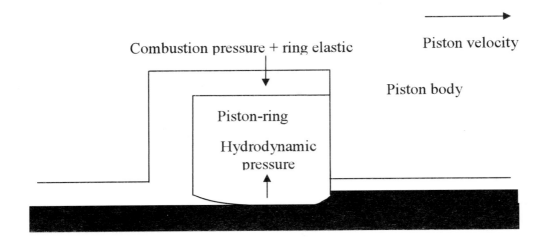

Figure 3. Principle of operation of piston-rings

The convergent geometry between the ring and liner arises from several contributions which may include the machining of a crowned or wedge shaped profile on the ring, piston-ring profile wear during operation (particularly running in), changes in the tilt of the ring face due to ring twist during operation and variations in the shape of the engine cylinder due to heating or dynamic distortion as a consequence of combustion.

3. INFLUENCES ON PISTON-RING OIL FILM THICKNESS IN LARGE DIESEL ENGINES

An understanding of the influences on piston-ring lubricant film thickness in large two stroke marine diesel engines is important because it can be used to establish the requirement for the minimum lubricant supply rate from the injection system. The thickness of the lubricant film depends on many primary and secondary influences. Since the 1970s detailed theoretical and experimental studies have focussed on building a more detailed understanding of piston-ring behaviour. Much of this work has been conducted on engines for road going vehicles. However, a small number of studies have also been performed on marine engines. Two recent examples of this kind of study are described in references [8,9].

The primary influences on film thickness in hydrodynamic lubrication are ring load, lubricant viscosity, ring sliding velocity and the geometry of the ring to liner gap. If the ring is assumed to be equivalent to a flat tilted pad (some rings have a simple inclined profile rather than a curved profile), it can be shown that in the hydrodynamic regime the minimum operating film thickness, h_{min}, is given by:

$$h_{min} = c' \frac{\eta \; velocity}{Load}$$

where c' is a constant of proportionality and η is the local lubricant viscosity. However, in reality the situation is complex and many influences other than these, mainly related to practical considerations, can become highly significant. This is illustrated extremely well by work of Moore [10,11] who conducted measurements of oil film thickness and ring rotation on board operating ships. Moore demonstrated the impact of many factors some of which are summarised below in table 1.

Table 1. Conclusions from film thickness measurements on board operating ships. (Summarised from [9,10].)

Variable	Notes
Pre-lubrication	Pre-lubrication of the engine prior to start up showed increased film thickness for up to 28 hours in the TDC region of the stroke.
Film thickness distribution	Correlation was identified between Port and Starboard film thickness with one increasing as the other increased. In rough sea this was seen to change with an increase in one side accompanied by a decrease on the other.
Feed rate variation	Increases in feed rate appeared to lead to film thickness changes that took tens of minutes to stabilise while decreases in feed arte led of film thickness falls much more quickly.
Viscosity grade	Use of high viscosity grade lubricants seemed to result in slightly thinner films near TDC due to reduced transport capacity.
Speed variation	Small changes in engine speed had an immediate and significant effect on film thickness.
Abrupt vessel motion	Appeared to promote ring rotation. (Believed to be beneficial for evening out wear patterns.

Moore's measurements begin to highlight the complexity of determining a satisfactory feed rate for the ring lubricant supply. However, it is by no means an exhaustive summary of the influences. From the direct experience of these authors and from information from other investigations, additional influences will include at least those listed in table 2.

Table 2. Additional influences on piston-ring operating film thickness.

Variable	Notes
Formation of deposits	Including soot from combustion and calcium carbonate derivatives (due to un-used components in the lubricant base agent) which can restrict ring movement and lead to scuffing between the top land and the liner.
Quality of lubricant and fuel	Fuel and lubricant may contain chemical or physical components which can influence wear which in turn changes the geometry of the interface.
Variation of the ring face profile due to wear	The circumferential profile of rings is often not the same after a period of operating time as wear is uneven.
Variation in cylinder roundness	May be static, due to manufacturing limitations, or dynamic, due to the combustion pressure and cooling profiles which will change the ring to liner clearances.
Variation in liner temperature.	Influences the local lubricant viscosity in a complex manner.
Mixing with fuel on cylinder wall	Changes local viscosity of lubricant from anticipated value
Impact of corrosion on surface quality	Changes in the liner topography may influence surface transport of lubricant along the liner.

4. INFLUENCE OF MARPOL VI ON ENGINE OPERATION

Annex VI of the marine pollution protocol, MARPOL 73/78, became effective in May 2005. It set limits for a range of emissions including NO_x and SO_x as well as ozone depleting substances. (These guidelines are summarised at the IMO web site [3]. The protocol sets a general upper limit of 4.5% for the sulphur content of bunker fuel. Few fuels exceed presently this limit so the impact of this requirement is not high [3]. However, the protocol also specifies a number of emission control areas, known as SECAs. Ships operating permanently in these areas may not use fuels with a sulphur content exceeding 1.5% by mass. SECA areas include the North Sea (from November 2006) and the Baltic Sea. Further SECAs may be introduced in the future in busy shipping areas such as Tokyo Bay, the Mediterranian, the Black Sea, the West Coats of Canada and Hong Kong [3]. Additionally California may also introduce stringent regulations to limit sulphur emission off its coast [12].

4.1. Meeting the standards

Ships operating entirely within a SECA are obliged to use fuels with a maximum sulphur content of 1.5% by mass. However, ships which spend only a proportion of their time in SECAs may choose to adopt one of two approaches to control emissions when in a SECA as follows:

- *Fuel switching* - By incorporating an arrangement to pump either high or low sulphur fuels into the service tank from the settling tank operators can arrange to have the correct grade of fuel when in a SECA.

- *Exhaust gas cleaning* - An alternative to fuel switching is to employ an exhaust gas cleaning system which maintains emissions below 6g SO_x $(KW\ h)^{-1}$ [3].

4.1.1. Fuel switching

The fuel switching strategy involves having supplies of low sulphur fuel (<1.5% sulphur) as well as higher sulphur content fuel (<4.5% sulphur). Some days before entry to a SECA the supply to the service tank can be changed from high sulphur to low sulphur so that as fuel is consumed the sulphur content of remaining fuel in the service tank is gradually diluted by new low sulphur fuel. The tank will be refilled on perhaps on 5 or 6 occasions, before the ship enters the SECA to bring the sulphur content in remaining fuel down to the required level.

One problem with this approach is that changes in fuel sulphur content will in many cases not be matched by a switch to a lubricant with a lower content of acid neutralising additive. (Specified by a parameter called the Base Number normally abbreviated to BN.) Instead a compromise lubricant will be employed for use with both fuels leading to situation where fuel sulphur neutralisation will not be ideal in either context. This will lead to the formation of deposits or greater corrosive wear as discussed in section 2 if not managed appropriately.

4.1.2. Exhaust gas cleaning systems

Exhaust gas scrubbers can be used to circumvent the need to user fuel switching. The implications of adopting such systems for engine lubrication arrangements are minimal. However, scrubbers are known to suffer a number of disadvantages and limitations. These include a relatively high installation cost, £0.5m to £1m and an apparent inability to meet the emission criteria at high gas flow rates.

5. AUTOMATIC CONTROL OF PISTON-RING LUBRICATION

5.1.   Impact of fuel and lubricant sulphur

The rate of delivery of fuel to an engine is dependent on a number of parameters, but it is normally around 175 g $(kW\ h)^{-1}$. This is much higher than the delivery rate for cylinder lubricant which normally falls in the range 0.9 to 1.2 g $(kW\ h)^{-1}$. Additionally the sulphur content of lubricant is low, about 0.5 %, so even when low sulphur fuel is used, the contribution to unwanted emissions from lubricating oil is relatively small. As a consequence there is very little value in attempting to reduce the sulphur content of lubricant to manage emissions. The main challenge for designers of lubrication systems are, therefore, to arrange minimal use of lubricant to keep costs low and to ensure a match between the BN of the lubricant and the fuel sulphur levels.

5.2.   Future developments

The last ten years or so have seen the introduction of electronic / computer based systems for the control and operation of marine diesel engines. This is seen as big step for the marine engine industry which is traditionally very conservative in its approach to design. The incorporation of electronic control has permitted a number of innovative developments in engine design, for example, the commercialisation of hydraulically operated exhaust valves [13].

The last decade has also seen improvements in the lubrication technology of large marine engines. The aims of these improvements have been largely twofold, ie., to improve the distribution of lubricant and to deliver smaller amounts of lubricant without an increase in wear rate. Examples of these technologies have entered the marketplace and include the HJ Jensen SIP system for positioning the lubricator and controlling injection timing to promote the swirl of the lubricant spray against a sector of the cylinder liner [14] and the MAN B&W Alpha Lubrication System for delivering varying quantities of oil by changing the interval between injection rather than adjusting the volume injected at each stroke [2].

In addition to commercial developments, a number of patent applications have also been filed which describe feedback control systems, based on electronics, for the delivery of lubricant and/or additives. Following the introduction of environmental controls and SECAs, it appears that the demand for systems of this type is likely increase considerably in the very near future as fleet operators move to meet the new standards.

Electronic feedback based lubrication systems have many advantages. One of their main assets is that they can strike an optimal balance between lubricant supply rate and adhesive and abrasive wear rates to minimise lubricant cost and maximise component lifetime. Some of feedback systems describe control of a separate additive supply which can be set to deliver additives to exactly match the sulphur level in the fuel supplied minimising corrosive effects. A comprehensive system of this type including feedback control for both the lubricant and additive supplies has been described by Sherrington [15].

Some potential additional advantages of electronic systems include:

- The volume of oil injected into the system can be automatically compensated to *accommodate for variations in the quality and type of lubricating oil* supplied to the ship.

- Lubricating conditions to be controlled in a manner which *is unique to each individual cylinder of an engine*. (This should extend the service period for the cylinder/engine, for example by extending the period between change of piston-rings. Such closely controlled operating conditions may also extend useful engine life in general.)

- The sealing of a piston-ring in the cylinder could be improved over the engine life. The *effect of changes in the clearance of engine components due, for example, to piston-ring or cylinder liner wear could be taken into account automatically*. This procedure can be conducted on an individual cylinder by cylinder basis. Such a system should allow a reduction in the occurrence of combustion gas escaping past the piston-rings (known as blow-by) and could be particularly useful in temporarily enhancing power output from engines with worn piston-rings/cylinder liners.

- Electronic systems increase the opportunity for the *incorporation of condition monitoring*. It is envisaged that the oil film thickness measurement system will be sensitive to certain types of problem elsewhere in the engine which could be observed through their influence on the oil supply control system.

- Feedback systems should offer the ability to *compensate for changes in the needs of an engine operating at sea which arise when the sea state changes*. Sea conditions have been reported to influence the operating film thickness of piston-rings.

- Feedback system can offer the ability to *account for differences in operating conditions in each cylinder which arise as a consequence of the marginal differences in the engineering assembly and manufacture* (e.g. tolerances on component sizes and variations in clamping forces) which inevitably arise in an engine and its components. Thus, the performance of each engine cylinder can be optimised.

- Software control permits *the control variables used by the algorithm to be modified readily*. This gives the engine operator flexible control and potentially provides the opportunity to take advantages of changes in thinking relating to oil film thickness control technology with reasonable ease.

6. CONCLUSION

The lubrication of piston-rings in large two stroke marine diesel engines is a complex process with many variables influencing the effectiveness of wear protection and lubricant film integrity.

The complexity of the lubrication process, the pressure to advance engine performance and the introduction of new pollution standards are factors which are likely to drive fleet operators and engine designer to consider new ways to lubricate engines.

Feedback based lubrication and additive delivery control systems have many potential attributes including their ability to:

- Minimise consumption of cylinder lubricant while maintaining an "ideal" hydrodynamic film.

- Match the corrosive effects of combustion compounds thus automatically controlling corrosive wear.

- Compensate for a wide range of influences on ring lubrication

REFERENCES

[1] Alpha adaptive cylinder oil control. CIMAC Circle 2002 – SMM
http://www.cimac.com/PDF/CIMAC%20Circle2002/pres2_jacobsen.pdf (Last accessed June 2006.)

[2] Lubricator system for cutting the cylinder oil bill and reducing emissions on MAN B&W two stroke engines
http://www.manbw.com/files/news/filesof2582/p384-0108.pdf (Last accessed June 2006.)

[3] Prevention of air pollution from ships Pub IMO. IMO Marpal Annex VI review.
http://www.imo.org/Newsroom/mainframe.asp?topic_id=233#review (Last accessed June 2006)

[4] Demmerle, R., Barrow, S., Jaquet, D., (2001) New insights into the piston running behaviour of Sulzer large bore diesel engines. Proc. CIMAC Congress

[5] Bushan, B. (Ed) (2001) Marine equipment tribology (by Schmid, S. and Schmid, K. J.) pp 1371 – 1384. Modern Tribology Handbook (Volume 2) Pub. CRC Press.

[6] Emission control – Man B&W Two-Stroke Diesel Engines. http://www.manbw.com/files/news/filesof4458/p9000.pdf

[7] Regulations for the prevention of air pollution from ships – Technical and operational implications. Pub DNV. Appendix 1
http://www.dnv.com/binaries/Marpol_Annex_VI_tcm4-125462.pdf (Last accessed June 2006)

[8] Saburi, S., Saitoh, Y., Yamada, T., Tribology between piston rings and cylinder liners of marine diesel engines. IHI Engineering review. 38(1) (February, 2005) pp 11 – 18.

[9] Dragsted, J. Lim, K. C., Aabo, K., (2004) "An insight into advanced cylinder lubrication issues. Proc. of CIMAC Congress (Kyoto) Paper 131.

[10] Moore, S. (1995) The influence of engine operating parameters on piston-ring oil film thickness in a marine diesel engine. Proc. of CIMAC Congress (Interlaken

[11] Moore, S. (1985) The complexities of piston-ring oil lubrication in a large two stroke marine diesel engine. Proc. ofCIMAC Congress (Copenhagen) pp 575 – 586.

[12] Charting the course – Marine fuel efficiency and emissions conference – 18th and 19th January 2005 – A report on the proceedings. Rod B. Taylor.
www.tc.gc.ca/programs/environment/Freight/training/marine/pdf/Chart.pdf (Last accessed June 2006)

[13] ME Engines – The new generation of diesel engines. Pub MAN B+W
http://www.manbw.com/files/news/filesof2810/p412-0503.pdf (Last accessed June 2006)

[14] Lauritsen, S., Dragsted, J., Buchholz, B. Swirl injection lubrication – A new technology to obtain low oil consumption without sacrificing wear rates. Proc. CIMAC Congress (2001) Hamburg.
http://www.met-online.com/download/CIMAC%202001.pdf (Last accessed June 2006)

[15] Sherrington, I., "Lubrication control system". UK patent Number GB 2357556B. (December, 1999).

Filtration of Oil and Related Benefits

C. J. Thomsen

C.C. JENSEN LTD, Unit 26 Enterprise City, Meadowfield Avenue, Spennymoor, Co Durham, UK

ABSTRACT

This article contains information about the negative influence oil contamination will have on machine component life time and the oil life time. It is also mentioning some of the existing oil filter types/principles available and the positive influence a good filtration system will have on any oil system.

The purpose of this article is to give an illustrative introduction to what can be done if a company is having problems with contamination causing machinery to break down. It also gives an idea to what can be done to prevent these problems occurring in the first place.

Keywords: Oil contamination, life of components and oil, removal of contamination, filter principles.

1. INTRODUCTION

One of the major problems in today's oil systems is the effect which particles, water and oxidation deposits (broken down additives) have on the lifetime of oil system components and the fluid itself. These factors are the cause of 80% of breakdowns, and can be avoided with improved oil management techniques. This test will mainly focus on particle influence on an oil system.

Figure 1. Bearing Wear

Figure 2. Water in Oil

Figure 3. Oxidation, Steering Gear

The key is to optimize oil "house keeping" – this should be delivered by installing efficient oil filtration systems in conjunction with an increased effort to limit contamination ingress and generation.

Figure 4. An example of a CJC Filter total solution, which removes particles (3μm), water and oxidation from oil.

If oil is kept clean and "dry" the optimal conditions for the oil additives are created and "the benefits are clear". Good oil environment will, in fact, offer savings in maintenance costs, production down time, component replacement and oil changes.

2. OIL CONTAMINATION AND GENERATION

As mentioned in the introduction we see one of the major problems in today's oil systems as the effect particles, water and oxidation deposits (broken down additives) have on the lifetime of oil system components and the fluid itself. The Danish Maintenance Association stated a few years ago that these factors are the cause of 80% of machinery breakdowns, and can be avoided with improved oil management solutions.

Concisely, the contamination of lube oil systems will therefore create much higher running costs for production equipment than is necessary.

If you take a look at the below mentioned illustration you will see an example of a lube oil system. On the right hand side of this illustration some of the common potential contamination sources are mentioned.

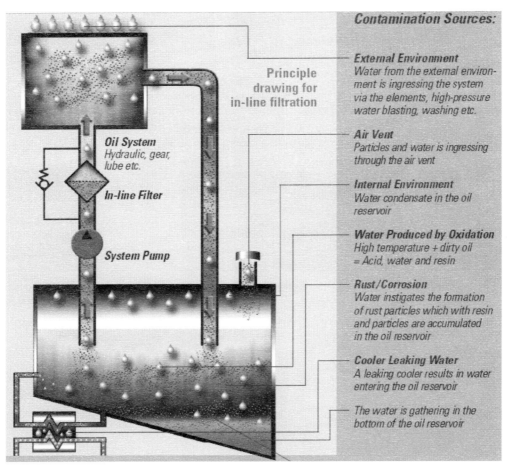

Figure 5. Contamination Sources

Additionally, to the above-mentioned contamination sources, contamination can be delivered with new machinery (built in). Also, new oil can be the source if it is not cleaned before it is poured into a lube oil system.

No matter how the fluid has been contaminated, a particle generation of will take place. Figure 6 shows some of the ways particle generation occurs.

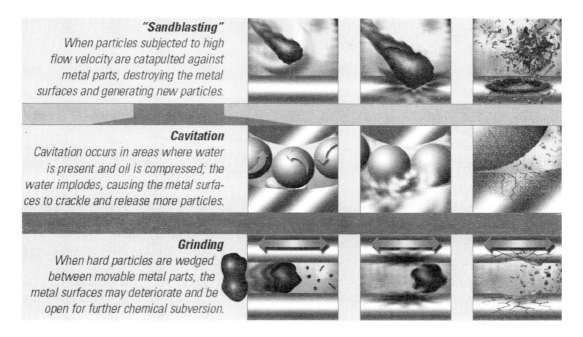

Figure 6. Wear caused by contamination

In lube oil systems the negative effect on lubricity is caused by particles, water and heat.

In an oil system there is always a level of particles present, however, the number should always be as low as possible. Figure 7 shows an observed particle average in a medium charged hydraulic oil system. The number of small particles is higher than the number of large particles.

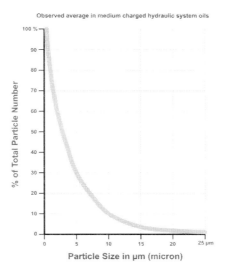

Figure 7. Particle size distribution

Looking at the above graph it can be concluded that 70% of the particles are smaller than 5µm and looking at component tolerances in oil systems they are often between 1 and 5µm. With this knowledge we can conclude that it will be beneficial to remove the very small particles from the oil system.

This conclusion has also been made by MacPherson who discovered the importance of small particles. The MacPherson Graph (Figure 8) [1] is based on an accelerated test of 10 roller bearings. The lubricating oil used was contaminated with dirt from gearboxes.

The MacPherson Graph indicates that the real component life time improvement is achieved when filtering below 10µm. Why is that?

Firstly, 90% of all particles in gear oil are smaller that 10µm i.e. a 10µm filter will leave 90% of the particles in the oil, only offering a very limited filtration.

Secondly, the dynamic tolerance in, for example, a wind turbine bearing is between 1-5µm, which indicates that only particles smaller than 5µm are able to enter and damage the bearing.

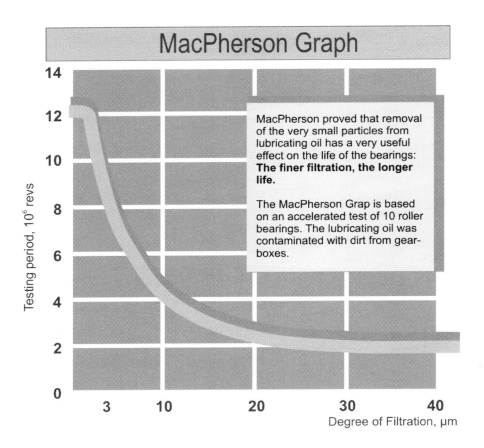

Figure 8. MacPherson Graph [1]

Looking at the graph you will find that increasing the filtration ratio from 30µm to 3µm will increase the component life 3 to 4 times.

3. INFLUENCE ON COMPONENT LIFE

CJC Off-line Oil Filter Application		Filtration time	0 hours	48 hours	1 month
Application: Wind Turbine 600 kW **Oil type:** Tribol 1710/320 **Oil volume:** 220 litres		Particles 2 µm	1,443,178	29,975	6,774
		Particles 5 µm	298,681	14,652	2,204
		Particles 15 µm	17,893	1,549	356
		ISO 4406 Code	21/19/15	15/14/11	13/12/9
		Water content	1,240	109	76
Before Filtration After Filtration		Colour of membrane filter disc	Black	Light	White

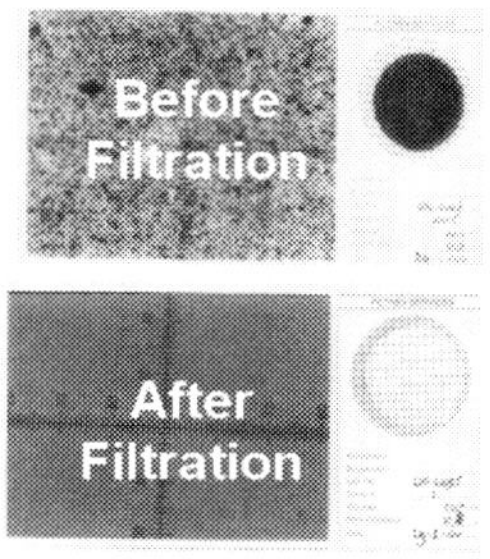

Figure 9. Results from a CJC Fine Filter mounted on a wind turbine gearbox

The above mentioned results shows what difference a good and efficient filtration system makes – in this case – to a gear oil contamination level.

Before filtration (0 hours) you can see the number of particles is high, which equates to an ISO code of 21/19/15. A month later (after filtration) the particle contamination has dropped dramatically (e.g.: 2µm particles have dropped from 1,443,178 to 6,774) which equals an ISO code of 13/12/9.

To quantify this in relation to prolongation of the component life, we can plot the two above-mentioned ISO Codes into the following Figure 10 which is a diagram concerning life extension of element bearings [2].

Life Extension Method (LEM)
Rolling Element Bearings

Life Extension Faxtor (LEF)									
	2	**3**	**4**	**5**	**6**	**7**	**8**	**9**	**10**
28/26/23	24/22/19	22/20/17	20/18/15	19/17/14	18/16/13	17/15/12	17/15/12	16/14/11	16/14/11
27/25/22	23/21/18	21/19/16	19/17/14	18/16/13	17/15/12	16/14/11	16/14/11	15/13/10	15/13/10
26/24/21	22/20/17	20/18/15	19/17/14	18/16/13	17/15/12	16/14/11	15/13/10	15/13/10	14/12/9
25/23/20	21/19/16	19/17/14	17/15/12	16/14/11	15/13/10	15/13/10	14/12/9	13/11/8	13/11/8
24/22/19	20/18/15	18/16/13	16/14/11	15/13/10	14/12/9	13/11/8	13/11/8		
23/21/18	19/17/14	17/15/12	15/13/10	14/12/9	13/11/8	13/11/8			
22/20/17	18/16/13	16/14/11	15/13/10	13/11/8					
21/19/16	17/15/12	15/13/10	13/11/8	◄					
20/18/15	16/14/11	14/12/9							
19/17/14	15/13/10	13/11/8							
18/16/13	14/12/9								
17/15/12	13/11/8								
16/14/11	13/11/8[1]								
15/13/10	13/11/8[2]								
14/12/9	13/11/8[3]								

(1) LEF = 1.8 • (2) LEF= 1.5 • (3) LEF = 1.3

Figure 10. Diagram on rolling element bearing lifetime [2]

The exact ISO Code is not in this diagram; however the above-mentioned 21/19/15 and 13/11/8 are very close. This is why we can conclude that the filter on the wind turbine gear oil will prolong the bearing life approximately 4 times.

4. DIFFERENT TYPES OF OIL FILTERS

To obtain good clean oil you need to choose a good and reliable filtration system. There are a lot of different filters and filtration equipment on the market, and to mention the most common filter types - please take a look at Figure 11.

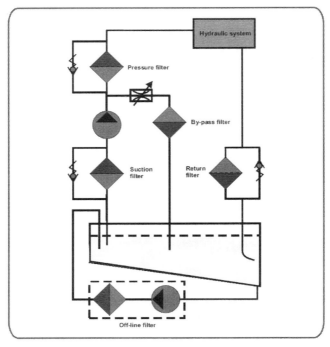

Figure 11. Filter types

The filters types: Suction, Pressure and Return filters are all **Inline surface** filters working with the full flow of, in this case, a hydraulic system. Please take a look at the illustration below regarding inline filter inserts.

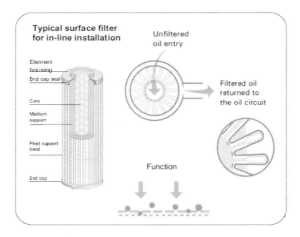

Figure 12. Inline surface filter

By-pass filters operate by drawing a limited stream of oil from the main oil circuit. The oil flows through the filter and returns to the sump/tank.

Offline filters are sucking the oil i.e. the bottom from the oil reservoir, with a dedicated pump which presses the oil through a cellulose **depth** filter insert (not a surface inline insert). The clean oil is returned to the oil reservoir below the oil surface. Please see the illustration below which shows the function of a true offline filter insert function.

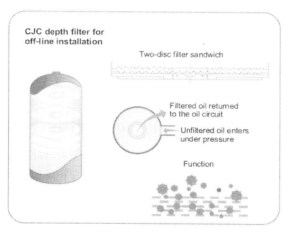

Figure 13. Offline Depth Filter

Offline filters are very important to oil systems as they are the only ones that can keep the oil reservoir clean. The reason being that the offline filters suck the dirty oil out from the bottom of the reservoir and thereby always take out particles, the settled sludge, water (some filter systems) and oxidation (some filter systems).

To illustrate the importance of offline filtration, please look at the photograph shown below. It shows the bottom of a tank in a hydraulic system where the oil system is equipped with a 3μm (beta value 200) inline filter, however, there is still a good deal of contamination in the tank.

Figure 14. The bottom of a tank in a hydraulic system, equipped with a 3μm (beta value 200) inline filter.

5. BENEFITS OBTAINED WHEN MAINTAINING CLEAN OIL

The key is to optimize oil "house keeping" – this should be achieved by installing efficient oil filtration, systems in conjunction with an increased effort to limit contamination ingress and generation in the first place.

If oil is kept clean and "dry" the optimal conditions for the oil additives are created and "the benefits are clear". Good oil environment will, in fact, offer you the following benefits:

- Prolonged life time of components
- Prolonged life time of oil
- Less unplanned production stops
- Longer machine service intervals
- Less man hours needed to keep machinery running

AT THE END OF THE DAY OPTIMIZING YOUR OIL SYSTEM IS A GOOD WAY OF EARNING MONEY FOR YOUR COMPANY!

REFERENCES

[1]   MacPherson
[2]   NORIA

Plenary Session 2
KEYNOTE ADDRESSES

Chair:　　　Dr. Ana Aranzabe

Mechanical Dynamic Test Equipment for Evaluation and Development of Lubricating Greases

R. W. ATKINSON

The Case for Condition Monitoring

R. F. W. CUTLER, A. FINDLOW

Additive Reaction Mechanisms on Coating Surface

J. VIŽINTIN, M. KALIN, E. ROMAN

Mechanical Dynamic Test Equipment for Evaluation and Development of Lubricating Greases

R. W. Atkinson

Kluber Lubrication (GB) Ltd

ABSTRACT

The expectation of machinery builders and operators today is that equipment should function reliably with minimum maintenance thus allowing maximum machinery uptime.

Industry demands reliable machine operation with minimum maintenance and where possible reduced operating costs. Longterm or lifetime lubrication is the expectation today and can be achieved by improved machinery design combined with appropriately selected synthetic lubrication technology.

As an integral ingredient the lubricant's primary function is to optimise the wear characteristics of friction components such that the machine or equipment fulfils its operating design requirements across a specified service lifetime.

The following paper, entitled, "Mechanical Dynamic Test Equipment for Evaluation and Development of Lubricating Greases" provides an insight into the behind the scenes testing that is undertaken in order to evaluate the suitability of a lubricating grease for use in a specific application. To this end a number of key test rigs are outlined including those used to evaluate, bearing wear protection, grease lifetime, corrosion protection, operating noise levels as well as low temperature torque and others.

1. INTRODUCTION

The performance of a lubricant is not only determined by the results attained from a test rig test.

In fact it takes a trained and experienced lubrication specialist to interpret this data and draw correct conclusions thus enabling selection of the most appropriate lubricant for a specific application.

This paper considers certain performance parameters which may be beneficial to support the decision-making process during selection of the lubricant.

In reality we refer to two types of lubricant related tests, these are Chemical-physical and Mechanical-dynamic Chemical-physical and Mechanical-dynamic

2. CHEMICAL-PHYSICAL AND MECHANICAL-DYNAMIC TESTS

Chemical-physical tests concentrate only on specific lubricant related properties, (such as base oil type, viscosity etc) whereas mechanical-dynamic tests attempt to simulate the effects of load, speed, media and temperature on the friction and wear behaviour in the tribo-system.

Regretfully there is no such thing as a universal test rig. When developing a lubricant the engineer has often to rely on "model test rigs" which may or may not entirely reflect the complete system requirements. Numerous model test rigs evaluating different test parameters are required to correctly evaluate the results correctly and relate them to the original design concept.

Chemical-physical tests generally precede mechanical-dynamic tests. Depending on the lubricant type and requirements there are many different test procedures to consider, some of which are listed in Table 1

Table 1. Chemical-physical characteristics of lubricating greases

Parameters	Test method	Description
Density	DIN 51 757	Quotient of a mass of a substance and its volume; facilitates identification
Base oil viscosity	DIN 51 561	Indicates the load-carrying capacity, friction and physical wear behaviour as well as flow characteristics
Drop point	DIN ISO 2176	Determines the "melting point" of the grease when the oil separates from the thickener medium
Penetration	DIN ISO 2137	Determines the consistency of a lubricating grease. The penetration depth of a metal cone into a grease-filled cup is measured in tenths of a millimetre The ranges are classified in NLGI grades
Apparent dynamic viscosity	DIN 53 018, part 1	Determination of the internal resistance of a grease to shear on the basis of its Newtonian flow characteristics
Flow pressure	DIN 51 805	Temperature-dependent pressure needed to force a grease through a tube. Indicates the lower service temperature
Corrosion of copper/steel	DIN 51 811	Corrosion protection effect on non-ferrous metal alloys or steels coated in a lubricant film
Oxidation resistance	DIN 51 808	Resistance of the grease to absorb oxygen indicating grease ageing
Water resistance	DIN 51 807, part 1	Emulsification test on the grease
Oil separation	DIN 51 817	Determination of static oil bleed as a in percentage by weight

2.1. Purpose of mechanical-dynamic tests

Lubricants developed by Klüber Lubrication and tested by the user are evaluated in terms of technical suitability against defined performance limits and expectations. Mechanical-dynamic tests which subject the lubricant and construction materials to the effects of temperature, load, relative movement and media provide invaluable data with regard to lubricant performance and help establish the limits necessary to predict component lifetime, warranty intervals etc. (see Figure 1)

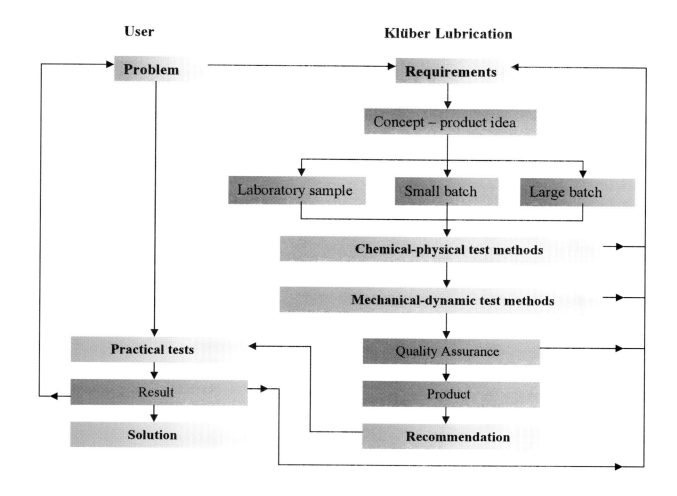

Figure 1. Flow chart outlining lubricant development

Mechanical-dynamic tests offer the following advantages:

❑ Simplified representation of the lubrication problem using selected test equipment to simulate specific operational conditions.
❑ Verification of the product concept and principles.
❑ Optimization of the lubricant formulation and manufacturing process
❑ Impact of the operating and test parameters on friction and wear behaviour.
❑ Confirmation of lubricant and component performance
❑ Reduction of time consuming and cost intensive practical tests
❑ Shortening of development time

The results of mechanical-dynamic tests prove the technological advantages offered by special lubricants. The interpretation of the test results serve different purposes, such as:

❑ They help the engineer to determine whether the lubricant fulfils all requirements.
❑ They allow the test engineer and designer to draw conclusions as to the lubricant's application and performance limits.
❑ They permit the production department to verify quality standards and prove quality assurance.
❑ They enable consulting engineers to provide competent and reliable recommendations.

3. MECHANICAL-DYNAMIC TEST EQUIPMENT

Table 2 below summarises the range of mechanical-dynamic test equipment used for evaluation of rolling bearing greases

Table 2. Mechanical-dynamic test equipment for evaluation of rolling bearing greases

No	Test Equipment	Description	Reference
1	FE 9 rolling bearing grease test rig	Used to determine the service life of greases, F_{10}, F_{50} lifetimes Test temperature: 100 to 250°C Speed: 3,000 / 6,000 rpm Axial load 1,500 to 4,500 N m Upper service temperature of greases	See Fig. 4
2	ROF rolling bearing grease test rig	Used to determine the service life of greases, F_{10}, F_{50} lifetimes Test temperature: 240°C Speed: 1,000 to 20,000 (30,000) rpm Radial load up to 800 N Axial load 50 to 200 N Upper service temperature of greases	
3	FE 8 rolling bearing wear and friction test rig	Antiwear behaviour under high load conditions, up to 80,000 N axial load Speed: 7.5 to 3,000 rpm Used to determine wear rate, steady-state temperature and friction torque behaviour	
4	SNR – FEB2 bearing test rig	Anti brinelling / tribocorrosion behaviour under oscillating conditions Angle ± 3°, observe bearing wear in mg.	
5	FAG "KSM" rolling bearing test rig	Noise behaviour of greases in rolling bearings. Measurement of solid-borne sound according to noise class or level Provides details on the noise related running-in behaviour of greases	
6	Vibrational quality test rig MGG 11, SKF-MVH 90 B		
7	GRW rolling bearing test rig		
8	SKF-BeQuiet rolling bearing test rig		
9	Low-temperature bearing torque test rig IP 186, – ASTM 1478	Determination of the starting and running torque at low-temperature. -70 to 0 °C. Determination of the lower service temperature for greases	
10	Emcor machine DIN 51 802, IP 220, ISO 11 007	Determination of the anti-corrosion properties of lubricating greases Corrosion degree (see table DIN 51 802, corrosion values 0 (no corrosion) to 5 (severe corrosion)	See Fig. 2
11	Water wash-out test rig DIN 51 807, ASTM D 1264	Water resistance of greases, grease loss as a % by weight	See Fig. 3
12	Roll stability tester ASTM D 1831	Roll stability of greases, determination of consistency change, oil separation effect.	

3.1. Emcor Machine

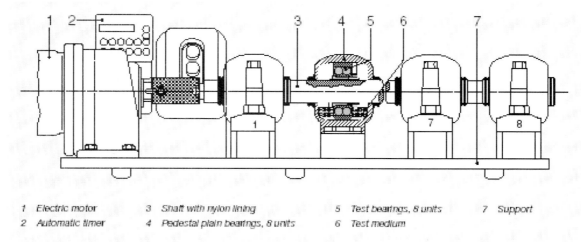

| 1 | Electric motor | 3 | Shaft with nylon lining | 5 | Test bearings, 8 units | 7 | Support |
| 2 | Automatic timer | 4 | Pedestal plain bearings, 8 units | 6 | Test medium | | |

EMCOR machine

Figure 2. EMCOR Machine

Scope
Determination of the anti-corrosion properties
of lubricating greases

Standard
DIN 51 802, IP 220, ISO 11 007

Specimen
Self-aligning ball bearings: 1306 K / 236725
Special type with steel cage

Test conditions

Duration of test:	168 h with alternating running and stop periods
Speed:	80 rpm
Test medium:	distilled water or other aqueous media
Grease volume:	11 cm^3 per bearing

Procedure
- ❑ Dismount and clean the test bearings
- ❑ Visually examine the outer bearing races for corrosion
- ❑ Grease the test bearings and mount them on the drive shafts of the test units
- ❑ Run the test
- ❑ Disassemble and clean the test bearings
- ❑ Examine outer bearing races visually without optical aids

Result
Corrosion rating on the outer bearing races (reference; 0 to 5, see above chart)

3.2. Water Wash Out test rig

Scope
Behaviour of a lubricant under
dynamic conditions at different
temperatures

Standards
DIN 51 807; ASTM D 1264

Specimen
Deep groove ball bearing 6204, open

Test conditions
Duration of test: 1 min to 10 h
Speed: 600 rpm
Temperature: 40 °C; 80 °C acc.to
                 DIN 38 °C;
                 79 °C to ASTM
Water flow: 5 ± 0.5 cm^3/s

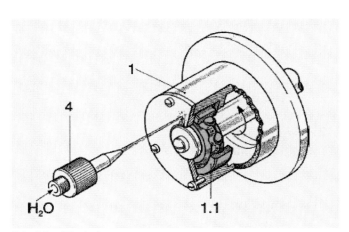

Principle of the test

Figure 3. Washer Wash Out test rig

Procedure
- ❏ Weigh the test bearing and the housing cover
- ❏ Lubricate the test bearing with 4 ± 0.05 g of grease
- ❏ Mount the test bearing in the bearing housing and fix the cover
- ❏ Run the test for 60 minutes directing a defined water jet onto the capped specimen
- ❏ Disassemble the test bearing
- ❏ Dry the test bearing and housing cover for 16 h at 95 °C in the drying cabinet or for 15 h at 77 °C in the drying cabinet, (ASTM) then weigh.

Test result
Determination of grease weight loss as a percentage. Visual rating 1-3 (see following chart)

Rating level	Loss in weight, %	Change
1	< 10	low
2	> 10 but < 30	moderate
3	> 30	high

3.3. FE 9 Rolling Bearing Grease test rig

Scope
Determination of the service life and the upper service temperature of lubricating greases in rolling bearings subject to medium speeds and medium axial loads

Standard
DIN 51 821, DIN 51 825 FAG Schweinfurt, Germany / Klüber test conditions

Test specimen
5 angular contact ball bearings FAG-special type 529689 S 2 (corr. to 7206 B open, with steel cage)

Test conditions
Axial load: 1500, 3000, 4500 N, DIN 51 821: 1500 N
Speed: 3000, 6000 rpm
DIN 51 821:   6000 rpm
Temperature: max. 240 °C, DIN 51 821: 120 to 240 °C in steps of 20 °C
Grease quantity
per bearing: * 2 cm^3
                 ** 10 cm^3
Various assemblies
*A: Test bearing without washer, open
*B: Bearing shielded on both sides with external washers
** C: As B; plus additional grease reservoir on one washer

Test procedure
❑ Disassemble, clean, mount and lubricate the test bearings
❑ Fix the 5 test bearings in the test units
❑ Set the test parameters
❑ Carry out the test run
❑ Record the running time of the test bearings, expressed in h

The 5 running time values are evaluated statistically and documented in a WEIBULL diagram.
This diagram indicates the F_{50} or F_{10} running times (h), i.e. where 50% or 10% of the bearings fail due to the selected test parameters and the lubricant.

Test result
Running times F_{10}, F_{50} with 90% confidence range, failure time ß

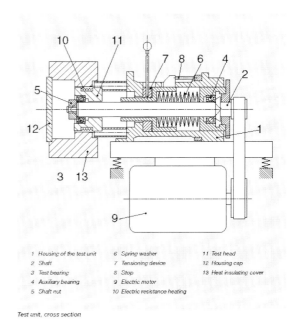

1	Housing of the test unit	6	Spring washer	11	Test head
2	Shaft	7	Tensioning device	12	Housing cap
3	Test bearing	8	Stop	13	Heat insulating cover
4	Auxiliary bearing	9	Electric motor		
5	Shaft nut	10	Electric resistance heating		

Test unit, cross section

Figure 4. FE 9 Rolling Bearing Grease test rig

4. CONCLUSIONS

Industry demands reliable machine operation with minimum maintenance and reduced operating costs. Longterm or lifetime lubrication is the expectation today and can be achieved by improved machinery design combined with approprieately selected synthetic lubrication technology.

Today's engineers can select from a wide variety of lubricating greases each with their own specific performance features. Selection of the most appropriate lubrication product however is the critical task. Unfortunately all aspects of the "suitable" lubricant cannot be fully realised without deeper investigation in the actual equipment required. Evaluation of the lubricant therefore by means of suitable mechanical-dynamic test equipment is an excellent way to determine the suitability of the lubricant under real time operational stresses such as load, temperature, speed etc. Indeed the evaluation of the lubricant in this way allows certain predictions to be made in respect to operating reliability, equipment lifetime as well as recognition of performance limitations.

Kluber Lubrication is committed to a process of continuous customer focussed product development to enable the extension of operating boundaries, achievement of simpler more economical and environmentally friendly designs.

The use of mechanical Dynamic test rigs form an important part of this process allowing assessment of new and variable base oil, thickener and additive combinations enabling development of "state of the art" tailor made lubricating grease solutions.

REFERENCES

[1] Kluber Lubrication   "Lubricant Testing Focusing on Mechanical-Dynamic Tests"
[2] Kluber Lubrication   "Lubricating Greases Classification, Selection and Application"

The Case for Condition Monitoring

R. F. W. Cutler [1], A. Findlow [2]

[1] ALcontrol Robertson Laboratories, Conwy, North Wales, LL32 8FA, United Kingdom
[2] Drive Management Services, Sheffield Technology Park, Sheffield, S9 3SP, United Kingdom

ABSTRACT

The principles and case for Oil Condition Monitoring (OCM) has long been established. However there remains a need to continuously prove the case financially; this paper will attempt, with an example, to show a means to do so and refers to formal training as a key factor in this debate. It will also be shown that in addition to OCM, there are other complementary techniques available, which must be considered. While these, especially OCM will always be required; there is a place for a relatively low priced and robust on-board oil condition oil sensor, which will also be discussed.

Keywords: Condition monitoring, Oil analysis, Vibration, Thermography, Acoustics, Ultrasonic, Shearography, training and certification, on-board oil sensor, gas engines, machinery, failure analysis.

1. INTRODUCTION

"For want of a nail, a shoe was lost. For want of a shoe, a horse was lost. For want of a horse, a message was lost. For want of a message, a battle was lost. For want of a battle, a war was lost. All for want of a horse shoe nail". - Extract from Reliability-centred Maintenance, by John Moubray. (Derivative of a quote assigned to Benjamin Franklin).

A strange way to begin a paper, but it summarises the whole case for Reliability Centred Maintenance (RCM), Root Causes of Failure Analysis, Failure Modes and Effects Analysis (FMEA) and Oil Condition Monitoring as well as others techniques to be discussed.

In the modern world the nail could be a screw or bolt, the shoe a small, but vital cog, the battle could be a machine driving the production line and the war - a lost contract or even the liquidation of the company.

John Moubray also rightly points out that drilling down too far to find the root cause of any failure, could prove less productive than necessary, as one could go on forever beyond the control of the organisation concerned. At the risk of doing just that, drilling down one step further below the loose nail or screw and say that the root cause could have been the lack of regular monitoring, which if it had been carried out properly would have detected this loose nail or screw and saved the war or contract. What price RCM?

It is not the intention in this paper to explain RCM, Oil Condition Monitoring in any detail or indeed any type of Condition Monitoring programme. It is however, to show among other topics, one way Condition Monitoring programmes can be justified in the work place to those who must sign up to it as an acceptable expense, such as the Financial Director.

Like many relatively new ideas, processes and disciplines, RCM is an enigma to most people outside the relatively small group of maintenance staff in any one company. This group feels that they have only too often, to justify their true value to the company and so somehow must steel themselves to find a simple way to quantify the cost of not using RCM.

It is reassuring to hear that some of the major UK companies and indeed a few small companies are now adopting the right attitude, recognising the value of RCM, employing it whole-heartedly and becoming successful leaders in the market place.

Nevertheless, it is still very difficult to convince others that RCM can reduce costs substantially and contribute positively to the P&L sheet. This is because some see it as a cost only: Pounds or Dollars they can "save" if they do not adopt it, or Pounds and Dollars they can "save" if times are tough and cuts have to be made in the organisation. This philosophy may be right in certain cases; it is uneconomical to adopt a regular CM programme using say Oil Analysis techniques, even at prices of less than £8 per sample to monitor small vans and car fleets, but this is not true for transport, manufacturing, quarrying or industrial organisations with static or mobile plant, trucks or buses etc. Why? Because a car or van for instance may be essential for the job, but if unavailable one day, can be replaced with a hire vehicle in these rare occasions, hence the cost of an RCM programme on small vehicle fleets is difficult to justify. However, simple options like this are not or rarely available for the specialised machines in the utilities, industrial, quarrying, mining and transport markets etc, not to mention the armed forces' predicament if a fighting vehicle fails in a war zone owing to an avoidable breakdown. – Remember the loose nail!

Considering only the commercial case, when an unscheduled stoppage occurs, livelihoods can be at risk. Production can grind to a halt, revenues cease, labour charges escalate owing to over time during repairs, orders are delayed, sales tumble, previous marketing efforts maybe ruined and in some cases penalty clauses can take effect, etc. When safety and the environmental issues are at risk, legislation is rightly in place, to direct companies to the proper solution, but when non-legislative financial considerations are at issue the accountants alone, with the usual brief to control spending, must be consulted. So for the maintenance engineer to go forward with a RCM programme, he/she needs to develop a strategy based not only on H&S issues, but on a financial one too. This can be quite difficult at times, as the maintenance engineer is not normally in a position to assess the true worth of his or her skills or his/her department, nor is he/she necessarily a competent statistician, but must persevere anyway.

The time of building in redundancy has long passed its sell-by date. There was a time in the early eighties and before, when a company would stock a number spare engines, gearboxes and other expensive components, depending on the size of its fleet. These would be readily available as replacements when a failure occurred and the money tied up this way was considered acceptable. Now minimum stock levels, just in time servicing and low staffing levels are now more realistic and prevalent today. In many cases transport companies see the OCM programme part of the costs to be borne by the lubricant suppliers and effectively free to them. Of course nothing is free, but when it does not actually show as an identifiable item on the P&L sheet it appears free; hence the need to sell the true value of RCM to the accountant and prove its value. Consequently a simple device is proposed, which may already be in use by some maintenance departments and their financial people, to help quantify the financial risks and costs of operating or not operating a regular condition-monitoring scheme.

For this idea to proceed, the engineer needs to consider the following alternatives set out in Table 1a and accept that failures in this analysis scheme come in three forms: Severe, Moderate and Minor. Note that while there are formal ISO methods (ISO 17359) available to deduce the probabilities of these events and choice of diagnostic tools to use in any maintenance situation, the probability values quoted in Tables 1a&b have been established from case histories, using OCM, hence can readily be used in such applications as mobile plant and road vehicles, although can be considered for other applications too. As will become obvious, the intention of this exercise at first is to reduce Severe and Moderate failures to minor ones. Table 1a sets out how to evaluate and consider costs of failures, Severe, Moderate or Minor, but only the company concerned is able to quantify the actual monetary value of a given failure to their business. Therefore they alone can replace the letters in the table with realistic numbers. The actual values must be considered by first assuming that minor failures will probably not include any downtime, moderate failures are those that involve loss of production, but can readily be fixed within a few hours and severe failures will involve a major, possible long-term shutdown, expensive labour and components costs, with the added problem of client dissatisfaction.

These assessments should be made by first carrying out a risk analysis on each piece of equipment, in terms of what would happen if the unit failed (again remember the horse shoe nail), how likely is it to happen and is the ultimate cost tolerable to the company. It is the view of the authors that severe and moderate failures are not tolerable, while minor failures can be "managed". So if Severe and Moderate failures could be turned into just minor failures, there will be just as many failures occurring, but the

RCM programme would instantly pay for itself. Then if RCM can be used to reduce the number of minor failures too, there is no question about whether RCM can be justified – it can!

Table 1b demonstrates that Condition Monitoring can be used to reduce costs by at least 67%. These are the arguments put forward by OEM's especially in the Mobile plant industry when rightly insisting on an OCM scheme to be in place before offering any form of extended warranty.

Table 1a. COST SAVING NON-RCM v RCM

COSTS	SEVERE FAILURE	MODERATE FAILURE	MINOR FAILURE	WEIGHTED TOTAL COST
Down Time	A	D	G	
Parts	B	E	H	
Labour	C	F	I	
Total	A+B+C	D+E+F	G+H+I	
Probability of type of failure <u>without</u> CM	20%	30%	50%	
Weighted cost	(A+B+C)*0.2 = X	(D+E+F)*0.3 = Y	(G+H+I)*0.5 = Z	X+Y+Z = S
Probability of failure <u>With CM</u>	5%	10%	85%	
Weighted cost	(A+B+C)*0.05 = P	(D+E+F)*0.10 = Q	(G+H+I)*0.85 = R	P+Q+R = T
Saving per event <u>With CM</u>				(S-T) as % (Typically 67%)

Table 1b: EXAMPLE OF VALUES IN A MOBILE PLANT SCENARIO

COSTS (US Dollars)	SEVERE FAILURE	MODERATE FAILURE	MINOR FAILURE	WEIGHTED TOTAL COST
Down Time	50000	10000	0	
Parts	10000	2000	500	
Labour	10000	3000	1000	
Total	70 000	15000	1500	
Probability of type of failure <u>without</u> CM	20%	30%	50%	
Weighted cost	14,000	4,500	750	19,250
Probability of failure <u>With CM</u>	5%	10%	85%	
Weighted cost	3500	1500	1275	6275
Saving per event <u>With CM</u>				12975 ~ 67%

2. CONDITION MONITORING TECHNIQUES

The debate then turns to which condition-monitoring programme is best suited for a given operation?

While table 1b shows the effect of using an Oil analysis Programme in a Mobile Plant scenario, many stationary plant and equipment operations in industry are equally suited to other RCM techniques or a combination of more than one; these include amongst others, Vibration, Thermography, Ultrasonic, and Acoustic techniques.

3. AUTHORISED TRAINING ORGANISATIONS

It is therefore necessary for the production engineer or maintenance manager to be aware of and understand the techniques available to him/her, so be able to choose the technique or combination of techniques most suitable for his/her application.

Assuming that the management are serious about RCM and seeking a proactive means to improve maintenance procedures, while at the same time wanting to be aware of the financial benefits of such schemes, it follows that training and awareness programmes should be available and undertaken to enable members of a team to learn and become skilled in some if not all the techniques currently available. While excellent training is available through the vendors of each type of equipment, there are now specific training programmes available through the British Institute of Non-Destructive Testing (BINDT). Here formal training programmes to ISO standards (ISO 18436 and ISO 17024) have been devised, examinations set and training organisations approved in Lubricant Management (LM), which includes Oil Condition Monitoring (OCM), Vibration Analysis (VA), Infrared Thermography (IRT) and Acoustic Emission (AE). Ultrasonic Analysis (UA) being a separate topic and a sixth technique called Laser Shearography is under consideration. These courses are planned to take place over several years to three different levels; each level course is followed by a formal examination, after which, officially recognised certificates are awarded to successful candidates. Beware some companies are falsely claiming 'accredited trainer' status, but are not! Check them out and contact the relevant organisation; in the UK this could be BINDT.

4. CERTIFICATION AND TRAINING

The benefits of these training courses are that the students, who are essentially practicing maintenance personnel and maintenance managers, become trained in RCM techniques and are able to understand and use the information to develop the ideal RCM programmes for their particular company or industry. In this way they will help to ensure their business is operating efficiently, make their jobs far more secure and in turn guide their colleagues and staff to become more aware of the advantages of using RCM. The certificates will also be recognised by formal training colleges and universities as well as industry, to help some students graduate further in their chosen profession.

5. ON-BOARD OIL SENSORS

Whichever technique is used in industry for the purpose of RCM, there is the risk that the condition of the machine or lubricant could become seriously contaminated or otherwise affected at a point just after or at least between sampling times. To reduce this problem a risk assessment programme is usually carried out to establish the ideal frequency of monitoring any given equipment. However, this ideal frequency of monitoring could prove difficult to justify both financially and practically in cases where safety of sampling is an issue or the equipment is in remote locations, such as isolated pumping stations, a windmill or landfill sites.

To overcome this problem and reduce the risk further it follows that an on-board monitoring device would prove advantageous in such cases. The problem is that such devices are only just being developed, remain expensive and somewhat unreliable, owing to the technologies they employ, the type of conditions they must operate in and the parameters they must be able to detect. One such device believed to meet most of these requirements and discussed also in other papers at this conference is an on-board oil ANALEX rs sensor (Kittiwake Ltd.), based on a variant of the dielectric properties of the oil. This oil sensor uses patented technology based on dielectric loss factor (Tan-delta), which is a more sensitive indicator of oil condition than Permittivity (often known as dielectric constant). For most oils, the loss factor will vary from perhaps 0.005 (fresh oil) to 0.1 when contaminated, a dynamic range of 20:1. This is compared with just 0.8:1 for dielectric constant (which changes typically from 2.3 to 2.9), and therefore it is evident that Tan-delta is many times more sensitive than the traditionally understood and used dielectric constant.

Figure 1 Shows data produced in the laboratory from oils in a forklift truck also fitted with Tandelta based oil sensor. Clearly there are direct relationships with the oil sensor readings and the typically measured oil condition monitoring laboratory data.

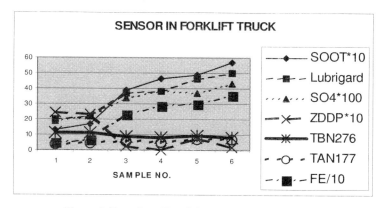

Figure 1. Data from Tan-delta sensor in fork lift truck

Table 2 shows the results of a set of gas engines samples, using the same lubricating oil, together with the overall status of the oil analysis laboratory report associated with these oil samples. The analyses show a fall in TBN, a rise in TAN and a rise in oxidation resulting in the laboratory recommending a caution value in some cases. While no oil change was effected at 1394 oil hours and 1533 oil hours, an oil change was done at 1693 oil hours showing an immediate fall in oil sensor reading and a corresponding fall in TAN and oxidation and rise in TBN as the used oil was replaced with fresh oil. The data in Table 2 confirms the oil sensor reliably tracked the oil condition.

Table 2. Data from gas engine trials

Oil Hours	Sensor Value	TBN Mg KOH/g	TAN Mg KOH/g	Oxidation Value	Report Status
484	11	6.0	2.4	6	Normal
653	12	6.1	2.6	7	Normal
886	19	5.8	3.1	7	Normal
1054	20	4.6	4.2	8	Normal
1227	24	5.3	3.9	9	Normal
1394	27	4.6	5.3	12	Caution
1533	27	5.3	4.5	12	Caution
1693	29	5.6	5.1	13	Caution
82	9	7.1	2.0	0	Normal
249	10	5.9	2.3	6	Normal

Nevertheless it must be stressed that this oil sensor, like all oil sensors, remains a "blunt" instrument, showing only that "something" is wrong, but not exactly which parameter is in an abnormal state. However, the engineer will have the advantage of a continuous real time early warning system and the added advantage that when the amber sign is alerted an oil change is recommended. He/she is also advised to send a sample to the appropriate laboratory for confirmation of the true oil and machine condition.

It is also often claimed that any oil sensor is required to identify exactly what the problem is, such as water or soot etc. This idea is unjustified and not really a problem, as even if such a sensor could distinguish between each parameter and one day such an oil sensor will be designed to do so, it would still be necessary to send a sample of oil to an oil testing laboratory to identify what damage if any has been caused to the machinery. Suggesting an investment in such technology may not prove any more advantageous, but a lot more expensive.

6. OIL SENSORS IN THE MARKET PLACE TODAY

One oil sensor proving itself in the market place today is the Tan Delta oil sensor. Currently it is being manufactured and marketed under licence by two companies under the name Analexrs Tribo and LubriGard. The Analexrs Tribo trademark is owned by Kittiwake whose paper today includes reference to this device and who primarily service the Marine market, while the LubriGuard trademark is owned by Drive Management Services (DMS), co-authors to this paper and who service the heavy engineering and manufacturing industries. DMS market this device under their own product name LubriGuard, as a variant of the patent owner's name of this technology, Lubrigard Ltd.

DMS offer the LubriGuard system for installation in various configurations, depending on the requirements of the client. It can be supplied in the following configurations:

- The basic LubriGuard oil sensor, illustrated in figure 2, communicating directly to the clients monitoring system, via a 4-20mA, a RS232 or a Canbus interface.

- The basic Simple LubriGuard system, comprising of the LubriGuard oil sensor, the MachineGuard instrument, with built in alarm facilities.

- The complex LubriGuard system comprising of the LubriGuard oil sensor, the MachineGuard instrument with data-logging facility, and wireless connectivity to an onsite monitoring PC.

- The sophisticated LubriGuard system comprising of the LubriGuard oil sensor, the MachineGuard instrument with data logging facility, and GPRS connectivity to a remote PC via the Internet.

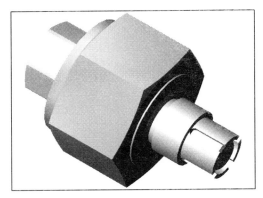

Figure 2 Basic LubriGard Sensor

The Basic LubriGuard Oil Sensor

This method of continuous monitoring is the most cost effective way of implementing a system on a site, which has an existing SCADA or other monitoring system.

The Basic Simple LubriGuard System

This system of continuous monitoring incorporates local alarms, such as klaxons, indicator lights and a relay interface to an existing local alarm system. This system is reliant on the "MachineGuard" instruments, built in intelligence, to handle temperature normalisation and the programming of multi-level alarms.

The Complex LubriGuard System

This is a continuous monitoring flexible and complex system developed to take advantage of a wide variety of wireless communication and networking technologies.

It can be supplied using DMS in-house developed telemetry modems. Alternatively, the system can be implemented, using a client's existing wireless or wired network, utilising the DMS range of network converters / interface devices. Both of these options dramatically reduce the need for site wiring.

The system will log required data and provide trend analysis of all historical information stored, on a site PC or from a remote location.

One major advantage of this system is its capability to warn customers and/or DMS support engineers, of impending deterioration of the lubricant in question. This warning can be sent instantaneously by SMS text message, e-mail or fax, direct to the contact concerned and the contact in question can then access the "LIVE" data with his/her own PC, to assist in making informed planning maintenance decisions.

The Sophisticated LubriGuard System

This system will deliver all the key features of the option detail above, without the need for any local infrastructure. This system has been specifically developed for remote unmanned locations, where all that is required is a local power supply and a mobile phone signal. One key aspect of the LubriGuard system is the MachineGuard instrument. The MachineGuard instrument is a self-contained device which will continually monitor the oil condition and temperature every second of the day.

Key features of this self-contained device are as follows

- The local storage of monitored information, up to 16,384 records from all input modules.
- Four input modules which enables the instrument to operate two (2) separate LubriGuard oil sensors, or if required additional monitoring conditions, such as vibration, temperature, motor current, etc.
- Local simple or complex multi-level alarms.

RS232 or RS485 communications

- Up to 255 instruments can be configured from one (1) wired or wireless monitored PC.
- All key parameters can then be configured remotely from the PC.
- Real time date stamping of all records.
- Wide range of input power supply from 9-30V DC, or 110V AC.
- Compact DIN rail mounted unit, for mounting in suitable enclosures and panels.

During the early stages of the system development, DMS identified that the majority of their prospective clients would benefit from a centralised collection of monitored data via a PC. The objective from day one was to ensure that all user interface functionality should be compatible with Microsoft Windows based operating platform. This would ensure familiarity and ease of access to the display system software, which can control communications with a large network of MachineGuard instruments. This package collects the data and interprets it to provide meaningful trends. The display is arranged with an image of the application or location as a backdrop. The instrument is identified by a graphical icon, which is positioned in an appropriate area to enable the operators to easily identify the exact location of the monitored equipment. The graphical icon represents a single or multiple reading which clearly shows the current reading and a "Traffic Light" colour coded indication of the each individual alarm status.

DMS believe that their LubriGuard continuous oil monitoring system is simple, cost effective and complements an existing laboratory oil-sampling programme. With the ever-escalating price of crude oil, it assists engineers on large expensive pieces of capital plant to make informed decisions when it comes to replacing the oil. With this LubriGuard system the guesswork is taken out of the process!

7. CONCLUSION

RCM is the future for industrial maintenance programmes and OCM is an integral part of that future. It has been shown how and why all maintenance staff should adopt an RCM policy. In doing so they should first carryout a risk assessment on all assets, prove by calculation the savings possible with RCM, carry out the appropriate RCM programme, which may involve more than one technique, invest in formal training by an authorised training organisation, such as BINDT and consider the option of on-board oil sensors to monitor vital equipment especially in hostile or remote environments. An on-board oil sensor will fill a vital role in the continual strives to reduce downtime and improve profits. Condition monitoring technologies discussed, particularly OCM, remain vital to the success of the Tan-Delta type oil sensor, to help identify the problems detected. Ideally, a Tan-Delta type oil sensor used in combination with regular Oil Condition Monitoring will prove probably the most effective force in the struggle to protect remote and vital oil lubricated equipment.

ACKNOWLEDGEMENTS

Mr. Chris Collister – Lubrigard Ltd. Inventor of the Tandelta Oil Condition Sensor

Wearcheck UK Laboratories (ALcontrol UK Ltd)

Drive Managements Services Ltd

Kittiwake Ltd

British Institute of Non-Destructive Testing (BINDT)

BIBLIOGRAPHY

Moubray, J. (2005) "Reliability-centred Maintenance". 2nd Edition Pub Elsevier ISBN 0 75 06 33 581.

Collister, C. (2000) "On board Oil Condition Oil Sensor" Presented at "Tribo 2000" (Munich).

REFERENCES

ISO 17359 (2003) "Condition monitoring and diagnostics of machines - General guidelines".

BS ISO 18436-1(2004) "Condition monitoring and diagnostics of machines - Requirements for training and certification of personnel."

ISO 17024 (2003) "Conformity assessment - General requirements for bodies operating certification of persons".

Additive Reaction Mechanisms on Coating Surface

J. Vižintin [1], M. Kalin [1], E. Roman [2]

[1] Center for tribology and technical diagnostics, University of Ljubljana, Slovenia
[2] Instituto de Ciencia de Materiales de Madrid, Madrid, Spain

ABSTRACT

Diamond-like carbon (DLC) coatings are generally considered as "inert" and to not react in contacts with oils and additives under boundary lubrication conditions. On the other hand, it was suggested in several studies that certain interactions between the DLC coatings and oil-additives must exist, because of their clear and well-differentiated influence on wear and friction behaviour, both of doped, but also of non-doped pure DLC coatings even in self-mated DLC/DLC contacts. However, a clear and non-disputable explanation of the chemical reactions was not obtained and the influencing parameters and the actual acting mechanisms in these contacts are still poorly understood. In this study we have investigated the wear and friction behaviour of boundary lubricated self-mated DLC/DLC contacts obtained at different contact conditions with different oils, including additivated and non-additivated. Several evidences from AES, XPS and Raman analyses about the chemical and structural changes of the DLC coatings when sliding in the presence of mineral oil, with and without additives are presented. We clearly show that these chemical reactions are highly condition-dependent, but they also depend whether - and what kind of - additives are used.

Keywords: DLC, oil, additive, temperature, friction, wear

1. INTRODUCTION

Until recently, most of the understanding of the tribological behaviour of DLC coatings was focused on their performance in environments like dry or humid air, vacuum and different gas atmospheres [1-5], with much less emphasis being placed on the oil-lubricated conditions. However, due to great improvements in the properties of coatings and their ability to operate under more severe conditions, it has become obvious that for the successful and broad implementation of DLC coatings in various machine components they also need to operate under lubricated conditions, remembering that these conditions are often poor and/or starved, i.e. in the boundary regime. So far, by employing mineral base oils we have studied the effect of the type of oil additives and the different doping elements in self-mated DLC/DLC [6,7] and steel/DLC [7,8] contacts, and we have also investigated the effects of the polarity and the saturation of different base oils [9]. In these, and most other reported studies, additives significantly affected the wear and friction of boundary-lubricated DLC contacts; however, the extent of the change depends on the type of oils, additives, coatings, counter-bodies, etc. However, despite our efforts to perform different surface-sensitive analyses [10], we have not yet succeeded in obtaining clear evidence for chemical reactions between these selected pure DLC coatings and the additives.

Therefore, in order to elucidate the effect of the temperature, we have investigated the tribological behaviour of lubricated self-mated DLC/DLC contacts at three distinctively different testing temperatures. Chemical and structural changes of the DLC coatings in contacts with mineral base oil with and without AW and EP additives were verified by AES analyses. The results show that DLC coatings already oxidise at room temperature and that chemical reactions between the DLC and the additives are highly temperature-dependent, as well as depending on the type of additives used.

2. EXPERIMENTAL

The tribological tests were performed using the ball-on-flat testing geometry, using balls and flats made from DIN 100Cr6 steel. The steel balls were standard, commercially available balls with a diameter of 10 mm; they had a hardness of 850 HV. The surface roughness was measured using a stylus-tip profilometer and the R_a value was better than 0.03 μm. The steel flat samples were heat treated to the same hardness as the balls. The steel discs were ground and polished to a final roughness R_a of 0.05 (+/-0.01) μm. All the steel balls and discs were then coated with a single-layer diamond-like carbon coating (without any doping elements) with a thickness of 2.67 (+/-0.04) μm. The surface roughness, R_a, of the samples, i.e., the balls and discs, was measured after the coating deposition, and the average value was about the same, or only slightly higher, i.e. by less than 0.01 μm.

The experiments were performed under two sets of conditions: using only a base oil, and using a mixture of a base oil and 1% of a single wear-reducing additive. A paraffin base oil (denoted as M) of viscosity grade ISO VG 46 was used for the tribological tests under selected conditions. Two different additives that provide the wear protection under a variety of possible conditions in mixed and boundary-lubrication conditions and are frequently used for conventional steel surfaces were employed. One of the additives was an ashless, multifunctional, mild, anti-wear/extreme-pressure (AW/EP) additive, i.e., a mixture of amine phosphates, having about 4.8% and 2.7% of P and N, respectively. The second additive used was a typical, strong, extreme-pressure (EP) additive, i.e., dialkyl dithiophosphate, containing 9.3% of P and 19.8% of S.

The wear experiments that involved self-mated DLC/DLC contacts were performed in a reciprocating sliding machine. In all the experiments, 10 N of normal load was applied through the loading system, which resulted in an initial Hertzian contact stress of about 700 MPa (1 GPa max). A stroke of 1 mm and an oscillating frequency of 50 Hz were used, resulting in a relative contact velocity of 0.1 m/s. In each test the total sliding distance was 100 m. A small amount of oil was spread on the surface of the flat specimen prior to each experiment. The experiments were performed at three different testing temperatures – 20, 80, and 150°C. The wear volume was calculated using the ball wear-scar diameter and a geometric equation for the volume of a spherical segment. Samples were examined using a scanning electron microscope equipped with a EDS detector. In addition, a number of samples tested under various conditions were analyzed with AES.

3. RESULTS

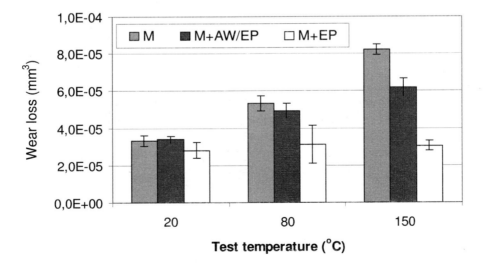

Figure 1. (a) Ball wear loss of DLC/DLC contacts tested with mineral oil (M), a mixture of mineral oil and AW/EP additive (M+AW/EP) and a mixture of mineral oil and EP additive (M+EP) at three different test temperatures.

The wear volume (Figure 1) generally increased with an increase in the test temperature as did the increase in the differences between the different lubricants used. At 20°C the differences between the lubricants were almost negligible and the wear was very low. At 80°C the variations in wear between the lubricants were already quite pronounced, with a significantly reduced wear when the additives were used. This was particularly the case with the EP additive, which led to an almost two-times lower wear compared to the base oil at this temperature. When the test temperature was increased to 150°C, the wear in the experiments with the base oil was the highest in this study. However, even under these conditions the coating was not worn through during the tests, but there was an obvious difference in the surface appearance when the base oil or the base oil with additives were used, Figure 2. The wear scar was noticeably more worn with the base oil only, and the scar, which contained several scratches, was noticed immediately (Figure 2a). The use of the AW additive quite noticeably reduced the wear compared to the base oil, i.e., by about 25% (Figure 1). On the other hand, the reduction of wear loss when using the EP additive was extremely high: almost three-times less wear was obtained than with the base oil at this temperature.

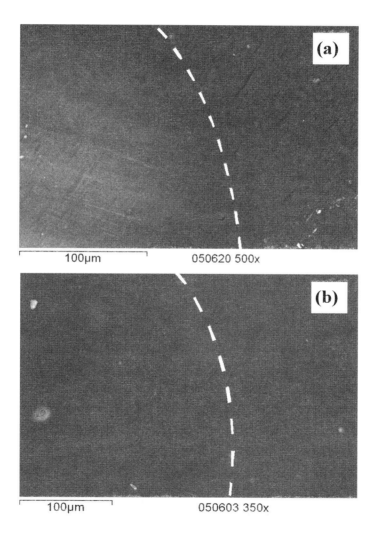

Figure 2. SEM images of the worn DLC-coated ball surfaces tested at 150°C with (a) mineral base oil M and (b) mineral base oil with EP additive. Dashed lines in Figures (a) and (b) represent the border of the wear scar.

In contrast to the wear, the coefficient of friction was reduced at higher testing temperatures, Figure 3. In all the tests at 20°C the coefficient of friction was approximately the same, irrespective of the lubricant used, with only a small reduction when the additives were used. In the experiments at 80°C, the coefficient of friction was also quite similar when using the base oil and the AW additive, and it was a few percent lower than for the experiments at 20°C. In these tests (80°C), the oil with the AW additive resulted in a slightly higher friction than when using the base oil. Moreover, when EP-additivated oil was used at 80°C, the friction increased more significantly and was clearly higher than for the base oil and the oil with the AW additive. A much more significant change in friction was, however, observed with the experiments at 150°C. The friction was also lower for the oil with the EP additive, but the decrease was smaller. The higher friction observed with the "stronger" additives at 150°C is the opposite to the case of the experiments at 20°C. However, a similar trend in the friction increase with the use of stronger additives was also observed for the experiments at 80°C.

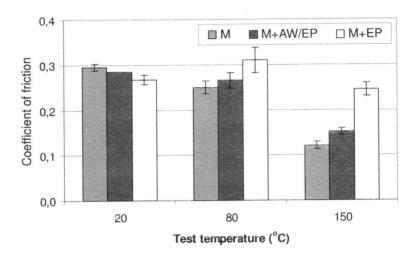

Figure 3. Steady-state coefficient of friction in DLC/DLC contacts tested with mineral oil (M), a mixture of mineral oil and AW/EP additive (M+AW/EP) and a mixture of mineral oil and EP additive (M+EP) at three different test temperatures.

Important chemical changes were found in some of the wear tracks using AES. Figure 4 shows the results of the AES analysis in the energy region 90–550 eV for the samples tested at 150°C with all three lubricants. Apart from the C KLL peak at 272 eV, which was found in all regions, as would be expected with DLC substrate, peaks were also observed for O, S, and P in the wear-track region for the samples tested with EP-additivated oil, see Figure 4c. The phosphorus (P) and sulphur (S) LVV transitions at 114 and 152 eV, respectively, represent evidence for a chemical change in the wear scar under selected tribological conditions as a result of the interaction between the DLC coating and the EP additive, which consists of the active elements S and P. No chemical changes could be observed at the surfaces of the samples tested with base oil (Figure 4a) or AW-additivated oil (Figure 4b), suggesting a higher chemical activity for the EP additive rather than the AW additive or the base oil only.

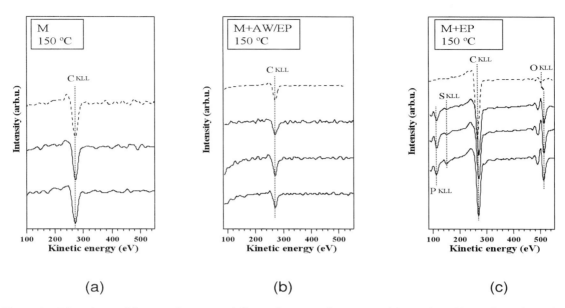

Figure 4. AES analyses of the worn DLC-coated disc surfaces tested at 150oC with (a) mineral base oil M, (b) a mixture of mineral oil and AW/EP additive and (c) a mixture of mineral oil with EP additive.

Our data show only one peak at energies of 114 eV for P and 152 eV for S, which could indicate that P is present mainly as phosphates and S as sulphide or organic sulphur. It can also be seen from Figure 4c that the intensity of the S peak is lower than that of the P peak. This decrease in the amount of sulphur, evident from the AES data in Figure 4, has already been observed in the past [11]. In that investigation, thermal-films and tribo-films are compared and the importance of surface effects and tribochemical reactions are pointed out.

To investigate the effect of the testing temperature on the interaction between the EP additive and the DLC coating, AES analyses of the worn surfaces tested at lower temperatures, i.e., 20°C and 80°C, were also performed. However, the spectra from the wear traces tested at 20 and 80°C do not show any noticeable changes related to the interaction with the additive active elements (S and P), indicating that the selected EP additive did not interact with the DLC coating with the same lubricating mechanism at temperatures lower than 150°C.

4. DISCUSSION

The effect of the testing temperature on the tribological behaviour of boundary-lubricated DLC coatings and their interactions with additives were investigated in this work. The results show that the wear (Figure 1) generally increases with the temperature, while the opposite is true for the friction (Figure 3). Moreover, it is clear that for all temperatures the wear is lower when using the stronger EP additive than the AW additive, and that these additivated contacts have lower wear than the base oil only, Figure 1. However, at 20°C, this behaviour is much less pronounced. On the other hand, the friction behaviour is just the opposite of the wear behaviour, but it is also consistently similar at 80 and 150°C, i.e., at these two test temperatures the friction increases more with the use of the stronger additive than it does with the base oil. The same can be said for the wear behaviour: the reverse friction performance is found at 20°C, and the differences are also smaller and less pronounced than at higher temperatures. So, as a general rule, some consistent trend and difference in the friction and wear behaviours can be found only at 80 and 150°C; this suggests that at 20°C any significant change related to an additive (chemical) effect is much less likely to exist.

On the other hand, it is clear that at higher testing temperatures (80 and 150°C) the additives significantly improve the wear resistance of the DLC/DLC contacts and the differences between the lubricants become very clear, Figure 1. This suggests that the chemistry of the oils starts to play a decisive role at higher temperatures. The use of the EP additive resulted in a clearly reduced wear of more than 40% at 80°C, and even more, i.e., about three times less, at the highest test temperature of 150°C. Adding the AW additive to the base oil also reduced the wear at 80 and 150°C, with a greater effect observed at 150°C.

As mentioned previously, the coefficient of friction increased consistently with the use of stronger additives at both higher temperatures, i.e., 80 and 150°C (Figure 3). This friction behaviour can be associated with the increased shear strength at the interface due to an interaction between the additives and the surfaces, as many times described for different lubricated systems [12-15] and also for DLC [6,9]. However, when only base oil was used at the highest temperature (150°C), the friction was very low, the lowest in this study, see Figure 3. From our and previous findings [16-18] it can be suggested that graphitisation occurred under these conditions and caused the reduced friction. The high wear that occurred in the experiments with the base oil at 150°C (Figure 1) also agrees with the formation of graphite layers at the surface. Namely, the graphite layers are softer than the original DLC surface, and thus more prone to mechanical damage and wear.

However, when additives were used at 150°C (or any other temperature), two major effects of the additives can be suggested. First, the AES analyses (Figure 4) provide direct evidence for the DLC coating's reaction with the EP additive and the formation of a tribochemical layer that consists of phosphates and organic sulphur/sulphates. Moreover, the results show that a decrease in the S/P ratio occurred at the tribochemical film. This is in agreement with the results reported in another study of additives at high temperatures [11], where this kind of depletion was also attributed to a tribochemical reaction of additives at the surface. Accordingly, it is reasonable to conclude that this tribochemical reaction resulted in a coherent lubricious interface layer, which produced the additive wear-protective effect that drastically changed the conditions at the interface, as seen from Figure 1. Second, another generally positive effect of the (soft) tribochemical layers that form at the surfaces is a reduction of the peak-stresses and a more uniform stress distribution (stress relief) at the interface [19-21]. This mechanism could also play a role in our contacts, and it is in agreement with the findings from this study. Namely, it could be (partially) responsible for the observed wear reduction (Figure 1). Therefore, from the presented results and the suggested mechanisms we can conclude that the EP additive reacts with the DLC diamond-like carbon films at high temperatures and forms a wear-protective layer at the interface. In this way, the wear was significantly reduced compared to the plain base oil under the same conditions.

5. CONCLUSIONS

1. The wear in self-mated DLC/DLC boundary-lubricated contacts generally increases with temperature, while the opposite is true for the friction. The use of additives effects the tribological properties at testing temperatures of 80 and 150°C, while during low-temperature experiments there is much less evidence for any additive effect.

2. AES analyses provided direct evidence for the reaction of the coating with the EP additive and the formation of a tribochemical layer at 150°C.

3. The beneficial wear-effect of the additives could be due to i) the formation of a coherent lubricious tribochemical layer at the DLC surface and/or due to ii) a reduction of the peak contact stresses within the tribochemical layer, thus reducing the surface strain and the consequent wear.

4. The strong EP additive reduces the wear much more effectively, but at the same time it increases the friction, compared to the AW additive. At the test temperature of 150°C the EP additive reduced the wear by almost three times compared to the base oil.

REFERENCES

[1] J. Andersson, R.A. Erck, A. Erdemir, Friction of diamond-like carbon films in different atmospheres, Wear, 254 (2003) 1070-1075.

[2] J. Jiang, S. Zhang, R.D. Arnell, The effect of relative humidity on wear of diamond-like carbon coating, Surf. Coat. Tech. 167 (2003) 221.

[3] Y.Liu, A.Erdemir, E.I.Meletis, Influence of environmental parameters on the frictional behavior of DLC coatings, Surface and coatings technology, 94-95 (1997) 463-468

[4] C. Donnet, J. Fontaine, A. Grill, T. Le Mogne, The role of hydrogen on the friction mechanism of diamond-like carbon films, Tribology Letters 9, [3-4] (2000) 137-142.

[5] J. Fontaine, C. Donnet, A. Grill, T. Le Mogne, Tribochemistry between hydrogen and diamind-like carbon films, Surface and coatings technology, 146-147 (2001) 286-291.

[6] 5th FP growth project, Lubricoat, Environmentally friendly lubricants and low friction coatings; A route towards sustainable products and production processes, (G5RD-CT-2000-00410).

[7] M. Kalin, J. Vižintin, J. Barriga, K. Vercammen, K. Van Acker, A. Arnšek, The effect of doping elements and oil additives on the tribological performance of boundary-lubricated DLC contacts, Tribology Letters 17 [4] (2004) 679-688.

[8] M. Kalin, J. Vižintin, A comparison of the tribological behaviour of steel/steel, steel/dlc and dlc/dlc contacts when lubricated with mineral and biodegradable oils, Wear, 261 (2006) 22-31.

[9] M. Kalin, J. Vižintin, Differences in the tribological mechanisms when using non-doped DLC, metal-doped (Ti, WC) DLC and non-metal-doped (Si) DLC, with and without additives, against steel under boundary-lubrication conditions, submitted, 2005.

[10] M. Kalin, J. Vižintin, K. Vercammen, J. Barriga, A. Arnšek, The lubrication of DLC coatings with mineral and biodegradable oils having different polar and saturation characteristics, Surface and Coatings Technology, 200 (2006) 4515-4522.

[11] M. Fuller, Z. Vin, M. Kasrai, G. M. Bancroft, E.S. Yamaguchi, P.R. Rayson, P.A. Willermet and K. H. Tam, Chemical characterization of tribochemical and thermal films generated from neutral and basic ZDDPs using X-ray absorption spectroscopy, Tribology International 30 (1997) 305-315.

[12] R.M. Mortier, S.T. Orszulik, Chemistry and technology of lubricants, Blackie Academic & Professional, Glasgow, 2nd ed., 1993.

[13] Z. Pawlak, Tribochemistry of lubricating oils, Tribology and interface engineering series 45, Elsevier, Amsterdam, 2003.

[14] P. Waara, J. Hannu, T. Norrby, A. Byheden, Additive influence on wear and friction performance of environmentally adapted lubricants, Tribology International, 34 (2001) 547-556.

[15] H. Spikes, The history and mechanisms of ZDDP, Tribology Letters 17 [3] (2004) 469-489.

[16] Y.Liu, A.Erdemir, E.I.Meletis; An investigation of the relationship graphitization and frictional behavior of DLC coatings, Surface and Coatings Technology 86-87 (1996) 564-568.

[17] K. Holmberg, J. Koskinen, H. Ronkainen, J. Vihersalo, J.P.Hirvonen, J. Likonen, Diamond Films Technol. 4 (1994) 113.

[18] J.C. Sanchez-Lopez, A. Erdemir, C. Donnet, T.C. Rojas, Friction-induced structural transformations of diamondlike carbon coatings under various atmospheres, Surface and Coatings Technology 163-164 (2003) 444-450.

[19] L. Lazzarotto, L. Dubar, A. Dubois, P. Ravassard, J. Oudin, Three selection criteria for the cold metal forming lubricating oils containing extreme pressure agents, Journal of Materials Processing Technology 80-81 (1998) 245-250.

[20] A. Ravikiran, S. Jahanmir, Effect of interfacial layers on wear behaviour of a dental glass-ceramics, J. Amer. Ceram. Soc. 83 [7] (2000) 1831-1833.

[21] M. Kalin, Said Jahanmir, G. Dražič, Wear Mechanisms of Glass-infiltrated Alumina Sliding Against Alumina in Water, J. Amer. Ceram. Soc., 88 [2] (2005) 346-352.

Session 7
LUBRICATION MANAGEMENT 2

Chair: Dr. Ramón Galllifa

Base Number and Acid Number prediction: A new application for FTIR Spectroscopy
E. GORRITXATEGI, E. ARANZABE, A. ARNAIZ, J. TERRADILLOS, S. FERREIRO

Oil analysis vs Oil based condition monitoring- What to expect and more importantly what to not
D. SHORTEN

Use of sensor technology for Oil Condition Monitoring
I. LAMONT, T. KENT, A. BALDWIN

Combining On-Site and On-Line Voltammetric Analyses to Improve Military and Industrial Oil Condition Monitoring Programs
R. E. KAUFFMAN, J. AMEYE

Base Number and Acid Number prediction: A new application for FTIR Spectroscopy

E. Gorritxategi [1], E. Aranzabe [1], A. Arnaiz [1], J. Terradillos [1], S. Ferreiro [2]

[1] Fundación Tekniker, Avda. Otaola, 20, 20600 Eibar, Spain
[2] Fundación de centros tecnológicos

ABSTRACT

Base Number (BN) and Acid Number (AN) are fundamental parameters of lubricant oil quality. BN is the measurement of a lubricant's reserve alkalinity and it decreases as acids are formed during combustion. AN is the measurement of acid compounds formed during lubricating oil degradation. Nowadays, methods used to analyze lubricating oil BN and AN are laboratory-based, time consuming, expensive and highly toxic for the environment.

Chemometric techniques use both statistical and machine learning methods in order to extract 'virtual' parameters from the data. One of the most interesting improvement is to develop these parameters that can be cheaper and/or easier to obtain than reference 'real' ones. Given this, a chemometric process on FT-IR analysis has been developed to predict the BN and AN parameters of gas engine oils, in order to assess the oil ageing.

This paper describes the process to achieve the prediction of BN and AN parameters from FT-IR analytical process. First of all, FT-IR analysis has been carried out, to get the best IR wavelengths for each parameter. Afterward, the chemometrics' (or intelligent data analysis) techniques have been applied to identify outliers and to build the prediction: the Partial Least Square (PLS – UnScrambler) Regression, Artificial Neural Nets (ANN) and different classifiers (Weka).

Keywords: Gas engine oil, Base Number (BN), Acid Number (AN), FT-IR Spectroscopy, Prediction, Aging, Reliability.

1. INTRODUCTION

The Base Number (BN) [1] is an indicator of the degradation state of the oil and it represents the oil alkalinity value. In other words, it is an indicator of the oil's ability to neutralize acids. During the oil aging process, the BN tends to diminish. Generally, it's considered that the oil is degraded when the BN original value decreases by 50%. Another way to know if the oil is degraded, is to compare the BN and the Acid Number (AN) values. The acid number is a measure of the amount of potassium hydroxide required to neutralize the acid contained in a lubricant. Acids are formed as oils oxidize with age and service. The acid number AN for an oil sample is indicative of the age of the oil and can be used to determinate when the oil must be changed. If the BN value is lower than the AN value, it's very probable that the oil is degraded. Thus, the BN and AN critical values are the interception values between them.

The obtaining of BN and AN parameters in the laboratory is quite expensive, as much in time as in materials. So, the prediction of these parameters, using indirect indicators, would give rise to a considerable saving for oil analysis laboratories. These kind of methods are shorter in time, less costly and safer for sample handling than standard lab methods. So, it improves the plant management, giving a faster decision support. In addition, the analysis carried out is very useful for the development of on-line sensors to measure oil degradation critical point because strategies must become on-line in order to respond to unforeseen events and to detect early stages of oil degradation.

But, there's a problem, it's not possible to handle all kind of oils together, because there are oils with very different properties, composition and therefore, very different behaviour with regard to Fourier Transform Infra Red (FT-IR) spectra. So, it's very difficult to develop a global model for all oils. Thus, it's necessary to simplify the problem of the BN prediction analysing one oil type each time. In this work the gas engine oil has been chosen. This selection is due to our preferences and data availability.

The use of gas engines has increased substantially in the last years, specially, in cogeneration plants, combined generation of thermal and electrical energy plants. Furthermore, it is an efficient and friendly source of power generation for a wide variety of industrial and domestic applications, reaching effectiveness levels up to 90%.They are used in industrial applications work regularly under constant high loads, high temperatures and during long periods of time. These high loads and temperatures promote the oil oxidation. Moreover the gas has some aggressive compounds. Thus, it's essential that the gas engine oil has a greater stability to the oxidation than the conventional oils.

2. EXPERIMENTAL METHODS

FT-IR spectroscopy measurements have been recorded from two different spectrometers; FT-IR Perkin Elmer Spectrum ONE and FT-IR Perkin Elmer Spectrum BX-I spectrometer. The Mid Infrared spectrum [2] has been considered in the present study. The spectra is recorded in the 4000-600 cm-1 range, by using SeZn. This test method is used to control of the state of the lubricant. It provides a spectral analysis that quantifies the presence of several chemical compounds. The differences between the spectrum IR of the used sample and the new one, indicate the chemical changes in the used oil, the different types from polluting agents are; Water, Soot , Glycol , Combustible , Nitration , Oxidation , Sulfatation.

For obtaining the BN values in the laboratory, the BN Titroprocessor Mettler-Toledo DL50 + Quanto has been used. D2896-03 Standard Test Method for Base Number of Petroleum Products by Potentiometric Perchloric Acid Titration has been chosen and the uncertainty (precision) of this method is +/-0.04 mgKOH/g.

To obtain the AN value in the laboratory a AN Titrator Mettler-Toledo DL53 has been used. The American Society for Testing and Materials ASTM D974-04 Standard Test Method for AN and BN by Colour-Indicator Titration has been chosen and the uncertainty (precision) of this method is +/-0.04 mg KOH/g.

3. CHEMOMETRICS

Chemometric methods are often applied in situations when no sufficient theory is available for describing or solving problems. Typical for problems of this type is the use of many variables to describe a system; furthermore often only hidden relationships exist between the available data and the desired information and the aim of chemometrics is to find out some of these relationships.

The typical chemometric strategy consists of the following steps [3]:

- Collection and pre-treatment of data.
- Generation of a mathematical model. This model is usually based on multivariate statistics, neural networks or machine learning techniques or algorithms.
- Interpretation of the model parameters in terms of the underlying chemistry.
- Application of the model to new cases, or often the search for a better model or for more appropriate variables.

The most important multivariate methods for chemometrics are listed in figure1.

data	aim of data analysis	criterion for latent variable (score)	method
features X	good representation of distances (similarities of objects) in feature space exploratory data analysis (cluster analysis)	maximum variance	PCA
X y class mem-ber-ship	discrimination between given classes (categories) of objects **classification**	optimum sepa-ration of two object classes	LDA PLS
X y pro-perty	modeling a property by the features **calibration**	optimum cor-relation with property y	MLR PCR PLS

Figure 1. Multivariate methods summary. PCA, principal component analysis; LDA, linear discriminant analysis; PLS, partial least squares regression; MLR, multiple linear regression; PCR, principal component regression; y, dependent variable.

Machine Learning is the study of computer algorithms that improve automatically through experience and can help in automating the time consuming process of knowledge acquisition that is essential to the development of a knowledge-based system. Machine learning approaches commonly used for classification include inductive learning algorithms such as decision tree induction and rule induction, instance based learning, neural networks and genetic algorithms. Some of these algorithms have been used to classify the degradation status of the oil.

Apart from classification, the main technique used in the prediction of AN and BN parameters has been the Artificial Neural Networks (ANN). ANNs are an approach to non-linear problems. Their structure is a net of interconnected nodes. Each node is weighted and in the nodes' interconnections is applied a formula. So at the end, we get an output, but it's difficult to know what has happened in the net.

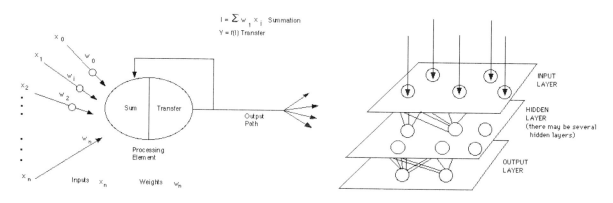

Figure 2. A basic Artificial Neuron and a simple Neural Network diagram.

4. DEVELOPMENT OF THE PREDICTION MODEL

In a prediction model development the most important steps to follow are:

- Pre-treatment – (Samples selection - outlier detection).
- Variable selection (FTIR bands selection).
- Construction of the calibration model (techniques & results).
- Model validation and evaluation (results validation).

Oil samples selected for the analysis can be seen in table 1. These samples are gas engine lubricating oils:

Table 1. Selected samples.

LUBRICATING OIL	Initial BN (mgKOH/g)	Samples
BP ENERGOL IC-DG 40	7.30	211
BP ENERGOL IC-DG 40S	5.45	720
BP ENERGAS NG 5	6.12	73
MOBIL PEGASUS 705	5.40	11

LUBRICATING OIL	Initial AN (mgKOH/g)	Samples
BP ENERGOL IC-DG 40	1.54	195
BP ENERGOL IC-DG 40S	1.55	691
BP ENERGAS NG 5	0.28	76
MOBIL PEGASUS 705	0.30	9

4.1. Pre-treatment

In "Wearcheck Iberica" there is a data base with many gas engines oil samples. At the time of selecting the training samples from the data base, it's necessary to take into account that these samples must represent all the other samples [6]. That way the models obtained from these samples, will fit also well any other samples.

Firstly, an important consideration in the FT-IR measurement is that the difference between fresh oil and used oil is measured, so in these analysis the variable to predict will be the variation of AN and BN from the fresh oil to avoid the differences in the initial BN and AN value.

Going on with the sample selection, for the BN prediction, 5506 gas engine oil samples have been selected from Wearcheck database and 4451 samples have been left out of the analysis because of different reasons. Selected samples have to fulfil some considerations:

- Sample with BN value measured in laboratory.
- Sample with FT-IR measured in laboratory.
- BN < 10mg KOH/g.
- Sample newer than May 2001.
- Fresh oil with FT-IR measurement.

For the AN prediction, above mentioned considerations have been carried out but with some differences. As it has been said above, variation of AN parameter from the fresh oil (catalogue value) has been predicted. The samples which exceed the catalogue values ie., negative AN variation < 0.3 and positive AN variation < 1.5, have not been considered in the analysis, in order to avoid the influence of the over additivation.

4.1.1. Outliers detection

Outliers may occur for many different reasons. There may be printing error, instrument error, objects from another population, chemical laboratory error, etc. For detecting outliers or these abnormal observations, there are different tools. Outlier detection has been carried out, first by means of visual and graphical inspection of the data and next with the use of multivariate analysis. This analysis can identify outliers taking into account the residual variance of each sample. In the figure 3 it can be seen some samples (outliers) are far from the rest of the data and with a very high residual variance. These samples can be considered as outliers, however it is necessary to conduct a thorough analysis of each sample.

Sometimes, an outlier may be highly informative. So, once we have obtained these extreme values, we have to check (asking experts) one by one, to be sure that they are really erroneous data and should be removed. For this task we have used other data apart from the spectra: viscosity, acidity number, density etc.

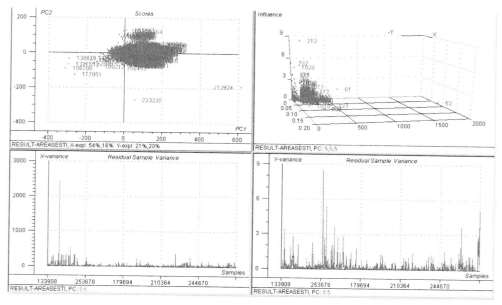

Figure 3. Outlier detection.

4.2. FTIR bands selection

In order to get the best wavelength bands related to BN, some characteristic bands have been selected, following the *"Wearcheck Ibérica"* laboratory experts' advice. Proposed wavelengths are shown in figure 4.

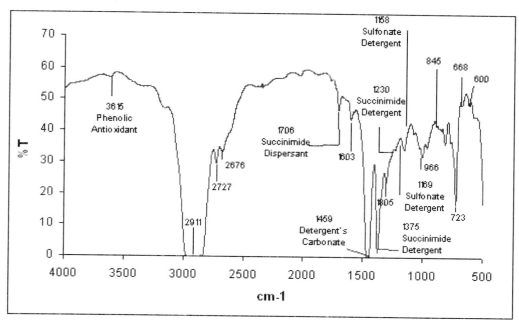

Figure 4. IR spectrum with oil aging characteristic bands.

These spectral regions are related with different chemical compounds (additives) which are also related to the oil alkalinity and acid resistance. These bands' values are the theoretical ones. But in practise these bands can be wider or narrower [8], and they can also move towards right or left, it depends on the influence of the other compounds. For instance, the phenolic antioxidant band 3648 cm^{-1} could be represented by different wavelength ranges 3653-3644 cm^{-1}, 3660-3640 cm^{-1}, etc. So here there's a problem to set bounds to the bands. In order to solve this problem, data mining techniques have been used, taking into account that the best bands will be those which better make the BN assessment. Finally, selected bands are listed in table 2.

Table 2. Selected IR bands.

Acid Number (AN)	Base Number (BN)
Water content (3520 -3220 cm^{-1})	Phenolic antioxidant (**3670 -3627 cm^{-1}**)
C=O Aldehydes carboxylic acids (**1850 -1612 cm^{-1}**)	Detergent's carbonate (**1520 -1500 cm^{-1}**)
C=O Conjugated ketones (**1750 -1700 cm^{-1}**)	Succinimide detergent (**1240 -1215 cm^{-1}**)
C=O Aldehydes, carboxylic acids (**1690 -1640 cm^{-1}**)	Sulfonate detergent (**1180 -1145 cm^{-1}**)
C-O Esters (1175 -1135 cm^{-1})	Zinc dialkyl dithiophosphate- ZDDP (**1050 -970 cm^{-1}**)
	Zinc dialkyl dithiophosphate- ZDDP (**690 -620 cm^{-1}**)

In order to check the selection of the bands, a Partial Least Square 1 (PLS1) regression was carried out. This regression method gives as result the regression model and a verification of whether the selected variables are significant or not. As can be seen in figure 5, most of the variables are significant and representative of the model.

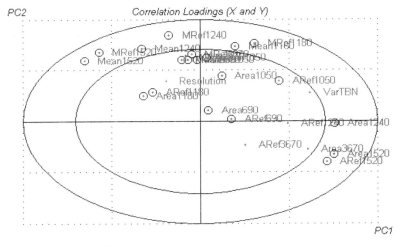

Figure 5. Most representative variables.

The figure 5 shows the variables that are significant into the model highlighted by a circle. It can be seen that almost all of them are significant, but some of them have a higher weight in the calibration of the model. Variables that are between the external ring are more significant than the other ones.

4.3.   Calibration Models RESULTS

Three different studies have been carried out using different techniques [3, 4] and three software applications have been used: UnScrambler (PLS), Predict (ANN), Weka Software (Machine learning algorithms).

4.3.1. Multivariate AN-BN prediction model

This model is a linear approach and it's based on the PLS regression. The Partial Least Square [5] regression reduces the data space, creating new factors (or latent variables). These factors are a linear combination of original data and the weight vectors are calculated maximising the covariance between the predictor variables (FTIR bands) and the response (BN or AN).

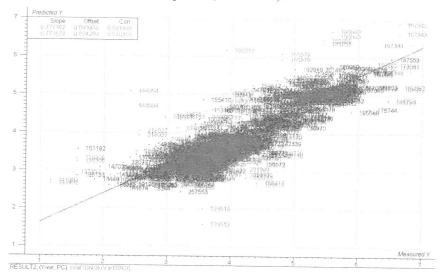

Figure 6. AN-BN prediction graph obtained by multivariate analysis.

A high correlation coefficient has been obtained by means of this method, R=0.88 and as it can be seen in the graphs it seems that the correlation between the data is linear.

4.3.2. Neural Networks AN-BN prediction model

The Artificial Neural Networks (ANN) are an approach to non-linear problems. Its structure is a net of interconnected nodes. Each node is weighted and in the node interconnections a formula is applied. So at the end, we get an output but it's difficult to know what has happened in the net.

Results obtained by ANN are listed in the table 3 and 4.

BN Variation Prediction									
OUT_1	R	Net-R	Avg. Abs.	Max. Abs.	RMS	Accuracy (20%)	Accuracy (10%)	Conf. Interval (95%)	Records
All	0.899	-0.899	0.285	2.026	0.384	0.971	0.827	0.749	1015
Train	0.911	-0.911	0.279	1.076	0.353	0.99	0.806	0.688	500
Test	0.902	-0.902	0.291	1.094	0.370	0.983	0.794	0.721	715
Manual	0.894	-0.892	0.271	2.026	0.416	0.943	0.903	0.814	300

Table 3. Statistics for measuring the predictive ability of the BN model.

AN Variation Prediction									
OUT_1	R	Net-R	Avg. Abs.	Max. Abs.	RMS	Accuracy (20%)	Accuracy (10%)	Conf. Interval (95%)	Records
All	0.716	-0.716	0.240	1.019	0.306	0.870	0.582	0.595	971
Train	0.767	-0.766	0.198	1.019	0.273	0.888	0.756	0.533	410
Test	0.752	-0.752	0.203	1.019	0.280	0.882	0.739	0.545	587
Manual	0.672	-0.672	0.295	0.815	0.341	0.851	0.341	0.666	384

Table 4. Statistics for measuring the predictive ability of the AN model.

The models' predictive ability is measured using the following statistics:

Table 5. Definition of statistics.

R	Also known as Pearson R, it is a measure of the interdependence of two random variables. It ranges from -1.0 and +1.0, indicating perfect negative correlation at -1.0, absence of correlation at 0, and a perfect positive correlation at +1.0..
Net-R	The linear correlation between the target outputs and the raw predicted outputs (before they are transformed into real-world values).
Avg.Abs	The average absolute error between the real world target and the real world predicted outputs.
Max.Abs	Max error.
RMS (Root Mean Square Error)	A measure of network performance during training. It is the average absolute error between the real-world target and predicted output values. $$RMSE = \sqrt{\frac{\sum_1^n (y_i - \hat{y}_i)^2}{n}}$$
Accuracy (%)	The percentage of real-world predicted outputs that are within the specified tolerance of the corresponding real-world target output.
Coef.Interval (%)	This interval establishes the range within which the corresponding predicted output occurs with a specifies degree of confidence.
Records	Number of samples used in train, test and manual mode.

4.3.3. Machine learning algorithms classification

As it can be seen, very good results have not been reached by means of previous methods for AN prediction, so machine learning techniques and algorithms have been applied to try to improve these results.

Machine Learning is the study of computer algorithms that improve automatically through experience [7]. In this task the objective was to build a classification model for the degradation of the oil status. Using a software tool (Weka), an AN status classification model has been carried out by machine learning techniques. For analysing the data we have selected the following machine learning algorithms: Bayesian classifier (NaïveBayes), Lazy classifier (IB1), DecisionTree Classifiers (J48, NBTree) and Rules (JRip) from the Weka software tool. Each algorithm has its advantages and disadvantages and many times there is no way to know which type fits better to the data. So, the best we can do is to take algorithms from the different types of classifiers.

Table 6. Classification algorithms results.

Algorithm	% Correctly classified	% Incorrectly classified
Naive Bayes	46.31	17.18
IB1	59.81	15.63
J48	59.32	13.88
NBTree	57.48	14.08
JRip	61.55	12.33

To validate our tests we have used the 10-fold-cross validation technique. At the same time, an external testing data set has been used for the validation.

It can be seen in the table 5, that the results of the different classifiers are in line with the results obtained with Neural Networks. The reason could be that many samples could belong to a status however the y could be near a status change. Because of this, the values that are considered as incorrectly classified (3rd column) are samples that are classified as status 2 when they really are status 0 [2-0] or samples classified as status 0 when they really are status 0 [0-2]. The percentage of them are exposed in the third column. With mentioned criteria, it can be seen in the table 5 that JRip algorithm results are close to 90%.

5. SUMMARY

It can be observed that the model prediction is very good for BN prediction and not so good for AN prediction. Taking into account previous works in the prediction of the BN parameter [11], an improvement in the results can be seen, above all because results obtained show similar performance (R statistic from 0.90 to 0.92) while a wider coverage of different oil types, samples and spectrometer data sources have been used for the analysis.

With reference to the AN prediction, an improvement of the results is necessary, using another pre-treatment method for example. Another task that it is pending could be the validation of the model with other kinds of lubricating oils. Finally, another step to carry out, also for BN prediction, is the search of good classification ensembles (boosting, bagging), where combined results of statistical and data mining analysis are expected to yield better performance.

These results are encouraging and the near future we expect to substitute the BN and AN analytical method by this FTIR-Chemometric method. This development's advantages, in contract to lab methods, could be: time saving, manual labour reduction, materials reduction, less wastes... Some of them are toxic wastes, so their disposal is quite expensive. A cost table is shown in table 7.

Table 7. Cost comparison.

	Time	Materials	Labour	Wastes	Cost
Lab method	10 min	solvents	Sample and solvent preparation	Acids, chlorinated wastes	80$
New method	<2 min	Null	null	<10gr oil	2$

This step would also open the door to other applications, for instance on line process control using FTIR spectrometers.

ACKNOWLEDGEMENTS

This work was partially funded by the Basque Government (RAMSIS II project).

REFERENCES

[1]   Web page about lubrication and maintenance: http://www.wearcheckiberica.es
[2]   Jay R. Powell. (1999), Practicing Oil Analysis Journal. *FT-IR Analysis in Lubricant Condition Monitoring: New Methodologies and Field Results.*
[3]   Varmuza K. (2000), *Applied Chemometrics: From chemical data to relevant information.* Conference on Chemistry.
[4]   B. Pavoni, N. Rado, Rossano Piazza and S. Frignani. (2004), Annali di Chimica 94, by Societa Chimica Italiana. *FTIR Spectroscopy and Chemometrics as a useful approach for determining Chemical-physical properties of gasoline, by minimizing analytical times and sample handling.*
[5]   Y.P. Du , Y.Z. Liang , J.H. Jiang , R.J. Berry , Y. Ozaki. (2003), Analytica Quimica Acta. *Spectral regions selection to improve prediction ability of PLS models by changeable size moving window partial least squares and searching combination moving window partial least squares.*
[6]   Martens H. & Naes T. (1989). *Multivariate Calibration.* John Wiley & Sons.
[7]   Michael Berthold, David J. Hand. (2003). *Intelligent data analysis.* Springer, second edition.
[8]   Richard G. Brereton. (2003). *Chemmometrics: data analysis for the laboratory and chemical plant.* John Wiley & Sons.
[9]   Paul Geladi and Bruce R. Kowalski. (1986), Analytica Chimica Acta, Volume 185, Pages 1-19. *Partial least-squares regression: a tutorial.*
[10] Aitor Arnaiz, Ana Aranzabe, Jesús Terradillos, Santos Merino and Ibón Aramburu. (2004). COMADEM 2004. pp. 466-475 *"New micro-sensor systems to monitor on-line oil degradation".*
[11] Jesús Terradillos, Ibon Aranburu, Aitor Arnaiz & J.I. Ciria (2005). Base Number prediction through spectroscopy & chemometrics Lubrication Excellence May 2005. USA.

Oil analysis vs Oil based condition monitoring - What to expect and more importantly what to not

D. Shorten

Lloyds Register EMEA

ABSTRACT

Oil Analysis (OA) and Oil Based Condition Monitoring (OBCM) are two very different things, yet as practitioners of failure analysis we are often provided with historical oil test data as a means to add value to our investigations. We find however, that such reports are often meaningless and of no real value to the job in hand. This presentation will seek to stimulate discussion in regard to the significant differences between checking the condition of the oil and using the oil to determine the condition of its parent plant. This is especially relevant where the reported data is being used as part of an operational activity such as insurance cost management or annual survey deferral.

The author, who has a direct understanding of the provision of both "oil analysis" and "oil based condition monitoring", will illustrate the common misconceptions and the pitfalls that can be encountered by users of oil analysis techniques and in addition he will seek to stimulate discussion regarding the best way for this industry to move forward in order to realise the initial promises of delivering savings in terms of increased safety due to improved asset reliability and a reduction in the actual number of component failures experienced.

Keywords: Oil analysis, Condition Monitoring, Reliability, Training

1. INTRODUCTION

In the 1980's the rapid emergence of information technology heralded an opportunity for the economic collection of oil analysis test data in such a way that could be compiled into test reports detailing used oil condition. This then became both an added value option for oil companies who wished to secure new business and also an independent chargeable service supplied to industry by specialist service providers.

Prior to this, the analysis of lubricants was very much a hands on activity and bound in what is often referred to as "wet chemistry". More importantly, analysis based upon "wet chemistry" would often be labour intensive and as such routine analysis was the preserve of customer service, research & development and failure investigation.

The move towards routine oil analysis, when carried out on behalf of protecting reliability, became known colloquially as OBCM. The aim of this paper is to demonstrate that OA and OBCM are two very different activities within the maintenance management and should not be confused and that there can be significant danger of making such an assumption which will ultimately lead to unplanned machinery downtime.

2. DEVELOPMENT OF OIL ANALYSIS TESTING

The test suites that made up early reports were ultimately based upon the types of quality assurance tests that were already a part of lubricating oil production standards and research and development procedures. That is, kinematic viscosity and additive chemistry via automatic viscometers and ICP(Inductively Coupled Plasma) Spectroscopy respectively.

By the addition of tests for acidity, base, insolubles, water content and flashpoint, a much more comprehensive report could be generated which enabled interpretation for indications of not only the condition status of the lubricant by comparison with new oil data, but also the operational condition of the plant from which the sample had been taken.

Contaminants such as water, air-borne debris, particulates of burnt/un-burnt fuel etc. could indicate evidence of poor sealing; inefficient engine performance; condensation; leakage; etc. in addition to indications of oil degradation via oxidation and additive depletion. Evidence of these indications would then be used to initiate work instructions for maintainers to incorporate into planned maintenance schedules.

The activities described here can all be achieved by basic analysis of the used oil and comparison with the new.

3. TYPICAL ASSUMPTIONS OF OIL TESTING AND ANALYSIS.

3.1. Data variance

One of the most frequent assumptions made when reviewing a completed oil analysis report is that the results are absolute. For example a reviewer believes that there is a real difference between two systems which have the same component and sub-assembly, oil, operational experience and duty, yet have not produced identical results. Ignoring the potential for sampling errors, differences in recorded data may have occurred as a result of;

1. Test methods repeatability and reproducibility factors,

2. Quality Assurance procedures, where some laboratories are be better at spotting and rectifying errors,

3. Differences in calibration standards

4. Staffing issues etc.

3.2. Method Scope

Data variance tends to apply mainly when comparing results from test to test and from different laboratories, however there are other assumptions based upon the expectation of the test itself, especially in relation to the significance of change and scale. For example, it is widely known that the predominant test used by most oil analysis houses to identify metal elements within a sample is by Plasma Emission Spectroscopy (PES) using a device called an Inductively Coupled Plasma (ICP) spectrophotometer. It is also widely recognized that the ability of this device to measure the amount of any metal within the sample is severely limited by the size and mass of the particle. So most metal debris in excess of 5µm may not be fully atomised within the plasma leading to inaccurate results. However, the casual reviewer will assume that the results are absolute and that all metal mass has been considered. This is also part of the reason why manufacturers are reluctant to provide limits of acceptability for any given asset and where they do they are very keen to state that the limits are for guidance only.

3.3. Trending for failure indications

The use of oil analysis in oil based condition monitoring is completely reliant upon the appropriate trending of those key variables which indicate changes which contribute significantly to the risk of machinery malfunction.

Issues indicated by variables such as water content and base number are normally allocated guidance limits based upon experiences of risk and are either expressed as a fixed numerical value or as a percentage change from new. However, the use of trending is becoming more prevalent within the field of oil analysis as a primary trigger for maintenance activities, especially where component wear debris is being monitored.

There are many tools available to the engineer for setting alarms based upon trends however; a simple multiple of standard deviation would appear to be a good start point when developing a CM system. Furthermore, if these limits are updated in real time, then the alarm system becomes automatically more sensitive to changes which are unusual and clearly require further investigation.

Accurate failure prediction is the ultimate goal of condition monitoring. By selecting variables which give indications of known failure modes, we hope to be able to witness a trigger point which can then be used to start a series of risk mitigation activities before returning to low risk equilibrium again and maintaining operation. This cycle could be as simple as a temperature control loop, through to the planned outage of a complete asset or production facility. It is the false indications that we hope to manage out and the selection of the most appropriate failure indicator monitor, which is the key to achieving this.

For example, it is of little use using oil analysis on a system that is known to fail due to excessive abrasive airborne contamination, when an inexpensive differential pressure device fitted to a filter may be more effective. Furthermore, an even more effective solution in this instance may be to install or improve air filtration and fit filter breathers, thus removing the potential for excessive abrasive presence, an RCM approach to maintenance.

4. OIL BASED CONDITION MONITORING

4.1. Data requirements

For oil based condition monitoring to be effective there must be a must greater depth of information made available to the service provider, whether these are internal or external. This information could include;

- OEM recommendations, new oil specification, used oil condemning limits,
- Rate of top up of oil, sump volume, filtration method,
- Oil/Machinery duty: Continuous, stop-start, periodic, well within/at limit,
- Metallurgy: Interacting components, alloys, normal wear limit specifications,
- Non interacting components: coatings, structures,
- System data: temperature, pressure etc, information from other condition monitoring techniques results form other techniques, e.g. fusion analysis

Most oil analysis providers will not have the facility to accommodate this additional information within their reporting and laboratory information management systems. One way around this is to invite the oil analysis provider to sit within the condition monitoring team and be privy to all relevant information.

4.2. People requirements

The people requirements cannot be underestimated here as without complete co-operation by all parties the benefits which are sought may not be found. It is of greatest importance that the "company" sees this approach as a functional part of its management strategy. Some elements of this are;

- Condition based maintenance requires commitment at all levels and should be a clearly defined management strategy for the company to achieve greater profitability..
- The benefits of condition based strategy should be clearly understood and supported at board level as well as on the factory floor or at the asset.
- One needs a global "buy-in" and not just a local "enthusiast", as this requires a long term approach
- It is a holistic approach and as such should not rely upon active individuals but a global ownership within an established company infrastructure

- In order to measure the fiscal benefit of condition based strategies, costs/investments should be recorded within a separate budget from other maintenance activities and then compared in the light of previous costs and the profits that these new investments have delivered– profit related not cost.

- Pre and post cost analysis needs to be carried out – to develop clear financial benefits against which to be measured going forward. It is only by using the universal language of profit and loss that such potentially radical shifts in underlying cultures can be changed.

- The processes must be regularly reviewed and ongoing performance analysed and distributed in plain concise language to everyone.

- As with any management of change, positive and negative feedback is actively encouraged to ensure that the change is inclusive and the individual has a voice.

Condition based maintenance and various analysis techniques often appear to fail because any benefits are not properly identified and attributed appropriately to condition based strategies.

For illustrative purposes we can consider the plant manager saying to the maintenance manager, "Why do we spend this much on condition monitoring when we have so few failures?" The following simple diagram (Figure 1) shows the cyclic expenditure of this fictitious maintenance department on condition based activities shown against the resultant reliability of plant and the effect that budgetary changes would have as the strategy moves between a "condition" based approach and a "reactive" approach.

The second diagram (Figure 2), illustrates the ideal path of cost and reliability. The unknown will be the point at which cost and benefit diverge positively and the acceptable differential between both lines, following the achievement of equilibrium.

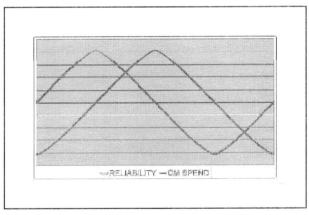

Figure 1.Where CM is poorly applied, reliability increases and falls with CM spend

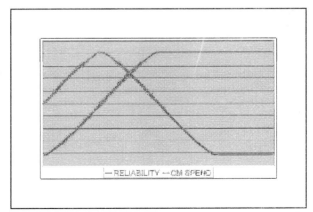

Figure 2. Well managed CM systems incur an initial increase in cost followed by a reduction over time whist reliability is maintained.

5. DEVELOPMENT OF MAINTENANCE MANAGEMENT STRATEGIES

As other monitoring techniques became more compact and affordable, strategies incorporating a fusion of these techniques came into being. This has resulted in the move from a predominantly planned maintenance regime to a condition based maintenance regime. Health monitoring has subsequently become a very broad basis of engineering development, utilising inputs from many sources such as vibration, thermography, process variables, human sensory recordings and also oil analysis data. However, the provision of these activities remains fragmented, with the oil analysis provider being very much an external feature of the maintenance strategy.

5.1. Which model to use?

It is at this point that the asset manager must decide where they will place the responsibility for analysis. For example the system could be based upon a third party management contract where responsibility for CM is placed outside of the organisation. The benefits of this may be that the contract holder can be given clear performance targets and audited on a regular basis, within clear financial constraints. The contractor may find however, difficulty in negotiating downtime for maintenance with the production or engineering manager, so may have to perform a more significant level of analysis to allow him to produce clear reasoning in support of such requests.

Another model could be that the asset manager holds the technical skills within the organisation and simply uses contractors to collect data, via meter readings and oil sampling/testing. This will result in a much lower initial cost for the data creation, but a higher cost in having the necessary interpretational and engineering decision makers on the payroll. Machinery access will be less problematic if the CM manager has sufficient presence within the management team and the costs of the CM system management will shared.

What appears to be evident is that there is a combination of these models in place in most companies whilst it is assumed to be one or the other. The result is that the negative aspects of each model could be compounded.

6. MAINTENENANCE MANAGEMENT AND STRATEGY

6.1. Training

Modern maintenance professionals have become extremely specialised and as such it is essential to ensure that the personnel involved with condition monitoring activities are accredited at the appropriate level. The ISO standard ISO18436 Condition monitoring and diagnostics of machines -- Requirements for training and certification of personnel – details the credentials for this. There are also a number of supplements within this standard which cover vibration, thermography, acoustic emission and lubricant management. It is highly likely that companies within the CM arena will be expected to offer services provided under this standard. Similarly, staff operating within organisations receiving CM reports could also be expected to meet these criteria, dependant upon the operational context of the relationship between the service supplier and the company.

6.2. External involvement

Specialists in CM should be actively encouraged to participate in external seminars and discussion groups to actively share successes and to reduce the incidence of repeated mistakes. Furthermore it is proposed that active participation in engineering institutions such as IMechE, IoP, BINDT, IMAREST etc to promote further the sharing of information should be considered to be an expected part of CM development.

7. CONCLUSIONS

- Oil analysis (OA) and Oil Based Condition Monitoring (OBCM) are two separate activities.

- Just having a contract with an oil testing company does not mean that you are using oil based condition monitoring.

- It is very important to select the correct failure indicating variables and effective monitors.

- A complete database of the operational and mechanical make-up of each oil filled system must be compiled and updated on a regular basis or the contractor given access to it.

- There must be sufficient trend data for OBCM to be used as an effective planning tool.

- Alarms must be carefully considered and action following alarms input to prevent false alarms in future and increase understanding of normal operational performance.

- People are at the core of these activities where responsibilities must be clear and fully supported by management at all levels.

- Assumptions of service delivery from contractors can lead to gaps in the provision of asset care and are usually a precursor for poor asset management.

- CM, including OBCM, if undertaken should reflect a companywide approach to asset management, the benefits of which should be clearly communicated as part of the company performance statistics.

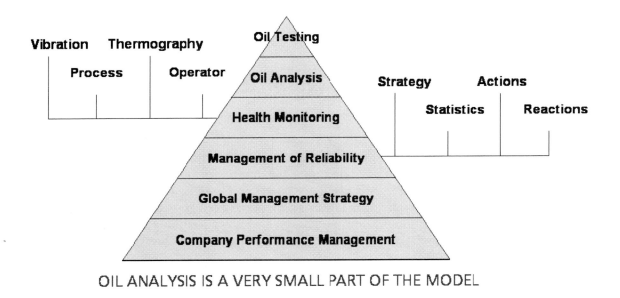

Figure 3. Relevant positions oil analysis and other various condition monitoring tools within a company structure.

REFERENCES

[1] Moubray, J. (1997) "Reliability Centered Maintenance". Pub. Elsevier ISBN 1-7506-3358-1
[2] Toms, Larry A. (1998) "Machinery Oil Analysis". Pub. Coastal Skills Training. ISBN 0-9664604-0-5
[3] ISO18436 Part 4 (2005) (Under validation.) "Condition monitoring and diagnostics of machines – Requirements for training and certification of personnel".

Use of sensor technology for Oil Condition Monitoring

I. Lamont, T. Kent, A. Baldwin

Kittiwake Developments Ltd, Littlehampton BN17 7LU, UK

ABSTRACT

A range of on-line labour saving condition monitoring sensors have been designed, tested and placed in real world situations. These sensors detect parameters such as metallic wear debris, emulsified and dissolved water, viscosity and oil condition.

This paper will show how well the sensors have performed out in the field, and prove that from this data, real time assessments of machinery condition can be made. Tests carried out on FZG rigs have shown for the first time the rate at which wear debris is produced as load stages increase, as well as the profile of wear during each load stage. Also both oil and machinery condition data has been collected from slow/medium speed diesel engines and wind turbine gearboxes. This shows how oil change intervals can be extended and maintenance can be scheduled in advance.

1. INTRODUCTION

Laboratory based oil analysis programs are currently the accepted method for assuring oil and machinery condition, often with additional expert interpretation from the lubricant supplier. Many applications also use local on-site analysis facilities where time is critical or the logistics of sending a sample to a remote laboratory are difficult. Typical examples would be naval and merchant marine diesel engine installations, wind turbines or mine operations.

The market for off-line lubricant analysis equipment is well served but coming under pressure especially from a requirement to reduce manpower or to continually monitor critical systems. A typical example would be the US Military who need a 70% reduction in manpower for the next generation of front line ships [1]. There is a need to develop reliable and relatively low cost on-line instrumentation capable of replicating a laboratory analysis providing information on both lubricant and machinery condition.

A 5 year research programme was undertaken to investigate the practicality of a number of techniques for monitoring machinery and oil condition, realised as on-line devices. Techniques included magnetometry, cyclic voltammetry, impedance spectroscopy, (Q) capacitive/resistive and microwave. Discussions of each method can be found in a previous paper [2].

Previous research has shown that it is possible to develop on-line instrumentation that does replicate laboratory techniques [3] but these types of systems again have cost and complexity considerations that severely limit their application.

A more practical solution, discussed in this paper, is a system that provides Monitoring of Machinery Condition by measuring both ferrous and non-ferrous metallic contamination, uniquely at the low levels routinely reported in a laboratory analysis. Augmenting this is a system that Monitors Lubricant Condition by sensors for Oil Condition and Moisture Level. Oil Condition sensing allows monitoring of the lubricant charge, resulting in much less frequent interventional off-line testing. Moisture sensing provides detection of absorbed & potential free water in the oil and hence prevents corrosion and lubrication failure due to water contamination. (see Figure 1)

Ferrous Debris	<0.5 micron	Measured as bulk
	60 - 200 micron	Individually counted
Non-Ferrous Debris	60-200 micron	Individually counted
Oil Condition, sensitive to:	BN , depletion; Insolubles (soot); AN; Glycol ; Free water	
Water in Oil	0-100% RH - marine systems contamination more likely	

Figure 1. Oil Parameters Investigated

2. MONITORING MACHINERY CONDITION

A body of experience currently exists for the accurate and non-interventional determination of ferrous contamination [4]. More recently, this has been developed specifically for use in the field by shielding the significant effects of movement and the proximity of rotating machinery.

2.1. Magnetometry for Ferrous and Non-Ferrous Debris

There are several methods for detecting ferrous debris in oil. These utilise similar principles of magnetometry [5] [6]. The most promising approach is to arrange for the oil to flow through an enclosed magnetic field. This technique has been previously utilised for metal in food applications, or as "chip" particle detectors for gross mechanical failure.

Two approaches are investigated here. The measurement of Total Ferrous Debris from sub micron to large particles; and a "chip" particle detector to, count, size and classify ferrous and non-ferrous metallic particles. The sensors investigated here include a novel shielding system and exploit two fundamental physical effects: The change of inductance due to the presence of a magnetic material; The change of energy losses due to electromagnetic induction in any conductive material. A full explanation of technologies can be found in previous papers [2]

2.2. Total Ferrous Debris

Figure 2. Piston Total Ferrous Debris Sensor

The Total Ferrous Debris Sensor detects the total amount of ferrous debris in the oil independently of the particle size. It reports ferrous debris as total ppm iron by weight. The total ferrous debris detector is designed in 2 versions, using either a mechanical (piston) or air driven mechanism to clear the oil chamber and provide a zero reference. In this investigation a Piston Total Ferrous Debris Sensor is used to monitor the onset of failure (see Figure 2).

It can be difficult to obtain real world wear debris data from an application that has failed in the field. There are, however, specialist test rigs whose design is such that mechanical test parts can be tested to destruction. One such device is an FZG machine developed by the Technical Institute in Munich. This method allows testing of oils to determine their ability to protect gears from wear but can also be used for the study of wear in gears and drive mechanisms. The results are recognised as an industry standard and test data can usually be found on gear oil datasheets.

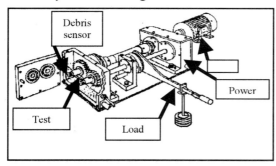

Figure 3. Schematic of FZG machine

Figure 4. Debris Sensor attached to gear chamber

The FZG rig (Figure 3) consists of two shafts with a pair of gears at each end. A weighted lever applies an adjustable amount of torque to the gears which is fixed for each load stage. The standard test consists of filling the chamber containing the wheel and pinion, with the trial oil to a set level. This chamber is then closed and an ever-increasing amount of torque is applied to the gears until they visibly fail. There are 12 load stages which each have the same number of shaft revolutions and last approximately 15 minutes. To obtain an oil sample from the test gear chamber a drain hole was opened and sensor was attached (see Figure 4).

The tests were carried out at an independent test house – (QinetiQ) over 2 days.

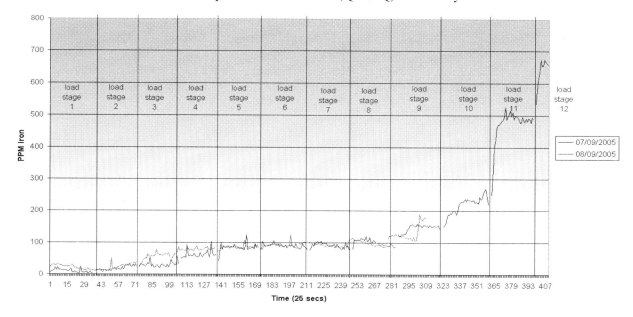

Figure 5. FZG Rig Day 1 and 2 Results Combined

During load stage 8 wear was only generated at the onset and then it stayed constant or even reduced for the rest of the load stage. Throughout At load stage 10 more severe damage occurs. These differing profiles appear to show running-in / bedding-in and failure damage (see Figure 6).

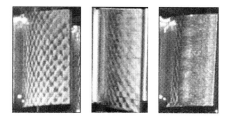

Figure 6. Pictures of New, Scratched and Worn Teeth (left to right respectively)

On Day2 the test was stopped at load stage 9 when damage had occurred to the pinion but not the wheel.

Weight of test gears: New pinion 726.798g; Used pinion = 726.761g; Difference = 0.037g

The two result curves for Day 1 and 2 correlate very accurately (see Figure 5).

We can conclude that the total ferrous debris sensor can detect failure even at low levels and at a point well before the damage becomes catastrophic. It is sensitive down to 10ppm of ferrous debris providing a large amount of information for a loss of less then 0.04g of gear material.

2.3.   Particle Content

Figure 7. Picture of Particle sensor

The Particle Content Sensor will detect individual metallic ferrous and non-ferrous wear debris particles in the lubricant flow and determine their size and quantity. This is different to the Total Ferrous Sensor which detects the sum of all size ferrous particles (i.e. submicron iron and larger). This sensor is suitable for any application where metal surfaces shed debris which is then taken away by the lubricant flow. The sensor is positioned up stream before any filters. Good examples of applications are bearings and gearboxes.

Tests were conducted at the Jost Institute for Tribotechnology which is based in the University of Central Lancashire, Preston, UK. The bearing test facility was used and Comparative Wear Debris Analysis was carried out using photomicroscopy [7] with debris being prepared on transparent filters.

The apparatus used for the testing is a bearing standard stand originally designed for determining the L10 life of 7305 and 6305 bearings (shown in Figure 8). The rig has been fitted with a magnetic debris extraction to study the particulate material shred throughout the test duration.

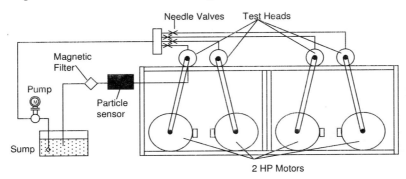

Figure 8. Bearing Test Stand

The bearing test stand was fitted with an up-rated lubricant system. The test bearing (7305 BE 2RS) 62mm diameter single row angular contact bearing, was subjected to an axial load of approximately 2 tonnes at a speed of 1500 rpm. The test oil was SAE10 automotive oil. In order to reduce the time to failure, various faults were seeded onto the inner race of the bearing closest to the lubrication outlet.

2.4.   Spark eroded bearing

The inner race was damaged by spark erosion to propagate the failure. The bearing failed by a scar in typical rolling pitting fatigue mode. The bearing operated normally (very little vibration) for the entire test, but upon inspection the inner race showed classic spalling over an area of 7 mm^2.(see Figure 9)

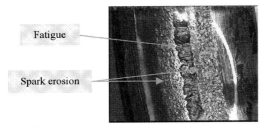

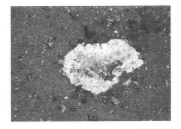

Figure 9. Spalling wear   Figure 10. Cracked & pitted debris   Figure 11. Debris with striations

Figures 10 & 11 show photo-microscopic detail of 250µm chord, 25µm thick particles collected from the magnetic filter at the end of the test. Figure 9 shows fatigue generated by spalling wear.

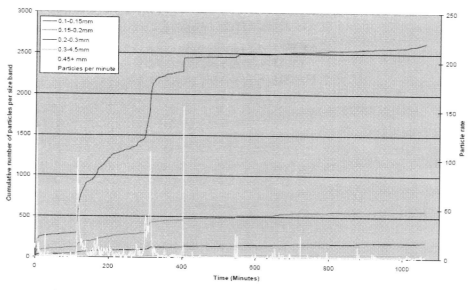

Figure 12. Bearing Data Graph showing spalling wear starting at 120 seconds

2.5. Diamond indented bearing

For this test an inner race was damaged using a diamond indenter to propagate failure. The bearing failed through rolling pitting fatigue. A small fatigue scar can be seen close to one of the indentations (see Figure 13).

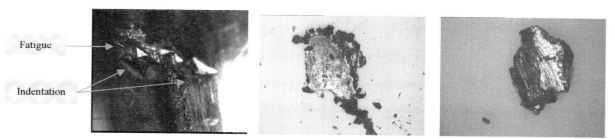

Figure 13. Fatigue wear   Figure 14. 450µm large particle   Figure 15. Chunky particle with striations

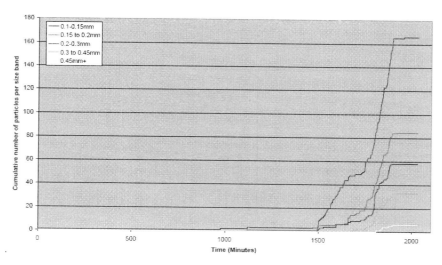

Figure 16. Test 3 bearing data graph

Figure 14 (450µm chord) and Figure 15 (200 µm chord) show photo-microscopic details of particles collected from the magnetic filter at the end of the test.

The first metallic particles appeared approximately 1500 minutes into the test and continued at a low level for 400 minutes. The sensor picked up the failure which was later confirmed through inspection of the inner race. From the data shown in Figure 16 it can be inferred that the fatigue occurred after 950 minutes and again after 1100 minutes. This is the same pattern of debris emission shown in the previous test

Both tests fail in a classical fatigue mode exhibiting spalling on the inner race close to an artificial stress raiser (a region of spark erosion in the former and close to an indentation in the latter test). In each case the particle detector has captured data relating to cyclic fatigue debris .The sensor detects particle platelets of 250 µm chord length. These particles are approximately 20 – 50 µm in thickness.

A more sensitive sensor has since been produced which can detect smaller particles It will also have the ability to give an indication of material type.

3. MONITORING LUBRICANT CONDITION

Current experience shows that changes in the condition of the lubricant are often a precursor to lubricant degradation and subsequent machinery failure. Monitoring optimum lubricant performance is explored here using an Oil Condition Sensor. Additionally detection of water contamination of oil is investigated using a Moisture Sensor.

3.1. Oil Condition

Figure 17. Oil Quality Sensor

The Oil Quality Sensor provides a measurement of how quickly the oil is degrading indicating when off-line or laboratory based analysis is required. The sensor uses Patented Technology [8] which is a subset of impedance spectroscopy called Tan Delta. See paper for a full explanation [2].

A test was carried out using the oil condition sensor and an industrial gearbox (11kW at 288rpm). After achieving a stable temperature, 1% water was added and results captured (Figure 19).

Figure 18. Gearbox Installation

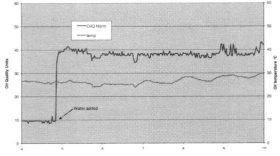

Figure 19. Step change due to water addition

Another test with was carried out using a polyalphaolefin (PAO) synthetic oil at 50°C to simulate a wind turbine gearbox. Sample was oxidised and water contaminated (0.5%) replicate a failure conditions. Successive measurements were taken using an oil condition sensor without turning the sensor off. The sensor head was purged between tests with dried and filtered (0.2μm) compressed air.

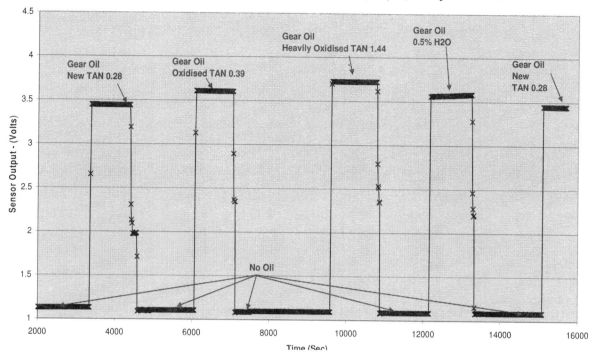

Figure 20. Oxidisation Graph

It can be seen from Figure 20 that the readings increase as the oxidation levels increase. Also there is an easily measurable change for the 0.5% water sample. A fresh sample of oil showed zero hysteresis.

3.2.   Moisture

Figure 21. Moisture sensor

The sensor detects the moisture [water] content of oil up to saturation point - volume of water oil will dissolve before the oil becomes saturated. The sensor expresses this moisture content as % relative humidity (RH) – 100% is saturation. Free, absorbed or emulsified water can damage lubricant and machinery. The sensor only allows water molecules to penetrate its polymer coating, it then tests the dielectric properties inside the polymer to determine the proportion of water molecules, and hence %RH

3.2.1.   Verifying sensor performance using salt solutions

The generally accepted principle is based on the fact that a saturated salt solution generates a certain relative humidity in the air above it. The sensor output can then be verified accordingly. Salt solution testing demonstrated close correlation between text book and measured %RH values.

3.2.2.   Verifying sensor performance when measuring water dissolved in oil

Sample oil was taken and a range of water levels were mixed in using a high shear mixer. This allowed a series of tests to be taken at different percentages of saturation. The results can be seen in Figure 22

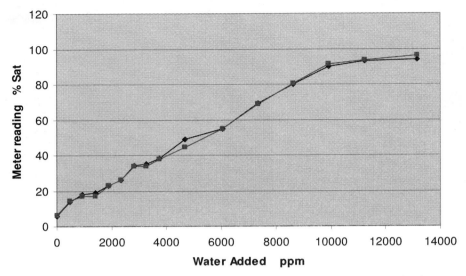

Figure 22. Comparison of Kittiwake & Other sensor at different moisture levels

4. CONCLUSION

Testing the sensors in real installations and simulated applications has been a way to not only prove the sensors work, but prove that the philosophy of continually monitoring certain oil parameters can be used to predict failure.

Machinery Condition Monitoring:

The Total Ferrous Debris Sensor detects metallic wear debris down to sub-micron levels repeatably. The data shows that it is possible to detect low levels of wear, down to the levels generated by the bedding in of new gear surfaces. It has been tested in the field under severe operating conditions.

Additionally it is possible to use a Particle Content Sensor to predict the onset of machinery failure by providing detailed analysis of particle evolution from a bearing surface. The ability to detect particle sizes is clearly demonstrated and this can be used to provide very early detection of failure, well before any vibration is evident. Future work will use this technology to identify non-ferrous metallic wear debris particles.

Oil Condition monitoring:

The oil quality monitor indicates that a change has happened and quantifies that change so as to instigate an off-line test only as and when necessary. It does not replicate individual laboratory tests. It works independently of oil type and temperature and is not biased by any particular type of oil contamination.

The moisture sensor detects increased levels of dissolved water in the oil, to enable prediction of absorbed and free water, hence allowing preventative action to be taken before water related damage occurs. The response to increasing water levels in oil has been clearly demonstrated.

The final configuration consists of prototype systems capable of identifying the following parameters:

- Oil condition
- Water in oil
- Ferrous debris
- Non-Ferrous debris

The sensors have been used individually in a range of applications but have also been supplied as a multi-sensor plug and play box for wind turbines and mining equipment (see Figures 23 & 24).

Figure 23. Online Sensor Suite

Figure 24. Suite fitted to Wind Turbine

5. NOMENCLATURE

PM   Planned Maintenance

RCM   Reliability Centred Maintenance

FZG   Forschungsstelle für Zahnräder und Getriebebau (Department of Research for Gears & Gearboxes)

REFERENCES

[1]   Internal conversation with Naval Sea Systems Command, Alexandria VA
[2]   C. Leigh Jones, Thomas Kent. CIMAC Paper "Development of a range of On-Line Lubricant and machinery condition sensors for Engine Monitoring" no:224 2004
[3]   Real Time Oil/Fluid Analysis System under development at Pacific Northwest National Laboratory operated by Battelle for the U.S. Department of Energy
[4]   Press release "ExxonMobil introduces Oil Analysis Program" p34 Diesel and Gas Turbine Worlwide, 11/2003
[5]   D.A.Parker 'A High Resolution Magnetometer' UK Patent No W08902083, Filed 24/08/1987
[6]   M.J.Hutchings 'Electromagnetic detector for measuring magnetic or conductive properties' US Patent No. US6051970, Filed 27/3/1998
[7]   Sperring TP, Roylance BJ, Nowell T, and Hodges D, 'From research to application – The development of the wear debris classification system SYCLOPS', International Conference on Condition Monitoring, Oxford, UK, 2001, pp 363 – 373.
[8]   Christopher John Collister 'Electrical measurement of Oil Quality' US Patent 6,459,995 B1 [1st October 1992] and UK Patent 2,306,660 A [7th May 1997]

Combining On-Site and On-Line Voltammetric Analyses to Improve Military and Industrial Oil Condition Monitoring Programs

R. E. Kauffman [1], J. Ameye [2]

[1] UDRI, 300 College Park, Dayton, OH 45404, USA, Kauffman@udri.udayton.edu
[2] FLUITEC International, Nieuwbrugstraat 73 B-1830 Machelen Belgium, j.ameye@fluitec.com

ABSTRACT

Combining on-site and on-line voltammetric analytical techniques will improve the capabilities of established oil condition monitoring programs to differentiate and monitor the different degradation mechanisms of lubricating oils used in a wide variety of applications. The additional knowledge obtained from the voltammetric techniques can be used to determine the correct maintenance actions to optimize equipment performance and reliability while minimizing downtime and costs. This paper presents on-line and on-site voltammetric results for seeded fault tests using aircraft and diesel engine stands as well as for normally and abnormally operating military aircraft engines and industrial equipment. The combination of on-site (RULER©) and on-line voltammetric results were able to detect and distinguish between oxidative, thermal, hydrolytic and contamination degradation mechanisms at much earlier stages than off-site, traditional oil condition monitoring tests (acid number, viscosity, color, etc.) preventing additional component damage and potential equipment failure.

Keywords: Additives, Lubricant Testing, Antioxidants, Dielectric, Voltammetry, RULER, Oxidation, Coolant Leak, On-line Sensors, Acid Number, Oil Condition Monitoring (OCM).

1. INTRODUCTION

The on-line voltammetric oil condition monitoring (OCM) sensors used in this study are based on voltammetric measurement techniques and have been previously described in detail [1,2]. The electronics of the OCM apply a 0.1 – 50 Hz waveform to the wire sensor of the OCM in contact with the heated oil, liquid or vapor, causing a current to flow (below 10 nanoamps). The current flow is converted into a voltage and recorded/displayed by a data acquisition system as well as being displayed on the face of the OCM as a series of lights. As the antioxidants deplete in the circulating oil, the oil degradation rate accelerates and the current flow between the sensor wires/voltage output of the OCM increases.

All of the previously reported research with the voltammetric based OCM sensors has been performed on used engine oils heated in vials in the laboratory to simulate on-line testing of engine reservoirs and liquid lines. The laboratory research [2,3] demonstrated that the OCM sensors had the potential to detect oils undergoing long-term oxidation due to antioxidant depletion as well as oils undergoing rapid degradation due to hot spots/oil fires. Antioxidant analyses with an off-line, portable voltammetric instrument (RULER©) were needed to distinguish between the two types of oil degradation, i.e., OCM reading increases with antioxidant depletion (oxidation) versus OCM reading increases without antioxidant depletion (hotspot/oil fire). In the case of biodegradable ester based oils being used in lower temperature applications such as forestry equipment, acid number measurements and voltammetric antioxidant measurements were used to distinguish between used oils undergoing hydrolysis versus oxidation, i.e., acid number increases with antioxidant depletion (oxidation) versus acid number increases without antioxidant depletion (hydrolysis).

Although RULER© antioxidant analyses were needed in the laboratory to identify the different degradation mechanisms, it was theorized that on-line OCM sensors could differentiate between the degradation mechanisms by the timing, size and rate of changes in the OCM readings. In the case of aircraft engine oils, the long-term oxidation would cause a slow, steady rise in the OCM readings over several flights followed by an accelerated rise as the oxidation accelerated due to loss of antioxidants, e.g., oxidation due to cracked seals experienced by military helicopters and aircraft [2-4]. Degradation due to hot spots/oil fires would cause a rapid, large increase in the OCM readings during a single flight, e.g., "black oil" problem of F-16 aircraft [2]. In diesel engines suffering coolant leaks or aircraft engine oils contaminated with corrosive ground fluids (motor oil, phosphate ester hydraulic fluid and ethylene glycol antifreeze), the OCM readings would increase between uses/flights.

This paper describes the test results for OCM sensors developed for the Joint Strike Fighter engine and for the diesel engine used in ground transportation vehicles, specifically the high mobility, multi-purpose wheeled vehicles (HMMWV). The development and optimization of the on-line voltammetric OCM sensors for evaluation on the engine test stands were performed in two main phases. In the first phase, the on-line OCM sensors were optimized in the laboratory for use in both liquid (reservoir and return lines) and vapor (breather tube, bearings and scavenge line) lubricant environments. The sensors' capabilities to detect oil oxidation, oil fires and oil contamination by other fluids were tested. In the second phase, the optimized OCM sensors were incorporated into the various liquid and vapor lubricant environments of the JSF and HMMWV engine test stands. The OCM sensors were used to monitor the oil as seeded faults were introduced into the engines in an attempt to cause known engine and lubricant failure modes. The OCM test results from the laboratory and engine tests are described and discussed in full detail in the following paper.

2. EXPERIMENTAL

2.1. On-Site Laboratory Analytical Instruments

Introduction. In order to monitor the condition changes of the in-service oils during the different engine test stand evaluations, the used oil samples removed from the engine test stand were fully characterized with a wide range of analytical instruments. To determine if the JSF accelerated oxidation engine test should be ended, the viscosity, acid number and COBRA instrument (related to the conductivity of the analyzed oils [5]) measurements were used. To determine when the diesel engine test evaluations should be ended, i.e., oil had been sufficiently degraded or contaminated to begin causing engine damage, the Fourier Transform Infrared (FTIR) spectrophotometric results were compared to the US Army condemnation values (ACV) used to identify field engines requiring oil changes or other maintenance actions. All of the other laboratory analytical results used for the diesel engine test stand evaluations are listed in Reference 6.

Fourier Transform Infrared (FTIR) Spectrophotometer. The FTIR technique was used to evaluate compositional changes and contaminant levels of the used oils. The FTIR was used to monitor the soot (ACV > 50), oxidation (ACV > 18), water contamination (ACV > 65), ethylene glycol contamination (ACV > 3) and diesel fuel dilution (ACV > 255) of the used oils.

Acid Number (AN) Measurements. The AN measurements were performed as described in ASTM D644. The JSF engine test was stopped when the AN reached 0.15 (mg KOH/gram of oil) and the HMMWV engine test was condemned when the AN for the used oil was double that of the new oil.

RULER Antioxidant Measurements. The RULER© instrument (Fluitec International, Dayton, OH) analyses were used to monitor the secondary aromatic amine antioxidants in the JSF ester oils and the zinc dialkyldithiophosphate (ZDDP) additive in the HMMWV hydrocarbon oils. The antioxidant/additive concentrations were reported in percent remaining useful life (%RUL) with respect to their original concentrations in the fresh oil using the following formula:

$$\%RUL = (\text{Used oil RULER© reading/ New oil RULER© reading}) \times 100\%$$

2.2.   On-Board Suite of Oil Condition Sensors

Introduction. Based on the first year of research [3] with used diesel oil samples removed from normally and abnormally operating HMMWV diesel engines, the following on-board sensors were incorporated into a steel tube used to by-pass the oil radiator hose of the diesel engine test stand. The suite of sensors was tested simultaneously as the circulating oil of the diesel engine test stand was diverted from the oil radiator hose into the steel tube containing the sensors. The locations of the on-board sensors built into the steel tube are shown in Figure 1. In the case of the JSF engine test, only the voltammetric OCM sensors were used due to the temperature limitations of the other sensors in Figure 1. The four on-line voltammetric sensors used for the JSF engine test stand were installed at three engine locations: supply line to a bearing compartment (2 sensors), bearing compartment and breather tube.

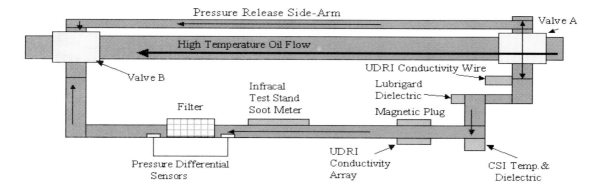

Figure 1. Sensor suite and side-arms used during diesel engine test stand evaluations.

Dielectric Sensors. The dielectric constant (temperature compensated) and temperature of the circulating oil of the engine test stand were measured directly in-line with the CSI Oil View Model 5500 Combined Temperature Sensor (CSI, Emerson Process Management, Knoxville, TN) as shown in Figure 1. When the display button was pushed, the dielectric constant and temperature readings were displayed. The Tan delta component of the dielectric constant of the circulating oil was measured with the Lubrigard sensor (Lubrigard Limited, Dorset, UK). The Lubrigard results were outputted continuously to a digital display.

Magnetic Wear Debris Plug. In an attempt to isolate magnetic wear debris from the circulating oil of the engine test stand, a magnetic plug (Super Plug, Houston, TX) was located directly in-line as shown in Figure 1. A different magnetic plug was used for each engine test stand evaluation. Each magnetic plug was removed at the end of engine test stand evaluation and submitted for particle size distribution and compositional analyses by a scanning electron microscope/energy dispersive spectrometer combination.

UDRI Voltammetric Array and Wire Sensors. The low frequency conductivity of the circulating oil of the engine test stand was measured in-line with the UDRI array and wire voltammetric sensors [1-4]. The array sensor consisted of nickel lines in an interdigitated pattern on a polyimide film. . The nickel line widths and spacings were 120 micron and the polyimide film had the dimensions of 25 mm x 5 mm x 1 mm. The wire sensor consisted of two, parallel nickel wires (25 mm in length and 2 mm in diameter) spaced 3mm apart. A 10-hertz square wave (± 3V) was applied to both sensors and the sensors' outputs (V) were read at 10-second intervals by a computer as previously described [2].

2.3. Engine Test Stand Evaluations

Introduction. The details of the engine test stand evaluations are given in References 6-8. For the JSF test engine test stand, the engine was put through simulated flights – take-off, cruise, full-throttle, cruise, and land. After each landing, an oil sample was obtained for antioxidant and oil condition analyses and comparison to the voltammetric OCM measurements made during the simulated flights in the temperature range of 100°C - 232°C (212°F - 450°F). For the HMMWV diesel engine test stand, the accelerated oxidation and coolant leak tests are described herein. The HMMWV engine test stand was operated for seven to eight hours each day during each seeded fault test. Once per day, the oil temperature was cooled to approximately 70°C (158°F) due to the stated temperature limits of the commercial sensors. Once the readings of the sensors stabilized (approximately 10 minutes), the readings of the different sensors were recorded and an oil sample (4 oz.) was obtained for antioxidant and laboratory analyses to establish the oil condition of the oil flowing through the sensor suite.

3. RESULTS AND DISCUSSION

3.1. Laboratory Voltammetric OCM Sensor Evaluations

Accelerated Oxidation Tests.   Prior to the JSF engine test stand evaluations [7], the capabilities of the on-line voltammetric OCM sensors to detect accelerated thermal-oxidation were tested. Three Generation I oils and two Generation II (HTS) oils [9] were oxidized at 200°C (392°F) in a flask with a bubbling air stream to determine the capabilities of the on-line OCM sensors to detect accelerated oil oxidation during higher than normal operating temperatures in both the liquid and vapor phases. The heated oils were sampled at set time intervals and analyzed for antioxidant and AN using the RULER© [10] and for kinematic viscosity at 40°C. At the end of each test, the liquid and vapor OCM, percent remaining antioxidant, AN and viscosity measurements of the stressed oil samples were plotted versus the heating time. The prepared plots were then used to compare the oil condition trending capabilities of the on-line OCM results with the capabilities of the on-site (off-line) analytical tests for the different oils. Figure 2 is the plot for one of the Generation II oils and is representative of the plots produced by the different Generation I and II oils.

The plots in Figure 2 show that the on-line OCM sensors (vapor and liquid), TAN and viscosity measurements undergo minimal increases as the percent remaining antioxidant decreases to 40 % of the original concentration of the fresh oil during the first 30 hours of heating. The oil drop that formed during the first 30 hours of heating between the wire pair of the vapor OCM sensor was yellow in color (oil vapor condensing). Between 40 and 20 % remaining antioxidant (30 – 60 hours in Figure 2), the OCM (liquid and vapor) and TAN measurements begin to increase at an accelerated rate, i.e., the useful life of the oil has ended. The oil drop on the vapor OCM sensor became thin and colorless (degradation products condensing in place of oil vapor) as the bulk oil darkened rapidly. Although the rate of increase in the liquid OCM readings slows with extended heating in Figure 2, the vapor OCM (5V maximum reading), TAN and viscosity measurements continue to increase rapidly until the end of the test. All of the accelerated oxidation tests for the Generation I and II oils produced plots similar in shape to Figure 2. However, the useful lives of the Generation I oils ended at 15 – 30 hours compared to 50 – 60 hours for the Generation II oils [9] and the baseline OCM readings of the fresh oils at 200°C (392°F) were initially 3 – 5 times higher for the Generation II oils than for the Generation I oils. Regardless of the oil type, the rapid rate of increase in the OCM readings was always in good agreement with the depletion of the antioxidant and the rapid increase in the AN and viscosity measurements, i.e., the oil condition measurements of the on-line OCM and on-site analytical techniques were in agreement regardless of oil type.

Oil Fire Test.   Next, the capabilities of the on-line voltammetric OCM sensors to detect oil fires were tested. A small pool (5 mL) of oil was placed on a watch glass, heated to 175°C (347°F) and ignited with a butane lighter. The oil drop held by the vapor sensor wire pair above the watch glass turned black in color and the sensor went off scale (> 5V) in less than 10 seconds for every oil ignited. For every oil tested at room temperature, the liquid OCM sensor reading was below 0.2V before the fire and was off-scale (> 5V) after the fire. As opposed to the oxidation test in which the antioxidants decreased to less than 10% (Figure 2), the antioxidants measured with the RULER only decreased 10% during the fires. Therefore, both the vapor and liquid OCM sensors are capable of detecting oil fires within seconds of initiation. As discussed in previous papers, the RULER could be used to distinguish between OCM sensor increases due to oxidation (antioxidants < 20%) and fires/hot spots such as F-16 "black oil" (antioxidants >80%) when only single measurements with the OCM sensors are available.

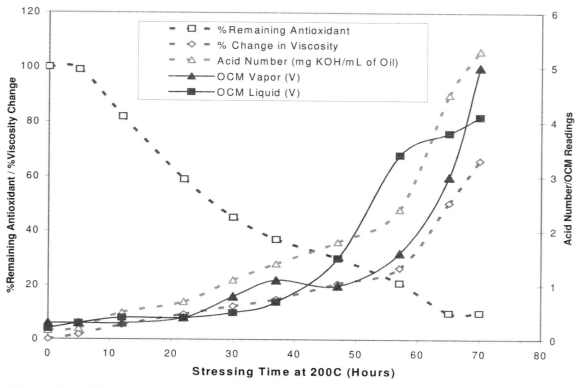

Figure 2. Plots of Percent Remaining Antioxidant, Viscosity, Total Acid Number, and OCM (Liquid and Vapor) Sensor Measurements Versus Stressing Time at 200°C (392°F) for a Laboratory Accelerated Oxidation Test of a Typical Generation II (MIL-L-23699 Type) Oil.

Oil Contamination Test. The final laboratory test was performed to evaluate the capabilities of the on-line voltammetric OCM sensors to detect liquid contaminants. External liquids may enter the oil supply of the engine due to oil additions with the wrong fluid (motor oil, hydraulic fluid or antifreeze) or due to fuel leaks (fuel can leak into oil lines through breach in oil cooler walls). To test the OCM sensors' capabilities to detect contaminant fluids in Generation I and II oils, oils were prepared with 1, 5 and 10% (by weight) contaminants and dispensed into 5-ml vials. The vials were heated to 150°C (302°F) and the wire pair of the liquid OCM sensor was submerged into the oil to simulate on-line monitoring during normal operating oil temperatures for aircraft engines.

The results indicated that the liquid OCM sensor can detect commercial hydraulic fluid (phosphate ester based), motor oil and antifreeze immediately at contamination concentrations above 5% and within minutes at concentrations below 1% due to increases in the OCM readings with time (contaminant unstable at temperature). The higher initial readings of the Generation II oil decrease the ability of the OCM sensor to immediately detect motor oil below 5%. The liquid OCM sensor was unable to detect jet fuel or military hydraulic fluid (petroleum based) at concentrations below 10% in Generation I or II oils.

With regard to the vapor OCM sensor positioned at the open mouth of the heated vial, the 5 and 10 % fuel dilutions caused the oil drop to thin and drop from the wire pair (OCM reading went from 0.3 to 0.02V).

Conversely, the vapor OCM sensor readings increased rapidly as the oils containing 10 % commercial hydraulic fluid, motor oil or antifreeze were heated.

Consequently, the liquid OCM sensor has better contamination detecting capabilities for commercial hydraulic fluid, motor oil and antifreeze while the vapor OCM sensor has better contamination detection capabilities for fuel. Neither sensor was able to detect military hydraulic fluid (petroleum based, stable at temperature) below 10% contamination.

3.2. JSF Engine Accelerated Oxidation Seeded Fault Test

Test Set-up of Engine Test Stand. Once the on-line voltammetric OCM sensors were evaluated and optimized using laboratory testing, four OCM sensors were packaged for testing on the JSF engine test stand. Minor modifications were made to engine components selected to be monitored by the sensors. Connectors containing the sensing wires were attached to fittings incorporated into an oil return line (2 sensors), the exterior surfaces of the bearing compartment and breather tube.

To initiate the JSF engine stand test, seven engine runs (Runs 1 – 7) were made under normal lubricant operating conditions [seeded fault was a bearing race with indents [8]. Then five more engine runs (Runs 8 – 12) were made with the oil cooler by-pass valve closed up to 80% resulting in increased oil temperatures and accelerated oxidation. The oil in the monitored return line reached a temperature of 232°C (450°F) when the engine speed reached 9900 rpm during the accelerated oxidation seeded fault. At the end of each engine run [approximately 90 minutes simulating take-off, flight with different engine speeds (with afterburners) then landing], oil samples were obtained for on-site oil analyses. The on-site analytical techniques used in this study were the RULER© (percent remaining antioxidant), the COBRA (oil degradation), and AN (buildup of organic acids from oil oxidation) measurements.

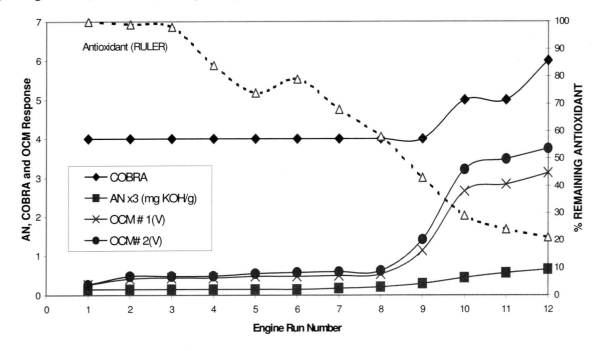

Figure 3. Plot of the Percent Remaining Antioxidant, COBRA, Acid Number (AN), and Two Liquid OCM Sensor Measurements Versus Engine Run Time for JSF Engine Test. Accelerated Oxidation Seeded Fault Engine Test: Engine Runs 8 – 12.

Liquid OCM Sensor Evaluation. For the first evaluation of the on-line monitoring capabilities of the four OCM sensors, the liquid OCM readings taken at 8600 rpm and the on-site oil condition measurements of the oil samples obtained at the end of each engine run were plotted versus the engine run number in Figure 3. The results in Figure 3 show that the oil was stable for engine runs 1 - 3 due to the high oil make-up rate between engine runs, i.e., the RULER© readings were ≈100% remaining antioxidant and the COBRA, AN and OCM sensor measurements were constant. During runs 3 – 7, the oil additions were minimized allowing the antioxidants to deplete at an accelerated rate due to the minimized antioxidant replenishments. By the end of engine run 7, the percent remaining antioxidant levels of the oils decreased to approximately 70% of the original concentration while the OCM, COBRA and TAN measurements remained constant (Figure 3) indicating that the oil was still stable but had reduced oxidation protection. The capability to detect rapid antioxidant depletion allows the RULER© to detect accelerated oil oxidation prior to the on-line OCM sensors and off-line COBRA and AN condition monitoring techniques.

For the accelerated oxidation seeded fault (runs 8 - 12 in Figure 3), the antioxidant levels decreased to 20% remaining antioxidant (RULER©) and the readouts of the liquid OCM sensors increased at a rapid rate for engine runs 8 and 9. The rate of increase for the liquid OCM sensor outputs slowed after engine run 10 similar to the liquid OCM outputs during the laboratory oxidation test in Figure 2. The COBRA and AN measurements in Figure 3 begin to increase after engine run 10 indicating the oil was beginning to oxidize. The results in Figure 3 also show that the two liquid OCM sensors had similar results illustrating the reproducibility of the OCM sensors' oxidation detection capabilities even though their wire pairs had different sensitivities to oxidation (different wire lengths due to location restraints).

Therefore, the results in Figure 3 demonstrate that the liquid OCM sensors detected accelerated oil degradation during the seeded fault test, one engine run prior to the on-site COBRA and AN analytical tests. The results in Figure 3 also indicate that the on-site RULER© instrument has the capability to detect accelerated oil oxidation at an early stage of oxidation, several engine runs prior to the on-line OCM and on-site COBRA and TAN techniques.

Vapor OCM Sensor Evaluation. In addition to the liquid OCM sensor readings, the readouts of the vapor OCM sensor were recorded every 10 seconds for the accelerated oxidation seeded fault test (engine runs 8 – 12). The breather air temperature varied between 93 up to 193°C (200 - 380°F) as the engine speed varied between 4400 rpm up to 9800 rpm, respectively, during each engine run.

The readouts of the vapor OCM sensor were constant during engine runs 7 – 10. At the ends of engine runs 9 and 10, the vapor OCM sensor readings rose sharply indicating the accumulation of degradation products onto the sensor's wires as the breather tube air temperature decreased. At the beginning of engine run 11, the vapor OCM sensor spiked and then decreased with increasing run time. Inspection of the vapor sensor after run 11 found that the degradation vapors had thinned the oil film between the sensors' wires resulting in the loss of the oil drop. A new drop of oil was added to the sensor wires. As in engine runs 9 and 10, the readouts of the oil replenished vapor OCM sensor increased rapidly at the end of run 12 (condensation of degradation products) as the breather air temperature decreased.

Visual inspection of the breather tube after engine run 12 detected the presence of coke on the inner walls of the breather tube. Consequently, the oil degradation detected by the vapor OCM sensor may be due to degradation products from the bulk oil or due to the degradation products from the oxidation of the oil (reduced antioxidant concentration) condensing on the hot walls of the breather tube.

Regardless of the source of the oil degradation products, a vapor OCM sensor could be used to detect oil oxidation in the breather air of the JSF engine. Since the oil degradation products concentrate in the breather tube, the vapor OCM sensor would have the added advantage of being less oil type dependent than the liquid OCM sensors. Small changes in the sensor designs such as the addition of Teflon mesh (tested in laboratory) to maintain the oil drop/accumulated degradation products would ensure the performance of the vapor OCM sensor in degradation rich vapor environments. Placing sensors at different positions along the inside of the breather tube at selected surface temperatures would allow degradation vapors produced from the bulk oil and produced inside the breather tube to be monitored separately.

Effects of Engine Speed and Temperature on Oxidation Detection by Liquid OCM Sensors. To determine the effects of engine speed and oil temperature on the oxidation detection capabilities of the liquid OCM sensors, the readouts of the liquid OCM sensors at three different engine speeds (4400, 8600 and 9900 rpm) were recorded and compared to engine run number. The ranges of the oil temperature readings during the five engine runs were 126 - 154°C (260 - 310°F) for 4400 rpm, 182 - 216°C (360 - 420°F) for 8600 rpm and 216 - 229°C (420 - 445°F) for 9900 rpm.

The results indicated that until engine run 8, the engine speed/temperature had minimal effect on the readouts of the liquid OCM sensors. However, the readings for the liquid OCM sensors at the different engine speeds/temperatures diverged as the oil degraded during engine runs 9 – 12, i.e., the sensitivities of the OCM sensors to oxidative degradation increase with temperature.

Consequently, two methods can be used to detect oil oxidation with the liquid OCM sensors. The first method is to record the OCM sensor reading at a preset engine speed/temperature range (Figure 3). The second method is to record the difference between the readouts of the OCM sensor at two preset engine speeds. The second method would make the OCM oxidation detection capabilities independent of oil type, i.e., Generation II oil has higher original OCM reading than Generation I oil but rate of increase due to oxidation is similar. Therefore, increases in the absolute value and/or increases in the differences of the OCM sensor readings with temperature could be used to detect accelerated oil oxidation directly on-line. These results also indicate that the OCM readings in Figure 3 would have been even more sensitive to accelerated oxidation if the 9900 rpm readings had been used instead of the 8600 rpm readings.

Fire and Contamination Seeded Fault Tests. The planned seeded fault tests to initiate a bearing compartment fire and to introduce liquid contaminants into the engine stand lubrication system were not accomplished. The spark plug installed into the bearing compartment failed to ignite the oil (the readouts for the OCM sensor in the bearing compartment also did not change, i.e., did not detect oil degradation due to fire/hot spot) under a wide range of oil:air ratios. Due to their expected detrimental effects on oil-wetted components and the excellent laboratory results commercial hydraulic fluid, motor oil and antifreeze were not injected into the engine oil system to ensure the other mechanical seeded faults could be performed [8] prior to engine failure.

3.3.   HMMWV Diesel Engine Accelerated Oxidation and Coolant Leak Seeded Fault Tests

Introduction. After the sensor suite and system of side-arms (Figure 1) were optimized in the laboratory [6], the system was incorporated into the diesel engine test stand oil radiator hose. With the suite of sensors in place, two diesel engine tests were performed to evaluate the individual sensors' capabilities to detect accelerated oxidation and coolant leaks. For the purposes of discussing the different engine test results, the analytical data for the diesel engine test stand evaluations was divided into three basic groups: Army oil condition techniques and on-board oil condition sensors.

Several types of on-board soot sensors were evaluated during this project [6], however, the soot sensors (Figure 1) did not perform properly during laboratory and initial engine tests and are not presented here in. The cause(s) of the erratic results produced by the on-board soot meters were not determined during this project. In addition to their analytical limitations, the on-board soot sensors would require extensive research prior to use on diesel engines both with regard to size and temperature limitations. The data for the pressure sensors upstream and downstream of the secondary filter (Figure 1) also was not included because the pressure data for both sensors was erratic and did not trend with engine operation time. The pressure release provided by the additional side-arm in Figure 1 is thought to have negated any effects of viscosity on the pressure readings at the secondary filter (Figure 1).

Accelerated Oxidation Seeded Fault Test. The first diesel engine test evaluation described herein was performed to determine the capabilities of the different on-board sensors to monitor accelerated oxidation. The categorized data and FTIR oxidation values were plotted versus engine operating time in Figures 5 and 6. The Army condemnation values (ACV) for FTIR oxidation, FTIR soot and viscosity at 40°C were also included in Figures 5 and 6 as points of reference in determining the oil condition according to Army specifications. The Army condition data in Figure 5 indicates that the oxidation level (FTIR) of the oil samples removed from the diesel engine test stand increased at a steady rate for the first 8000 minutes, then leveled for the next 2000 minutes before increasing for the rest of the accelerated oxidation test.

With respect to the ACV for FTIR oxidation, the sampled oils exceeded accepted oxidation levels after 2130 minutes of test engine operation.

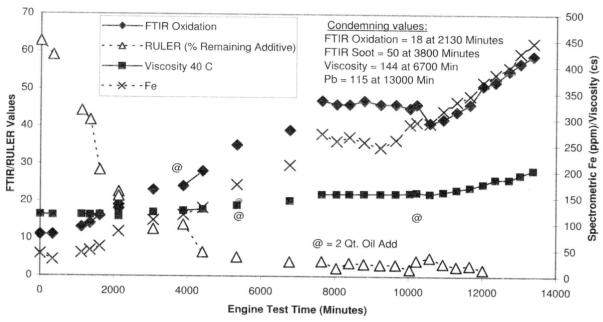

Figure 5. Army oil condition and RULER© analyses for HMMWV diesel engine accelerated oxidation seeded fault test samples

In addition to oxidation levels, the oil samples exceeded the ACV for soot (FTIR soot) and viscosity (40°C) after 3800 and 6700 minutes of test engine operation, respectively. In addition to the basestock degradation, the Fe and Pb wear metal concentrations in Figure 5 increased during the engine test with the Pb concentrations exceeding the ACV after 13000 minutes of operation.

The data from the on-site RULER instrument (additive depletion) for the test stand oil samples in Figure 5 indicates that the ZDDP multifunctional additive depletes rapidly to 20 percent of the new oil during the first 2130 minutes of operation and decreases to below 5 percent after 5300 minutes of operation. The 20 percent ZDDP level coincides with the FTIR oxidation value exceeding the ACV for oxidation for the test oil samples.

For the on-board sensors in Figure 6, the CSI dielectric sensor data (multiplied by 20) increases at a slow rate for the entire engine test, basically unaffected by the oil additions at 3800, 5300 and 10200 minutes. The trend of the Lubrigard sensor was similar to the CSI data and was not plotted in Figure 6. The dielectric sensors underwent similar rates of change for the HMMWV diesel accelerated soot accumulation tests [6]. In contrast to the dielectric data in Figure 6, the data for the UDRI array and wire voltammetric sensors decreases rapidly for the first 2000 minutes of operation, then increase for the next 6000 minutes, before becoming constant, slight decrease for the remaining minutes of engine operation. The dips in the voltammetric plots that occur at 6000 and 10000 minutes coincide with the fresh oil addition as designated in Figure 6.

The FTIR technique used by the Army to monitor the oxidation levels of used HMMWV diesel engine oil samples indicated that the oil samples obtained from the accelerated oxidation test exceeded the ACV for oxidation after 2100 minutes of engine operation (Figure 5). The RULER analyses indicated that the ZDDP additive was depleted to 20% after 2100 minutes of operation. Consequently, the FTIR oxidation measurements and additive depletion measurements indicated that the oil in the diesel engine test stand should be changed out after 2100 minutes of operation. The oil samples exceeded the ACV for viscosity (40°C) after 6700 minutes of test engine operation indicating viscosity measurements to monitor oxidation would allow severe oxidation to occur prior to detection.

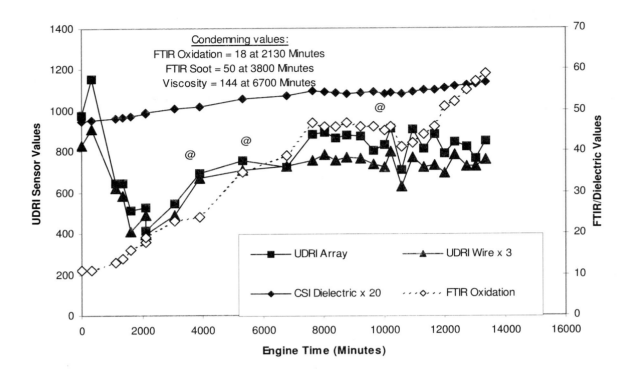

Figure 6. On-Board Sensor Outputs for HMMWV diesel engine accelerated oxidation seeded fault test samples

The on-board dielectric sensor results and the FTIR oxidation levels showed similar trends in Figures 5 and 6, i.e., dielectric and oxidation values increased at a constant rate up to 8,000 minutes, leveled off for 2,000 minutes, and then increased slightly/moderately during the remaining engine test. In contrast to the dielectric results, the outputs of the on-board UDRI voltammetric sensors decreased rapidly for the first 2000 minutes of engine operation, then increased for the next 6000 minutes, before becoming constant/slight decrease for the remaining minutes of engine operation. These results correlate well with the ZDDP additive depletion of the used oil samples measured with the RULER in Figure 5 followed by accelerated oxidation measured with FTIR in Figures 5 and 6. As opposed to the dielectric plots in Figure 6, the UDRI voltammetric sensor plots have distinctive rate changes that could be used to determine oil change intervals, i.e., voltammetric sensor outputs decrease indicating additive decrease, then level indicating additives no longer effective, then increase indicating oxidation accelerating (in agreement with ACV for FTIR oxidation).

Coolant Leak Seeded Fault Test. An additional diesel engine test evaluation was performed to determine the capabilities of the different on-board sensors to monitor coolant leaks. The coolant leak test was performed differently from the accelerated oxidation test in that the diesel engine was operated for 2185 minutes prior to initiating the test. The coolant leak test was then performed by adding 100 mL quantities of a 50/50 solution of coolant/water to the oil flowing through the side-arm containing the suite of sensors and then obtaining a sample for analysis. The coolant additions and sample removals were performed at 15-minute intervals for approximately two hours (eight samples obtained). No oil additions were made during the coolant leak test. The FTIR water in petroleum values (Army technique for detecting coolant leaks) were plotted versus sample number in Figure 7. The ACV for FTIR water and Karl Fisher titration technique were included in Figure 7 as points of reference in determining the water concentrations in the obtained oil samples according to Army specifications.

Although the on-board CSI dielectric sensor output appears level in Figure 7, the value increased with coolant addition from 2.54 (sample 6) to 2.66 (sample 8) in agreement with the on-site water analyses. The changes in the output of the on-board Lubrigard dielectric sensor were more complex with the coolant additions in Figure 7.

As reported in previous work [3], the capabilities of the UDRI voltammetric sensors to detect the water/coolant additions are dependent upon the sensor geometry. As expected, the array Voltammetric sensor readout increases rapidly for samples 5 thru 8 in agreement with the on-site sensors. Whereas, the readouts for the wire voltammetric sensor are level, decreasing slightly for samples 5 thru 8. It is believed that suspended coolant/water droplets (20-30 micron range) accumulate on the array polymer surface bridging adjacent, 120 micron spaced conductive lines in the array causing the increase in the sensor readout. The suspended droplets are not able to bridge the one-millimeter gap of the wire voltammetric sensor, and consequently, have no effect on the sensor readout.

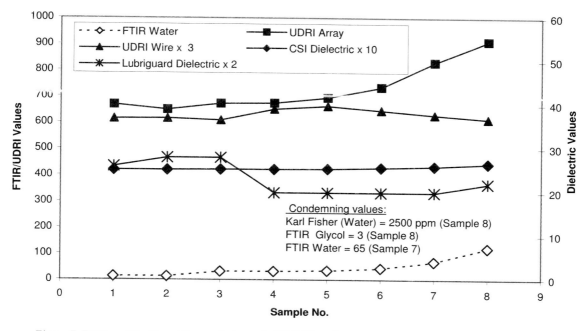

Figure 7. FTIR and On-Board Sensor Outputs for HMMWV diesel engine coolant leak seeded fault test samples

The laboratory FTIR and Karl Fisher techniques used by the Army to monitor the water levels of used HMMWV diesel engine oil samples indicated that the oil samples obtained from the coolant leak test exceeded the ACV for water between samples 7 and 8 of the test. The on-board (Figure 7) and on-site dielectric sensor results [6] detected the coolant/water increases after sample 5 prior to the ACV. Similar to the dielectric results, the on-board UDRI voltammetric array sensor was able to detect the coolant/water increases after sample 5 in Figure 7 in agreement with the on-site analyses. In contrast to the array sensor, the wire voltammetric sensor did not detect the coolant/water additions.

On-Board Sensor Trends. The diesel engine test stand seeded fault evaluations of the on-board dielectric and voltammetric sensors indicate that the following combinations would accurately assess the condition of in-service diesel engine oils:

- Voltammetric decreasing and dielectric increasing = oil normal.
- Voltammetric level and dielectric increasing = detergents depleted, soot building (Previous research [6]).
- Voltammetric increasing and dielectric increasing = oil oxidizing
  Increase more evident at operating temperature than room temperature.
- Voltammetric array increasing/wire constant and dielectric increasing = coolant leak.
- Voltammetric array constant/wire decreasing = oil level dropping
  (Dipstick sensor in previous work [6]).
- Voltammetric increasing and dielectric constant = fuel leak
  Increase more evident at room temperature than operating temperature [6].

Previous results [6] also showed that the use of a magnetic debris sensor (Figure 1) would be of use for diesel engines in trending abnormal operating engines because the trapped particles were too large for spectrometric detection.

4. CONCLUSIONS

Regardless of the sensor location (lubricant or vapor), lubricant temperature/flow rate, lubricant composition or engine application, the on-line voltammetric sensors successfully monitored the lubricant condition changes caused by all of the seeded faults during the JSF and HMMWV test stand evaluations. The capability of the on-line voltammetric sensors to distinguish between different degradation mechanisms could be greatly improved by recording the voltammetric sensor outputs at two more temperatures for aircraft engine applications and by combining them in a system with other on-line sensors (e.g., dielectric, viscosity, etc.) for diesel engine applications. In addition to the sensor system built into the radiator hose in Figure 1, another sensor system [6] was constructed from a HMMWV dipstick, two voltammetric sensors (array and wire) and a battery operated electronics package to power the sensors and display their outputs. The "dipstick sensor" could be used in place of the current HMMWV dipstick to monitor lubricant level as well as condition. A magnetic plug, electronic or manual, could be used in place of the oil drain plug to monitor the production of magnetic (iron) debris.

The results also indicate that the on-site RULER© instrument could be used to detect the initiation of accelerated oil oxidation prior to detection by the on-line or typical laboratory oil condition monitoring techniques. The RULER© instrument could also be used to help distinguish between the different degradation mechanisms being monitored by the on-line voltammetric sensors. Once the on-line voltammetric sensor detects an abnormal condition for a diesel engine, the on-site RULER© instrument could be used to determine if the abnormal condition is accelerated oxidation (antioxidant concentration decrease) or fuel dilution (antioxidant concentration constant, spectrum change [6]).

REFERENCES

[1]   Kauffman, R., "Development of a Remaining Useful Life of a Lubricant Evaluation Technique. Part III. Cyclic Voltammetric Techniques," Lub. Eng., V. 46(1), 1990.

[2]   Kauffman, R., "On-Line and Off-Line Measurements of Thermal and Oxidative Degradation in Used Lubrication Oils - Part I: Laboratory Evaluations," Lub. Eng., V51, No. 11, p. 914-921,1995

[3]   Kauffman, R., Wolf, J., and Moyer, S. "Development and Laboratory Evaluation of On-Board Oil Condition Monitoring Sensors for HMMWV Diesel Engines". Technology Showcase 2002, JOAP International Condition Monitoring Conference, Mobile, AL, 2002.

[4]   Ameye, J., "The Results of a Program for Quick Determination of Antioxidants on O-160 Helicopter Turbine Lubricants by Using the RULER Oil Analysis Instrument," Technology Showcase 2000, *JOAP International Condition Monitoring Conference Proceedings,* Mobile, Alabama, pp 86 –98, 2000.

[5]   Saba, C.S., et al, "Lubricant Performance and Evaluation II," Report No. AFWAL-TR-91-2111, Aero Propulsion Laboratory, Wright-Patterson AFB, Ohio, 1992.

[6]   Kauffman, R., et al. "Diesel Engine Test Stand Evaluations of On-board Oil Condition Monitoring Sensors for U.S. Army Ground Equipment," Proceedings of NORIA Excellence in Lubrication, Nashville, OH, April 22 – 24, 2004.

[7]   Kauffman, R., and Ameye, J. "Combining On-Site and On-Line Voltammetric Analyses to Better Understand the Degradation Mechanisms of Lubricants and Equipment - Part I: Joint Strike Fighter". Lub. Eng., V. 51(11), pp. 19-27, 2002.

[8]   Humphrey, G.R., "Joint Strike Fighter—Analysis of Filter Debris by Energy Dispersive X-Ray Fluorescence," Technology Showcase 2000, *JOAP International Condition Monitoring Conference Proceedings,* Mobile, Alabama, pp 86 –98, 2000.

[9]   Karasek, K., Feng, A. and Kauffman, R., "Coke Formation from Aircraft Oils. Part II: Effects of Oil Formulation and Surface Composition," *Tribology Transactions,* 43, 4, pp 677 –681, 2000..

[10] Kauffman, R.E., "Rapid, Portable Voltammetric Techniques for Performing Antioxidant, Total Acid Number (TAN) and Total Base Number (TBN) Measurements," *Lub. Eng.,* V54(1), pp.39 – 46, 1998.

Session 8
LUBRICATION TECHNOLOGY 3

Chair: Mr. Richard Atkinson

The Effect of Lubricants on the Repeated Use of Threaded Fasteners
W. ECCLES, I. SHERRINGTON, T. SPERRING

The Influence of Lubricating Oil on the Plain Slideway FailuresThe Influence of Lubricating Oil on the Plain Slideway Failures
R. RAKIĆ, M.A. ZLATA RAKIĆ

Magnetic Fluid based Squeeze Film between Rotating Porous Rough Annular Plates
G. M. DEHERI, H. C. PATEL, R. M. PATEL

Tribological behaviour of DLC coated gears lubricated with ester-based oil
B. KRŽAN, M. KALIN, J. VIŽINTIN

The Effect of Lubricants on the Repeated Use of Threaded Fasteners

W. Eccles [1,2], I. Sherrington [2], T. Sperring [2]

[1] Bolt Science Limited, Chorley, Lancashire, PR7 2PU, UK
[2] Jost Institute for Tribotechnology, University of Central Lancashire, Preston PR1 2HE, UK

ABSTRACT

Threaded fasteners are used widely in critical applications in engineering plant and equipment world-wide. They are usually supplied dry, with a surface finish applied for corrosion protection purposes but without any lubricant being present. Practice varies between industries and companies on the use of lubricants with fasteners. Due to a lack of availability, or for economic reasons, fasteners are often re-used following disassembly of a joint. To understand the impact of differing practice, this study reports on the effect that a range of lubricants (including oil, lithium grease and molybdenum disulphide) can have on the repeated use of fasteners compared to fasteners without a lubricant applied. The study focuses on fasteners having an electro-zinc plated (EZP) finish that are commonly used across a wide range of industries. Results of torque-tension tests, used to determine friction coefficients during tightening, are reported together with the effect that repeated use, with and without, lubricants has on the friction coefficient.

A significant reduction (54%) in the bolt preload occurs between the first and tenth tightening of an EZP bolt tested in the "as-received" condition with no lubricant applied; with a 51% reduction occurring between the first and fourth tightenings. This contrasts with the cases where lubricants were used where there was no significant reduction in the preload values between the first and tenth tightening. These results indicate that the use of an appropriate lubricant can ensure that a consistent preload is achieved from bolts re-tightened to a constant torque value. The effect of using a dry lubricant on stainless steel also resulted in a consistently higher preload when the fastener was reused compared to the unlubricated condition.

This study shows that there exists a potential for large economic savings if lubricants are employed on re-used fasteners. Presently when parts are removed from assemblies for repair or servicing, OEM's typically recommend using new fasteners. By ensuring that a consistent preload is achieved when the fasteners are re-tightened, the use of lubricants could allow fasteners to be reused in many instances.

Keywords: Fastener, Lubricant Testing, Bolt, Nut, Preload, Coefficient of Friction

1. INTRODUCTION

Replacing parts on most items of mechanical equipment requires the removal and subsequent re-tightening of threaded fasteners. It is the fastener's preload (the clamp force that is generated when the fastener is tightened) that ensures the structural integrity of the joint. The preload clamps the joint together and prevents relative movement between its constituent parts. Insufficient preload generally results in the joint moving and the fasteners failing by fatigue or self loosening and subsequently being dislodged leading to significant problems [1-4].

In the majority of applications, the preload provided by the fastener is indirectly controlled by specifying a tightening torque. The relationship between the applied torque and preload during the tightening process is linear and so increasing the torque value leads to a proportional increase in the preload. To provide guidance and a measure of quality control, many manufacturers provide the appropriate tightening torque to which specific fasteners should be tightened on assembly drawings and in their maintenance handbooks. Such torque specifications are usually based upon values quoted in a table that was compiled on the basis of knowing the friction conditions present in the fastener derived from tests.

It is not widely appreciated that re-tightening a threaded fastener can significantly affect its performance. Damage to the fastener's surface, incurred during the tightening process, affects the friction characteristics that prevail under the nut face and the bolt head. If the friction increases as a result of surface damage sustained during previous tightenings then the fastener's preload will decrease for a given tightening torque. It is usual to specify a single tightening torque in a maintenance handbook, independent of the number of times the fastener has been tightened. If the performance of the product was proven based upon the preload achieved on the fastener's first tightening then there is the risk of structural integrity problems if a decrease in preload occurs as a result of an increase in friction due to the fastener being re-tightened.

Many OEM's specify that if a part is removed, the fasteners should be replaced. However in many applications this is not feasible for economic or practical reasons. The market for threaded fasteners is considerable. According to the Freedonia Group [5], the world-wide demand for fasteners in 2006 is expected to be US$46.3 billion. The policy of disposing of fasteners that are capable of providing a satisfactory function can be regarded as wasteful in both in economic and environmental terms.

There has been little published work on the influence that re-tightening has on the performance of threaded fasteners. One paper by Morgan and Henshall [6] reports on the effect of re-tightening M22 x 1.5 nuts on commercial vehicle wheels with and without a lubricant (engine oil). Their report indicated that degreasing the nuts resulted in a 70% reduction in the preload after three tightenings.

In this present study, the effect of re-tightening M12 x 1.75 electro-zinc plated (EZP) bolts and nuts on their torque-preload characteristics is investigated. Fasteners are commonly zinc plated to prevent corrosion of the underlying steel - the zinc providing both a barrier and sacrificial protection. The fasteners were not degreased in the tests but used in their 'as received' condition. The majority of the tests were performed on property class 8.8 bolts [7] however a number of tests were also completed on stainless steel bolts and nuts of property class A4-70 [8]. Stainless steel fasteners are used across a range of industries for their corrosion resistance properties and their retention of fracture toughness at low temperatures. A common issue with the assembly of such fasteners is galling in the threads that can result in problematic tightening.

2. EQUIPMENT

To allow the bolt preload to be measured, a test apparatus was designed and built. This device included a specially designed test frame, with torque, angle and clamp-force measuring instruments. These were connected to a computer via an analogue to digital converter to allow data to be collected throughout an experiment.

Nuts were "hand tightened" using an electronic torque wrench which was used for tightening the nuts had cabling that connected to the A/D converter allowing sampling of the torque-angle measurements to be made. A 12 bit analogue to digital (A/D) converter was used to sample the analogue signals from the load cell and the electronic torque wrench. The sampling rate is variable, but an acquisition speed of 10 samples per second was found to produce consistent results. The test apparatus allowed either the bolt head to be rotated with the nut held stationary or the nut to be rotated with the bolt head stationary. In the tests reported here, the nut was rotated with the bolt head held stationary. The equipment is illustrated in figure 1.

Figure 2 illustrates the torque/preload measuring device. It consists of a load cell to measure the preload and a torque transducer to measure the thread torque. A roller thrust bearing allows the thread torque to be reacted by the torque transducer. With knowledge of the overall applied torque, the thread torque and the preload, the device allows the thread and under head friction coefficients to be determined.

For one set of tests, standard property class 8.8 bolts were used with property class 8 nuts and plain washers were used under the nut face. Bolts, nuts and washers had an EZP finish, the coating thickness typically varied between 5 μm to 9 μm. A constant tightening torque of 50 Nm was used in the tests. It was found that if a higher torque was used, the bolt yield point would be reached when a high

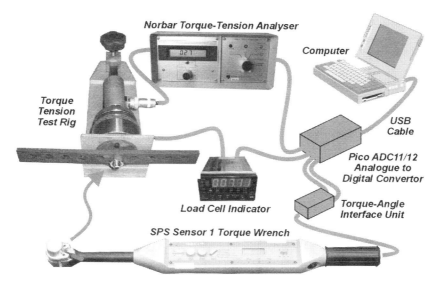

Figure 1. Overview of the Test Apparatus

performance lubricant was used. To ensure that the nut surface rotated against the washer surface rather than the washer rotating against the support, a tabbed washer was used to prevent the washer rotating.

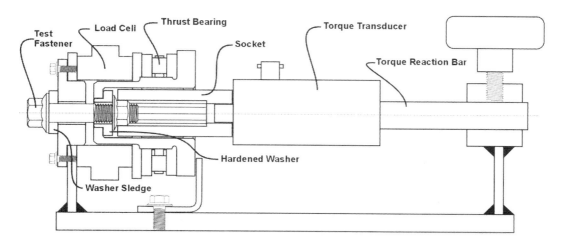

Figure 2. Section through the fastener test apparatus

3. TEST CONDITIONS / SPECIMENS

Two series of tests were performed:

1. Tests on as received property class 8.8 EZP bolts and nuts in the following conditions:
   ▪ As received with no lubricant applied.
   ▪ With a molybdenum disulphide paste applied.
   ▪ With Copaslip[1] applied.
   ▪ With litium grease applied (Duckhams LB10 lithium grease)
   ▪ With a light oil applied (Castrol Everyman Oil)

In each case, the lubricant was applied prior the the first tightening to the threads and the nut bearing face but was not re-applied between subsequent re-tightenings.

2. Tests on as received stainless steel property class A4-70 bolts and nuts in the following conditions:
   ▪ As received with no lubricant applied.
   ▪ With a dry coating of molybdenum disulfide applied via a spray prior to the first tightening.

4. RESULTS

Bolt preloads arising during multiple tightening on the EZP bolts and nuts to a torque of 50 Nm are summarized in figure 3.

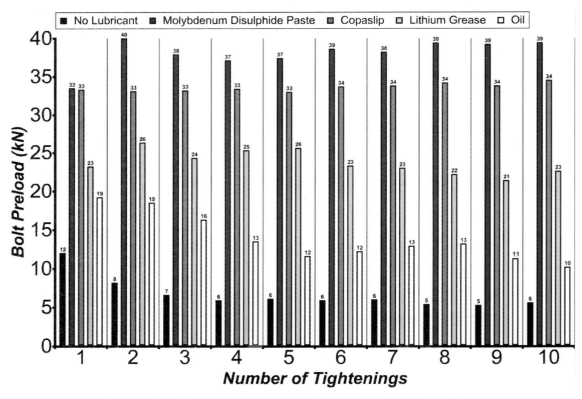

Figure 3. The Effect on the Bolt Preload of Repeated Tightening of EZP Bolts

---

[1] Copaslip is a high temperature anti-seize compound that incorporates a non-melt grease with copper. It is a registered trademark.

Bolt preloads arising during multiple tightening on the stainless steel bolts and nuts to a torque of 50 Nm are summarized in figure 4.

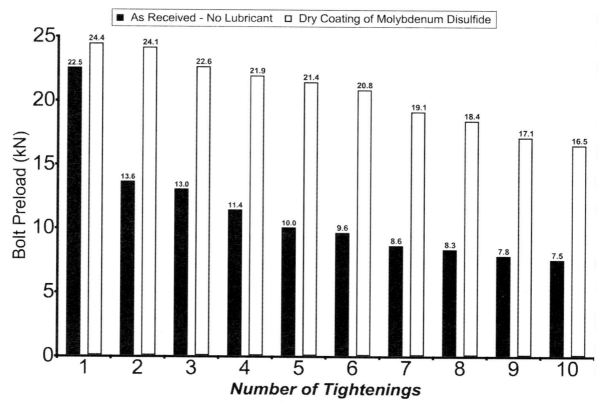

Figure 4. The Effect on Bolt Preload of Repeated Tightening of Stainless Steel Bolts

5. MATHEMATICAL MODEL

A mathematical model relating the applied torque to the tension induced into the bolt is described by [9].

$$T = \frac{F}{2}\left[\frac{p}{\pi} + \frac{\mu_t d_2}{\cos \beta} + D_e \mu_n\right]$$ Equation 1

$$\text{with } D_e = \frac{d_o + d_i}{2}$$ Equation 2

where

T	Total tightening torque
F	Bolt preload
μ_t	Coefficient of friction for the threads
d_2	The basic pitch diameter of the thread
β	The half included angle for the threads
p	Pitch of the thread
μ_n	Coefficient of friction for the nut face or bolt head
D_e	The effective bearing diameter of the nut
d_o	The outer bearing diameter of the nut
d_i	The inner bearing diameter of the nut face

The three terms inside the bracket in equation 1 represent the torque resulting from the circumferential component of the normal reaction between the nut and bolt threads due to the thread's helix angle. The second term is from torque to overcome the friction between the bolt and nut threads and the final term the torque needed to overcome friction under the nut face.

As can be seen from inspection of the equation 1, if the terms in the bracket are constant during the tightening process a linear relationship exists between the applied torque and the preload. A typical graph of change in preload as torque increases from the authors' experimental data is shown in figure 3. A roughly linear relationship between torque and the bolt preload is evident.

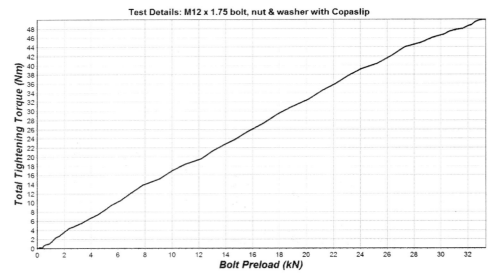

Figure 5. Torque-Force Graph

Based upon this experimental confirmation, it is safe to determine the coefficient of total friction μ_{tot} by the formula (from [10])

$$\mu_{tot} = \frac{\dfrac{T}{F} - 0.15915p}{0.57735d_2 + \dfrac{D_e}{2}} \qquad \text{Equation 3}$$

6. DISCUSSION

From inspection of figure 3 it is evident:

- A significant reduction (54%) in the bolt preload occurs between the first and tenth tightening of an EZP bolt, a 51% reduction occurs between the first and fourth tightenings.

- Use of a specialist high pressure lubricant (molybdenum disulfide or Copaslip) applied under the nut face and in the threads results in no significant change in the bolt preload between the first and tenth tightenings. Use of a lithium grease also provided a consistent bolt preload between the first and tenth tightenings.

- The use of a light machine oil resulted in a significant decrease (47%) in the bolt preload value. This was probably a result of the oil being displaced from the moving contact surfaces as a result of the high contact pressures involved.

From inspection of figure 4 it can be seen that:

- The preload change on the tenth tightening on unlubricated stainless steel was 33% of that achieved on the first tightening (from 22.5 kN to 7.5 kN). The use of a dry coating of molybdenum disulfide on the stainless steel resulted in the preload on the tenth tightening being 68% of the first tightening (24.4 kN to 16.5 kN).

Table 1 - Friction Values

	μ_{tot} First Tightening	μ_{tot} Fifth Tightening	μ_{tot} Tenth Tightening
EZP bolt as received	0.276	0.566	0.620
EZP bolt with molybdenum disulfide paste	0.086	0.075	0.070
EZP bolt with Copaslip	0.086	0.087	0.083
EZP bolt with lithium grease	0.133	0.118	0.137
EZP bolt with machine oil	0.165	0.286	0.329
Stainless steel bolt – as received	0.137	0.332	0.449
Stainless steel bolt with a dry molybdenum disulfide coating	0.125	0.145	0.193

Table 1 presents coefficient of friction values calculated using equation 3. It can be seen that a lubricant can play a vital role in ensuring a relatively constant friction value between tightenings. VDI 2230 [9] indicates that a reliable design must be based upon the minimum bolt preload value. Having a large scatter in the preload results in bolts larger than would otherwise be needed having to be specified. The bolt diameter has to be sized based upon the maximum preload in order that the minimum preload still meets the functional requirement.

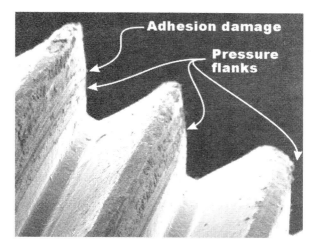

Figure 6 - The pressure flank of an unlubricated EZP bolt thread after five tightenings

As can be seen from the results, there is a significant increase in friction occurs with unlubricated EZP bolts as the number of tightenings is increased. Previous work [11] using a scanning electron microscope indicated that, in an unlubricated condition, a significant amount of surface damage can be observed on the pressure flanks of the threads. This is shown in figure 6 which illustrates damage on a thread pressure flank i.e. the side of the thread that sustains the loading, after five tightenings.

7. CONCLUSIONS

This study has shown that the use of high pressure lubricants, such as molybdenum disulfide, on threaded fasteners offers considerable potential in ensuring that a high and repeatable preload is achieved when the fasteners are re-tightened after parts are removed from an assembly. By reducing the thread friction and hence the torsional stress incurred during tightening, lubricants also provide the opportunity for a greater utilization of the bolt strength. That is, a greater preload is achievable using a lubricated fastener since the yield point is reached as a combination of tensile and torsional stresses. Decreasing the torsional stress due to lower friction allows a higher tensile stress to be present when the yield point is reached and hence a higher preload.

Considering that many companies specify that the fasteners should be replaced if parts are removed, this study shows that with the use of lubricants, fasteners tightened using the torque control method can be re-used so that a repeatable preload is achieved. Detailed advice on how the fasteners could be reused, by using a lubricant, could be provided in maintenance handbooks and similar publications. The potential economic savings that could be made if this was adopted would be considerable. This approach is also in line with the increasing importance of re-cycling and sustainability.

REFERENCES

[1] M.E. Stevenson, J.L.M., and K.G. Cline, Metallurgical Failure Analysis of Titanium Wing Attachment Bolts. Practical Failure Analysis. 3 (4).
[2] Graves, F.E., Fastener Failure and Product Liability. Fastener Technology, 1981.
[3] Trilling, J.A., Causes and Prevention of Fastener Failures. Machine Design, 1972.
[4] Eliza, N., Failures of bolts in helicopter main rotor drive plate assembly due to improper application of lubricant. Engineering Failure Analysis, 2003. 10: p. 443-451.
[5] World Fasteners. Freedonia Group Report 1545, 2002: p. 344.
[6] Morgan, R.C. and J.L. Henshall, The torque-tension behaviour of 22 x 1.5 bolts for fixing spigot located wheels on heavy commercial vehicles. Proceedings of the Institution of Mechanical Engineers, 1996. 210: p. 209-214.
[7] ISO 898-1 Mechanical properties of fasteners made of carbon steel - Part 1: Bolts, screws and studs. 1999.
[8] ISO 3506-1 Mechanical properties of corrosion-resistant stainless steel fasteners - Part 1: Bolts, screws and studs. 1997.
[9] VDI 2230 - Part 1 Systematic calculation of high duty bolted joints. Joints with one cylindrical bolt. 2003, Verein Deutscher Ingenieure.
[10] ISO 16047:2005 - Fasteners - Torque/clamp force testing.
[11] W. Eccles, I.S., T. Sperring, Changes in Friction during Repeated Tightening of Zinc Plated Fasteners. In preparation, 2006.

The Influence of Lubricating Oil on the Plain Slideway Failures

R. Rakić [1], M.A. Zlata Rakić [2]

[1] NIS-Petrol, Naftagas promet, Narodnog fronta 12, 21000 Novi Sad, Serbia and Montenegro,
e-mail: rrakic@nap.co.yu
[2] Javorova 2A, 21000 Novi Sad, Serbia and Montenegro

ABSTRACT

Progress in the fundamental understanding of tribology is crucial for the design and engineering of mechanical components. The slideways are frequently the most troublesome to lubricate on machine tools. There are plain slideways, hydrostatic slideways and ball / roller slideways. The aim of this study is to investigate the influence of lubricating oil on the reliability of plain slideways. The experimental investigation of the influence of lubricating oil on the tribological behaviour of plain slideways has been carried out at a metalworking factory.

The paper presents the following:
- the classification of lubricating oil for plain slideways,
- the analysis of the symptoms of failure to plain slideways and
- the curves of plain slideways reliability in function of tribological properties of lubricating oil under presented operating conditions of investigation.

The following conclusions can be drawn from this study:
- The reliability of plain slideways was found to be affected by both type of lubricating oil and viscosity grade,
- the hydraulic oil ISO-L-HG gives a longer life of plain slideway compared with the case of the hydraulic oil ISO-L-HM,
- the viscosity grade ISO VG 68 gives a longer life of plain slideway compared with the case of the viscosity grade ISO VG 46.

Keywords: Lubricating oil, failures, plain slideways.

1. INTRODUCTION

The majority of plain slideways in use today are oil lubricated. There are many published papers on the mechanisms of oil lubrication in plain slideways. Hydrodynamic lubrication is generally characterized by surfaces that are conformal.That is, the surfaces fit snugly into each other with a high degree of geometrical conformity, so that the load is carried over a relatively large area. Fluid film slide bearing, slideway and other slide parts exibits conformal surfaces [1].

The important future task include research and development leading to the identification of tribological causes of tribo-deformation and damage and to the establishment of adequate models of frictional wear processes [2]. A wear process of the operating surfaces of a body induced by fluid medium containing abrasive particles between the interacting solid surfaces in relative motion may be termed wet abrasion and hydro-abrasive wear [3]. Slideway elements on metal cutting machines where the penetration of metal particles cannot be reliably prevented. The solution of the problem of increasing the life time and reliability of tribomechanical system elements on machine cutting tools is closely connected with the revealing of abrasive wear of their contact surfaces. The probability of system survival is a measure of the probability that a system will not reach a completely failed state during a given time interval, given that at the beginning of the interval the system was in a fully operable state [4]. The effectiveness of lubricating oils has been studied in several projects and more detailed explanations can be found in [5, 6, 7, 8, 9, 10].

2. PLAIN SLIDEWAYS

The slide guides have been widely used for precision motion applications because of their high load-bearing capability and high damping property [11]. However, because slide-guide dynamic friction properties vary with external load, speed and running time, it has become necessary to monitor and compensate for these effects to achieve precision motion. Further, in order to maintain a high degree of reliable accuracy over long periods of operation, it is of paramount importance that an appropriate control model of the slide guide is established in terms of preload, wear and operating conditions.

The slide guide has large frictional surfaces compared to other types of guides. Hence, motion of the moving table is strongly dependant on the tribological characteristics. Due to the difference between the static and the dynamic friction, a stick-slip motion can cause adverse effects which may vary with the external load and significantly affect the positioning accuracy of the motion, especially at low speed.

The slideways are frequently the most troublesome to lubricate on machine tools. There are plain slideways, hydrostatic slideways and ball / roller slideways. The plain slideway system has been widely used in machine tools because of its sensitive moving, high precision of positioning and repositioning.

If lubrication breaks down, even momentarily, during traverse movements, the table may stick, then jump away as the actuating force increases. This phenomenon, which is repeated intermittently during the slideway movement, is known as "stick – slip", and is especially pronounced at the slow feeds that are frequently needed in machine tools. Stick – slip affects surface finish, causes vibration and chatter marks, and makes it difficult to hold fine tolerances. On long slideways the oil tends to be wiped or scraped from the bearing surfaces. To reduce this possibility the oil is fed to regularly – spaced orifices and the slideway split into smaller sections by grooves in the underside of the moving member. Grooving (in, for example, "v" or "fishbone" formation) helps to distribute the oil across and along the slideway. Stick-slip is the phenomenon of unsteady sliding, consisting of a stick phase and a slip phase, caused by a decreasing friction force with increasing relative speed, in combination with elasticity of the mechanical system of which the friction contact is part. Stick-slip is the well-known phenomenon of intermittent motion caused by a negative slope of the friction-relative speed relative in combination with tangential elasticity of the tribomechanical system of which the friction interface is part. It causes among others low accuracy in positioning and poor control lability of machining processes like cutting, extrusion and deepdrowing [12].

3. SELECTING LUBRICATING OIL

In order to avoid "table – float", the sliding bearing must be lubricated under thin – film or boundary conditions. Thus lubrication and the properties of the lubricating oil – particularly its viscosity, adhesion and friction-reducing properties – are extremely important.

Lubrication under boundary conditions is dependent not only on the lubricant but also, because of their frictional characteristics, upon the constructional materials used for the stationary and sliding components, and upon their working conditions. The lubricant must adhere tightly to the moving surfaces, and be of sufficiently low viscosity to avoid table-float. If the sliding speed is decreased, hydrodynamic effects are thereby lessened and the lubricating oil can have a higher viscosity.

The problems of table and slideway lubrication have been greatly eased by the development of adhesive and friction – reducing additives for oils. These additives cause the oil to cling to the sliding surfaces and are relatively insensitive to changes in oil viscosity. Slideways may form part of a circulatory system or be lubricated as total – loss components. The kinds of lubricating oils for plain slideways with standpoint the recommendations for the choice of lubricants for machine tools [13, 14, 15] and author ' s investigations [9, 10] are presented in Table 1.

Table 1. Recommendations for the choice of lubricants for plain slideways of machine tools

Letter symbol	Category symbol	Examples of applications
G	G68 G 100 G 150 G220	Lubrication of plain bearings slideways. They should be particularly useful at low traverse speeds to minimize vibrations due to discontinuous sliding (stick – slip)
H	HM 32 HM46 HM68	General hydraulic systems which include highly loaded components. These oils are also suitable for the lubrication of plain or rolling bearings and all types of gears normally loaded (worm and hypoid gears excepted)
H	HG 32 HG 68	Machines with combined hydraulic and plain bearings slideways, lubrication systems where vibration or intermittent sliding (stick– slip) at low speed is to be minimized.

Lubrication is the significant importance to the prevention of plain slideways from tribological processes which cause failure of machines tools. Among many requirements that must be satisfied is optimum lubricant viscosity.

4. TRIBOLOGY IN RELIABILITY OF TRIBOMECHANICAL SYSTEM

The basic tribological phenomena friction, wear and lubrication are all reliability related. Friction in machinery and equipment resists motion and can result in energy losses and failure. Wear is a process of material deteration that will result in failure if it can proceed far enough. Lubrication is the method of controlling friction and wear by introducing a third material between the interacting moving surfaces, which can reduce energy losses and help avoid failure [16]. What is important from a reliability point of view is to produce more and better tribological data on the endurance life and on the critical wear and friction levels of tribomechanical elements, both in general and specific operational conditions. The important question from a reliability point of view is to produce tribological data and techniques with which the endurance life can be estimated. In addition to endurance life, another reliability parameters that are important from a practical point of view are the probability of failure, failure rate, average life and reliability curve. With this kind of basic reliability data of tribomechanical elements it should be possible to estimate with a good degree of accuracy the reliability of machine tools and the availability of plants.

During operation of machine tool actions can be taken to improve the reliability and tribology has an important role to play in this. By condition monitoring of the performance, on-line information is obtained about the stage of functional deteration that may be due to, e.g. the wear of surfaces. The most common machine tool condition monitoring techniques used today are: vibration analysis, oil analysis and performance measurements such as measuring chatter marks, tolerances, clearances, temperatures, etc. This emphasizes the importance for the tribology society to produce friction and wear data for different material combinations, as well as different contact and environmental conditions in the form of endurance life, probability of failure and so on. The data can then be of use in reliability estimations and functional predictions of tribomechanical elements and machine tools. The reliability curve defined by R(T), which is the probability that the tribomechanical system is operating for a time T, where are R(0)=1 and $1 \geq R(T) \geq 0$, for T>0 . The rate of failure λ(T) is defined in the following way:

$$\lambda(T) = \frac{f(T)}{R(T)}$$

(1)

Thus, the reliability curve is:

$$R(T) = \exp\left[-\int_0^T \lambda(T)\,dT\right]$$

(2)

The density function is:

$$f(T) = \lambda(T) \bullet \exp\left[-\int_0^T \lambda(T)dT \right]$$ (3)

and the mean time to failure is:

$$T_c = \int_0^\infty R(T)dT$$ (4)

5. EXPERIMENTAL INVESTIGATION

The experimental investigation of the influence of lubricating oils on the tribological behavior of plain slideways of machine tools has been carried out on machine tools in two periods of time. During the cutting process a certain amount of workpiece material transforms into chips (particles). The coolant system for metalworking and slideways of machine cutting tools are typical examples of tribomechanical systems where is abrasive wear the most often observed tribological process. The wear process in wet abrasion caused the coolant with particles flows between the interacting solid surfaces of tribomechanical system under load contact. Particulate composition varies significantly as a function of cutting process, operating conditions as well as coolant characteristics and coolant system. The machine tool slideway, because of its sliding components, are very susceptible to deterioration by particulate and therefore are much less reliable. Materials of the slideways are similar by their characteristics to grey cast iron. The region of mixed lubrication, where the roughness of the two opposing surfaces has a high comparable to the lubricant film thickness is complex and poorly understood [17]. Between the regimes of hydrodynamic or elastohydrodynamic lubrication on the one hand and boundary lubrication on the other lies the territory known as "mixed" or "partial" lubrication. To properly chart this region requires a detailed understanding not just of both hydrodynamic and boundary lubrication but also of the influence of surface topography on fluid behavior and of the influence of contact and fluid pressure on surface topography. A number of workers have studied the practical implications of mixed lubrication [18, 19, 20]. The most important area of computational modeling however probably lies in further attempts to deterministically model contacts with load sharing, as has been started by Chang [21]. But, such modeling by supported by experimental work, without experimental verification computation is valueless. However, there appear to be a number of promising developments that make study of mixed lubrication possible. Liang [22] gave one of the methods of for measuring and mapping the real area of contact. The working conditions of these plain slideways are shown in Table 2.

Table 2. Working conditions of plain slideways

Operating Conditions:	
1. Contact geometry	Area
2. Sliding velocity	V=15 – 500 mm / min
3. Contact stress	$P \leq 1,5$ MPa
4. Frequency of motion	Intermittend
Environment:	
1. Lower operating temperature	$t_l \geq 0^0$ c
2. Upper operating temperature	$t_u \leq +55^0$ c
3. Medium	Moisture and contamination with metal particles
4. Coolant for cutting	Semisint water based fluid (5%)
Lubricant:	
1. Type	Hydraulic oils ISO-L-HM and ISO-L-HG
2. Viscosity	ISO VG 46 and ISO VG 68

The relevant parameters of test procedure on the experimental plain slideways of machine tool are shown in Table 3.

Table 3. The relevant parameters of test procedure for plain slideways

Main symptoms of failure	Relevant parameters
	Indication
Uneven motion ("stick – slip")	Surface finish Vibration Chatter marks
3. Decrease of machining accuracy	τ - tolerance $\tau > \tau_{max}$ of cutting operation
3. Excessive clearance	h – clearance $h > h_{max}$ =0,015–0,040 mm
4. Contamination	Contamination with metal particles from coolant system
5. Other symptoms (corrosion and so on)	Corrosion due to moisture and contamination; insufficient oil and so on.

Typical characteristics hydraulic HM oils and hydraulic HG oils are listed in Table 4. Hydraulic HM oils are high quality oils containing anti-oxidant, anti-rust, anti-wear and anti-foam additives for general hydraulic applications and also for circulating or oil bath lubrication systems.

Hydraulic HG oils designed for hydraulic systems and the lubrication of machine tool slides and tables. They are high quality oils of high oxidation stability, incorporating oilness, anti-wear and non-drip additives. The additive combination imparts the frictional characteristics necessary to prevent "stick-slip.

Table 4. Typical characteristics of hydraulic oils

No	Typical characteristics	ISO - L - *HM*		ISO - L - HG	
		VG 46	VG 68	VG 46	VG 68
1	Viscosity at $40\,^0$ C, mm^2 /s	46	68	46	68
2	Viscosity at $100\,^0$ C, mm^2 / s	6,9	8,7	7,0	9,3
3	Viscosity index	100	95	115	105
4	Pour point, ^{0}C, max	205	220	220	230
5	Flash point, ^{0}C, min	-25	-25	-30	-30
6	Density at $15\,^0$ C, kg/m^3	880	885	880	885
7	Rust (Turb. Corr.) ASTM-D 665A	-	p a s s		-
8	FZG (A/8.3/90) Failure Load Stage	11	12	11	12
9	Static friction coefficient	-	-	0,080	0,080
10	Kinetic friction coefficient	-	-	0,100	0,102

6. RESULTS OF EXPERIMENTAL INVESTIGATION AND DISCUSSION

Author discussed three major measures of plain slideways reliability effectiveness:

- Failure rate - λ,
- Average life - $\overline{T}_c$
- Reliable curve - R(T)

The majority of failures of machine tool plain slideways are connected with tribological processes of the elements in the sliding contact. Figure 1 shows the main symptoms of plain slideway's failure.

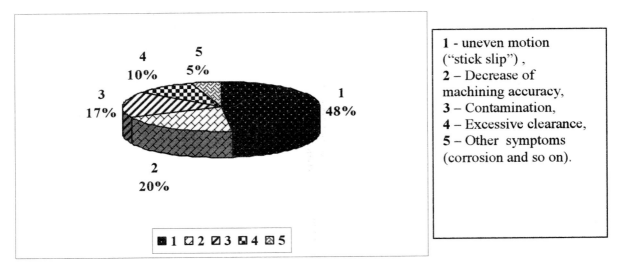

Figure 1. Symptoms of plain slideway failure for oil ISO-L-HG 68

Analysis of the results showed that the most common single symptom of plain slideways was uneven motion due to "stick – slip" and vibration. Contamination leading progressively to decreased of machining accuracy and excessive clearance. Corrosion resulting from moisture, contaminants and the presence of metalworking coolant.

When the friction force in this tribomechanical system suddenly increases (e.g. by a local increase of the surface roughness due to influence of present particle), the relative sliding speed decreases due to motion of the sliding element to the back. This relative deceleration occurs during a relatively large time-length so that enough time is available for part of the lubricant to be squeezed out of the contact. This leads to enhanced metal – metal contact and a further increase of the friction force. This process continues until a relative stick occurs which may be followed by a subsequent slip-phase and so on. The life time of the plain slideways up to the failure mostly shows deviation. Using a probability and statistic methods, it was possible to determine the influence of lubricating oil on the reliability of plain slideways. The results for two periods of time were plotted in reliability curves (R) versus time (T) are shown in Table 5 and Figure 2. Based on statistical χ^2 goodness-of-fit-test to those data (confidence interval is 95%) i.e.

$$\chi_k^2 = \sum_{i=1}^{n} \frac{(f_i - f_{t_i})^2}{f_{t_i}} \qquad (5)$$

it can be concluded that reliability curves are approximately exponentialy distributed. These curves represent the probability of plain slideways reaching the moment"T "without failure. As evident from Figure 2, the lubricating oil ISO - L - HG 68 gives the most plain slideways reliability, but the lubricating oil ISO - L - HM 46 gives the least plain slideways reliability. According to Figure 2, the following observation can be made:

- Increasing the viscosity grade of these lubricating oils led to a longer average life.
- In the same the viscosity grade, hydraulic oils ISO – L – HG give better results than hydraulic oils ISO – L - HM.
- The effect extent of viscosity grade to lives was less compared with that of changing oil type.

Table 5.

R1 (T)	ISO – L – HG 68	$e^{-6,667*10**(-4)*T}$	$\overline{T_c}$ =1500 h
R2 (T)	ISO – L – HG 46	$e^{-7,143*10**(-4)*T}$	$\overline{T_c}$ =1400 h
R3 (T)	ISO – L – HM 68	$e^{-7,692*10**(-4)*T}$	$\overline{T_c}$ =1300 h
R4(T)	ISO – L – HM 46	$e^{-8,333*10**(-4)*T}$	$\overline{T_c}$ =1200 h

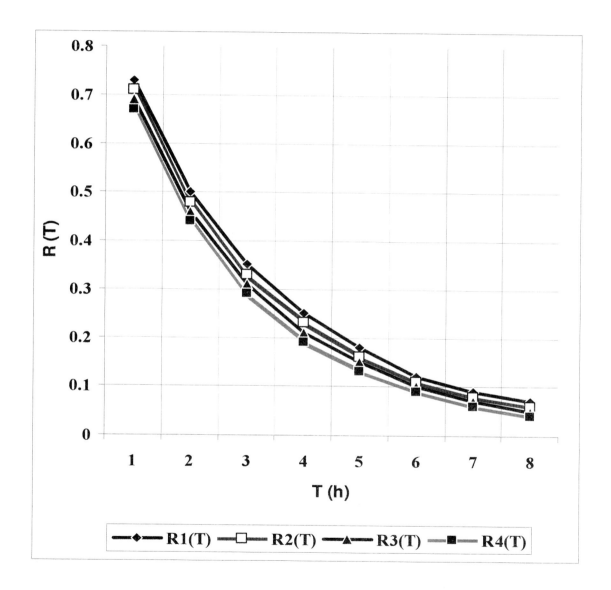

Figure 2. Reliability curves of plain slideways versus time for ISO-L-HM and ISO-L-HG; Values on X- axis are:
1- 500 (h), **2**- 1000 (h), **3**- 1500 (h), **4**- 2000 (h), **5**- 2500 (h), **6**- 3000 (h), **7**- 3500 (h), **8**- 4000 (h)

7. CONCLUSION

The following conclusion can be drawn from the results presented here:

- The reliability of plain slideways was found to be affected by both type of lubricating oil and viscosity grade.
- The hydraulic oil ISO-L-HG gives a longer life of plain slideway compared with the case of the hydraulic oil ISO-L-HM,
- The viscosity grade ISO VG 68 gives a longer life of plain slideway compared with the case of the viscosity grade ISO VG 46.

The paper presents the following:

- The clasification of lubricating oils for plain slideways,
- The analysis of the symptoms and the causes of the failures to plain slideways and
- The curves of plain slideways reliability in function of tribological properties of lubricating oils under presented operating conditions of investigation.

REFERENCES

[1] Hamrock B. J., "Elastohydrodynamic Lubrication of Elliptical Contacts", *Proc. of 1st Symposium Intertribo'81*, High Tatras, 1981, pp. 6 -16.

[2] Jost P. H., "The First Years and Beyond – Achievements, Shortcomings and Future Task", *Proc. of 8th Int. Colloquium*, Ostfildern, 1992, pp. 1.1.1 - 1.1.17.

[3] Zhang W. S., Chang X., "Wet Abrasion of Nitrile Rubber", *Proc. of Japan Int. Tribology Conference*, Nagoya , 1990, pp. 249 - 254.

[4] Sandler H. G., *System Reliability Engineering*, Prentice – Hall, Inc. Engewood Cliffs, N.J., 1963.

[5] Rakić R., "The Influence of Tribological Properties of Lubricants on Contact Surfaces of the Elements of Tribomechanical Systems", *Proc. of 4th Symposium Intertribo'90*, High Tatras, 1990, pp. 64 - 67.

[6] Rakić R., "The Influence of Tribological Properties of Lubricants on Tribological Processes of Machine Elements in the Sliding Contact", *Proc. of Japan Int. Tribology Conference*, Nagoya, 1990, pp. 1707 – 1711.

[7] Rakić R., "Lubricant Selection for Tribomechanical Systems of Machines in Function of Lubricant Properties", *Proc. of 8th Int. Colloquium*, Ostfildern, 1992, pp. 5.3.1 - 5.3.6.

[8] Rakić R., "Analysis of Tribological Processes on Machine Elements in the Sliding Contact", *Proc. of Tribological Seminar Tribologia'92*, Sozopol, 1992, pp. 62 -67.

[9] Rakić R., " Lubricant Selection for Plain Slideways of Machines", *Proc. of 5th Int. Symposium Intertribo'93*, Bratislava, 1993, pp. 69 - 74.

[10] Rakić R., "The Influence of Lubricants on Operation of Machine Tools", *Proc. of 10th Int. Colloquium*, Ostfildern, 1996, pp. 213 - 219.

[11] Lee S-K, Yoo J-H and Yang M-S, Effect of Thermal Deformation on Machine Tool Slide Guide Motion, *Tribology International 36*, 2003, pp.41-47.

[12] Van De Velde F. and De Baets P., Interaction between Friction and System Dynamics during Stick-Slip, *Proc. Symposium on Computational and Experimental Methods in Mechanical and Thermal Engineering*, Gent, 1998, pp.283-283.

[13] *** *Lubricants, industrial oils and related products* (class L) – Recommendation for the choice of lubricants for machine tools, ISO Technical Report 3498, 1986.

[14] *** *Lubricants, industrial oils and related products* (class L) – classification – part 4, Family H (hydraulic systems), International Standard ISO 6743 / 4, 1982.

[15] *** *Lubricants, industrial oils and related products* (class L) – classification – part 13, Family G (Lubricants for slideways), International Standard ISO 6743 / 13, 1987.

[16] Holmberg K., Tribology in Reliability Engineering, *Proc. of 2nd World Tribology Congress*, Vienna, 2001, pp.13-19.

[17] Spikes A.H., "Mixed lubrication – An Overview", *Proc. of 10th Int. Colloquium*, Ostfildern, 1996, pp. 1713-1734.

[18] Chang L., "Deterministic Modelling and Numerical Simulation of Lubrication between Rough Surfaces- a Review of Recent Developments", *Wear 184*, 1995, pp. 155-160.

[19] Cheng H.S., "The Lubrication of Rough Surfaces", *Proc. of 11th Leeds - Lyon Symposium*, 1984.

[20] Greenwood A.J. and Johnson L.K., "The Behaviour of Transverse Roughness in Sliding Elastohydrodynamically Lubricated Contact", *Wear 153*, 1992, pp. 107 – 117.

[21] Chang . L. "A Deterministic Model for Line Contact Partial Elastohydrodynamic Lubrication", *Tribology International 28*, 1995, pp. 75-84.

[22] Liang X, Linquing Z., "A New Method for the Experimental Investigation of Contact in Mixed Lubrication", *Wear 132*, 1989, pp. 221-233.

Magnetic Fluid based Squeeze Film between Rotating Porous Rough Annular Plates

G. M. Deheri [1], H. C. Patel [2], R. M. Patel [3]

[1] Department of Mathematics, Sardar Patel University, Vallabh Vidyanagar, Gujarat – 388 120, India.
[2] Government Engineering College, Chandkheda, Gandhinagar, Gujarat – 382 424, India.
[2] Gujarat Arts and Science College, Ahmedabad, Gujarat – 380 006, India.

ABSTRACT

Efforts have been directed to study and analyze the behavior of magnetic fluid based squeeze films between porous rotating transversely rough annular plates. The roughness of the bearing surface is modeled by a stochastic random variable with nonzero mean, variance and skewness. The Reynolds' equation is stochastically averaged with respect to the random roughness parameter which in turn, is solved with appropriate boundary conditions. Results for performance characteristics such as pressure, load carrying capacity and response time are numerically calculated for various values of the mean, standard deviation and measure of symmetry and presented graphically as well as in tabular form. First of all it is observed that the bearing suffers on account of transverse surface roughness. Further, it is noticed that load carrying capacity decreases with the increasing values of the aspect ratio and the rotational inertia. However, it is seen that negatively skewed roughness improves the performance of the bearing system for suitable values of the variance. Besides, the performance of the bearing system improves significantly owing to the presence of the magnetic fluid lubricant. In addition, the response time follows the trends of load carrying capacity. This article reveals that the roughness, rotational inertia and the aspect ratio must be taken into account while designing the bearing system even if there is the presence of the magnetic fluid.

Keywords: Reynolds equation, roughness, squeezes film, pressure, load carrying capacity, rotation and aspect ratio.

NOMENCLATURE

a = outer radius of the plate (m)

b = inner radius of the plate (m)

p = lubricant pressure (Pa)

$P = -\dfrac{h_0^3 p}{\mu \dot{h}_0 a^2}$ = dimensionless pressure

w = load carrying capacity

$W = -\dfrac{h_0^3 w}{\mu \dot{h}_0 a^4}$ = dimensionless load carrying capacity

Δt = response time

$\Delta T = \dfrac{w h_0^2 \Delta t}{2 \mu \pi^2 a^4}$ = non-dimensional response time

α = mean of the stochastic film thickness

σ = standard deviation of the stochastic film thickness

σ^2 = variance

ε = measure of symmetry of the stochastic random variable

$\bar{\sigma} = \sigma / h_0$

$\bar{\alpha} = \alpha / h_0$

$\bar{\varepsilon} = \varepsilon / h_0^3$

$R = r / a$

$k = b / a$

ϕ = permeability of porous facing

$\psi = \dfrac{\phi H}{h_0^3}$

μ = absolute viscosity of the lubricant (Pa.s)

$\bar{\mu}$ = magnetic susceptibility (m^3/kg)

μ_0 = permeability of the free space (N/A^2)

$\mu^* = -\dfrac{h_0^3 \mu_0 \bar{\mu}}{\mu \dot{h}_0}$ = magnetization parameter

Ω_l = angular velocity of lower plate (rad/s)

Ω_u = angular velocity of upper plate

$\Omega_r = \Omega_u - \Omega_l$

$\Omega_f = \Omega_l / \Omega_u$ = rotation parameter.

$S = -\dfrac{\rho \Omega_u^2 h_0^3}{\mu \dot{h}_0}$

1. INTRODUCTION

In most conventional bearing systems the induced effects due to inertia appear to be of almost negligible significance. However, inertia effects are of crucial nature especially, in bearings with higher rotational speeds and extremely small squeeze velocities. Wu [1-2] investigated the squeeze film behavior between rotating porous annular plates and showed that rotation caused reduced load carrying capacity and response time. Ting [3] simplified the analysis of Wu [2] considerably by taking only the lower disk to be rotating. Gupta and Sinha [4] extended the analysis of [1] by considering the effects of the axial current. Subsequently, Bhat and Patel [5] improved the analysis of [3] by including the effect of an axial current. In all the above discussions the bearing surfaces were considered to be smooth but it is a well-known fact that the bearing surfaces develop roughness after having some run in and wear. Various methods have been adopted to analyze the effect of surface roughness on the performance of squeeze film bearings. Several investigators have proposed a stochastic approach to model the random character of the roughness [6,7,9]. Later on Christensen and Tonder's [7] approach laid down the basis for the analysis to study the effect of surface roughness on the performance of the bearing system in a number of investigations [10-14]. Andharia, Gupta and Deheri [15-16] presented the study of the effect of surface roughness (both transverse and longitudinal) on the performance of a squeeze film bearing using the general stochastic analysis. All these above studies made use of conventional lubricant. Bhat and Deheri [17] analyzed the squeeze film behavior between porous annular disks and found that its performance with a magnetic fluid lubricant was relatively better than that with a conventional lubricant. Further, Bhat and Deheri [18] studied the magnetic fluid based squeeze film in curved porous circular plates. This analysis was extended by [19] by considering the rotation. Patel and Deheri [20] analyzed the behavior of the squeeze film formed by a magnetic fluid between curved annular plates. Patel and Deheri [21] dealt with the behavior of magnetic fluid based squeeze film between rotating porous plates with a concentric circular pocket and studied the surface roughness effect. Recently, Patel and Deheri [22] discussed the behavior of a magnetic fluid based squeeze film between rough annular plates. Here we propose to analyze the above configuration by considering the rotation of both the plates.

2. ANALYSIS

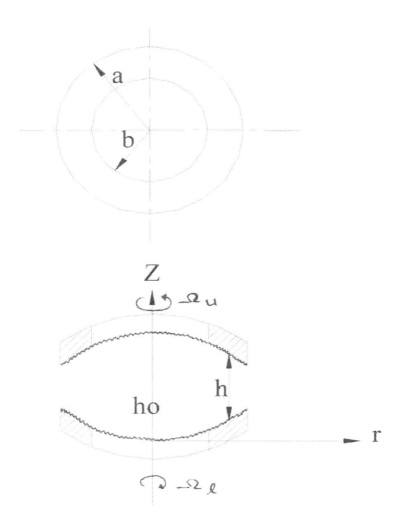

Figure 1. Configuration of the bearing system.

The configuration of the bearing depicted in Figure 1 consists of the annular disks. The upper face moves normally towards the lower disk with uniform velocity $\dot{h} = dh/dt$. Both the disks are considered to have transversely rough surfaces. The upper and lower disks rotate with angular velocities Ω_u and Ω_l respectively. Assuming an axially symmetric flow of the magnetic fluid between the disks under an oblique magnetic field $\overline{H} = (H(r)\cos\phi,\ 0,\ H(r)\sin\phi)$ whose magnitude H is a function of r vanishing at $r = a$ and $r = b$, the modified Reynolds' equation governing the film pressure p is given by [21-22]

$$\frac{1}{r}\frac{d}{dr}\left\{r\frac{d}{dr}\left(p - \frac{\mu_0\bar{\mu}H^2}{2}\right)\right\}$$

$$= \frac{12\mu\dot{h}}{g(h)} + \frac{24\rho\phi H\ \Omega_u^2}{g(h)} + 2\rho\left(\frac{3}{10}\Omega_r^2 + \Omega_r\Omega_l + \Omega_l^2\right) \qquad \ldots\ \ldots\ \ldots\ (1)$$

where

$$g(h) = h^3 + 3\sigma^2 h + 3h^2\alpha + 3h\alpha^2 + 3\sigma^2\alpha + \alpha^3 + \varepsilon$$

and the film thickness has been considered to be $h(r,t)+h_s(r,\xi)$ wherein, h denotes the smooth part of the film thickness and h_s is the part due to surface roughness measured from the mean level. Since the magnetic field arises out of a potential, the angle ϕ can be determined from

$$\cot\phi\,\frac{\partial\phi}{\partial r}+\frac{\partial\phi}{\partial z}=\frac{2r-a-b}{2(a-r)(r-b)}$$

whose solution is

$$c^2\cos ec^2\phi=(a-r)(r-b)$$

and

$$\sin\left(\frac{z}{c}\right)=\frac{2r-a-b}{\left[(a-b)^2-4c^2\right]^{1/2}}$$

Introducing the non-dimensional quantities

$$R=\frac{r}{a}\ ,\quad P=-\frac{h_0^3 p}{\mu\dot{h}_0 a^2}\ ,\quad k=\frac{b}{a}\ ,\quad S=-\frac{\rho\Omega_u^2 h_0^3}{\mu\dot{h}_0}\ ,\quad \psi=\frac{\phi H}{h_0^3}\ ,\quad \Omega_f=\frac{\Omega_l}{\Omega_u}$$

we observe that the dimensionless film pressure P satisfies the equation

$$\frac{1}{R}\frac{d}{dR}\left[R\frac{d}{dR}\left\{P-\frac{\mu^*}{2}(1-R)(R-k)\right\}\right]=-\frac{12}{G(h)}+\frac{24\,S\,\psi}{G(h)}+\frac{S\Omega}{5}\ . \qquad \ldots\ \ldots\ \ldots(2)$$

where

$$G(h)=1+3\overline{\sigma}^2+3\overline{\alpha}+3\overline{\alpha}^2+3\overline{\sigma}^2\overline{\alpha}+\overline{\alpha}^3+\overline{\varepsilon}\ .$$

Solving this equation under the boundary conditions $P(1)=0$ and $P(k)=0$ one gets the pressure distribution as

$$P=\frac{\mu^*}{2}(1-R)(R-k)-\frac{1}{4}\left\{\frac{-12}{G(h)}+\frac{24\,S\,\psi}{G(h)}+\frac{S\Omega}{5}\right\}\left\{1-R^2-\left(1-k^2\right)\frac{\log R}{\log k}\right\} \qquad \ldots\ \ldots(3)$$

The load carrying capacity

$$w=2\pi\int_b^a r\,p(r)\,dr$$

of the bearing in non dimensional form can be expressed as

$$W=\int_k^1 R\,P(R)\,dR$$

$$=\frac{\mu*}{2}\left(\frac{1}{12}-\frac{k}{6}+\frac{k^3}{6}-\frac{k^4}{12}\right)+\frac{c\left(1-k^2\right)^2}{4}+\frac{c\left(1-k^2\right)^2}{4\log k}+\frac{ck^2\left(1-k^2\right)}{2} \qquad \ldots\ \ldots(4)$$

where

$$c=-\frac{1}{4}\left\{-\frac{12}{G(h)}+\frac{24\,S\,\psi}{G(h)}+\frac{S}{5}\left(3\Omega_f^2+4\Omega_f+3\right)\right\}$$

The response time Δt taken by the upper plate to reach a film thickness h_2 from an initial film thickness h_1 can be determined in dimensionless form from the equation,

$$\Delta T=\frac{W}{2}\left(\frac{1}{\overline{h}_2^2}-\frac{1}{\overline{h}_1^2}\right) \qquad \ldots\ \ldots\ \ldots(5)$$

where

$$\overline{h}_1=\frac{h_1}{h}\quad\text{and}\quad \overline{h}_2=\frac{h_2}{h}\ .$$

3. RESULTS AND DISCUSSION

Equations (3-5) represent expressions for dimensionless pressure P, load carrying capacity W and response time ΔT respectively. These performance characteristics depend on various parameters such as μ^*, ψ, $\bar{\sigma}$, $\bar{\alpha}$, $\bar{\varepsilon}$, S and the aspect ratio k. Setting the magnetization parameter $\mu^* = 0$ in these above equations we obtain the pressure, load carrying capacity and response time for the non magnetic case. Further, this study reduces to the investigation of [19] in the absence of roughness. In addition, when neither plate rotates this present analysis leads to the non-rotating case presented by [17]. First of all we have the distribution of load carrying capacity with respect to μ^* for different values of standard deviation $\bar{\sigma}$, skew- ness $\bar{\varepsilon}$, variance $\bar{\alpha}$ and porosity ψ in Figures:2 - 5 respectively.

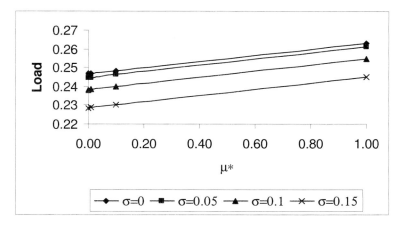

Figure 2. Variation of Load carrying capacity with respect to magnetization parameter μ^* where $\bar{\alpha}$ = -0.05, $\bar{\varepsilon}$ =-0.05, ψ = 0.01, k =1/3, Ω_f= -0.667

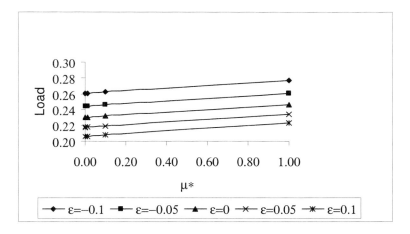

Figure 3. Distribution of Load carrying capacity with respect to magnetization parameter μ^* where $\bar{\alpha}$ = -0.05, $\bar{\sigma}$ =0. 05, ψ = 0.01, k =1/3, Ω_f= -0.667

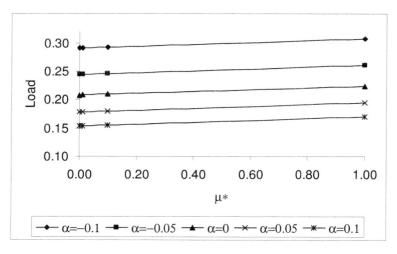

Figure 4. Variation of Load carrying capacity with respect to magnetization parameter μ^* where $\bar{\sigma} = 0.05$, $\bar{\varepsilon} = -0.05$,
$\psi = 0.01$, k =1/3, Ω_f= -0.667

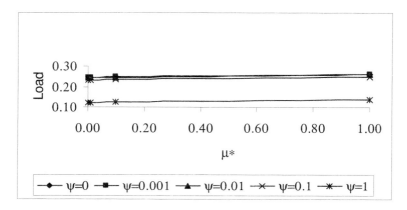

Figure 5. Distribution of Load carrying capacity with respect to magnetization parameter μ^* where $\bar{\alpha}$ = -0.05, $\bar{\sigma}$ =0. 05,
$\bar{\varepsilon}$ = - 0.05, k =1/3, Ω_f= -0.667

It is clearly seen that the performance of the bearing system improves substantially due to $\mu *$ and negatively skewed roughness $-\bar{\varepsilon}$. Besides, porosity decreases the load carrying capacity of the bearing system while the increasing values of standard deviation $\bar{\sigma}$ and variance $\bar{\alpha}$ cause decrease in load carrying capacity. Figures: 6-7 present the distribution of load carrying capacity with respect to $\bar{\sigma}$ for various values of variance and skew ness while Figure 8 describes the variation of load carrying capacity with respect to skew ness for various values of standard deviation $\bar{\sigma}$.

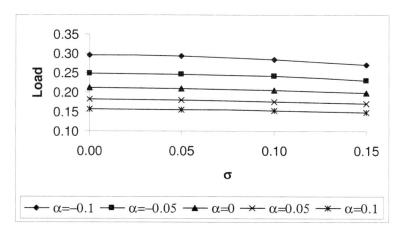

Figure 6. Variation of Load carrying capacity with respect to standard deviation $\bar{\sigma}$ where $\mu^* = 0.1$, $\bar{\varepsilon} = -0.05$, $\psi = 0.01$, k =1/3, Ω_f= -0.667

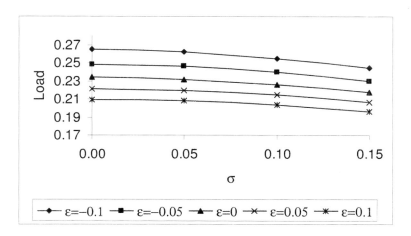

Figure 7. Distribution of Load carrying capacity with respect to standard deviation $\bar{\sigma}$ where $\bar{\alpha} = -0.05$, $\mu^* = 0.1$, $\psi = 0.01$, k =1/3, Ω_f= -0.667

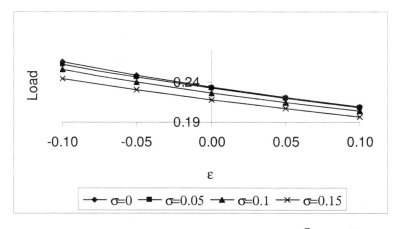

Figure 8. Variation of Load carrying capacity with respect to skew ness $\bar{\varepsilon}$ where $\bar{\alpha} = -0.05$, $\mu^* = 0.1$, $\psi = 0.01$, k =1/3, Ω_f= -0.667

From these figures it is revealed that the standard deviation has a considerable adverse effect on the performance of the bearing system. However, the effect of variance is also equally significant. Figure 9 is concerned with the distribution of load carrying capacity with respect to the rotation parameter Ω_f for different values of μ^*.

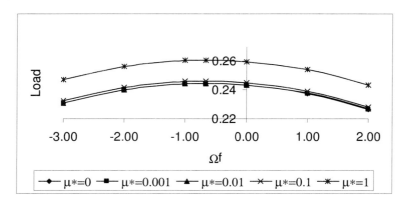

Figure 9. Distribution of Load carrying capacity with respect to rotation parameter Ω_f where $\bar{\alpha}$ = -0.05, $\bar{\varepsilon}$ =-0.05, $\bar{\sigma}$ =0. 05, ψ = 0.01, k =1/3

It is clearly seen that the load carrying capacity tends to attain a maximum value when the plates rotate in opposite direction $(-1 \prec \Omega_f \prec -0.5)$ but the maximum value occurs when Ω_f is closer to -0.67 for different values of μ^* and the roughness parameters $\bar{\alpha}, \bar{\sigma}$ and $\bar{\varepsilon}$. Further, the maximum value occurs at $\Omega_f = 0$ for the case of non rotating lower plate. In Figure 10 we have the distribution of load carrying capacity with respect to the magnetization parameter μ^* for different values of the aspect ratio k. Figures 10-11 make it clear that the aspect ratio results in decreased load carrying capacity even if, there is the presence of magnetic fluid. A comparison of Figure 10 and Figure 11 indicates that the effect of k is sharper as compared to the effect of μ^* .In Figure 12 we have the distribution of load carrying capacity with respect to standard deviation $\bar{\sigma}$ for various values of the porosity ψ. Figures 6-8 and Figures 11-12 suggest that the load carrying capacity decreases significantly.

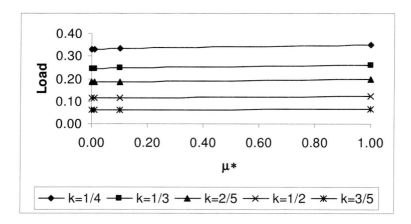

Figure 10. Variation of Load carrying capacity with respect to magnetization parameter μ^* where $\bar{\alpha}$ = -0.05, $\bar{\varepsilon}$ =-0.05, ψ = 0.01, $\bar{\sigma}$ =0. 05, Ω_f= -0.667

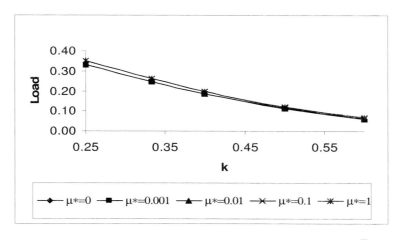

Figure 11. Distribution of Load carrying capacity with respect to aspect ratio k where $\bar{\alpha}$ = -0.05, $\bar{\varepsilon}$ =-0.05, $\bar{\sigma}$ =0. 05, ψ = 0.01, Ω_f= -0.667

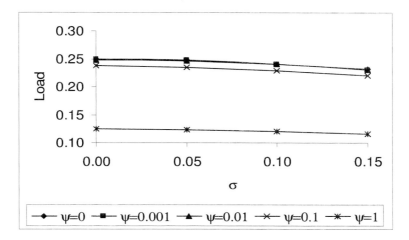

Figure 12. Variation of Load carrying capacity with respect to standard deviation $\bar{\sigma}$ where $\bar{\alpha}$ = -0.05, $\bar{\varepsilon}$ =-0.05, μ^* = 0.1, k =1/3, Ω_f= -0.667

Table 1. Distribution of Load carrying capacity with respect to skew ness $\bar{\varepsilon}$ for different values of μ^* where $\bar{\alpha}$ = -0.05, $\bar{\sigma}$ =0. 05, ψ = 0.01, k =1/3, Ω_f= -0.667

	μ^*=0	μ^*=0.001	μ^*=0.01	μ^*=0.1	μ^*=1
ε = -0.1	0.260646	0.260663	0.260811	0.262292	0.277107
ε = −0.05	0.244560	0.244577	0.244725	0.246206	0.261021
ε = 0	0.230335	0.230351	0.230499	0.231981	0.246796
ε = 0.05	0.217665	0.217681	0.217829	0.219311	0.234126
ε = 0.1	0.206308	0.206325	0.206473	0.207955	0.222769

Table 2. Variation of Load carrying capacity with respect to skew ness $\bar{\alpha}$ for different values of μ^* where $\bar{\varepsilon}$ = -0.05, $\bar{\sigma}$ =0. 05, ψ = 0.01, k =1/3, Ω_f= -0.667

	μ^*=0	μ^*=0.001	μ^*=0.01	μ^*=0.1	μ^*=1
α = -0.1	0.290739	0.290755	0.290904	0.292385	0.307200
α = -0.05	0.244560	0.244577	0.244725	0.246206	0.261021
α = 0	0.207827	0.207843	0.207992	0.209473	0.224288
α = 0.05	0.178192	0.178209	0.178357	0.179838	0.194653
α = 0.1	0.153989	0.154006	0.154154	0.155635	0.170450

Table 3. Distribution of Load carrying capacity with respect to standard deviation $\bar{\sigma}$ for different values of μ^* where $\bar{\alpha}$ = -0.05, $\bar{\varepsilon}$ = -0.05, ψ = 0.01, k =1/3, Ω_f = -0.667

	μ^*=0	μ^*=0.001	μ^*=0.01	μ^*=0.1	μ^*=1
σ = 0	0.246731	0.246747	0.246895	0.248377	0.263192
σ = 0.05	0.244560	0.244577	0.244725	0.246206	0.261021
σ = 0.1	0.238270	0.238287	0.238435	0.239917	0.254731
σ = 0.15	0.228473	0.228490	0.228638	0.230119	0.244934

Table 4 Variation of Load carrying capacity with respect to porosity ψ for different values of μ^* where $\bar{\alpha}$ = -0.05, $\bar{\varepsilon}$ = -0.05, $\bar{\sigma}$ =0. 05, k =1/3, Ω_f = -0.667

	μ^*=0	μ^*=0.001	μ^*=0.01	μ^*=0.1	μ^*=1
ψ = 0	0.245796	0.245813	0.245961	0.247442	0.262257
ψ = 0.001	0.245672	0.245689	0.245837	0.247319	0.262133
ψ = 0.01	0.244560	0.244577	0.244725	0.246206	0.261021
ψ = 0.1	0.233436	0.233453	0.233601	0.235082	0.249897
ψ = 1	0.122199	0.122215	0.122364	0.123845	0.138660

Table 5 Distribution of Load carrying capacity with respect to porosity ψ for different values of $\bar{\sigma}$ where $\bar{\alpha}$ = -0.05, μ^* = 0.1, $\bar{\varepsilon}$ = -0.05, k =1/3, Ω_f = -0.667

	σ=0	σ=0.05	σ=0.1	σ=0.15
ψ = 0	0.249624	0.247442	0.241121	0.231275
ψ = 0.001	0.249499	0.247319	0.241000	0.231159
ψ = 0.01	0.248377	0.246206	0.239917	0.230119
ψ = 0.1	0.237155	0.235082	0.229077	0.219723
ψ = 1	0.124936	0.123845	0.120684	0.115761

Table 6. Variation of Load carrying capacity with respect to rotation parameter Ω_f for different values of μ^* where $\bar{\alpha}$ = -0.05, $\bar{\varepsilon}$ = -0.05, $\bar{\sigma}$ =0. 05, ψ = 0.01, k =1/3

	μ^*=0	μ^*=0.001	μ^*=0.01	μ^*=0.1	μ^*=1
Ω_f=-3	0.230858	0.230874	0.231022	0.232504	0.247319
Ω_f=-2	0.240086	0.240102	0.240250	0.241732	0.256547
Ω_f=-1	0.244280	0.244297	0.244445	0.245927	0.260741
Ω_f=-0.667	0.244560	0.244577	0.244725	0.246206	0.261021
Ω_f=0	0.243442	0.243458	0.243606	0.245088	0.259902
Ω_f=1	0.237569	0.237586	0.237734	0.239215	0.254030
Ω_f=2	0.226663	0.226680	0.226828	0.228309	0.243124

Table 7. Distribution of Load carrying capacity with respect to aspect ratio k for different values of Ω_f where $\bar{\alpha}$ = -0.05, $\bar{\varepsilon}$ =-0.05, $\bar{\sigma}$ =0. 05, ψ = 0.01, μ^* = 0.1

	Ω_f=-3	Ω_f=-2	Ω_f=-1	Ω_f=-0.667	Ω_f=0	Ω_f=1	Ω_f=2
k=1/4	0.313585	0.326032	0.331690	0.332067	0.330558	0.322637	0.307927
k=1/3	0.232504	0.241732	0.245927	0.246206	0.245088	0.239215	0.228309
k=2/5	0.176982	0.184007	0.187199	0.187412	0.186561	0.182091	0.173790
k=1/2	0.109122	0.113453	0.115421	0.115552	0.115028	0.112272	0.107154
k=3/5	0.059386	0.061743	0.062814	0.062885	0.062600	0.061100	0.058315

From Tables 1-4 one can observe the variation of load carrying capacity with respect to $\bar{\varepsilon}$, $\bar{\alpha}$, $\bar{\sigma}$ and ψ for various values of the magnetization parameter μ^*. Table 5 depicts the distribution of load carrying capacity so far as the effect of porosity ψ and standard deviation $\bar{\sigma}$ are concerned. Table 6 presents the variation of load carrying capacity with respect to μ^* for various values of the ratio of rotations. Figure 9 and Table 6 make it clear that the effect of rotational inertia is equally sharp so far as reduction in load carrying capacity is concerned. Lastly, Table 7 shows the effect of the aspect ratio k for various values of rotation parameter. Also, it is observed that the response time follows the trends of the load carrying capacity which is even demonstrated in Equation (5).

A closed scrutiny of the variation of load carrying capacity in graphical as well as tabular form indicates that the adverse effect induced by different parameters (e.g. $\bar{\sigma}$, $\bar{\alpha}$, ψ, k) can be marginally compensated by negatively skewed roughness $-\bar{\varepsilon}$ and the magnetization parameter μ^*. This study establishes that the aspect ratio and rotation must be given due consideration while designing such bearing systems even if there is the presence of magnetic fluid.

REFERENCES

[1]   Wu, H., Squeeze film behavior for porous annular discs, Trans. ASME 92; 1970.p.593-596.
[2]   Wu.H., The squeeze film between rotating porous annular disks, Wear 18; 1971.p. 461- 470.
[3]   Ting L. L. A mathematical analog for determination of porous annular disks squeeze film behavior including the fluid inertia effect, Journal of Basic Engineering 94 (2); 1972. p. 417-421.
[4]   Gupta, J. L., Sinha, P. C., Axial current induced pinch effect on squeeze film behavior for porous annular discs, Journal of Lubrication Technology 97(1); 1975. p. 130-133.
[5]   Bhat, M. V., Patel, K. C., The effect of axial current induced pinch on the lubrication of   rotating porous annular and circular discs, Wear 50; 1978. p. 39-46.
[6]   Tzeng, S. T., Saibel, E., Surface roughness effect on slider bearing lubrication, Trans. ASLE 10; 1967. p. 334-340.
[7]   Christensen H., Tonder K.C., Tribology of rough surfaces: Stochastic models of hydrodynamic lubrication, SINTEF, Report No. 10/69-18; 1969.
[8]   Christensen H., Tonder K.C., Tribology of rough surfaces: Parametric study and comparison of lubrication models, SINTEF, Report No. 22/69-18; 1969.
[9]   Christensen H., Tonder K.C., The hydrodynamic lubrication of rough bearing surfaces of finite width, ASME-ASLE lubrication conference; Paper No. 70-Lub-7; 1970.
[10] Ting L. L., Engagement behavior of lubricated porous annular disks Part I : Squeeze film phase, surface roughness and elastic deformation effects, Wear 34; 1975. p.159-182.
[11] Prakash J. Tiwari K., Roughness effects in porous circular squeeze-plates with arbitrary wall thickness, J. Lub. Tech. 105; 1983. p. 90-95.
[12] Prajapati B. L.,Behavior of squeeze film between rotating porous circular plates: Surface roughness and elastic deformation effects, Pure and Appl. Math. Sci.33 (1-2); 1991. p. 27-36.
[13] Guha S. K., Analysis of dynamic characteristics of hydrodynamic journal bearings with isotropic roughness effects, Wear 167; 1993. p. 173-179.
[14] Gupta J. L., Deheri G. M., Effect of roughness on the behavior of squeeze film in a spherical bearing, Tribology Transactions 39; 1996. p. 99-102.
[15] Andharia P. I., Gupta J. L.and Deheri G. M., Effect of longitudinal surface roughness on hydrodynamic lubrication of slider bearings, Proc. Tenth International Conference on Surface Modification Technologies, The Institute of Materials 1997. p. 872-880.
[16] Andharia P. I., Gupta J. L. and Deheri G. M., Effect of transverse surface roughness on the behavior of squeeze film in a spherical bearing, Journal of Applied Mechanics and Engineering 4; 1999. p. 19-24.
[17] Bhat, M. V., Deheri, G. M., Squeeze film behavior in porous annular disks lubricated with magnetic fluid, Wear 152; 1991. p.123-128.
[18] Bhat, M. V., Deheri, G. M., Magnetic fluid based squeeze film in curved porous circular disks, Journal of Magnetism and Magnetic Material 127; 1993. p. 159-162.
[19] Shah, R. C., Bhat, M. V.,Magnetic fluid based squeeze film in curved rotating circular disks, Journal of Magnetism and Magnetic Materials 208; 2000. p. 115-119.
[20] Patel, R. M., Deheri, G. M., On the behavior of squeeze film by Magnetic fluid between curved annular plates, Indian Journal of Mathematics 44(3); 2002. p. 353-359.
[21] Patel, R. M., Deheri, G. M., Magnetic fluid based squeeze film behavior between rotating porous circular plates with a concentric circular pocket and surface roughness, effects, International Journal of Applied Mechanics and Engineering 8(2); 2003. p. 271-277.
[22] Patel, R. M., Deheri, G. M., Magnetic fluid based squeeze film behavior between annular plates and surface roughness effects, AIMETA International Tribology conference 2004, Rome, Italy; 2004. p. 631-638.

Tribological behaviour of DLC coated gears lubricated with ester-based oil

B. Kržan, M. Kalin, J. Vižintin

University of Ljubljana, Centre for tribology and technical diagnostics

ABSTRACT

The development of new transmissions and gearboxes is characterized by increasing levels of torque and power, improved efficiency, increased life expectancy, prolonged service intervals, reduced amount of lubricant, and more stringent noise and environmental requirements. The environment, as a new factor in the design process, increases the focus on product improvements that are designed to avoid environmental problems before they occur. Surface coating is one of the future technologies for improving performance of case-hardened gears. A main limiting factor to extend the use of hard coatings to machine component application is the lack of knowledge about how these inert coatings perform using today's lubricants, that were originally designed for the steel/steel contact situation. The influence of an ester-based lubricant on the scuffing capacity of WC-containing DLC coated spur gears was evaluated in a non-standard FZG test procedure. The properties of the formulated ester-based lubricant were investigated in comparison with the conventional mineral gear oil. The results show that under present conditions W-DLC coated gears could provide satisfactory wear resistance for moderate loads.

Keywords: wear, gears, ester oils, hard coatings

1. INTRODUCTION

Generally, the gears for power transmission drives are lubricated with the lubricants based on petroleum derived base stocks. With rapid advancement of gear design and manufacturing technology, gearboxes have become smaller, and output power has increased significantly. The net results are higher contact stresses, higher speeds and lower amount of lubricant. With the decreased oil capacities, the lubricant must provide appropriate lubrication at higher operating temperatures, more effective cooling and suspension of contaminants. Therefore, selecting high performance lubricants becomes more and more important. Moreover, there is also a clear trend to use lubricants that cause less harm to the environment. The current view is that the depletion of scarce resources and the increasing environmentally pollution cannot continue in the same way for the next fifty years as they have in the past fifty, without drastically affecting our quality of life. Use of environmentally adapted lubricants is one of the lubrication strategies to avoid environmental problems before they occur. Very good or even superior technical performance of some esters combined with very favorable ecological properties enable the formulation of high performance lubricants, with extremely low evaporation rates, very high viscosity index and good boundary lubrication characteristics. Diesters, polyol and complex esters are biodegradable in the terms of one of the internationally recognized test methods and they have low aquatic toxicity. Their advantage is also that they can be partly derived from the renewable resources, including vegetable oils and animal fats. From ecological point of view, the prospects for the use of renewable raw materials are favorable, provided the full potential of natural synthesis by means of energy from the sun is used. The production of vegetable oils constitutes a cycle in which no net release of carbon dioxide occurs [1,2].

During recent years, significant progress has taken place in the development of advanced coatings used in tribology technology. The unique tribological properties of diamond-like carbon (DLC) films, such as low friction, high wear resistance and low deposition temperature, have made them very attractive for machine element applications. DLC films doped with metal (Me-C:H) have advantages over pure carbon coatings as internal stress is reduced and adhesion to steel substrates is improved. Beside tools and dies, diamond like and related coatings are starting to find application in some mechanical component applications, including bearings and gears. They provide a great opportunity to improve durability and to reduce frictional losses of machine components [3,4].

The present work attempt to combine the excellent friction properties of W-DLC coating with the established lubricating abilities of ester-based lubricant for improving gear performance. The modified FZG scuffing tests were carried out to investigate and compare the scuffing capacity of uncoated steel gears and W-DLC coated gears, lubricated with the conventional mineral gear oil and environmentally adapted ester-based formulation.

2. EXPERIMENTAL

2.1.   Test equipment

The gear tests were performed on a FZG back-to-back test rig. Test conditions were similar to the standard procedure for load carrying capacity of lubricants according to ISO DIS 14 635-1 [5].

The test oils were subjected to the load, increased through 12 load stages, defined in the above-mentioned standards. Duration of each load stage was 20 minutes (29 000 revolutions of the motor) at constant pinion shaft speed of 1450 rpm. Starting bath oil temperature in each load stage was 50 °C and was allowed to rise freely during the test. As the duration of load stages was prolonged with regard to the standard A/8.3/90 test procedure, the total work transmitted by the test gears up to the end of load stage, was 25 percent higher. At the end of the last load stage total work transmitted by the test gears was 184 kWh.

The gear teeth flanks were visually examined after each load stage for cumulative damage in particular scuffing marks and excessive wear. Beside visual inspection, test gears were weighted to the nearest milligram after every 3rd-load stage.

The method used for the quantitative evaluation of the wear particle concentration was a direct reading (DR) ferrography. DR ferrography magnetically separates wear particles from lubricants and optically measures the relative concentration of particles present in the oil sample. The instrument is able to detect particles in the length range of 1 to 300 micrometers.

2.2.   Test gears

Test gears used were standard FZG type "A" spur gears. Type "A" test gears have been designed with a large profile modification, which increases their sensitivity to adhesive wear modes of failure.

Uncoated test gears were made of DIN 20MnCr5 steel and case carburised. The surface hardness after tempering was 60 to 62 HRC and a case depth of 0.6 to 0.9 mm. The surface roughness was 0.35 microns for the pinion and 0.30 for the wheel.

The W-DLC coatings were deposited onto case carburized type "A" spur gears by using a magnetron sputter deposition process, at a substrate temperature of about 200°C. The microhardness was about 1200 HV. The primary coating constituents included W, C and H, with Cr used as a thin adhesion layer (150 nm). The coating thickness of W-DLC layer was typically 1 micron at the root of the gear teeth and 2 microns at the tip.

2.3. Lubricants

The test lubricants were complex ester formulation and conventional mineral based ISO VG 68 gear oil. Physical and chemical properties of test lubricants are summarized in Tab. 1.

Saturated complex ester was composed of multifunctional synthetic alcohol, some petrochemical di-acids and some short chain (C8 – C10) fatty acids from natural resources. Complex ester used as a base stock was almost not toxic for aquatic organisms and according the OECD 202 method was classified as relatively harmless. Primary biodegradation in the CEC-L-33-A-93 test was 76.7 % and ultimate biodegradation in OECD 301F test was 62.2 %. The degradation results identify a material that can be rapidly and extensively biodegraded in the environment.

Esters are inherently good boundary lubricants, however some performance additives are still necessary. The additive system selected was based upon ashless components with mild EP being provided by an organic phosphorous-based chemistry. The EP additive was an amine neutralised phosphoric acid ester, a common type of general purpose EP additive. The AW additive was a dialkyl ditiophosphate ester. Each additive was blended with the complex ester in the concentration of 1 % (wt).

Table 1. Test lubricants.

Property	Unit	Test method	Mineral oil formulation	Ester formulation
Density	kg/m^3	ISO 12185	887	921
Viscosity @40 °C	mm^2/s	ISO 3104	68	48
Viscosity @100 °C	mm^2/s	ISO 3104	8.6	8.0
Viscosity index		ISO 2909	96	138
Pour point	°C	ISO 3016	- 27	<- 42
Elemental compositon phosphorous sulphur	%m/m	PML 07.18 (int.) ISO 14596	0.022 1.0	0.101 0.158

According to the producer, the reference petroleum based oil is recommended for heavily loaded gearboxes with surface hardened tool metallurgies. One ISO viscosity grade higher viscosity was chosen to compensate the effect of viscosity index difference.

3. RESULTS

The most informative method for plotting wear results was found to be cumulative plots of the test gears weight loss and wear particle concentration on the same graph with the reference to the total work transmitted and FZG load stage.

The results of the scuffing investigations for steel test gears are presented in Fig. 1. It is evident that the scuffing load capacity of ester formulation is higher compared to the mineral oil formulation. For the mineral oil the weight loss of test gears is within the acceptable limits as long as 140 kWh of total work transmitted was reached. At 184 kWh the cumulative weight loss of pinion and gear equals 610 milligrams and all pinion flanks were damaged. With the ester formulation the test gears weight loss is significantly lower. After completion of the test cumulative sum equals only 18 milligrams and just a few scoring marks above the pitch line could be noted. The wear particle concentration results completely follow the gears weight loss trend for both oils. The rate of wear particle concentration for mineral oil is seen to give rather high values especially after the 6th load stage.

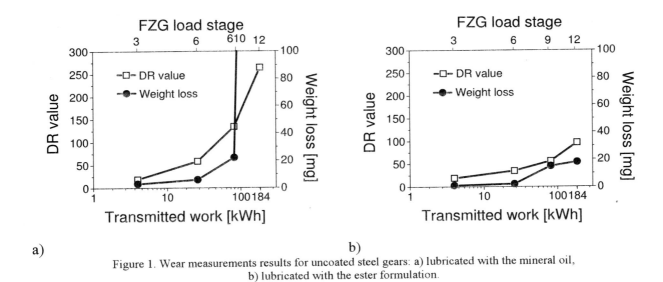

a)   b)

Figure 1. Wear measurements results for uncoated steel gears: a) lubricated with the mineral oil,
b) lubricated with the ester formulation.

The wear results for W-DLC coated gears as presented in Fig. 2, show a steady progressive increase of test gears weight loss and wear particle concentration for both oils.

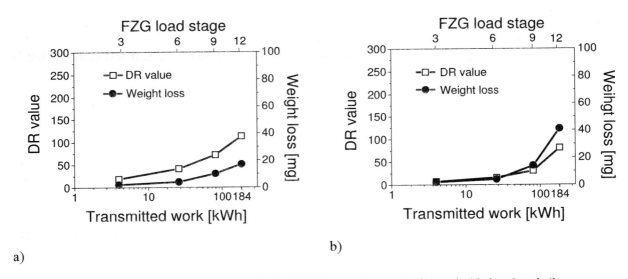

b)

a)

Figure 2. Wear measurements results for W-DLC coated gears: a) lubricated with the mineral oil,
b) lubricated with the ester formulation.

Use of the ester formulation resulted in higher weight loss of gears, while the wear particle concentration is lower compared to the mineral oil formulation. For ester formulation scuffing marks became visible after the 8 kWh work transmitted and started first at the root and later at the tip of the pinion teethes. After 15 kWh mostly the all pinion tooth flanks were tiny polished. The first breakthrough of the W-DLC coating was observed after 26 kWh work transmitted at the root of the pinion. For mineral oil formulation the coating breakthrough started at the same time after 26 kWh work transmitted but visible damages were more severe. Developing scoring damages were observed during the following runs for both oils. After the completion of the test the pinion flanks were polished and the W-DLC coating was totally worn out from the root of the pinion.

Figure 3 shows the increase of bath oil temperature at the end of the each scuffing load stage for both oils and uncoated steel and W-DLC coated test gears. The bath oil temperature increases steadily with the applied load for both oils and material combinations. Tests with the W-DLC coated gears resulted in lower bath oil temperature, suggesting that the surface tooth flank material is stronger influence factor on temperature rise than lubricant used. The lowest oil bath temperature is found for the W-DLC coated gears lubricated with the mineral oil formulation.

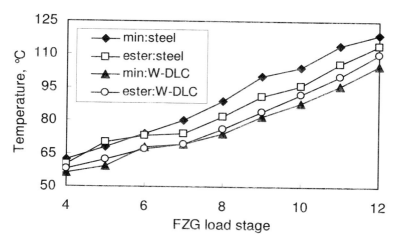

Figure 3. Bath oil temperature after the completion of load stage.

4. DISCUSSION

Wear results for mineral oil formulation suggest that scuffing capacity is strongly influenced by the surface material of the test gears (see Fig 1a and 2a). The mineral oil and steel gear test combination is seen to exhibit the highest wear. Visual inspection of the pinion tooth flanks indicate the failure in the 12th load stage after 184kWh work transmitted. On the other hand, mineral oil in the combination with the W-DLC coated gears resulted in significantly lower wear and passes the 12th load stage. Contrary, when using ester formulation wear results for steel and W-DLC coated gears are comparable and of low value.

Additional information about wear mode and mechanism could be obtained with the analytical wear particle analysis. Wear particle is the final product of surface damage and its shape, morphology, size and concentration can give some information on the mode and the mechanism of wear. The wear particles are first fixed to a glass slide and then analyzed under an optical microscope.

Figure 3 displays the particles separated from the mineral oil formulation and Fig. 4 displays the particles separated from the ester formulation after 146 kWh total work transmitted that is equivalent to the 11th test run in the modified FZG test procedure. On Fig. 3a, 3b and Fig. 4a, 4b are presented typical wear particles from the entry region of the glass substrate. Particles at this location are typically the largest particles separated from the oil because the magnetic force which attracts the particles is proportional to the volume whereas the viscous resistance of the particles to motion in the fluid is proportional to surface area. From comparing the photos it is evident that wear particles obtained from the tests with W-DLC coated gears are larger than wear particles from the lubricants tested in combination with uncoated steel gears. It can also be observed that wear particles from mineral oil are larger than particles from ester formulation for both gear tooth flank materials.

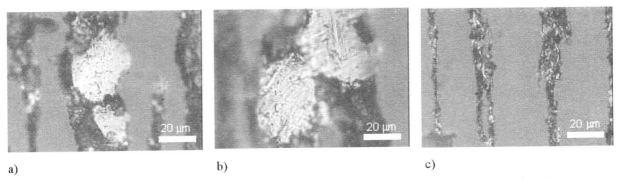

a)   b)   c)

Figure 3. Entry region of the glass slide made from mineral oil, magnified 500 times. a) uncoated steel gears;
b) W-DLC coated gears; c) W-DLC coated gears – the largest cutting wear particles.

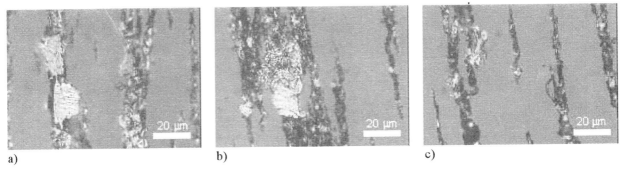

a)   b)   c)

Figure 4. Entry region of the glass slide made from ester formulation, magnified 500 times. a) uncoated steel gears;
b) W-DLC coated gears; c) W-DLC coated gears – the largest cutting wear particles.

Larger size of the wear particles separated from the mineral oil formulation for steel gears is expected, because the coefficient of friction for ester-based lubricants and steel contact surfaces is typically lower [6,7]. The lower bath oil temperature (see Fig.3) also indicates the lower coefficient of friction for ester formulation.

Even through the particles found in different gear material combinations discussed above are of different sizes and compositions, the most of them are flat flakes having irregular shapes and generally featureless surfaces without characteristic striations indicating severe wear. In fact, this is the morphology observed for the majority of wear particles larger than 15 microns. This implies that they were all produced by the same wear mechanism. However, wear particles produced by the interaction of two component surfaces, such as gear teeth, are subjected to continuous high contact pressures and would therefore have a strong tendency to be flattened and smoothed by the forces acting on them. This process would account for the typical particle morphology observed and suggests considerable alternation to wear particle morphology occurs after the particles are produced.

Another characteristic group observed is cutting wear particles, presented on Fig. 2c and Fig. 3c. Cutting or abrasive wear particles are produced by the penetration, ploughing or cutting of one surface by another. They take the form of miniature spirals, loops and bent and their presence is abnormal. It is indicative, that these types of particles are found only on the glass slides from the tests with the W-DLC coated gears. They are not found on slides made from lubricants obtained from the tests with steel gears. Distinctive are also very large flat particles obtained from test with mineral oil formulation and W-DLC coated gears. Figure 5 shows the largest particles separated from the oil. They ranged from 70 to 125 micrometers in major dimension indicating the lubrication problems.

  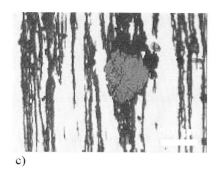

a)   b)   c)

Figure 5. Glass slide made from the mineral oil from the test with the W-DLC coated gears, after 146 kWh work transmitted, magnified 500 times a) large particles; b) the largest particle; c) the largest particle, magnified 100 times.

Very large wear particles and presence of abrasive particles all these imply that the wear mechanism for uncoated and W-DLC coated gears is different. For W-DLC coated gears the wear probably starts under the surface while prevailing wear mechanism for uncoated gears is adhesive wear.

5. CONCLUSIONS

The following conclusions can be derived from this study:

- Ester-based formulation resulted in higher scuffing load capacity than mineral oil formulation in the test with the steel gears.

- The scuffing performance of mineral oil in the combination with the W-DLC coated gears is significantly improved as regards to the combination with steel gears. However, some particles exciding the 100 micrometers in the major size indicate the lubrication problems. The wear rate for ester-based formulation is similar for steel and W-DLC coated gears.

- The surface tooth flank material is a stronger influence factor on temperature rise than lubricant used.

- The wear mechanism for uncoated and W-DLC coated gears is different.

REFERENCES

[1]   Kržan B., Vižintin J.: Use and development of biodegradable oils, in Tribology of mechanical systems; a Guide to present and future technologies, ed. by Vižintin J., Kalin M., Dohda K., Jahanmir S., ASME Press, New York, 2004.
[2]   Willing, A.: Lubricants based on renewable resources, Chemosphere, Vol.43, pp.89-98, 2001.
[3]   Jiang, J.C., Meng, W.J., Evans, A.G., Cooper, C.V.: Structure and mechanics of W-DLC coated spur gears, Surface and coatings technology, Vol.176, pp. 50-56, 2003.
[4]   Mercer, C., Evans, A.G., Yao, N., Allameh, S., Cooper, C.V.: Material removal on lubricated steel gears with W-DLC coated gears, Surface and coatings technology, Vol.173, pp.122-129, 2003.
[5]   ISO DIS 14635-1: FZG test procedure for relative scuffing load capacity of oils, Part 1: Test method A/8.3/90, 1996.
[6]   Kalin, M., Vizintin, J.: A comparison of the tribological behaviour of steel/steel, steel/DLC and DLC/DLC contacts when lubricated with mineral and biodegradable oils, Proceedings of the 11th Nordic Symposium on Tribology, pp. 549-564, 2004.
[7]   Krzan, B., Vizintin, J.: Tribological properties of an environmentally adapted universal tractor transmission oil based on vegetable oil, Tribology International, Vol.46, pp. 827-833, 2003.

Session 9
LUBRICANTS & ADDITIVES 3

Chair: Prof. R. Derek Arnell

The Effect of Friction Modifiers in Shock Absorber Oils
P. LAFONT, J. L. MUÑOZ, J. ECHÁVARRI, P. LEAL,
J. M. MUÑOZ-GUIJOSA, H. LORENZO, A. DÍAZ

Performance and Selection of Pour Point Depressants
P. HUTCHINSON, J. ARCHIBALD, C. NEVEU

Synthesis of some lubricant additives, investigation of antioxidant characterization and the synergism effect of them on ZDDP
M. SHEKARRIZ, M. SOLEYMANI JAMARANI, S. TAGHIPOOR,
A. A. KHALILI, B. GHANBARI, F. HAJIALIAKBARI

The Effect of Friction Modifiers in Shock Absorber Oils

P. Lafont, J. L. Muñoz, J. Echávarri, P. Leal, J. M. Muñoz-Guijosa, H. Lorenzo, A. Díaz

División de Ingeniería de Máquinas (Universidad Politécnica de Madrid)
José Gutiérrez Abascal, 2, 28006 Madrid, Spain

ABSTRACT

The main aim of this work is to develop an experimental method capable of finding a relationship between the friction behaviour of an oil used in a shock-absorber and the type and quantity of the friction modifiers used in its formulation. For this purpose, a complete design of experiments has been done, based on a long series of additives and shock-absorbers. The results obtained, in a damper test system, prove that the shock-absorber performance varies greatly according to the friction modifier selected. In many cases the combination of different types of additives, such as friction modifiers and antiwear additives produces interactions and the corresponding variation in test results. In some cases, a small variation in the quantity of chemical species used as additives has also an important impact in the results. The conclusions obtained in this research have been applied to develop a new shock-absorber oil, that fulfills the most strict requirements in friction tests specified by the automotive industry.

Keywords: Shock-absorber, Friction, Lubricants and Additives.

1. INTRODUCTION

In the shock-absorber sector, unlike in other industrial sectors, there are no reference standars. Each automobile manufacturer specifies some trials in test bench and some rejection/acceptance criteria, and thereby decides if a shock-absorber is suitable or not for its vehicles. These tests vary according to the customer and the subsequent use of the shock-absorber, but they always include performance tests at different speeds and some friction tests that are representative of the shock-absorber in service behaviour.

Moreover, comfort and safety requirements in the automobile industry are constantly evolving, which means that companies in the sector come up with specifications for shock-absorbers that are ever more numerous and demanding, and which require made-to-measure lubricants. Therefore, lubricant oils for shock-absorbers require a continuous research process in order to develop oils that are capable of adapting to changing and ever stricter demands.

All the above means constant changes to oil formulation and the use of different additives in different proportions. The problems of interaction between them are solved by using "packs", a name used to refer to the groups of additives that are added jointly, and whose compatibility must be known beforehand.

This paper reflects a broad study on friction, taken from the internal specifications of manufacturers, which has enabled the different substances used as additives to be classified, as well as enabling the most suitable ones to be selected.

Friction has its origin in the different contacts produced during the movement of a shock-absorber: piston-sleeve, piston-rod-guide and piston-rod-seal. The first two, which are designed with the aim of reducing friction, are each covered by a layer of teflon, and are located in an area of appropriate lubrication. To the contrary, the seal is conceived as a hermetic device, and lubricant reaches this area with difficulty, which means that friction in its slip against the piston-rod may be very high and produce problems of wear and the appearance of noise when working [1], [2].

This is why the friction value is limited in the friction trials of different manufacturers. However, to reduce this friction, it is not sufficient to add a good anti-friction additive to the lubricant but it is necessary to contrast experimentally the appearance of interactions between additives, or use packs of known compatibility. Friction and wear enhancers, in particular, are combined with the utmost care, as both additives are of a strong polar nature and adhere to sliding surfaces [3].

In order to measure this friction force, different types of tests are defined in each manufacturer's specifications [4]. All are performed at very low speed [5] (below 1mm/s), so that hydraulic forces, due to oil passing through the valves, do not influence the measurement..

2. INITIAL EXPERIMENTAL METHOD

Friction tests on shock-absorbers are performed on an MTS hydraulically controlled test-system, which allows movements at sufficiently low speeds and different types of displacement (sinusoidal wave, ramp, square, etc.). The joint between the test bed and the shock-absorber is made by using spherical joints, which enable the shock-absorber to be aligned during the test and avoid the introduction of lateral forces that might distort the friction measurements [5]. Temperature control is carried out in all the trials.

The tests for taking and comparing friction results are performed on the same model of a type 1 shock-absorber, of which several units that can be disassembled are used and which allow the oil to be changed and to be pressurised with nitrogen. This is a twintube type shock-absorber with an oil chamber between the casing and the sleeve and another between the piston-rod and sleeve. It has two valves for oil flow in the piston and at the base of the sleeve. Instructions for filling the shock-absorbers have been received.

The precision and repeatability of the results in the performance and friction tests has been verified by using tests on shock-absorbers that can be disassembled, as is shown below:

- In the manufacturer's laboratories on the units of shock-absorbers supplied.

- In the "División de Ingeniería de Máquinas", on the same units, before the first opening.

- Second test in the "División de Ingeniería de Máquinas"; after opening, a thorough cleaning and filling with in-origin fluid.

The deviations observed in the performance and friction test results are always below 5%, which shows that the test and cleaning procedure followed has been appropriate.

2.1.   Study of different fluids in the shock-absorber

The effect of using different fluids is studied below. In each case, the typical curve is determined on the MTS test machine, by four test configurations: without gas pressure in the shock-absorber and without applying any lateral load on the piston-rod-seal sliding contact; without pressure and loaded; pressurised but with no lateral load; pressurised and loaded.

The friction of a series of eight shock-absorber fluids is evaluated, based on the same composition, but with a different type of friction modifier in a proportion of 1%:

- Oil 1: Base oil with 1% no. 1 friction modifier (FM) additive

- Oil 2: Base oil with 1% no. 2 FM additive

- Oil 3: Base oil with 1% no. 3 FM additive

- Oil 4: Base oil with 1% no. 4 FM additive

- Oil 5: Base oil with 1% no. 5 FM additive

- Oil 6: Base oil with 1% no. 6 FM additive

- Oil 7: Commercial oil with 1% no. 7 FM additive

- Oil 8: Oil without friction modifier

For this test, the Force-Displacement curve is recorded in a complete cycle and the amplitude of this curve is measured at the positions of minimum and maximum displacement that correspond to the sum of the friction forces under compression and rebound, in R-C passes from rebound to compression, and C-R passes from compression to rebound (figure 1). The results for the eight oils are showed in figure 2.

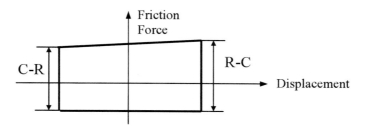

Figure 1. Force-Displacement curve for a shock-absorber.

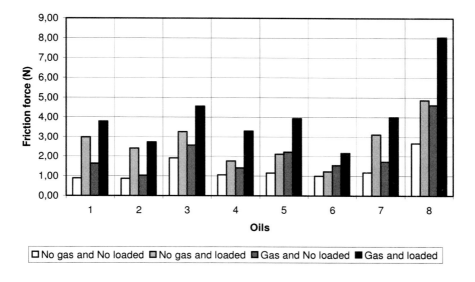

Figure 2. Results of mean R-C and C-R friction force, for eight oils tested on a shock-absorber test machine.

2.2. Friction study in a tribometer

The lubricated piston-rod-seal contact is reproduced in a tribometer, and an alternative movement is applied to the contact with an amplitude of movement of one millimetre. Although the value measured in this test is not friction force but the average friction coefficient during the test, the results obtained can be used to check the results for the previous eight oils. These results for the tribometer (figure 3) show the same tendency for all the oils studied.

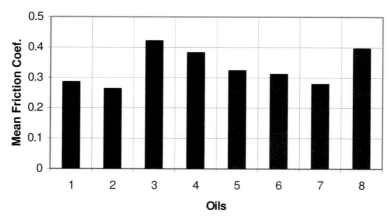

Figure 3. Results of mean piston-rod-seal friction coefficient for eight oils tested in a tribometer.

3. SELECTING THE BEST FRICTION MODIFIER

Once it has been verified that differences between oils can be found by using the friction test on a shock-absorber test machine, the test is systematically performed on a series of more than 50 different types of friction modifiers at a percentage of 1 % on the same base.

With the results obtained, a slightly lower number of series of friction additives is selected in order to develop a more thorough study, which includes the effect of different proportions of additive, and combinations of anti-wear additives in different proportions.

3.1. Experimental design for studying interactions among additives.

As the friction tests progress, it is useful to apply a design of experiments tool, such as Statgraphics, that will enable the results of friction in the shock-absorber, for different proportions and types of friction and anti-wear modifier additives, to be distinguished. To this end, a $6 \cdot 2^{3-1}$ design fractional factorial is designed for each type of friction modifier using the following variables:

A: Oil sample with combinations of additives, which may take the form of the following six levels:

   A1: Base oil with 2% friction modifier additive (FM) but without anti-wear (AW)

   A2: Base oil with 1% FM additive and 1% of a first type of AW additive

   A3: Base oil with 1% FM additive and 0.5% AW of the first type of AW

   A4: Base oil with 1% FM additive and 0.5% AW of a second type of AW

   A5: Base oil with 1% FM additive and 0.5% AW of a third type of AW

   A6: Base oil with 1% FM but without AW

B: Gas pressurisation of the shock-absorber, with two levels:

   B0: Without gas pressurisation

   B1: Shock-absorber at 5 bar

C: Lateral load application, with two possibilities:

   C0: Without lateral load

   C1: Test with 11 daN

D: R-C or C-R transition:

   D0: Pass from rebound to compression R-C

   D1: Pass from compression to rebound C-R

In some oils, in no. 5 oil for example, a complete model has been made (without fraction), to check that the results with half the model offer the same information (with 95% reliability) as the complete model, for any of the possible fractions. To the contrary, it has been verified that the same does not happen if it is attempted to make extrapolations with a quarter of the data.

Some results are shown (figure 4) for the complete factorial model of this oil as well as the fractional model (with the two possible fractions) for half the tests. It becomes evident that with half of the results, the comparative parameter bands for the friction force show more uncertainty, but allow the same conclusions to be reached.

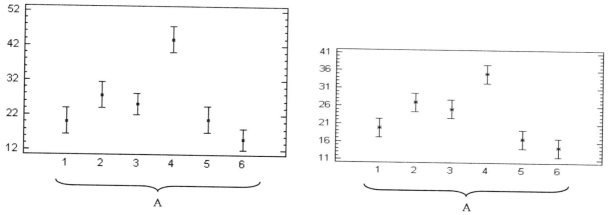

Figure 4. Friction comparative parameter for tests without gas or load for oils with friction modifiers and anti-wear additives. Left: $6 \cdot 2^{3-1}$ Fractional model. Right: $6 \cdot 2^3$ Complete model.

4. RESULTS AND DISCUSSION

Figure 5 shows the results of a friction test on a test machine for no. 5 oil, for the test case without gas or lateral load. If the additive concentration is varied, the results show that the friction force is not reduced by adding 2% anti-friction additive instead of 1%, as may be seen by comparing samples A1 and A6 in figure 5. Adding anti-wear additive increases friction in every case. This increase varies depending on the type of anti-wear that is added and in what proportion (samples A2, A3, A4 and A5 in figure 5). When this proportion is increased, a greater deterioration in the friction characteristics is observed. A compromise between wear and friction criteria is the deciding factor for the type of additives and the most suitable proportions.

Although the contacts between piston-rod and seal are very similar in the most widely used shock-absorbers, the friction can be changed by using the same lubricant in different types of shock-absorbers. In order to study the variations in friction measured in a type 1 shock-absorber, tests are performed with another type of shock-absorber that can be disassembled (type 2). The example of results for oil no. 5, obtained for the test without gas and without load, indicate that qualitative tendencies are preserved, but the variation in force is less than for type 1 (figure 6). This aspect should be taken into account when studying the compliance of a particular quantitative specification.

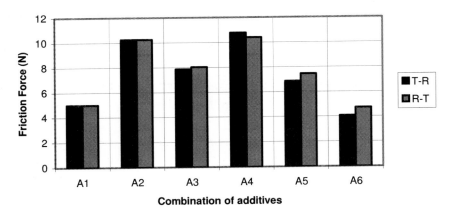

Figure 5. R-C and C-R friction in tests without gas or load, for different type and proportion of FM and AW additives.

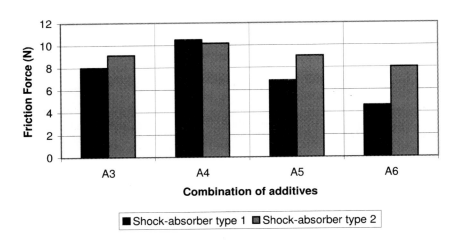

Figure 6. Mean R-C and C-R friction in tests without gas or load for type 1 and 2 shock-absorbers.

The process described has been used to select a set of additive components for an oil that complies with the strictest specifications required in the sector, and which at present is used by a leading automotive company.

5. CONCLUSIONS

Once the repeatability and precision of the test has been verified, the tests with different oils allow differences in the friction curves to be detected. The highest values correspond to oils with worse anti-friction additives.

The friction results in a tribometer for the eight oils indicate that the measures taken in the shock-absorber evaluation equipment are good and correspond to the piston-rod-seal contact tested in a tribometer.

In the tests performed, the components with the best anti-friction properties are determined, the differences between oils being very considerable. It has been observed that the effect of increasing the concentration of friction modifier additives in a shock-absorber oil is of little significance from one percent upwards.

The results of selecting types and proportions of oil additives using different shock-absorbers, have enabled it to be verified, that in friction tests, a noticeably higher friction force is measured when the anti-friction additive is combined with some types of anti-wear. The increase in friction turns out to be different depending on the anti-wear additive that is added and in what proportion. When the proportion is increased a greater deterioration in friction characteristics is produced.

When different types of additive are used in the oil, the friction results enable the most suitable set of additives to be selected to be combined with a particular friction modifier and obtain a lubricant with the best possible level of friction.

If the experiments are properly planned, the number of tests to be performed can be reduced to half without the loss of any relevant information, given that an error interval of the same order of magnitude as the measured results may be obtained. Furthermore, the same significant variables are found in both the complete and the fractional design.

ACKNOWLEDGEMENTS

Jorge Insa and Luis Fernández, REPSOL-YPF, Head Office of Technology, Refining and Marketing, and Lubricants. And Ramón Gutiérrez, Mechanical Engineer, U.P.M.

REFERENCES

[1]   J. Echávarri. "Vibraciones en Adherencia-Deslizamiento Lubricado. Aplicación a Amortiguadores de Automóviles". Thesis. Universidad Politécnica de Madrid, December 2005.
[2]   E. Bautista, J. Echávarri, J.L. Muñoz, E. Olmeda. "Vibraciones en Adherencia-Deslizamiento Lubricado. Aplicación a Amortiguadores de Automóviles". III-Congreso Ibérico de Tribología, Guimaraes (Portugal), June 2005.
[3]   J. Echávarri, E. Bautista, E. Olmeda, H. Lorenzo "Evaluación de fricción en amortiguadores y contraste de resultados", XVI-Congreso Nacional de Ingeniería Mecánica, December 2004.
[4]   Jo hn C. Dixon, Shock Absorber Handbook, SAE, Warrendale U.S.A, 1999.
[5]   Database of Shock-absorbers Oils, Repsol-YPF, 2006.

Performance and Selection of Pour Point Depressants

P. Hutchinson, J. Archibald, C. Neveu

RohMax Additives GmbH, Kirschenalee, D-64293 Darmstadt, Germany

ABSTRACT

Mineral base stocks contain waxy hydrocarbons that come out of solution when temperature decreases. They form a three-dimensional wax crystal network that can totally immobilize the oil. In formulated engine oils some additives have a "waxy" or crystalline structure and further contribute to the formation of a crystal network that impairs oil flow. Waxiness is evidenced at low temperature by higher pour-point, yield stress and viscosity compared to a wax and additive free oil. Inadequate oil flow to critical parts of the equipment may result in costly failures and must be avoided by selecting the appropriate type and content of Pour Point Depressant (PPD).

Selection of a suitable PPD must take into account many factors. These include the PPD type and addition rate, the base stocks used, the influence of other additives and the different cooling rates and shear rates to which the oil will be submitted in service.

As new, more diverse base-stock types are used, more waxy additives are utilized and ever more stringent low temperature requirements on fresh and used oils are imposed, the selection of a suitable PPD is becoming increasing challenging. Key aspects for the proper selection of PPDs are presented in this paper.

Keywords: Pour-Point Depressant, Wax, Low Temperature Lubricant Testing.

1. INTRODUCTION

Prior to the 1930s, the options for dealing with poor lubrication due to the thickening or gelation of engine oils due to wax crystal effects at low temperature were very limited. These included heating the sumps of vehicles, dilution of the oil with kerosene or addition of one or several naturally occurring materials, which were removed at various stages of the refining process, such as asphaltic or resinous hydrocarbons or microcrystalline waxes.

The structures of natural hydrocarbon pour point depressants, all waxy materials themselves, provided clues to the early synthetic efforts and, in 1931, alkylated naphtalenes, wherein the alkyl groups contained linear waxy paraffinic structures, were introduced. This development encouraged the examination of other waxy materials as candidates, and in 1937 Rohm and Haas patented the first polymeric pour point depressant, polyalkyl methacrylates (PAMAs), again based on waxy alkyl groups.

Over the years, a wide variety of synthetic materials has been introduced commercially as pour point depressants. Chlorinated wax is the most notable example of small molecule chemistry, but most commercial products are moderate to high molecular weight polymers, such as polymethacrylates, polyacrylates, acrylate-styrene copolymers, esterified olefin- or styrene maleic anhydride copolymers, alkylated polystyrene, vinyl acetate-fumarate copolymers and ethylene-vinyl acetate copolymers.

2. PAMA POUR POINT DEPRESSANT CHEMISTRY

Even though polymethacrylates were the first of the polymeric pour point depressants, they are still, by far, the most widely used because of the exceptional flexibility of this chemistry. PAMA pour point depressants are obtained by the free radical polymerization of a mixture of methacrylic esters with alkyl groups ranging typically from Cl2 to C22.

$$- (-CH_2 - \underset{\underset{CO_2R}{|}}{\overset{\overset{CH_3}{|}}{C}} -)_x - (-CH_2 - \underset{\underset{CO_2R'}{|}}{\overset{\overset{CH_3}{|}}{C}} -)_y -$$

In order for the PAMA to interact with wax, alkyl groups must be linear and contain typically more than twelve carbon atoms. Because there is a distribution of wax molecule chain lengths in the oil, the best pour point depressancy is achieved when there is also a distribution of alkyl groups in the polymer. In general, the interaction of an alkyl group with wax intensifies as its length increases, and optimum positive interaction with wax requires a very careful balance of the waxy alkyl groups.

2.1. Mechanism of Action.

Pour point depressants do not significantly affect either the temperature at which wax crystallizes from solution or the amount of wax that precipitates. They do however provide nucleation sites to seed wax crystal formation, and also co-crystallize on the edges of the growing wax crystal plate, thereby sterically interrupting the growth in that plane. Growth is redirected in a perpendicular direction, resulting in the formation of needle-like crystals rather than plates. PPDs can thus limit the growth of three-dimensional gel structures that impair the oil.

 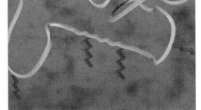 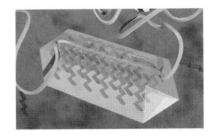

3-Dimensional Wax Structure   **PAMA Waxy Alkyl Chains**   **Co-crystallization with Waxes**

Figure 1. Interaction of PPD with the growth of wax crystals

Even in the absence of linear paraffins, decreasing temperature results in viscosity increase. When viscosity becomes too high the oil stops flowing under the influence of gravity. The temperature at which this happens is called the viscous pour point.

Addition of a PPD lowers the temperature at which the oil transitions from a viscous liquid to a solid like material under the effect of the three dimensional waxy structure. Thus the Pour-Point of a paraffinic oil lies between its cloud point and the viscous pour-point of its non-waxy hydrocarbons.

A properly selected PPD will provide a very large enhancement of low temperature performance at very low concentrations. Further addition of PPD can bring further improvements, but once wax crystallisation is completely under control the performance response becomes flat. Further increases in PPD concentration are, in effect, only adding additional wax to the system and contributing to viscosity, thereby eventually leading to a reversal of performance gains.

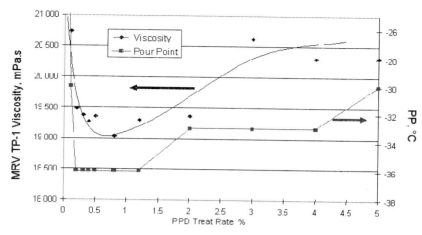

Figure 2. Effect of PPD concentration on low temperature performance

3. LOW TEMPERATURE PERFORMANCE REQUIREMENTS

When selecting a PPD, one needs to consider the effect of the rate at which the temperature of the oil is decreased on paraffin crystallization. Cooling the oil slowly promotes the formation of large crystals while fast cooling favours the creation of a large number of small crystals. Thus, at a given temperature, the physical characteristics of the crystals that have to be controlled by a PPD may be significantly different even though the total quantity of wax is the same.

Furthermore, many wax related phenomena are a function of time. Hence, one sometime finds acceptable performance in a fresh fluid, only to discover that the beneficial effect of the PPD is lost during storage. The wax solution behaves like a supercooled liquid, in which wax crystallisation takes place over an extended period of time, thereby converting a fluid system to a gel.

The control of low temperature properties of lubricants is such an incredibly complex phenomenon that no single test can ensure that an oil will remain fluid over a wide range of conditions. Most engine oils are extremely non-Newtonian at low temperatures, and the range of shear rates involved in oil flow is quite large. Furthermore, thermal history, including temperature cycling and/or cooling rates, plays a major role in low-temperature rheology. Hence, various test methods have been developed over the years, many in response to a specific issue encountered in the field. The most common of these include:

Test	Test Method
Pour Point	ASTM D 97
Stable Pour Point	FTM 791b, Method 203, Cycle C
Mini Rotary Viscometer	ASTM D 3829
Mini Rotary Viscometer using TP-1 cycle	ASTM D 4684
Brookfield Viscosity	ASTM D 2983
Scanning Brookfield Technique (SBT)	ASTM D 5133

All these tests differ by their cooling rate and rate of shear under which viscosity and/or yield stress are measured.

The low temperature properties of most lubricants (for example, automatic transmission fluids, gear oils and hydraulic fluids) are normally specified by the use of pour point and Brookfield or kinematic viscosity. Evaluation of engine oils is far more complex. SAE J300 includes viscosity requirements in the Cold Cranking Simulator (ASTM D 5293) and the MRV TP-1 (ASTM D 4684) and calls for no measurable yield stress in the MRV TP-l. The ILSAC GF-4 specification also includes a maximum Gelation Index in the Scanning Brookfield (ASTM D 5133).

4. SELECTION OF POUR POINT DEPRESSANTS

The screening of pour point depressants is best conducted on lubricants that are fully formulated except for PPD because additives containing a hydrocarbon structure, which is wax-like, can have a dramatic effect on low-temperature performance. For example, multigrade engine oils are based on a combination of two or more base stocks, a DI package and a VI Improver. High-ethylene-content OCP VI improvers contain long runs of ethylene that can exert a profound influence on PPD selection because of their crystalline nature. Also, some alkyl-aryl sulfonates have linear alkyl structures, which can have an effect on pour point.

The following example shows the effect on PPD type and addition rate by the use of high ethylene OCP type Viscosity Index Improver (VII). A 15W-40 engine oil was formulated with identical components (two base-oils and DDI package) except in one version the VII type used was a low ethylene OCP and in another version a high ethylene OCP type VII of similar SSI characteristics was used.

For each oil a range of PPD's was tested at different treat rates to determine the PPD level required to achieve the MRV TP-1 limits as required by the SAE J300 standard.

Alongside the low ethylene type OCP VII, a greater number of PPD's were found acceptable (PPD 1 to PPD 8) whereas far fewer were found acceptable alongside the high ethylene type OCP VII. Also, for those PPD types which did perform in both fluids, a higher PPD treat level was required alongside the high ethylene OCP type VII.

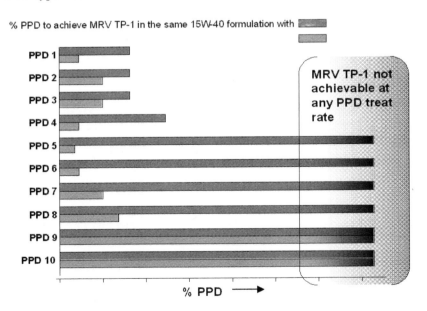

Figure 3. Effect of OCP VII type on PPD selection and content to meet MRV TP-1 requirements in 15W-40 engine oil.

Another major issue in PPD selection results from the need to satisfy the battery of low temperature tests that are specified by OEMs to protect their equipment at low temperature. To satisfy the sometimes conflicting requirements of low-temperature tests, a PPD has to be able to control wax crystallization over a wide range of conditions.

In some engine oil formulations, the MRV TP-1 and the Scanning Brookfield tests show different appetites because of their different cooling profiles and shear rates. The following example shows that the selection of the PPD can be highly dependent on the low temperature method used, and also that more careful consideration of the PPD type and use level is required when meeting multiple test requirements.

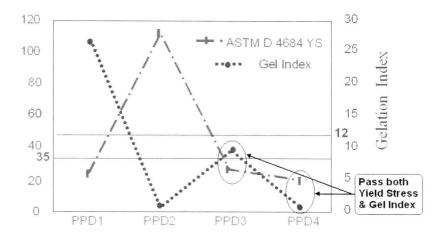

Figure 4. Effect of PPD selection on the oil yield stress in the MRV TP-1 and on Gelation Index in the Scanning Brookfield.

In this example, the same engine oil has been tested by two separate low temperature test methods; MRV TP-1 Yield stress and Scanning Brookfield Gelation Index. The limits for these tests are 35 Pa and 12 respectively, and so passing results are points below these values. It can be seen PPD 1 and PPD 2 are acceptable in only one out of the two tests, showing that the performance of a PPD in one low temperature test cannot be predicted from the performance in a different low temperature test in the same oil. Also a lower number of PPD's is likely to found acceptable for multiple low temperature test requirements; here two acceptable PPD's for both tests combined compared to three if just a single low temperature test pass was required.

In addition to trade-offs between tests within a specific application, there must also be consideration of the requirements within the viscosity grades of a product line, as well as the requirements across product lines. While it would be possible to define an optimum PPD for every lubricant, this is obviously not practical. It is unusual that a single, universal PPD would be optimized for all of the products in a blend plant. However, one PPD will sometimes meet all of the needs with a modest up-treat in a few products. The blender must weigh this option against the logistics issues of handling a second PPD for part of the product mix.

Another major issue that has surfaced in the last few years is the need to ensure that the low temperature of engine lubricants will not be lost due to non wax related phenomena even after severe service in gasoline and heavy duty diesel engines. ILSAC GF-4 now includes low temperature requirements after the Sequence IIIG engine test to ensure that, even after being submitted to severe oxidation, the lubricant will still have acceptable low temperature performance. For heavy-duty diesel engines, the need to control the viscosity increase that is induced by soot accumulation has led several OEMs to specify low temperature viscosity measurement on used oils.

5. BASE STOCK TRENDS

The range of base stocks in the market today is becoming increasingly diverse. Since the dewaxing process is the most capital-intensive process in a refinery, change has come slowly. So one can find on the market oils produced with the older, classic solvent-dewaxed stocks and oils produced by hydro-cracking or hydro-isomerization.

Variability in crudes may also be an issue for some refiners. Economic pressures encourage the use of multiple sources or spot purchases on the open market, leading to a constantly changing slate of crudes going through a refinery. This makes control of dewaxing processes particularly difficult. At the same time that the CMA Code of Practice and API Base Oil Interchangeability Guidelines have complicated life for the many oil blenders that are trying to take advantage of the flexibility of purchasing from multiple suppliers and/or from the spot market. .

Base stocks produced by hydro-cracking and/or catalytic dewaxing are becoming more common. These differ dramatically in their solvency, wax type and total wax content from solvent-refined stocks, thereby introducing their own unique set of problems.

Finally, biodegradable base stocks, i.e., vegetable oils that are used in some specific applications need to be treated to improve their low temperature performance. These stocks do not contain wax in the normal sense, but the molecular structure of the fluids themselves is in part wax-like. Hence, the effective concentration of wax-like material is extremely high, and control of low temperature fluidity is a major challenge for the PPD.

6. CONCLUSION

Overall, the range of wax-related issues confronting the formulation chemist has never been more complex. All indications are that this trend will continue. This increasing complexity will lead to the development of new PPD's that will provide the required low temperature performance to both fresh and aged lubricants over a wide range of cooling cycles, shear rates and using a large variety of base stocks and additives.

Synthesis of some lubricant additives, investigation of antioxidant characterization and the synergism effect of them on ZDDP

M. Shekarriz, M. Soleymani Jamarani, S. Taghipoor, A. A. Khalili,
B. Ghanbari, F. HajiAliAkbari

Research Institute of Petroleum Industry, Tehran, Iran
Shekarriz@ripi.ir

ABSTRACT

In this study we synthesized some antioxidant additives such as: molybdenum dithiophosphate, molybdenum dithiocarbamate, borate esters containing hindered phenolic substitution. They were measured the antioxidant characterization. The antioxidative actions of them with ZDDP were evaluated. The results showed a synergistic effect on the antioxidative action with certain mixtures of the additives in mineral oil.

Keywords: ZDDP, MoDDP, MoDTC, borate esters, antioxidant

1. INTRODUCTION

Modern lubricants are formulated from a range of base fluids and chemical additives. The base fluid has several functions but primarily it is the lubricant, which provides a fluid layer separating moving surfaces or removing heat and wear particles while keeping friction at a minimum. Many properties of lubricants are enhanced or imparted by the addition of additives to the base fluid. For example, stability against oxidation and degradation in characteristic engine oil can be improved by the addition of antioxidants while extreme pressure (EP) anti-wear properties needed in gear lubrication are created by the addition of special EP additives. The base fluid also functions as the carrier for these additives and must therefore be able to keep the additives in solution under all normal working conditions [1].

Most crankcase engine antioxidant needs are met by the zinc dialkyldithiophosphate (ZDDP). Todays higher-temperature engines require supplemental ashless antioxidants to pass the sequence IIIE engine. Therefore, modern engine oils use three or more different types of antioxidants, with the highest level being the ZDDP. An important phenomenon is known as inhibitor synergism. It defines as, "levels of two compounds produces a greater benefit than a full level of either alone". Synergistic combinations of inhibitors can extend a lubricant's temperature and use ranges, thereby boosting its performance [1, 2]. The most common friction modifiers are zinc diyhiophosphates and molybdenum-containing compounds such as molybdenum dithiophosphates (MoDDP) and dithiocarbamates (MoDTC).

In recent years, much effort has been focused on the research and development of new types of additives for lubricating oils without any environmental side effects [3]. Antioxidants used in lubricants include sulfides, disulfides, sulfoxides, phosphates, amines, and phenols. Antioxidants produce SOx and NOx gases and phosphorous oxides [1]. It is commonly accepted that boron-containing compounds, e. g. borate esters, not only have excellent antiwear and antifriction characteristics, but also possess good oxidation stability and compatibility with seals. Furthermore, they are non-volatile, relatively non-toxic, and have a pleasant odor [3-9].

In this study we synthesized molybdenum dithiophosphate (MoDDP), molybdenum dithiocarbamate (MoDTC), borate esters containing hindered phenolic substitution. They were measured the antioxidant characterization. The antioxidative actions of them with ZDDP were evaluated.

2. EXPRIMENTAL

Molybdenum dialkyldithiophosphates were prepared via the procedure in the literature [10]. The number of carbon of alkyl group was 4 to 8. The procedure in brief is:

$$MoO_3 \xrightarrow[\Delta]{NaOH} \xrightarrow[96\%]{H_2SO_4} \xrightarrow[(DDPA)]{acid} \xrightarrow[2\ h]{\Delta} [(RO)_2P(S)S]_2Mo_2S_2O_2$$

Molybdenum dialkyldithiocarbamate also prepared in four steps [11].

1) $Mo(VI) + Na_2S \xrightarrow{time} Mo_2X_4^{4+} + NaOH + H_2O$

2) $Mo_2X_4^{4+} + Na_2SO_3 \xrightarrow{time} Mo_2X_4^{2+} + Na_2SO_4$

3) $Mo_2X_4^{2+} \xrightarrow[\text{organic solvent}]{CH_3OH} Mo_2X_4^{2+} \downarrow$

4) $Mo_2X_4^{2+} + 2\ R_2NH + 2\ CS_2 \xrightarrow{time} \xrightarrow[time]{H_2SO_4}$

$$\underset{\substack{\| \\ S}}{R_2N\text{-}C}\text{-}S\text{-}\underset{\substack{\| \\ X}}{Mo} \underset{X}{\overset{X}{<}} \underset{\substack{\| \\ X}}{Mo}\text{-}S\text{-}\underset{\substack{\| \\ S}}{C\text{-}NR_2}$$

X=O, S

R is alkyl (C$_4$-C$_8$), cyclohexyl or benzyl.

Borate esters containing hindered phenolic substitution were prepared by transesterification of trialkyl borate (like tributyl borate or trihexyl borate) with hindered phenolic compounds (such as 2,6-di-t-butyl-p-cresol (BHT), 2,6-di-t-buthylphenol) at distillation apparatus and heated till no alcohol was distilled [6]. The mole ratio of phenolic compounds to trialkyl borate is 1 to 3.

Note: In these reactions all solvents are reproducible. Salts, acids and bases don't recover. The excess amount of CS$_2$ and amins can be recoverd.

OXIDATION TEST

The oxidation tests were carried out according to the reports [12, 13] as follow: in a jacketed rector a 0.001M solution of sample (containing additive and cumene) was placed while the temperature was set to 60°C by circulating warm water through the reactor jacket. Then 0.2 g of azabisbutyronitril was added and the oxygen pressure was set to 1 atm. The reduction in oxygen pressure was measured by a barometer.

3. RESULTS & DISCUSSION

In most environments in which lubricating oil is employed, it comes in contact with air, often at high temperatures and in the presence of metals or chemical compounds which act as "pro-oxidants" or oxidation catalysts. Under such conditions, the lubricant, whether it is a mineral or synthetic ester- based oil undergoes a complex series of oxidation reactions. The harmful results of such oxidation include principally an increase in the viscosity of the lubricant, the development of acidic contaminants such as "petroleum oxyacids", and the formation of carbonaceous matter. There is general agreement among independent investigators that the oxidation of lubricating oil involves a chain reaction in which initially-formed organic peroxides attack unoxidized oil and is subsequently regenerated by oxygen in the air to continue such attack. According to this "peroxide theory", an effective anti-oxidant is a material, which reduces organic peroxides and thereby causes the chain oxidation reaction to cease [1].

In this work we synthesized MoDDP [10], MoDTC [11] with different alkyl group (C_4-C_8) and borate esters containing hindered phenolic substitution [6]. The possibility that our compounds might act as chain breaking agents, by reaction with peroxy radicals, has been investigated in this work. A test method was used involving measurement of the oxidation rate of a suitable hydrocarbon containing an initiator such as azonitrile. Cumene oxidation in the presence of azonitril was chosen as a suitable system [12, 13]. The oxidation reaction is readily initiated at 60°C in the presence of oxygen. Oxidation of cumene without additive is shown in Fig 1.

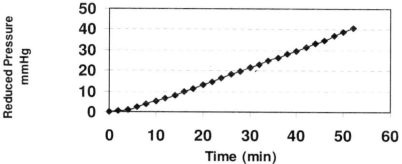

Figure 1. Oxidation of Cumene without antioxidant additive

Inhibition time of MoDDP and ZDDP for oxidation reaction of cumene was investigated. Both of them acted as oxidation inhibitor and the time of inhibition was 20 minutes (Fig. 2). Alkyl group substitution didn't effect on antioxidant characterization.

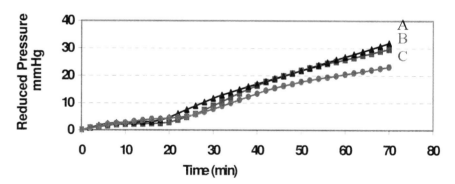

Figure 2. Antioxidant Characterization of MoDDP and ZDDP
A: ZDDP (Lubrizol), 18 min; B: MoDDP (dibutyl), 20 min; MoDDP (2-ethylhexyl), 23 min.

The mixtures of ZDDP and MoDDP showed the better antioxidative performance; however, the synergism effect of MoDDP is low (Fig.3).

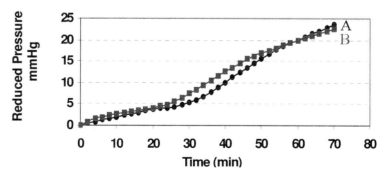

Figure 3. Synergism effect of MoDDP on ZDDP
A: 5% MoDDP (2-ethylhexyl), 25 min; B: 10% MoDDP (2-ethylhexyl), 27 min.

Molybdenum dialkyldithicarbamates have been shown the excellent antioxidant ability in comparison of ZDDP (Fig. 4).

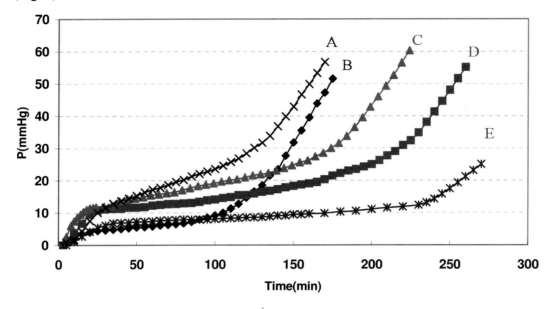

Figure 4. Antioxidant Characterization of MoDTC
A: MoDTC (di-benzyl), 80 min, MoDTC (bis-2-ethylhexyl), 105 min; C: MoDTC (dihexyl), 150 min; D: MoDTC (dibutyl), 200 min; E: MoDTC (dicyclhexyl), 225 min.

As it was shown antioxidant characterization depended on the number of carbon atom of alkyl groups. With increasing of carbon atom the antioxidant characterization has been decreased but the solubility in lubricant has been increased.

The mixture of MoDTC (bis-2-ethylhexyl) and ZDDP has also been investigated (Fig. 5).

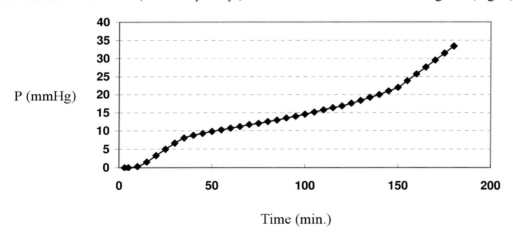

Figure 5. The Synergism effect of 5% MoDTC on ZDDP; 140 min

The antioxidant characterization of borate esters has been investigated. The effects of borate esters and hindered phenols are shown in Fig. 6. These results clearly show that the borate esters can act as chain-breaking inhibitors.

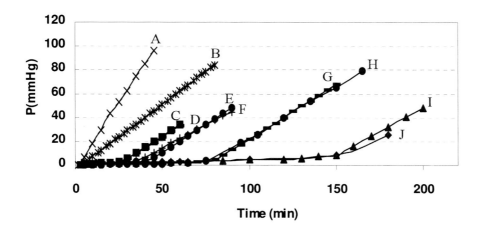

Figure 6. Effect of borate ester compounds on the oxidation of Cumene
A: No oxidant (0 min.), B: Trihexylborate (0 min.), C: Dihexyl[2,6-di-t-butylphenyl]borate (35 min.), D: Dihexyl[2,6-di-t-butyl-p-cresyl]borate (35 min.), E: Triphenylborate (40 min.), F: Tris(p-cresyl)borate (40 min.), G: Hexyl-bis[2,6-di-t-butylphenyl]borate (75 min.), H: Hexyl-bis[2,6-di-t-butyl-p-cresyl]borate (75 min.), I: Tris[2,6-di-t-butylphenyl]borate (150 min.), J: Tris[2,6-di-t-butyl-p-cresyl]borate (150 min.)

As it could be inferred from this Fig, the borates with tri substituted phenolic compounds inhibit oxidation reaction for a longer period of time. That inhibition occurs from the beginning of oxidation under mild temperature conditions, indicating that borate esters remove peroxy radicals. The inhibition time of oxidation reaction of commercial antioxidant zinc dialkyldithiophosphate was found to be for 20 minutes though this result was 150 min for tris[2,6-di-t-butyl-p-cresyl]borate. Borate esters didn't show any synergism effect on ZDDP.

4. CONCLUSION

In conclusion, molybdenum dialkyldithiocarbamates (MoDTC) have excellent antioxidant characterization and also good synergism effect on ZDDP. The antioxidant characterization of MoDDP is the same as ZDDP and has slightly synergism effect on ZDDP. Borate esters are good antioxidants for hydrocarbons and lubricants (such as engine oil) in comparison with commercial antioxidants (ZDDP). The borate esters are environmentally friendly additives. They do not contain heavy metals, do not poison exhaust catalysts and decompose in environment.

REFERENCES

[1]   R. M. Mortier and S. T. Oraszulik, "Chemistry and Technology of Lubricants", 2nd edd., Edmundsbury Press, 1997. L. R. Rudnick, "Lubricant Additives: Chemistry and Application", M. Dekker, New York, 2003.
[2]   T. V. Liston, "Lubricating Additives", Lubr Eng 1992, 48 (5), 389.
[3]   J. B. Yao, Q. L. Wang, S. Q. Chen, J. Z. Sun, J. X. Dong, Lubrication Science 2002, 14, 416.
[4]   M. Braid, US patent US 4530770, 1985. M. Braid, US patent US 4474670, 1984.
[5]   J. B. Hinkamp, US patent US 3356707, 1967.
[6]   M. C. Croudace, US patent US 4701274, 1987.
[7]   I. Ching Chiu, US patent US 5672727, 1997. J. R. Baranski, US patent US 5698499, 1997.
[8]   A. Erdemir, US patent US 6025306, 2000.
[9]   S. Haber, US patent US 6576789 B1, 2003.
[10] E. Rowan, H. Farmer, US patent US 3400140, 1968.
[11] N. Tanaka, US patent US 5631213, 1997.
[12] A. J. Burn, Tetrahedron 1966, 22, 2153.
[13] L. Bateman and J. I. Cunneen, J. Chem. Soc. 1955, 1596.

Session 10
LUBRICANT TESTING 2

Chair: Mr. Francisco Velasco

Grease Contamination and Ferrography Analysis
B. GRAÇA, J. SEABRA, A. CAMPOS

Used Grease Analysis
P. WEISMANN, S. BOTS

Basic principles of wear phenomena, mechanisms and lubrication – a review
M. A. KHAN, A. G. STARR

Grease Contamination and Ferrography Analysis

B. Graça [1], J. Seabra [2], A. Campos [3]

[1] INEGI – Instituto de Engenharia Mecânica e Gestão Industrial
Rua Dr. Roberto Frias s/n, 4200-465 Porto, Portugal
[2] FEUP - Faculdade de Engenharia da Universidade do Porto
Rua Dr. Roberto Frias s/n, 4200-465 Porto, Portugal
[3] ISEP – Instituto Superior de Engenharia do Porto
Rua Dr. António Bernardino de Almeida 431, 4200-072 Porto, Portugal

ABSTRACT

The artificial contamination of greases can be used to test the grease behaviour and the contaminant influence when the grease is in service. Grease analysis, as a condition monitoring tool to evaluate the wear of mechanical components, is also an actual demand since there are many grease lubricated applications.

The development of a mechanical device for the mixing of contaminant particles into grease is described, involving a combination of procedures and materials to obtain a homogeneous mixture of the particles into the grease.

Several grease samples were collected and were dissolved with appropriated solvent to be analysed by ferrography techniques. Very good correlation was obtained between the contamination levels and the ferrometry indexes.

Keywords: Artificial Contamination, Grease Mixer, Mixing Procedures, Grease Dissolution, Grease Analysis, Ferrography.

1. INTRODUCTION

Many grease lubricated mechanical components, mainly bearings, fail prematurely due to contamination. Understanding grease lubrication problems related with contamination can have a major role in improving grease performance and reliability [1, 2].

Grease lubrication is far more complex than oil lubrication and the influence of contaminants in a grease lubricated contact involves different conditions that require a perceptive knowledge about all interactions that are taking place. Artificial contamination of greases can have a useful contribution to better understanding those interactions, since a controlled and well defined level of contaminants are used.

In this work some greases have been contaminated with metal and non metal particles using the mechanical mixer device developed and applying the mixing procedures defined. Subsequently, different samples of the contaminated greases were collected, dissolved with appropriated solvent and analyzed using ferrography techniques.

2. GREASE CONTAMINATION

2.1. Grease Mixer

The batches of deliberately contaminated grease were prepared using a Thermal Bath Circulator (Julabo F10-VC) and an Electronic Stirrer (Heidolph RZR 2102), modified for this purpose at INEGI, as shown in Figure 1.

The mixer processed the grease performing a combination of rotating and vertically reciprocating motions of a mixing head in the glass beaker.

The mixing head consist of a laboratory stirrer (Ø 58 mm propeller with Ø 7 mm x 400 mm shaft, both made from stainless steel). The stirrer was complemented with a scraper support made from bronze and three scraper blades of 13 x 30 mm with rounded corners, cut from a 2 mm thick polytetrafluoroethylene (PTFE) plate. A PTFE cover avoids the leak of grease from the glass beaker when the propeller rotates and oscillates (see Figure 2).

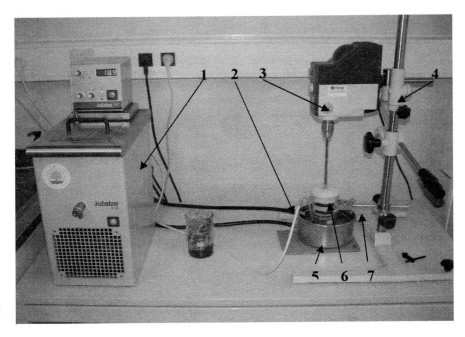

Figure 1. Grease Mixer and Thermal Bath assembly, developed at INEGI: (1) Thermal Bath Circulator; (2) Temperature Sensor PT100; (3) Electronic Stirrer; (4) Lift Stand; (5) Thermal Bath; (6) Glass Beaker Cover; (7) Clamp.

Figure 2. Scraper blades and PTFE glass beaker covers.

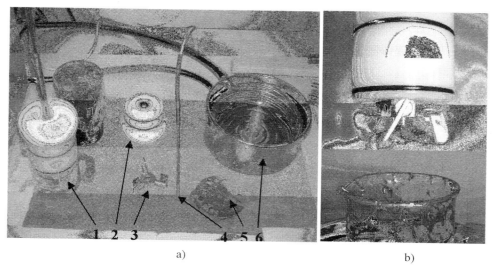

Figure 3. a) Mixer and Thermal Bath accessories; b) Mixing head mounted: (1) Mixing Head Mounted, (2) Glass Beaker Cover, (3) Scraper blades, (4) Temperature Sensor (PT 100), (5) Thermal Bath Base, (6) Thermal Bath.

The rotation of the propeller causes a vertical-lateral intermixing of the grease layers located within some millimeters above and below the propeller centre. The lateral and vertical intermixing was assisted by the three scraper blades, making 40° with the rotating shaft, which was particularly important for improving the lateral mixing close to the cylindrical glass wall and at the rounded corner at the bottom of the glass beaker (see Figure 3b). Due to the reciprocating vertical motion of the mixing head, the vertical intermixing was enhanced.

To decrease grease consistence and improve mixing, the glass beaker and grease were submerged in a water bath heated at about 60 ºC.

2.1.1. Mixing Procedure (evaluation and validation)

Before establishing a grease contamination procedure, all the mixing equipment and procedures were evaluated and validated to produce a homogeneous mixture of the contaminant particles into the grease. Small rolling bearing spheres, 1 mm in diameter and weighting 4.075 mg, were used for that purpose. They can be easily counted and visually give a reasonable approach of the homogeneity of the mixture. A contamination level of 1% (weight 1g/100 g) in concentration was used.

The following equipment and accessories were used to support the analysis: an Analytical Balance (Mettler PR 1203, 1 mg readability), a Membrane Filtering (Millipore), an Ultrasonic Bath (Sonorex Super RK 106) and an Oven (Fisher Isotemp 500 Series).

Lithium soap-thickened greases, made of mineral base oil and having NLGI grade 2, were used.

Prior to starting the mixture, the glass beaker, its cover and the mixing head (in parts) were cleaned using the ultrasonic bath with hexane. Once all parts were well dried, a glass beaker was used to weight the grease where the metal spheres, in a known number (400) and weight, have been added. This procedure has been used to prepare the samples indicated in Table 1.

Table 1. Grease samples prepared.

Sample	Grease mass (g)	Spheres mass (g)	Nº of Spheres
1	152.162	1.630	400
2	160.007	1.630	400
3	160.009	1.631	400

Mechanically, each grease sample mixture was prepared during 30 minutes according to the following procedures [3]:

1. Turn on the circulating water bath to reach a bath temperature of 60 °C;
2. Mount the mixing head (the propeller, the scraper blades and the glass beaker cover) and fix it to the electronic stirrer;
3. Place the glass beaker, with the grease and contaminants, on the mixing head and cover it conveniently;
4. Set the rotation speed to 48 RPM (5 Hz) on the electronic stirrer;
5. Manually (holding the glass beaker by hand), execute about twenty (20) rapid up and down movements, during one (1) minute;
6. Manually and slowly (during two (2) minutes), perform about ten (10) up and down movements;
7. Place the glass beaker in the water bath and fix it to the lift stand using the clamp. Set the mixing head at the grease top level and kept in rotation during eight (8) minutes;
8. Move the mixing head and leave it at the grease medium level and kept in rotation during eight (8) minutes;
9. Move the mixing head and place it on the grease bottom level and kept in rotation during eight (8) minutes;
10. Repeat step 5;
11. Repeat step 6;
12. The mixing head is stopped on the top of the grease and the mixture is ready to be analyzed.

When the mixing head was lifted and the glass beaker was opened, most of the grease remained inside the glass beaker. However, a considerable volume of grease was retained on the mixing head and cover.

The question arises about which part of the grease was more homogeneously mixed: the grease on the glass beaker or the grease on the mixing head and cover. This evaluation was made through the small spheres counting taking various portions of grease (sub-samples), from different locations:

- **Sample 1** - eight sub-samples (8) were taken from the glass beaker grease and three (3) sub-samples were made (about 16 g each) with all the grease retained between each scraper blade;

- **Sample 2** - eight sub-samples (8) were taken from the glass beaker grease and three (3) sub-samples were taken (about 9 g each) from the grease retained between each scraper blade;

- **Sample 3** – eight sub-samples (8) were taken after all the grease retained on the mixing head and cover was removed with a spatula and joined to the glass beaker grease;

Each sub-sample was weighted, dissolved in hexane and filtered through a large pore stainless steel membrane on the Millipore filtering system. The small spheres retained on the steel membrane were been counted.

Subsequently, the counting results were compared with the expected number of spheres to be encountered on each weighted sub-sample for a homogeneous mixture.

The results have shown that the grease was uniformly mixed with the small spheres in both locations: on the glass beaker and on the mixing head and cover. However, the results differences between the expected and the real counted spheres were lower and more consistent on the glass beaker grease. Therefore, and taking into account that most of the grease was retained on the glass beaker, the grease on the mixing head and cover will be not used on the subsequent grease artificial contamination.

2.2.   Contaminants

SAE Fine Test Dust and Steel Wear Particles were used to contaminate the greases. The SAE Fine Test Dust is characterized in Table 2. The Steel Wear Particles were collected from the used oil of a gearbox. To obtain the particles, the oil was submitted to a centrifugation and filtration process with consequent solvent washing and drying.

The contaminant concentration (weight-%) on the grease batches prepared was calculated taking into account the dissolution process. It involves a specific mass of solvent, normally 20 milliliters, corresponding to 14.85 grams in weight, which is a considerable mass when compared with the contaminant mass. It was intended to achieve a pre-established contaminant concentration after the grease sample dissolution.

Table 2. Characteristics of SAE Fine Test Dust powder.

SAE Fine Test Dust (PTI)	
Boiling Point (°F):	4040
Specific Gravity:	2.65
Solubility in Water:	Insoluble
Chemical composition:	%
▪ SiO_2	68 – 76
▪ AlO_3	10 – 15
▪ Fe_2O_3	2 – 5
▪ Na_2O	2 – 4
▪ CaO	2 – 5
▪ MgO	1 – 2
▪ TiO_2	0.5 – 1.0
▪ K_2O	2 - 5

Particle Size Distribution

Particle size distribution (% by Particle Size (μm)):
- 0 - 5: 33,5%
- 5 - 10: 19,1%
- 10 - 20: 18,5%
- 20 - 40: 18,1%
- 40 - 80: 10,6%
- > 80: 2,0%

2.2.1. Contamination with Steel Wear Particles

To define an appropriated level of the wear particles contamination, a sample of white oil was contaminated with a 0.05 weight-% of wear particles and analyzed by Direct Reading Ferrography (DR III). The wear indexes (Dl and Ds) resulted were much higher than 90 and consequently the sample was subjected to a dilution ratio of 0.01, obtaining a concentration of 0.0005 weight-%. The sample was then analyzed by Direct Reading Ferrography (DR III) and Analytical Ferrography (FMIII). The results obtained are shown on Table 3.

The Figure 4 shows, the microphotography's of the Steel Wear Particles deposited on a ferrogram prepared with white oil contaminated with a 0.0005 weight-% concentration.

Table 3. Direct Reading Ferrography results of white oil sample contaminated with steel wear particles.

Dilution factor (d)	Concentration (w-%)	Dl	Ds	CPUC	ISUC
1	0.05	> 90	> 90	-	-
0.01	0.0005	37.7	7.6	4530	136 353

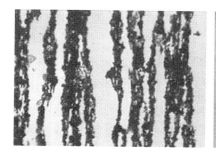  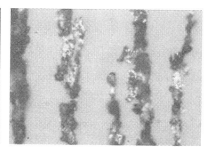

Figure 4. Steel Wear Particles: a) Ferrogram entry; b) Large particles (41 x 36   m); c) Small particles.

As can be seen on Figure 4, the presence of wear particles (small and large particles) is very significant for the contamination level concentration defined – 0,0005 weight-%.

2.2.2   Contamination with SAE Fine Test Dust

The concentration level of SAE Test Dust to be used on grease contamination was based on the concentrations previously defined for oil contamination (previous study made to evaluate the effectiveness of Ferrography in monitoring artificially contaminated lubricating oils [4]). Several new oil samples have been contaminated with different particle concentrations and have been analyzed by Ferrography techniques. The results have been compared with real oil lubricated applications and the contamination concentration levels have been established as low, medium and high.

Considering that in real grease lubricated applications, the grease contamination is higher when compared with oil contamination on oil lubricated applications, the concentration level used was the highest – 0.1 weight-%.

2.3.   Grease Contamination Procedure

The deliberately contaminated grease batches were prepared adding the contaminant powder into the grease before starting the mixing.

In the case of Steel Wear Particles, a concentrated contaminant-oil has been manually prepared in a glass bottle with 3 milliliters of white oil (GALP WON 65) and 60 milligrams of Steel Wear Particles.

The Table 4 shows the grease batches prepared.

The mixing procedure described above was used to evenly disperse the contaminants into the grease.

Table 4. Deliberately contaminated grease batches.

	Grease	Contaminant	Concentration (weight-%)
	SgM2	SAE Test Dust	
Mass (g)	162.522	12.067	0.1
	BgM1	Steel Wear Particles	
Mass (g)	162.502	approx. 0.060[1]	0.0005
	BgM3	SAE Test Dust + Wear Particles	
Mass (g)	162.005	12.024 + approx. 0.060	0.1005

[1] There was a residual mass of particles that remains on the bottom of the glass bottle.

3.   GREASE FERROGRAPHY RESULTS

Considering the sampling results obtained on the previous experiments with steel spheres, the grease samples to be analyzed were taken from the grease in the glass beaker on different locations.

Three samples of about 100 mg and 200 mg from each deliberately contaminated grease batch have been weighted and submitted to the following dissolution procedure:

1. Put a small portion of the grease sample (about 100 mg, depending on particle concentration) in a 50 ml (minimum) glass bottle;

2. Add 20 ml of the solvent mixture. The solvent mixture to be used can be a mixture of 15% of Toluene and 35% of Hexane, to which about 50% of a diester synthetic oil was added, to suspend high-density large particle material and avoid co-settling of wear particles. It was shown before that this solvent mixture was efficient to dissolve a wide variety of lubricating greases [5];

3. Agitate the bottle with the lubricating grease and the solvent during, at least 5 minutes, to get a homogeneous mixture. The agitation process can be assisted by ultrasonic agitation and heating or under manual shaking, using 3 mm diameter glass balls, which should be putted into the bottle before the grease and the solvent.

The results obtained by Direct Reading Ferrography (DRIII) are presented in Table 5.

Table 5. Direct Reading Ferrography Wear Indexes for the grease samples.

Wear Indexes

Grease Contaminated		Weight-%	Grease Sample (mg)	Dl	Ds	CPUC	ISUC
SgM2	SAE Test Dust	0.1	100	37.1	12.9	50.0	1210.0
			99	27.0	10.0	37.0	629.0
			101	27.6	9.7	37.3	667.7
			199	59.5	19.1	78.6	3175.4
			201	47.8	18.2	66.0	1953.6
			201	46.4	18.2	64.6	1821.7
BgM1	Wear Particles	0.0005	200	29.2	2.2	31.4	847.8
			204	35.9	3.1	39.0	1279.2
			204	38.4	3.9	42.3	1459.6
BgM3	SAE Test Dust + Wear Particles	0.10005	100	52.1	15.2	67.3	2483.4
			99	60.8	16.6	77.4	3421.1
			101	60.5	18.6	79.1	3314.3
			199	88.5	33.7	122.2	6696.5
			201	83.5	30.7	114.2	6029.7
			201	75.4	24.4	99.8	5089.8

Table 5 shows that the Ferrometric Wear Indexes (Dl – Large Particles, Ds – Small Particles, CPUC – Wear Particles Concentration and ISUC – Wear Severity) of the grease samples taken at different locations in the glass beaker reveal some confidence on the mixing process used to mix up the grease with the contaminant particles. The variations obtained are within normal intervals for Ferrometric analysis. Particle analysis was carried out using Analytical Ferrography. The two ferrograms made show no evidence of grease thickener presence and/or interference on the analysis of both types of contaminant particles (see Figure 5 and Figure 6).

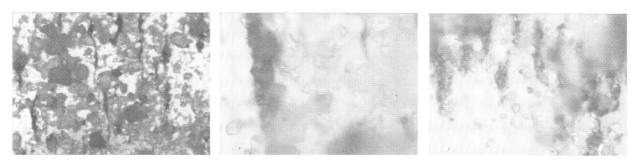

Figure 5. SAE Test Dust particles on the ferrogram (SgM2 contaminated grease).

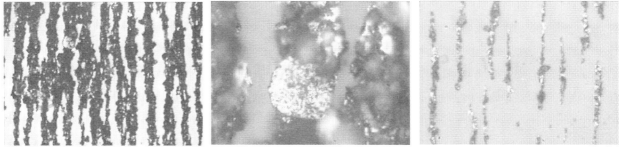

Figure 6. Steel Wear Particles on the ferrogram (BgM2 contaminated grease).

As can be seen, the metal and non metal contaminant particles are well documented and efficiently detected by Ferrography.

4. CONCLUSIONS

The experiments made showed that the assembly device developed for the mixing of the contaminant particles into the grease can be effectively used to obtain a homogeneous mixture.

The analysis through Direct Reading Ferrography (DRIII) of the grease contaminated samples shows that:

1) the mixing procedure used is efficient in obtaining a homogeneous mixture;

2) the solvent used – *mixture of toluene, hexane and diester synthetic oil*, is able to dissolve lithium greases;

3) there is no interference between different types of contaminants (metal and non metal) on the grease mixing process;

4) the grease thickener remaining undissolved does not interfere with the analysis (including the Analytical Ferrography).

AKNOWLEDGEMENTS

The authors wish to thank the European Union for the financial support of this research through project "BIOMON - Towards long-life bio-lubricants using advanced design and monitoring tools" (Contract N°: COOP-CT-2004-508208) and to Fundación Tekniker for all technical information exchanged during this study.

REFERENCES

[1]   Dwyer-Joyce, R. S. and Heymer, J. The entrainment of solid particles into rolling elastohydrodynamic contacts. Proceedings of the 22nd Leeds-Lyon Symposium on Tribology, 1995 September, Lyon, France, Elsevier, Amsterdam, ed. D. Dowson et al., Tribology Series N° 31, p. 135 – 140.

[2]   Dwyer-Joyce, R. S. Dirty Oil – A study of the effects of lubricant debris on contact failure, Dep. of Mechanical & Process Engineering, University of Sheffield (http:www.shef.ac.uk/~mpe/tribology/visitrtdj.html).

[3]   Andersson P., Graça B., Seabra J. and Sainio H. Development of procedures to analyse contaminant particles in lubricating greases. Tribologia – Finnish Journal of Tribology, Vol. 17 (1998) N° 3-4: 44-55.

[4]   Graça B. and Seabra J. TR07: Effectiveness evaluation of the Ferrography Analysis technique in monitoring artificially contaminated lubricating oils. Technical Report of BIOMON Project - Towards long-life bio-lubricants using advanced design and monitoring tools, Contract N° COOP-CT-2004-50820, 2005 March, Porto, Portugal, 29 pages.

[5]   Wear Particle Atlas (revised), Standard Oil, Engineered Materials, Sohio (about 1981).

Used Grease Analysis

P. Weismann, S. Bots

WEARCHECK GmbH, Kerschelweg 28, 83098 Brannenburg, Germany

ABSTRACT

The analysis of used greases is much more complicated than used-oil analysis. Only a few laboratories in the world are equipped to perform in-depth analyses of used greases based on extremely small sample volumes. OELCHECK Germany performs such used-grease analysis on a daily basis. The combination of analysis methods is selected according to the questions that need to be answered or on the application. Special prepaid analysis kits are delivered. As with oil analysis, the results are provided within 24h after the sample is received in the laboratory. The data are interpreted by experienced mechanical engineers and recommendations are made in a detailed diagnosis.

1. A MUST: THE CORRECT TECHNIQUE FOR TAKING SAMPLES

The basic requirement for a valid sample result is the proper sample-taking technique. It is obviously much more difficult to take a representative grease sample out of a bearing than to take an oil sample.

OELCHECK supplies a special kit for taking grease samples, so the sampling procedure can be standardized and less complex. The kit consists of:

- a reusable syringe to produce a very high vacuum
- a tube, in which the grease is sucked by the syringe-operation
- a sample container marked as "pre-paid analysis kit" for the shipment of the used grease
- a sample information form with specific questions for used greases
- pre-addressed mailing envelope for the sample shipment
- the complete content of the grease kit is packed in a robust red box

2. HOW TO TAKE A GREASE SAMPLE

1. Remove the inspection screw on a slew bearing. Take off the grease nipple from a rolling element bearing, which does not contain such a special grease sampling point.
2. If the bearing is "filled for life" the shield or cover has to be removed or the seal lip has to be lifted, so that the used grease sample can be taken as close as possible to the area where the grease sample is representative and contains the most information.
3. Cut off approximately 10 cm of the supplied sampling tube. Mount the clean tube on the syringe.
4. Press the opening of the tube on the corresponding greased area. Operate the syringe and suck the used grease for a length of at least 1cm (up to max. 5cm) into the sampling tube. Repeat the procedure on different sampling points of same bearing. Usually 3 g by small bearings app. 1g of grease is enough for the analysis. Don't understand the last sentence
5. Watch out for color change. Avoid taking fresh grease too close to the re-greasing point.
6. For trend analysis samples always should be taken at the same points.
7. A sample of the fresh grease should be send as a reference sample for all further analysis.
8. After sampling remove the tube from syringe, fold it and place it into the sample bottle.
9. Remove the sticky barcode label from the sample information form and stick it on the sample.
10. Fill out the questions on the sample information form. Place the sample container and the sample information form into the mailing envelope and send it to the OELCHECK Laboratory.

3. WHAT ARE GREASES?

Lubricating greases are not straight forward chemical substances. They contain approx. 90% of base oils and additives. The rest is thickener which works similar to a sponge and which holds the oil in suspension. Base oils of all types of mineral and synthetic oils are used. The additives are similar to the additives used in lubricating oils. For the thickener, mostly metallic soaps based on lithium, calcium, sodium, aluminum, or a combination of these, are used. In a cooking procedure out of the powder a sponge-like basic grease structure is formed. During the grease cooking process, water is vaporized and replaced by base oil. In the final stage, the additives are added and the grease is homogenized and de-aerated. The lubrication performance is provided by the base oils and additives but not by the thickener. The sponge-like thickener is responsible for holding and releasing in a very slow way the liquid components, so they are able to lubricate.

Machine elements are lubricated by grease if continuous lubrication by oil is technically not possible, or only achievable with a high technical impact. Also if oil can drip-off lubrication points the oil should be replaced by the grease. For a selection of the right grease type, it is important that the grease will not melt at elevated temperatures but still remain sticky and flexible. It should always stick at the lubrication point.

4. ANALYSIS METHODS FOR USED GREASES

Well-defined analysis kits for detailed information

OELCHECK provides several analysis kits with pre-defined sets of analysis methods for lubricating greases. The experts of OELCHECK consult in the selection of the best analysis methods, the optimized kit, the sample taking procedures and sample quantity. They also provide information regarding the individual analysis intervals. The tests packed in the analysis kits are sorted in a way that the kit with a higher number always contains all the tests of a kit with a lower number (like in kit 3 all tests of kit 1 and 2 are included). Besides of the complete test kit, also individual tests can be performed.

4.1. Wear-additives and contamination elements by OES

All grease samples at OELCHECK will be analyzed by the optical emission spectroscopy (OES) acc. to the Rotrode principal. Up to 21 elements will inform about wear, contamination and additives.

➢Wear metals: iron, chromium, tin, copper, lead, nickel, aluminum, molybdenum, zinc and, if present at all, particles of silver, vanadium, titanium antimony and tungsten.

➢Contamination elements: silicium, calcium, sodium, potassium and aluminum

➢Additives or thickeners: magnesium, calcium, phosphorous, zinc, barium, silicium, aluminum, molybdenum and boron.

4.1.1. Test principle

A small quantity of approximately 0.3 g grease will be smeared on a Rotrode graphite wheel. It is distributed on the complete radius of the 3 mm wide and 14 mm diameter electrode. According to the Rotrode-principle, in less than a minute all particles on the graphite electrodes are heated up in an arc which is created at 40,000 volts and provides temperatures of above 8,000°C. This temperature forces each of the present elements to create its characterized light which is typical for its metal. The element emits this light. The light beam will be distributed by means of a griter (prism principle) in its spectral colors (rainbow principle).

In a dark room, photomultiplier tubes are in a radius mounted behind slits in a way so they can absorb only the light that is typical for the measured element. The voltage change caused by the intensity of the light will be calculated into the mass of the present metal.

4.1.2. Result

Especially of interest for the diagnosis of a bearing- or grease-condition are the iron and chromium contents, which are present as wear particles from the bearing material. Non-ferrous materials like copper, lead or tin are indicated of corrosive or abrasive wear from the bearing cage. If dust in the form of silicium or calcium (limestone) or if hard water, which contains minerals like sodium, potassium or magnesium, is present, that information can be helpful in determining the reasons for the presence of wear metals. The content of elements of the metallic soap, or a comparison of the additive content between fresh and used grease, can inform whether the recommended grease is in use.

4.2.   Magnetic wear particles by PQ-Index

The PQ-Index (Particle Quantifier Index) is specialized on the determination of all magnetic iron particles. An Index value between 0 and 9999 informs independent of the particle size, about all iron particles present in the sample. Because rust particles are non-magnetic, those are not measured. The test is performed at OELCHECK by the Analex Ferrous Debris Monitor PQ-90 A.

4.2.1. Test principle

The test principle of the PQ-Index is based on the principle that iron, and therefore also iron wear, is magnetic and can be detected by a magnet. If a grease sample contains magnetic iron wear particles, a magnetic field is disturbed. This change in the magnetic field can be measured. The test result, named as PQ-Index because of the particle quantifier test unit, will be recorded.

In the PQ-90 A unit 2 magnetic coils are placed in a way that the magnetic fields are in balance. If the test starts, one of the magnetic coils has the function of the sample coil while the other acts as a reference coil. On top of the 2 magnetic coils a sensor is mounted. The sample, which is 1g of grease placed in the cap of the sample bottle, will be set on the sensor. If the sample contains only traces of iron wear, only a small influence on the magnetic field is recorded. If the sample contains a high concentration of particles of magnetic iron, the balance of the magnetic fields between the sample and the reference coil is changed. The "out of balance" signal is electronically filtered. The change is displayed as PQ-index. The index has no dimension; it can not be rated to a quantity of iron present in the grease.

4.2.2. Result

The PQ-Index or Ferrous-Index informs about the total content of magnetic wear particles. Contrary to the information about iron wear determined by the OES, the PQ-Index informs about all iron wear particles. By the OES usually in used grease samples only particles up to 5 microns can be detected, because larger particles are not excited.

For the interpretation of the results, the difference between the iron content measured by the OES in mg/kg will be compared with the result of the PQ-Index. The following conclusions can be made:

➢ An extremely high PQ-Index above 500 indicates, independently from the iron wear by OES (mg/kg) an ongoing wear situation in combination with pitting formation and fatigue.

➢ A high PQ-Index above 100 and iron by OES in a similar range is typical for fatigue and a sign for "normal" wear.

➢ A high PQ-Index above 100 and a low iron reading by OES indicates pitting and actual wear with large particles created.

➢ A high iron wear measured by OES (above 100 mg/kg) but a low PQ-Index (below 50) is always a sign for corrosion and rust formation.

4.3. Type and condition of the base oil based on FT-IR

The FT-IR (Fourier-Transform Infra-Red) Spectroscope identifies the type and condition mainly of the base oil in used grease. Also compared to the unused grease, contamination by another grease type or depletion of additives can be determined.

4.3.1. Test principle

FT-IR spectroscopy is based on the principle that the molecules present in a lubricant can absorb infrared light at corresponding wavelengths depending on its typical structure. Changes in the used grease in comparison to the fresh grease reference spectrum are calculated on the typical peaks at predefined wave numbers and interpreted as oxidation, water etc. A very small grease sample (less then 0.1g) is applied onto an ATR cell. In the contact zone the grease sample will be exposed to infrared light. An infrared spectrum, showing the absorbance of the infrared light on the corresponding wave number, will be recorded and interpreted.

4.3.2. Result

The infrared spectrum of a sample informs in comparison to a reference spectrum about changes and contamination. Absorbance at peaks where oxygen-reactions are shown indicate the oxidation of the base oil. Changes in another region of the infrared spectrum are a sign for water and can be related by comparison methods into % of water in the sample. By spectra-subtraction of used grease with a reference grease, the FT-IR method shows what kind of unknown grease is in use. Also a mixture of different greases in many cases is shown. The identification of the original grease and the base oil type can be found by a search in a library of reference spectra and supports the cause of a failure.

The FT-IR can indicate whether synthetic or mineral oil base oils are used.

If a mineral oil is used as base oil, the FT-IR will show whether the base oil is oxidized by a too long time without regreasing or at a too high temperature.

➢ If the grease contains EP additives on zinc-phosphor basis, the degradation of the additives can be seen.

➢ Information about the water content in the grease is provided.

4.4. Water in used grease by Karl-Fischer Titration

Besides solid contaminates - which can be identified by the OES-elements silicium, calcium or aluminum - water is a contaminant which is very often the cause of corrosion and bearing damage. Also often short regreasing intervals are caused by too much water. Unfortunately the determination of water in grease is not so easy as in an oil sample.

4.4.1. Test principle

For the water determination according to the Karl-Fischer method, a small grease quantity (app. 0.3 g) is filled into a glass vial and closed by a septic cap. In a small oven the sample is heated to approx. 120°C. The steamed out water is transferred by nitrogen into a titration vessel in which an electrochemical reaction between the water and a Karl Fischer reagent takes place. A titration curve is recorded and the water content gets defined very precisely.

4.4.2.   Result

Depending on grease type and application, the water content in a grease should not exceed the recommended limit values. Too much of water in grease can have an impact on different damage mechanisms:

➢ corrosion on all bearing metals

➢ increased oxidation of the base oil

➢ cavitation on parts with mixed friction

➢ softening of the grease

➢ water-wash out of the grease

If the result for water according to the KF-method is compared to the elements determined by the OES it can be decided, whether the water in the sample is "hard"-water, which contains minerals like sodium or potassium or whether it is "soft"-water, like condensate or rain water. If sodium, potassium, calcium or magnesium are newly found in the used grease as elements that are not present in the fresh grease, mostly "hard"-water is the reason. The comparison of these 2 methods, KF-water and OES can also indicate, whether the water was already present in the fresh grease as a part of the production process.

4.5.   Indication for wear and contaminates by sulfate ash

The ashes of grease consist of components of the metallic soap or of the thickener, of solid contaminants, of metal-organic grease additives and of wear metals. The quantity of the sulphate ash in comparison to reference grease is changed by wear particles and contaminants.

4.5.1.   Test principle

The sulphate ash is determined by annealing and burning a small grease quantity of app. 0.5 to 1g at a temperature of 775 °C. At this temperature all organic components are "burned" by a treatment with concentrated sulphuric acid. The oxides in the ash are converted into the corresponding sulphates. The sulphate ash is the residue, which remains in the container if all organic components from base oil, thickener and contamination are burned. Only metallic oxides and the contaminants remain at 775 °C. The difference between the original and the remaining quantity is given as Sulphate Ash by weight %.

4.5.2.   Result

The increase of the ash content in grease samples in comparison with reference grease indicates contamination and wear. If the sulphate ash is completed by the metal detection by OES, it is possible to rate the ash as wear or as contaminant, by comparing the iron and chromium content with silicium and calcium content. The sulphate ash is changed by:

➢ metallic wear particles, which indicate bearing wear

➢ solid contaminants (dust), which inform about the correct re-greasing intervals

➢ metallic soap and organic thickeners for determination of contamination by a different grease type

➢ solid lubricants like MoS2

➢ metal-organic EP-additives as anti-wear grease additives

4.6.   Bleeding out characteristics

Conventional greases are composed of approx. 90% oil. The rest is thickener that looks, observed under a microscope, often like a sponge. If the oil leaks out of the thickener it will be called "bleeding". This bleeding-out characteristic is influenced by the grease type and quality, as well as the temperature, vibration or load. If the oil gets lost, the grease becomes dry and loses its lubrication properties. Re-greasing in shorter intervals can overcome the problem.

4.6.1.   Test principle

A ring with a diameter of 10mm and 3mm height is filled with approx. 1g of grease and placed on a defined filter paper. The arrangement is stored for 6 hours at 80°C in an oven. Supported by temperature, during this period the filter paper will suck the oil as far as possible out of the thickener. After completion of the test, the filter paper shows an oil spot that can be measured. The grease quantity that remains in the ring after the test is scraped off from the paper and compared to the original quantity. The difference will be recorded as bleeding out-loss in % weight. Also the comparison of the diameter of the oil spot provides information with respect to the reduction of remaining oil and the lubricity of the used grease.

4.6.2.   Result

Long term use without re-greasing, high temperature, or oxidation will cause a separation of the oil from the grease thickener. To allow good interpretation of the oil loss, the bleeding-out characteristic of the fresh grease or of the previously analyzed grease should be compared with the sample result.

➤ the grease can be used without additional re-greasing if the bleeding-out characteristic remains within a +/- 15% range which means it is nearly the same

➤ if less oil is bleeding out, and the oil spot gets smaller, the bearing should be re-greased because the grease is already getting dry

➤ if the used grease is losing much more oil than the fresh grease, the thickener is not longer stable enough to keep the oil in its structure. The grease is softer. Very often, water also has an impact on the increased bleeding-out characteristic. The bearing should be greased in shorter intervals.

4.7.   Penetration and consistency

For oils, the viscosity is measured to inform whether the oil is more thick or thin. For greases, the penetration or the consistency indicates whether the grease is softer or more solid or stiff. But the grease penetration has nothing to do with the base oil viscosity. For used greases, the consistency is measured by a penetrometer with a quarter cone. The penetration is an indication of the identity of the grease and provides information on whether it can be pumped by a central lubrication system or used for a certain application at all.

4.7.1.   Test principle

2 g of the grease sample are filled at room temperature in a standard beaker. The tip of a standardized double cone is touching the surface. During 5 seconds the penetration depth of the cone is. Soft greases exhibit higher penetration than hard greases, because the loaded cone displaces more grease.

4.7.2.   Result

The consistency of the grease is characterizing by its ability to deform in the application. The consistency is grouped in NLGI classes from 000 to 6. If the penetration of the used grease is compared to the fresh grease, the following information can be gathered:

➤ a higher penetration, and therefore a softer grease, indicates often a contamination by another grease or high mechanical stress. Greases with different thickener types always soften if they are mixed.

➤ the penetration will be higher, and the grease, softer because of water or other liquid contaminants

➤ the grease will be softer if it is sheared by mechanical stress in a bearing which destroys the soap structure and shears its long fibered components.

➤ the penetration gets lower and the grease gets harder if it contains less base oil and more thickener. This may happen if the base oil is "bleeded-out" because of vibrations, or if it is vaporized by high temperature or oxidation.

4.8. Instability of grease thickeners by dropping point

The dropping point indicates the temperature in °C at which a small sample volume under defined condition builds a drop. The test shows the end point of a softening process under static conditions.

The dropping point should not be used as an indication of the temperature-limit for grease. Lubricating greases do not have a melting point like natural greases. They are not thinned in a uniform way, they only get softer because of the type of thickener. The oxidation of the base oil and the destruction of the thickener,   determine the operating temperature of grease, not the dropping point.

4.8.1. Test principle

A small sample volume of approx. 0.5 g is filled into a nipple which is equipped with a thermometer. The test unit is heated until a drop is formed on the bottom opening of the nipple. This drop, consisting of a thickener oil mixture, of oil or of soap, will fall into the test tube. The temperature, at which the drop formation starts, is recorded as "dropping point". The test units operate up to 300°C.

4.8.2. Result

The dropping point only indicates whether grease is not running at a defined operating temperature. The maximum operating temperature for a grease should always be far below the dropping point temperature. The base oil type and the thickener will give information on how far below the dropping point the operating temperature can be listed. Usually the dropping point should be at least 50 °C higher than the operating temperature.

If the analysis of used grease shows a lower dropping point than the fresh grease, the following problems might exist:

➤ Contamination by a different grease-type based on another thickener-type. A mixture of different grease-types lowers the dropping point. Due to the mixing of different greases, the product will become thinner; sometimes it looks like semi-fluid grease.

➤ water or other liquids in the grease will thin-down the product in such a way that it starts dropping much earlier

➤ the grease has been so heavily worked in the lubrication area that the soap structure is sheared into such small particles, that the oil is no longer kept within this structure

In all of the cases of a lower dropping point, the problem can only be solved by the removal of the present grease, by a cleaning process, or by re-lubrication in a shorter interval.

4.9. Oxidation and re-greasing intervals by RULER

Besides AW- , EP- or HD-additives which improve the anti-wear properties, a grease also contains anti-oxidants which prevent the base oil ageing and oxidizing too quickly. Usually oxidation is observed by the FT-IR spectrum, but especially when synthetic base oils are used, the peaks in the spectrum present for the synthetic product and the peaks for oxidation are in the same region. The infrared spectrum therefore does not deliver any valuable information about oxidation or the ageing of base oil based on temperature or operating time. One of the most important criteria for the recommendation of the optimum re-greasing intervals is missing.

With the RULER-test, the content of oxidation inhibitors on the aminic or phenolic base can be exactly determined. A comparison of the fresh grease can show the remaining useful lifetime of the grease and allows a prediction of the next re-greasing intervals.

4.9.1. Test principle

Any grease which contains an oxidation-inhibitor additive on the basis of phenols or amines can be tested. In the sample tube, which simulates an electrolytic cell, 0.25 g of the grease sample is mixed with solvent and special sand. By shaking the sampling tube very heavily, the solvent-sand-mixture will free the anti-oxidants from the base oil of the grease. Within 5 minutes the solid particles and the grease contaminants, as well as the thickener and the base oil, settle themselves on the bottom of the glass tube. An electrode dips approx. 1cm in the upper, liquid phase of the electrolytic solvent where the additives are kept. Using a voltametric principle, a well defined voltage curve will be applied on the electrode, which is reacting in the sample. As voltage increases, the anti-oxidants become chemically active and as a result a current is generated, which drops shortly after further increase of the voltage. The time depending increase of the voltage is selected with the way that the typical curves of anti-oxidants can be very well measured. Peaks in the measurement curve of the current indicates the antioxidants. The higher the peak, the more antioxidants are in the oil. The time stamp on the x-axis references to the height of the voltage and informs what type of antioxidant is detected.

4.9.2. Result

The RULER value is a number for the concentration of the oxidation inhibitors. This result is compared to the sample of the fresh grease of the same formulation. By trend analysis or a comparison of samples out of similar equipment, it can be observed by the Ruler, whether the oxidation inhibitor of a grease is strongly reduced. Based on this information, the remaining lifetime of the grease under similar conditions, and the interval for the next re-greasing, can be calculated.

5. SUMMARY

5.1. Predefined analysis kits for detailed used grease diagnosis

OELCHECK Analysis kits contain test combinations for more than 25 single values. Even if only extremely small grease quantities of less than 1g are available, the OELCHECK grease analysis is a well proven method for detailed information about the condition of the grease and of the bearing. The experienced OELCHECK experts combine the data received by different test methods. This way they can comment about wear and its cause, or about reasons for bearing failures. Also information for the correct re-greasing interval or quantity will be provided.

Based on the experience from more than 10,000 analyzed grease samples at the OELCHECK laboratory, some guidelines for the interpretation of wear in grease-lubricated applications can be provided:

5.2. Normal wear

- a moderate increase of the OES wear-metals
- iron (Fe) up to 80 mg/kg, chromium (Cr) up to 10 mg/kg and copper (Cu) up to 50 mg/kg
- a slight increase PQ-Index up to 60
- water below 500 ppm
- RULER value about 25%
- small differences in the bleeding out characteristics

5.3. Corrosive wear

- a relatively strong increase of the most OES wear-metals
- iron (Fe) above to 150 mg/kg, chromium (Cr) above 15 mg/kg and/or copper (Cu) above 50mg/kg
- PQ-Index less than 15% below the OES-iron (Fe). Rust particles are hardly magnetic, therefore the grease containing rust particles will show only a low PQ-Index
- more than 2% increase of the sulphate ash compared to fresh grease
- a decrease of the RULER-value below 25%
- a water content of more than 2.000 ppm, increase of sodium(Na) and potassium (K)
- TAN of more than 2 mgKOH/g above fresh grease, oxidation of more than 20 A/cm. (The reason for rust and corrosion are usually water, acids or oxidation)

5.4. Fatigue wear

- a moderate increase of the wear metals determined by the OES
- iron (Fe) more than 50% lower than the value of the PQ-Index. The iron particles present in the grease are too large to be detected by the OES-method.
- the PQ-Index is far above 300.
- the sulphate ash has increased by more than 2 %
- the bleeding out characteristic and the remaining oil content in the grease has significantly changed.
  (The reason for such wear condition is that the bearing has reached the end of its lifetime or the grease was no longer suitable. Both reasons lead to pitting, spalling or similar damage)

5.5. Mechanical abrasive wear

- a relatively strong increase of the OES-determined wear metals
- iron (Fe) above 100 mg/kg, chromium (Cr) above 10 mg/kg
- silicium (Si) very often also potassium (K), calcium (Ca) or aluminum (A) above 50 mg/kg
- increase of the PQ-Index above 150
- increase of the sulfate ash of more than 2%

The detailed interpretation of the analysis results, and the individual data of an OELCHECK grease sample, are clearly visualized in a detailed laboratory report. Information about the individual test methods may be found in the internet.

Basic principles of wear phenomena, mechanisms and lubrication – a review

M. A. Khan, A. G. Starr

Through Life Support Research Group, School of Mechanical, Aerospace and Civil Engineering, The University of Manchester, M60 1QD, UK

ABSTRACT

Due to the complex nature and behaviour of wear, in terms of theoretical and experimental aspects, the research literature provides diverse information regarding the basics, classification and mechanisms of wear. In this paper, a detailed study of available literature has been made. Furthermore, each classification with respect to mechanisms is sub-divided into respective wear modes, which provides a comprehensive wear classification description in a hierarchical manner. A brief review of lubrication mechanisms and their influence on wear and friction is also provided.

Keywords: Wear, classification, mechanisms, modes, lubrication.

1. INTRODUCTION

The term wear technically involves damage on the surface of a solid which usually (but not necessarily) causes progressive material loss, whenever there is a mechanical interaction between the surface of a damaged solid substance and some other contacting substance/substances that has/have motion relative to it [1]. Apart from the general understanding regarding the phenomenon of wear, which results in a significant material loss, it may not be restricted in the boundaries of material loss.

2. WEAR BETWEEN SOLID SURFACES

Irrespective of material type, atomic scale defects and surface roughness are most significant during generation of wear in solids [2]. Usually in solids, roughness is found distributed over the surface in an arbitrary manner, sometimes modified by manufacturing processes. Roughness prevents the meshing of two solid surfaces, because surface asperities or higher areas come in contact with each other. At a microscopic level it can easily be seen that the real contact area of the two surfaces is distributed in terms of several microscopic asperity contact zones or junctions, which is significantly different from the apparent area of contact as shown in Figure 1 [3].

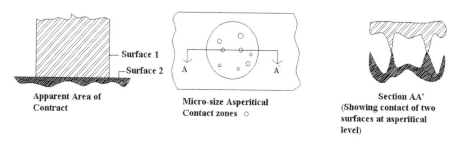

Figure 1. Apparent and real area of contact [3].

The sum of the individual contact areas of the junctions is the real area of contact between the two surfaces. The number of the junctions is proportional to the external load [4]. As the load increases new junctions will be created as a number of new asperities or higher areas on the two surfaces come into contact. Due to subsequent loading, the contact zones deform plastically [5] and initiate the degradation of the surfaces. This degradation of surfaces (wear) might tend towards surface material loss depending on the loading conditions.

The quantification of wear at the asperity contacts presents difficulties for making a realistic mathematical formulation as follows [6]:

- wear surface behaviour is not just associated with extreme local conditions;

- the wear process itself changes the composition and properties of the surface and near-surface regions;

- surface topography normally changes during the wear process;

- the mechanisms by which wear occurs are often complex and can involve a mixture of mechanical and chemical processes, e.g. un-lubricated sliding of two steel surfaces;

- the arbitrary nature of surface roughness needs complicated analytical considerations.

In order to make a step forward, many of the analytical discussions on wear use the relationship of normal load and wear rate (in volume per unit time) given by Holm (1946) and further experimentally tested and analyzed by Burwell and Strang (1951) [7]:

$$Wear\ rate = \frac{Wear\ coefficient \times Sliding\ speed}{Hardness\ of\ wearing\ surface} \qquad (1)$$

The wear coefficient is commonly symbolized by 'K' and quite useful for checking the severity of wear process.

3. WEAR CLASSIFICATION

The scope of wear is quite broad and difficult to classify in a rigid manner. Table 1 below shows some features [3, 8] on the basis of which wear may be classified:

Table 1. General Features for Wear Classification

Base of Classification	Examples
Visual Aspect	Scuffing, Spalling, Pitting, Polishing etc.
Cause	Adhesion, Abrasion, Corrosion, Cavitation, Erosion etc.
External Effecting Conditions	Lubrication, High temperature etc.
Type of Relative Motion	Rolling, Sliding etc.
State of Contacting surfaces	Solid, Liquid and Gas
Nature of Process (mechanisms)	Mechanical, Chemical and Thermal

The above table attempts to cover almost every base feature of classification available in the current literature.

4. WEAR CLASSIFICATION WITH RESPECT TO MECHANISMS

Researchers like Rabinowicz treated adhesion, abrasion, and corrosion directly as mechanisms [9]. Kato described the classification of wear in a very broad manner as described below [10]. The three main mechanisms may be further classified. The mechanical wear mechanism can be classified into seven wear modes, while the chemical and thermal wear mechanisms can be further classified into two modes each [10, 11, 12].

4.1.   Mechanical

The phenomena of material deformation and fracture are mainly involved in mechanical wear. Deformation mainly occurs in ductile material wear processes, while fracture is usually occurs in brittle materials.

4.1.1.   Abrasive mode

When hard particles or protuberances which are present at the surface of a body, or reside as loose particles between the contacting surfaces, are forced against or move along in the surface contact zone then wear which occurs, irrespective of hardness, is known as "Abrasive Wear"[13].

In the past, due to the observed sharpness of hard particles, it was thought that abrasive wear was similar to the cutting process of a machine tool or file, but now advances in microscopy visualization makes it clear that there are other complex processes involved in the case of abrasive wear as illustrated below in Figure 2 [14].

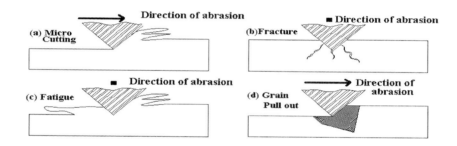

Figure 2. Complex processes in abrasive wear mode [14].

In above figure 2(a) abrasive micro-cutting represents the model where a sharp grit or hard asperity cuts the softer surface, and the material which is cut is removed as wear debris. Figure 2(b) represents a model where the abraded material is brittle in nature, and fracture of the worn surface may occur due to abrasive wear. In this kind of abrasive wear mode, wear debris will generate due to crack convergence. Figure 2(c) represents the model where a ductile material is abraded by a blunt grit, due to which cutting is unlikely to happen and the worn surface is repeatedly deformed. Figure 2(d), abrasive grain pull-out, represents the model where the boundary between grains is relatively weak and an entire grain is lost as wear debris. This process mainly happens in ceramics.

4.1.2.   Adhesive mode

The tendency of contacting surfaces to adhere arises from the attractive forces which exist between the surface atoms of the two materials. If the two surfaces are brought together and then separated, either normally or tangentially, these attractive forces act to attempt to pull the material from one surface to the other. Whenever material is removed from its original surface in this way, an adhesive wear fragment is created as shown in Figure 3 [15,16].

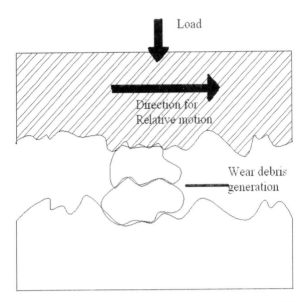

Figure 3. Wear debris generation in Adhesive wear mode [16].

In wear literature, the term sliding wear is quite often used in place of adhesive wear. Some researchers like Rigney strictly criticize adhesive wear as defined above and termed it as an adhesion process and recognize it as a part of sliding wear [17]. According to the American Society for Testing of Materials, adhesive wear is occur due to localized bonding between contacting solid surfaces leading to material transfer between the two surfaces or loss from either surface, while sliding wear is occur due to the relative motion in the tangential plane of contact between two solid bodies [1]. By treating these descriptions critically, it may be said that the property of adhesion in materials is the main cause which generates both adhesive and sliding wear. But the manner and effective physical parameters (like plane of relative motion), which are used to contact and separate two surfaces for generating wear, might be different or the same.

Adhesive wear can be classified into three sub types [18] as given below in Table 2;

Table 2. Subtypes of adhesive wear mode

Type	Lubrication scheme	Value of wear coefficient	Wear debris size
Severe galling	Poor lubricated	$10^{-2} - 10^{-4}$	$20 - 200 \ \mu m$
Moderate	Less / well lubricated	$10^{-4} - 10^{-6}$	$2 - 20 \ \mu m$
Burnishing	Very well lubricated	$10^{-6} - 10^{-8}$	$< 2 \ \mu m$

4.1.3. Flow mode

When the two surfaces are in a repeated sliding process, plastic deformation of surfaces occurs progressively and the accumulation of plastic strains causes thin plate-like metallic wear particles termed "flow wear mode or plastic ratchetting" [19]. The generation of thin particles when a hard ball is slid on a soft rough surface is illustrated schematically in Figure 4.

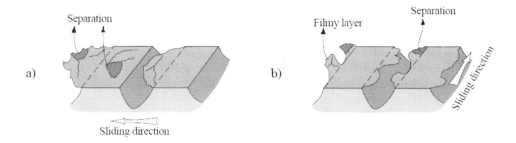

Figure 4. Filmy wear particles generation due to plastic ratchetting [19] adapted by [14].

When the asperities, as shown in figure 4(a) as machining grooves, are perpendicular to the sliding direction, the material is extruded from one side of the grooves only. When the asperities are parallel to the sliding direction as shown in figure 4(b), the material is extruded from both sides. The plastic ratchetting model is largely restricted to cases when one surface is much harder than the other and plastic deformation occurs on the softer surface. However, the case when both contacting surfaces are deformed (often the more realistic case) is not yet well defined.

4.1.4. Fatigue mode

The fatigue wear mode occurs when two rough surfaces move along each other. A non-homogeneous cyclic stress field with high amplitudes occurs in the subsurface layer. This causes damage accumulation near the surface in terms of propagated cracks, as shown in Figure 5 [20]. The wear under these conditions can be determined by the mechanics of crack initiation, growth and fracture.

Figure 5. Schematic for fatigue wear mode [10].

Fatigue wear may occur in two different ways: sliding, and rolling, depending on the relative contact of the two surfaces.

4.1.5. Erosion mode

Erosion is caused by a gas or a liquid which may or may not carry entrained solid particles, impinging on a surface, usually at high velocity as shown in Figure 6 [21]. When the angle of impingement is small, the wear produced is closely analogous to abrasion. When the angle of impingement is normal to the surface, material is displaced by plastic flow or is dislodged by brittle failure.

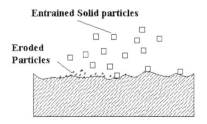

Figure 6. Schematic for erosive wear mode [22].

The severity of the erosive wear mode depends on parameters like particle material, angle of impingement, speed of particle, shape of particle and particle size.

4.1.6. Cavitation mode

Any liquid usually contains either gaseous or vaporous bubbles, which serve as the cavitation nuclei. When the pressure is reduced to a certain level, bubbles become the repository of vapour or of dissolved gases. The immediate result of this condition is that the bubbles increase rapidly in size. Subsequently, when the bubbles enter a zone of reduced pressure, they are reduced in size as a result of condensation of the vapours that they contain. This process of condensation takes place fairly quickly, accompanied by local hydraulic shocks, the emission of sound, the destruction of material bonds and other undesirable phenomena that are collectively termed 'cavitation' [23].

4.1.7. Fretting mode

When components are subjected to very small relative vibratory movements at high frequency, an interactive form of wear, called fretting, takes place that is initiated by adhesion, is amplified by corrosion, and has its main effect by abrasion [24]. Examples of vulnerable components to fretting mode are shrink fits, bolted parts and splines. This wear mode generally occurs between components that are not intended to move, like press fits.

4.2. Chemical

The growth rate of chemical reaction films mainly governs chemical wear processes. This rate of growth might be increased due to mechanical friction and in that case the wear will be 'tribo-chemical wear'. There are two modes of wear under chemical wear process, corrosive and oxidation.

4.2.1. Corrosive mode

This type of wear is due to the dynamic interaction between the environment and the mating material surfaces [25]. It occurs in a two-step cyclic manner:

- The contacting surfaces react with the environment and reaction products are formed on the surface.

- The reaction products are removed from the surfaces by crack formation and/or abrasion in the contact interactions.

4.2.2. Oxidation mode

The oxidation wear mode is a special type of wear mode indicated by the flaking off or crumbling of metal surfaces, which takes place when unprotected metal is exposed to a combination of heat, air, and moisture [26]. Rust is an example of oxidation.

4.3. Thermal

The thermal wear mechanism is a local surface melting phenomenon, in which the primary cause of the wear is due to friction and hysteretic heating that are generated as a effect of relative motion. As per Kato, there are two modes of wear under thermal wear process, melt and diffusion [10].

4.3.1. Melt wear mode

This wear mode is not considered as a dominant steady wear mode in general tribo-elements; however, it is generated by unexpected contact conditions, such as hard inclusions at the contact interface or a sudden overloading due to vibration.

4.3.2. Diffusive wear mode

Diffusive wear on the atomic scale may not play an important role in practice. Even though the original material properties of a contact surface are degraded by losing significant chemical compositions as a result of diffusion, the wear rate can still be increased by enhancing other wear modes, such as adhesive or abrasive wear.

5. ROLE OF LUBRICATION IN WEAR

5.1. General Discussion

The main aim of lubrication is to separate two surfaces sliding past each other with a film of some material which can be sheared without causing any damage to the surfaces [27]. By this separation of surfaces, the main goal is to reduce the severity in friction and wear phenomena. Since both friction and wear are two distinct phenomena, it not necessary that a specific lubricant that is used during any machine operation is evenly effective for both friction and wear as demonstrated by Table 3 [3].

Table 3. Different lubricants and their effect on wear and friction for three different metal couples – abstracted from [3]

Couple No.	Metal Couple Identity	Lubricant A Value of coefficient friction	Lubricant B Value of coefficient friction	Lubricant C Value of coefficient friction	Minimum reduction in system wear	Friction coefficient without lubrication
1	52100/415	0.15	0.13	0.17	5×10^{-4}	0.97
2	52100/1060	0.20	0.20	0.32	0.02	0.73
3	302/1060	0.15	0.15	0.16	1×10^{-3}	0.88

From table 3, one can see that for different metal couple combinations, the effects of lubricants on friction and wear are different. Consider couples 1 & 2: all three lubricants increase the friction coefficient for the couple 2. But at the same time, wear is reduced. Now if values of friction coefficient and wear reduction of couple 2 are compared with couple 3, a different behaviour is found, with a different balance of friction and wear.

5.2. Lubrication mechanism and its influence on wear and friction

The primary means through which a lubricant influences friction and wear is by reducing adhesion [28]. Three general mechanisms are available as described below [3]. Each is illustrated in Figure 8.

5.2.1. Adsorption

The lubricant forms a thin layer over the solid contacting surface, and tends to reduce the adhesive bond strength at the junctions.

5.2.2. Chemical Activation

Lubricant is used to modify the contacting surface chemically. Similar to the mechanism of adsorption, it also tends to reduce the adhesive bonds strength at the junctions.

5.2.3. Separation

Lubricant is used to separate the two contact surfaces physically, which tends to reduce the number of junctions and ultimately reduce the adhesion effect.

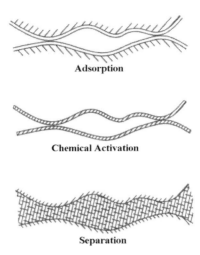

Figure 8. Lubrication mechanisms [3].

6. CONCLUSION AND FUTURE WORK

A review on the basic principles of wear and affiliated mechanisms has been presented. Analysis of the basic features of wear classification from the available literature has provided a comprehensive and methodological structure. The description of wear classification and mechanisms has been provided in a hierarchical manner that is normally not available in wear-related research literature. By this review material may provide an opportunity for new researchers to understand the basics of wear phenomena and affiliated mechanisms in order to gain knowledge for future research in wear related areas like wear debris analysis.

The next stages of the work will:

- review wear debris measurement techniques;

- examine in detail the descriptors for wear debris;

- identify relationships of quantifiable wear debris descriptors with degradation processes and hence diagnostics;

- automate the analysis of wear debris with application to health monitoring.

REFERENCES

[1]   ASTM G40-05 Standard Termninology Relating to Wear and Erosion: ASTM Standards. Book of Standards : v. 03.02) West Conshohocken : International Standards Worldwide; 2006.
[2]   Lagally MG, Welkie DG. Defect Structures at Solid Surfaces. Surface and Interface Analysis 1981; 3(1): 8-11.
[3]   Bayer RG, Mechanical wear fundamentals and testing. 2nd edition. New York: Marcel Dekker Inc; 2004.
[4]   Burnham N, Kulik AA, Bhushan B. editors. Handbook of micro/nano tribology. 2nd edition. Boca Raton: CRC; 1999.
[5]   Students E, Rudzitis J. Contact of Surface asperities in wear. Tribology International 1996; 29(1): 275-279.
[6]   Hutchings IM, Stachowiak GW. editors. Wear materials, mechanisms and practice. Chichester: Wiley; 2005.
[7]   Burwell JT, Strang CD. On the Empirical Law of Adhesive Wear. Applied Physics 1952; 23(1): 18-28.
[8]   Department of Material Engineering: Online Course Material on Ceramics. The University of British Columbia [Online] [access 2006 April]. Available from URL http://www.mmat.ubc.ca/courses/mmat382/sections/cnc763.doc
[9]   Rabinowicz E. Wear. Materials Science and Engineering 1976; 25: 23-28.
[10]   Kato K. Classification of Wear Mechanisms/Models. Engineering Tribology 2002; 216(6): 349-355.
[11]   Hutchings IM, Tribology friction and wear of engineering materials. London: Arnold; 1992.
[12]   Dasgupta A, Pecht Michael. Material Failure Mechanisms and Damage Models. IEEE Transactions on Reliability 1991; 40(5): 531-536.

[13]   Department of Solid Mechanics: Online Course Material on Wear. Chalmers University of Technology [Online] [access 2006 April]. Available from URL http://www.am.chalmers.se/~anek/research/wear.pdf

[14]   Stachowick GW, Batchelor AW, Engineering tribology. 2nd edition. Boston: Butterworth-Heinemann; 2000.

[15]   Rabinowicz E, Friction and wear of materials. New York: John Wiley; 1965.

[16]   Pall Corporation: Why is Filtration important? [Online] [access 2006 April]. Available from URL http://www.pall.com/hydraulic_3779.asp?level0=2

[17]   Rigney DA. Sliding Wear of Metals. Annual Review Material Science 1988; 18: 141-163.

[18]   Rabinowicz E. The Least Wear. Wear 1984; 100(1): 533-541.

[19]   Johnson KL. Contact Mechanics and the Wear. Wear 1995; 190(2): 162-170.

[20]   Goryacheva IG, Contact mechanics in tribology. Verlag: Springer; 1998.

[21]   Williams JA, Engineering tribology. New York: Oxford university press; 1994

[22]   Gordon England: Wear Resistance [Online] [access 2006 April]. Available from URL http://www.gordonengland.co.uk/wear.htm

[23]   Fitch EC. Cavitation wear in hydraulic systems [Online] [access 2006 April]. Practicing Oil Analysis 2002 Sept. Available from URL http://www.practicingoilanalysis.com/article_detail.asp?articleid=380&relatedbookgroup=Hydraulics

[24]   Bhushan B, Gupta BK, Handbook of tribology materials, coatings, and surface treatments. New York: McGraw-Hill; 1991.

[25]   Bunshah RF. editors. Handbook of deposition technologies for films and coatings science, technology and applications. 2nd edition. Noyes: William Andrew Publishing; 1994.

[26]   Key to Steel: Surfacing of Wear Resistance [Online] [access 2006 April]. Available from URL http://www.key-to-steel.com/Articles/Art139.htm

[27]   Cameron A, The principles of lubrication. London: Longmans; 1996.

[28]   Neale M. editors. Tribology handbook. New York: John Wiley & Sons; 1973.

Session 11
LUBRICANTS & ADDITIVES 4

Chair: Mr. Javier Barriga

Tribological Studies of Titanium Nitride Coatings Deposited By Combined Pulsed Magnetron Sputtering and Pulsed Biasing
Z. LIU, R. D. ARNELL, P. J. KELLY, F. VELASCO

Effective Lubricants: New Friction Modifier
V. A. LEVCHENKO, V. A. MATVEENKO

Influence of Lubricant on Rolling Fatigue Life – a Case Study
N. MANDAL, N. C. MURMU

The Effect of Degree of Refining of Base Oils on Grease Properties
V. SERRA-HOLM

Tribological Studies of Titanium Nitride Coatings Deposited By Combined Pulsed Magnetron Sputtering and Pulsed Biasing

Z. Liu [1], R. D. Arnell [1, 3], P. J. Kelly [2], F. Velasco [3]

[1] Institute for Materials Research, University of Salford UK
[2] Surface Engineering Group, Manchester Metropolitan University, Manchester, M1 5GD, UK
[3] Jost Institute for Tribotechnology, University of Central Lancashire, UK

ABSTRACT

Titanium Nitride (TiN) is widely used as a hard coating material in industrial applications, principally to protect cutting and forming tools against corrosion and wear. Despite this excellent wear resistance, until recently, it has been observed to have high friction against most metallic counterfaces. However, recent work by some of the authors of this paper has shown that TiN coatings deposited by pulsed magnetron sputtering (PMS) at 20kHz pulse frequency can have enhanced tribological and structural properties compared with conventionally deposited films. In particular, TiN coatings deposited using this technique can have friction coefficients as low as 0.09 against steel counterfaces. The first section of this paper reports the results of extending the frequency range of the pulsed magnetron sputtering to 350kHz.

The use of pulsed DC power at the substrate is a recent development in the field of magnetron sputtering that offers a means significantly to increase the ion current drawn at the substrate, and it is thought likely that the improved coating properties observed with PMS could be further enhanced by pulsing the power to the substrate during coating deposition. This paper reports an investigation of such a process. Pulsed DC power has been applied at both the target (zero, 20, 50 and 100kHz) and the substrate (100-350 kHz) during the deposition of TiN coatings in a closed field unbalanced magnetron sputtering system, and the effects on the structural, mechanical and tribological properties of the coatings are being studied.

This paper initially reviews the enhancements to be gained by pulsing the target voltage during coating deposition and then describes the results to date of the current investigations of the effects of including pulsed substrate power.

Keywords: Titanium Nitride Coatings, Tribology; Pulsed Sputtering

1. INTRODUCTION

Titanium nitride (TiN) coatings are very widely used in tribological applications, where they can provide a hard, wear-resistant surface to protect the underlying substrate. Despite these advantageous wear properties, until recently, the coefficient of friction for TiN against metallic counterfaces has been observed to be of the order of 0.4 – 0.8 in unlubricated conditions. However, recent work by some of the authors has shown that TiN coatings deposited by pulsed magnetron sputtering (PMS), can have substantially improved tribological properties, in terms of coefficient of friction, surface roughness and coating to substrate adhesion, compared to coatings deposited by conventional sputtering [1].

The extraordinary improvement in friction coefficient is illustrated in Figure 1. This shows the friction coefficient of eighteen TiN coatings against bearing steel (100Cr6) counterfaces. The coatings were deposited according to a fractional factorial array, which included eight different variables, and in each case, the coatings were deposited onto both rough (0.4μm Ra) and smooth (0.1μm Ra) tool steel substrates. It was found that by far the most significant variable was whether the sputtering source was powered by constant DC or by a power source that was pulsed at 20kHz. It can be seen that, with one exception, the coatings pulsed by constant DC had much higher friction coefficients than those produced when pulsing.

The friction coefficients observed in this study for coatings deposited by pulsed sputtering are comparable to those normally obtained with solid lubricants, such as graphite and molybdenum disulphide.

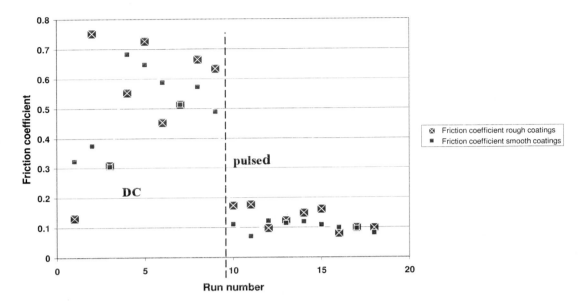

Figure 1. Showing the coefficient of friction for TiN coatings deposited onto tool steel substrates by Dc sputtering and sputtering with 20kHz pulsed power.

When examined by high resolution electron microscopy, the films produced by pulsed processing were found to have denser structures, with smoother surfaces than those produced by continuous DC processing, as shown in Figure 2. It was postulated that the enhancement in tribological properties observed was primarily a result of these structural modifications. Studies of surface topography are therefore a major component of the current programme.

(a)   (b)

Figure 2. High resolution SEM images of the surfaces of TiN coatings deposited by (a) DC sputtering and (b) sputtering with 20kHz pulsed power (courtesy of Professor Ivan Petrov, University of Illinois)

Pulsing the magnetron discharge is known to substantially modify the characteristics of the deposition plasma, with increased plasma densities and electron temperatures being measured close to the substrate in pulsed discharges [2]. As a result, higher ion energy fluxes are transported to the growing film, and the increased flux and energy of the particles incident at the substrate would be expected to contribute to the observed improvements in the structure and properties of films produced by pulsed processing.

Following this very promising initial study, it seemed likely that a further improvement in structure and properties could be obtained, firstly, by increasing the pulse frequency at the target and, secondly, by pulsing not only the magnetron power, but also the substrate power A comprehensive programme is therefore under way to study the effects of such changes on the structural, mechanical and tribological properties of TiN coatings.

This paper describes the initial results from the programme.

2. EXPERIMENTAL DETAILS

Titanium nitride coatings are being deposited by reactive unbalanced magnetron sputtering in a Teer Coatings Ltd. UDP350 rig [3]. Sputtering takes place from a single 300 x 100 mm, 99.5 % pure titanium target, with a second, unpowered, vertically opposed magnetron also installed in the chamber, to provide a closed magnetic field and thus maximize the ion-to-atom ratio incident at the substrate. The reactive sputtering process is controlled by optical emissions monitoring (OEM), using conditions selected to produce stoichiometric TiN coatings, based on previous experience [3]. The magnetron and substrate are powered by the two channels of a dual channel Advanced Energy® Pinnacle Plus power supply. This unit can operate two channels independently at pulse frequencies from DC to 350kHz and at duties in the range 50-100%.

The programme is being carried out for DC sputtering, for pulsed DC magnetron driving frequencies of, 20, 50, 100, and 350 kHz, and for an AC driving frequency of 40kHz.

Coatings are being deposited onto both polished SEM pin stubs and M2 tool steel coupons, to suit different analytical techniques. All substrates are ultrasonically pre-cleaned in propanol.

For the investigation of the extension of the sputtering frequency range, the substrates were sputter cleaned at -1000V DC for 20 minutes prior to deposition of coatings using -50V DC bias.

Following this initial work, coatings are being deposited, at each of the sputtering frequencies onto substrates with pulsed bias and the effects of etching voltage and frequency, and substrate bias voltage and frequency are being investigated using the fractional factorial experimental array shown in Table 1.

Table 1. Fractional factorial experimental array carried out for each magnetron driving frequency

Expt No.	Etch voltage (V)	Etch frequency (kHz)	Substrate bias (V)	Substrate bias frequency (kHz)
1	-450	100	-50	100
2	-650	100	-50	350
3	-450	350	-50	350
4	-650	350	-50	100
5	-450	100	-100	350
6	-650	350	-100	100
7	-450	100	-100	100
8	-650	350	-100	350
9	-550	225	-75	225
10	-550	225	-75	225

Standard operating conditions are: target power 1.5kW; sputtering pressure 0.24Pa; substrate-to-target separation 110mm; TiN deposition time 57.5 minutes. A thin Ti-only interlayer is deposited in all cases before introducing the nitrogen gas to the process to form TiN.

The structures of the coatings are being investigated by scanning electron microscopy (SEM) and X-ray diffraction (XRD); the surface topographies by Talysurf profilometry, Atomic Force Microscopy (AFM) and White Light Interference microscopy (WLI), the mechanical properties by micro-hardness testing, nanoindentation and scratch testing; and the tribological properties by pin-on-disk and thrust washer wear testing and drill testing.

It is a feature of fractional factorial experimental arrays that firm conclusions cannot be drawn until the full array of experiments has been completed. Nevertheless, some interesting comparisons have emerged from the results produced to date, and these are reported here.

3. RESULTS AND DISCUSSION

3.1. Coatings Deposited By Pulsed Magnetron Sputtering

3.1.1. Effects of pulse frequency and counterface material on friction coefficient

Thrust washer friction tests were carried out on the coated specimens at an interfacial pressure of 0.23 MPa and a sliding speed of 45mms-1 with a test duration of 15 minutes. Tests were carried out both for 100Cr6 steel washers, hardened and tempered to 7.5 GPa and for a silicon carbide washer. The results are shown in Figure 3.

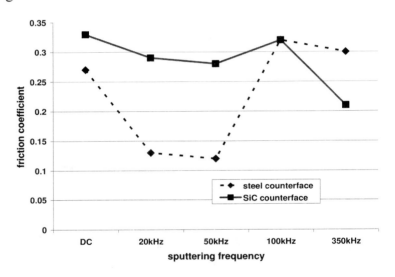

Figure 3. Effects of sputtering frequency on coefficient of friction for steel and SiC counterfaces

It can be seen that, for the steel counterface, the earlier results, shown in Figure 1 are confirmed; with the friction being low for both 20kHz and 50kHz sputtering frequencies. However, the friction at higher frequencies is higher than that observed for DC sputtering. Also, the friction against the SiC counterface does not exhibit the marked minimum observed with the steel counterface.

3.1.2. Effects of pulse frequency on mechanical properties

Coating hardnesses were measured using a Fischerscope H100 with a Vickers indenter at 50mN load, and critical loads were measured using a Teer Coatings ST3001 scratch tester with a 200µm diameter diamond indenter. The results are shown, with the friction results for the steel counterface repeated, in Figure 4.

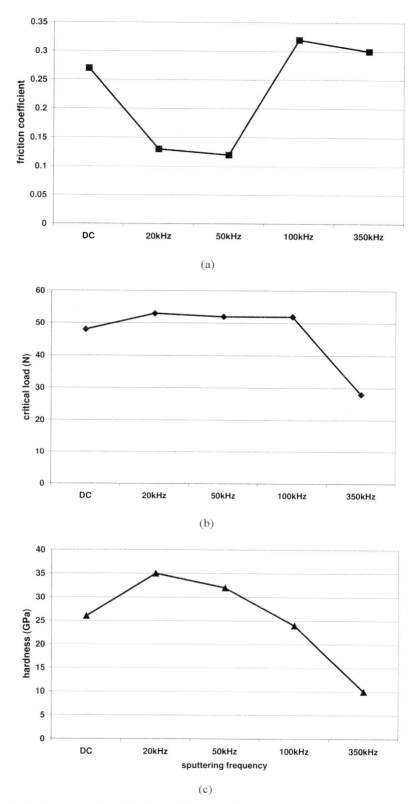

Figure 4. Effects of sputtering frequency on (a) friction coefficient against steel, (b) coating critical load and (c) coating hardness

It can be seen that the minimum friction against the steel counterface is obtained over the frequency range where the hardness and the critical load of the coatings have their maximum values.

3.2. Coatings deposited using pulsed bias

3.2.1. Effects of pulsed bias on coating morphology

Figure 5 shows SEM micrographs of typical fracture sections of coatings deposited by DC sputtering, pulsed magnetron sputtering and pulsed bias sputtering.

Figure 5a shows the dense, columnar structure normally observed for TiN coatings produced by a variety of techniques, and figure 5b shows a very similar structure produced by PMS. In contrast, Figure 5c shows a fully dense, non-columnar structure with many fracture facets. No structure of this quality has been reported previously and it is clear evidence that the extra energy input resulting from pulsed biasing is having a marked effect on the coating structure.

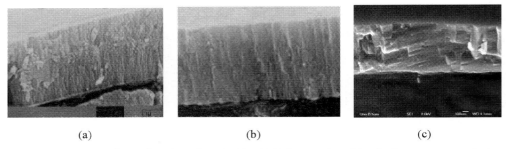

(a)   (b)   (c)

Figure 5. Cross sections of coatings deposited by (a) DC sputtering, (b) pulsed magnetron sputtering and (c) pulsed bias sputtering

3.2.2. Effects of pulsed bias on friction coefficient

As stated earlier, it is not possible to draw firm conclusions from fractional factorial experimental arrays until the full array has been investigated. However, significant comparisons have been made by pooling results for DC and pulsed 20kHz sputtering frequencies, 50V and 100V substrate bias, and steel and SiC counterfaces, as shown in Figure 6. These results were all obtained with substratev frequencies of either 100kHz or 350kHz, as shown in Table 1.

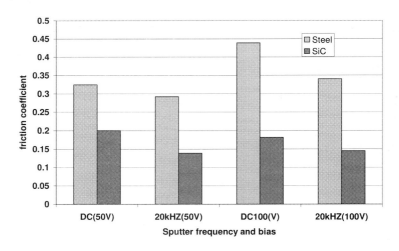

Figure 6. Comparison of friction coefficients against steel for sputtering frequencies of DC and 20kHz and substrate biases of 50V and 100V

It can be seen that the friction is substantially lower for SiC than for steel, significantly lower for 50V bias than for 100V, and somewhat lower for the 20kHz sputtering frequency than for DC sputtering. However, the very low friction observed against steel for DC substrate bias is not observed for pulsed bias.

3.2.3.   Effects on Surface topography

A wide variation in surface topography of the coatings has been observed. It is not possible to draw conclusions from this at this stage, but two extreme examples are shown in Figure 7, which shows the surfaces and three-dimensional views of samples 7 and 8 from Table 1. It can be seen that the surface appearance of specimen 7 is similar to that of the SEM micrograph of the low friction surface shown in figure 2(b).

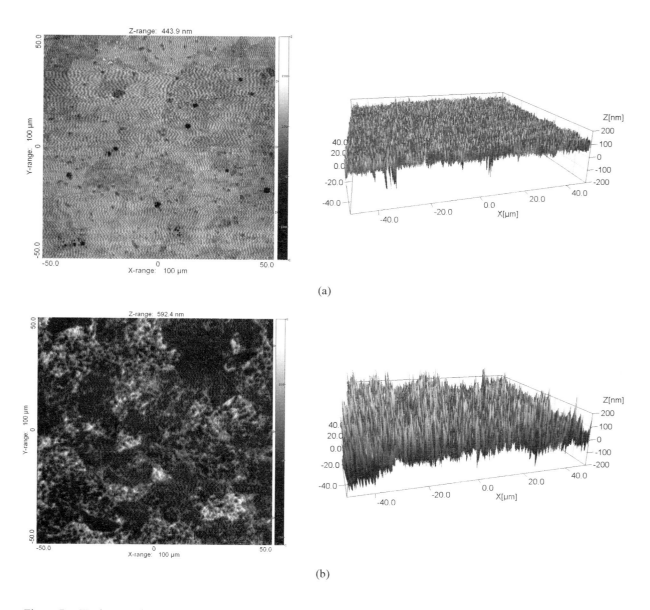

Figure 7. AFM images showing surface and three-dimensional views of (a) Specimen 7 and (b) Specimen 8 of DC sputtered coatings with substrate bias and frequency as shown in Table 1

3.2.4.   Effects on coating adhesion

Measurements have been made for coatings sputtered with constant DC power and with pulsed DC frequencies of 20, 50 and 100kHz, and with all the substrate conditions shown in Table 1.

Figure 8 shows the pooled results, at each of the sputtering frequencies, for substrate biases of 50 and 100V and substrate bias frequencies of 100 and 350 kHz.

There is a clear difference between the results with substrate biases of 50V and 100V. At 50V bias, the critical load continuously increases with sputtering frequency, whereas at 100V bias the critical load peaks at a sputtering frequency around 20 kHz. This behaviour is similar for both the bias frequencies of 100 and 350 kHz. As increases in both the sputtering frequency and the substrate bias voltage increase the energy arriving at the substrate, these results imply that there is an optimal energy arrival rate that would maximise the critical load. This optimum, in terms of both bias voltage and sputtering frequency, will be identified as part of the analysis of the fractional factorial array.

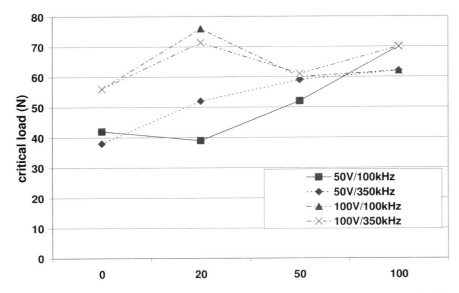

Figure 8. Effects of sputtering frequency, substrate bias and substrate frequency on critical load

4. DISCUSSION

The work described here confirms that pulsing of the magnetron power and the substrate power during the deposition of titanium nitride coatings can substantially modify the structures and tribological and mechanical properties of the films. In particular, the fully dense, faceted fracture section shown in figure 5c has not been previously reported for such coatings. The work also confirms that there is a range of pulsed magnetron frequencies over which the friction coefficient of TiN against steel is comparable with those of solid lubricants such as graphite and molybdenum disulphide. For substrates with DC bias, this frequency range corresponds to that in which the coating hardness and critical load are maximised, so it is likely that wear of the coating will also be minimised in this range. Investigations of the wear rate are currently taking place.

5. CONCLUSIONS

Pulsing of the power supplied to the magnetron and the substrate during reactive deposition of TiN coatings has the potential to substantially improve the tribological properties of the coatings.

REFERENCES

[1]   HA Jehn, 'Multicomponent and multiphase hard coatings for tribological applications.' Surf. Coat. Technol., 131 (2000) 433

[2]   WD Sproul and KO Legg (eds) 'Opportunities for Innovation: Advanced Surface Engineering.' Technomic Publishing Co., Inc., Switzerland, 1995.

[3]   I Efeoglu, RD Arnell, and DG Teer, 'The mechanical and tribological properties of titanium aluminium nitride coatings.' Surf. Coat. Technol., 57 (1993) 117.

Effective Lubricants: New Friction Modifier

V. A. Levchenko, V. A. Matveenko

Lomonosov Moscow State University, Leninskii Gory 1, Moscow 119992, Russia

ABSTRACT

This paper presents a new friction modifier. Increased requirements for the quality of lubricating oils are considered. The composition and structure of polymer additives compounds that serve as a lubricant base are discussed. The mechanism of anticorrosive and antiwear action is considered. The mechanism of action of antiwear and load-carrying additives is discussed. New high-index thickened oils are discussed and the mechanism of action of the viscous additives is considered.

Keywords: Friction Modifiers, Lubrication Technology, Lubricant Testing.

1. INTRODUCTION

Friction modifiers continue to be of high interest to the lubricant industry due to the ongoing pressure on fuel economy and energy efficiency. Current emphasis is on longevity of friction reduction to ensure proper performance during the lifetime of the oil.

A new polymer friction modifier, forming part of the additive package is described. Its anti-frictional action is caused by the formation of a layer of friction modifier on all the rubbing surfaces. Under the influence of high contact pressure and high temperatures in the friction zone, a local chemical reaction is initiated, the products of which fill the roughness and defects of the surfaces. The layer is formed of ordered macromolecules (structure Lengmuir), generated as spirals, which retain the lubricant environment. The friction modifier operates at the sites where it is most strongly required, identifying the necessary sites by an excessive rise in temperature due to frictional heating. Thus, friction modifier is bonded to the metal surfaces at the level of the crystal lattice, forming with it strong chemisorptions and chemical bonds.

2. MATERIALS AND TEST PROCEDURE

2.1. Lubricants tested

The lubricating oils used were (1) Castrol GTX and (2) a mineral base commercially available oil with viscosity corresponding to SAE 30 (viscosity: $v50 = 11, 5$ mm^2/s, $v100 = 10, 5$ mm^2/s, density-900 kg/m^3). Each oil was tested both with and without the polymer additive. The friction modifier content of the modified oils was 0.1% wt/wt.

2.2. Experimental apparatus and test procedure

The investigations of the effects of the friction modifier were conducted on a ball-disc tribometer, as shown in Fig.1. A steel ball with a diameter of $12,7 \times 10^{-3}$m was rubbed against a rotating aluminum disk (diameter 6×10^{-2} m; thickness – 4×10^{-3}m) placed in an oil bath with a heater. The oil bath temperature was increased at the rate of 100^{0}C/min.

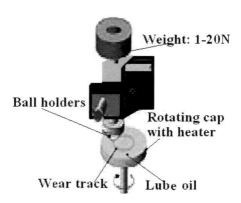

Figure 1. The ball-disc test scheme

The roughness parameter R_a of disk friction surfaces was 0,07 µm; that of the balls was 0.05µm. The balls were made of hardened ball-bearing steel (1,30-1,65% Cr; 1,0% C; Mn-0,20-0,40%,(Fe - remain). The disks were made of hardened disk-bearing aluminum.

The specimens were tested under constant sliding speed V = 0,9 mm/s, constant load P = 10 N, initial Hertz pressure Hz =56 MPa. The tests of discs and balls with and without friction modifier were conducted in the range of oil bath temperatures 40 – 200 0C.

3. TEST RESULTS

The test results in two the commercially available brands of lubricating oil with and without 0.1% wt/wt polymer additive are shown given in Fig. 2.

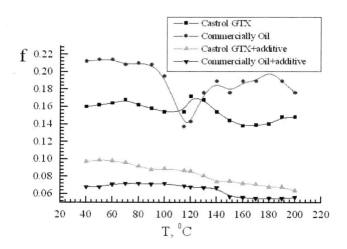

Figure 2. The friction coefficient dependence via temperature

The values of friction coefficient in pure Castrol GTX (f=0,14-0,18) are higher than those for Castrol GTX with additive (f=0,098-0,065) over the full range of test temperatures.

The values of friction coefficient in pure commercial oil (f=0,137-0,214) are higher than those for commercial oil with additive (f=0,076-0,058) over the full range of test temperatures.

4. CONCLUSION

The proposed new polymer as friction modifier operates at the metal surfaces and not through modification of the lubricant's physical properties. The friction modifier is stable in lubricating oil and does not affect the stability or function of other lubricating additives. Reductions in friction are seen over a wide temperature range varying from 40°C to 200°C. The proposed friction modifier is environmentally friendly.

Influence of Lubricant on Rolling Fatigue Life – a Case Study

N. Mandal, N. C. Murmu

Central Mechanical Engineering Research Institute,
M.G. Avenue, Durgapur, West Bengal, India

ABSTRACT

The elastohydrodynamic film thickness, which separates the ball or roller surface from those of the raceway of the bearings, directly affects bearing life. Due to this reason, lubricant considerations for rolling element bearings have taken an added importance in the design and operation of mechanical systems within the last few decades. The phenomenon, which limits the usable life of bearings, is the surface pitting fatigue on rolling elements. Chemical additives added to the lubricant can also significantly affect the bearing life and reliability. The interaction of these physical and chemical effects is important for the design engineer and user of these systems. Here an attempt has been made to evaluate the elastohydrodynamic effect of different lubricants on fatigue life of bearings. This work presents and discusses the results of rolling contact fatigue tests with three different lubricants using a four-ball E.P. lubricant tester. The lubricants' grades are SAE-90, SAE-140 and ISO-100. The test machine used was a four ball E.P. tester and the IP 300/87 standard was applied. The result indicated that the lubrication has an important influence on the rolling fatigue life of mechanical components. This paper depicts the comparative study of lubricants using Four Ball Tester, and information obtained can be used for accelerated life testing of rolling element bearing.

Keywords: Four-ball E.P.lubricant tester, Elastohydrodynamic (EHD) film thickness.

1. INTRODUCTION

Contact fatigue occurs on or close to the surface of any rigid body that sustains repeated rolling contact involving only a limited amount of sliding. The prime cause of contact fatigue is the high stresses generated by Hertzian contact between any pair of curved solid bodies. Examples of contact fatigue, which occurs when there is contact in both lubricated and non-lubricated situations, are found in gear teeth, rolling bearings, steel rails, and wheels. The presence of oil in lubricated contact fatigue modifies the mechanisms involved [1]. Factors influencing the contact fatigue life of hardened steel bearings and gears can be roughly classified into four categories: material, lubrication and surface finish, dimensional precision, and environmental conditions [2]. In Rolling Element Bearing application, the lubrication can have a marked effect on bearing life and load capacity. A lubricant has four major functions:

Provides a separating film between rolling and sliding contact surfaces, thus preventing wear.

Acts as a coolant to maintain proper bearing temperature.

Prevents the bearing from being contaminated by dirt and other foreign particles.

Prevents corrosion of bearing surfaces.

Since the establishments of lubrication mechanism maps are helpful to understand the lubrication ability for various lubricants and to select proper operating conditions, research on the transition between lubrication mechanisms is a very important work in the field of Tribology. Since Stribeck (1902) first investigated the functional characteristics of plain journal bearings, which are frequently referred to as the Stribeck curve, various lubrication mechanisms have been experimentally studied [3-13]. Generally, these mechanisms can be classified into three regions as

Elasto Hydrodynamic Lubrication (EHD) and Partial Elasto Hydrodynamic Lubrication (PEHD)

Boundary Lubrication (BL)

Severe Scuffing or Initial Seizure (IS)

It should be noted that the transitions between these three regimes have been well defined.

Tallian et al. [14,15] was first to report that the fatigue life of the bearing is dependent upon the dimensionless film parameter Λ, which is defined as $\Lambda = h_{min}/\sigma$ where h_{min} is the minimum fluid film thickness as calculated by one of several available equations of EHL theory and σ is the composite surface roughness of the sliding pair, defined by $\sigma = \sqrt{\sigma_1^2 + \sigma_2^2}$

2. DETAILS OF EXPERIMENT

2.1. Test Machine

The test machine used in this work was a Four-Ball E.P. Lubricant Tester with a driving shaft speed of 1470 rev/min.

2.2. Test Lubricants

The properties of the lubricants used are listed in the table below. The two oils SAE-90 and SAE-140 are hypoid gear oils containing extreme pressure additives, and the manufacturer claims that they have long service life due to their extremely good oxidation stability. These oils meet API service classification GL-4, IS: 1118-1957, US Military MIL-L-2105 and UK Defense CS 3000A specifications. The remaining oil ISO-100 is an extreme pressure type industrial gear oils, which contains sulphur, phosphorus compounds, and the manufacturer claims that they have better thermal stability and higher oxidation resistance compared to conventional lead-napthenate gear oils. This oil has good demulsibility, low foaming tendency and provides rust and corrosion protection to metal surfaces. ISO-100 oils meet AGMA standard 250.04 IS: 8406-1985.

Table 2.1. Properties of lubricating oils

Lubricant Description	Kinematic Viscosity cSt at 100°C	Viscosity Index (VI)	Flash Point COC°C Min
SAE-90	16-18	90	180
SAE-140	28-34	90	190
ISO-100	95-105	90	204

2.3. Test Method

The tests were carried out by Seta Shell Four Ball E.P. Lubricant Tester to ASTM D 2266 Standards. The tester was operated with one steel ball under load rotating against three steel balls held stationary in the form of a cradle. The rotating speed is 1475 rpm. The series of tests was carried out with the different lubricants by varying the loads from 60 to 100 kg with a time interval. The balls used in the tests are 12.7 mm in diameter with a roughness of R_a=0.035μm and made from a single heat of carbon-vacuum-deoxidized AISI 52100 steel with a hardness of RC 65.The experiments were conducted for 1 min for each run and then the scar diameter (if it appears) was measured for the three bottom balls by optical microscope. Two measurements for each wear scar were taken, one normal and the other parallel with the striations in the wear-scar surface. The arithmetic mean of the measurements was then obtained.

2.4. Test Results

The results are summarized in the following tables for the load of 80kg, 90kg, 95kg and 100 kg with different lubricants used written below (N.A abbreviates the term 'not appeared' in the tables given below).

Table 2.2. Results showed for lubricating oil SAE-90

Sl No	Temperature (°C)	Applied Load (Kg)	Scar Diameter (mm)						Average Scar Diameter (mm)
			Ball 1		Ball2		Ball3		
			Horizontal reading	Vertical reading	Horizontal reading	Vertical reading	Horizontal reading	Vertical reading	
01	Ambient	80	N.A	N.A	N.A	N.A	N.A	N.A	N.A
02		90	0.740	0.740	0.650	0.500	0.700	0.670	0.667
03		95	0.943	0.945	1.050	0.098	0.890	0.855	0.796
04		100	1.497	2.073	1.500	1.867	2.057	1.467	1.743

Table 2.3. Results showed for lubricating oil ISO-100

Sl No	Temperature (°C)	Applied Load (Kg)	Scar Diameter (mm)						Average Scar Diameter (mm)
			Ball 1		Ball2		Ball3		
			Horizontal reading	Vertical reading	Horizontal reading	Vertical reading	Horizontal reading	Vertical reading	
01	Ambient	80	N.A	N.A	N.A	N.A	N.A	N.A	N.A
02		90	N.A	N.A	N.A	N.A	N.A	N.A	N.A
03		95	N.A	N.A	N.A	N.A	N.A	N.A	N.A
04		100	0.700	0.730	0.720	0.710	0.710	0.720	0.715

Table2.4. Results showed for lubricating oil SAE-140

Sl No	Temperature (°C)	Applied Load (Kg)	Scar Diameter (mm)						Average Scar Dia (mm)
			Ball 1		Ball2		Ball3		
			Horizontal reading	Vertical reading	Horizontal reading	Vertical reading	Horizontal reading	Vertical reading	
01	Ambient	80	N.A	N.A	N.A	N.A	N.A	N.A	N.A
02		90	N.A	N.A	N.A	N.A	N.A	N.A	N.A
03		95	0.555	0.620	0.600	0.550	0.600	0.600	0.587
04		100	0.730	0.740	0.720	0.730	0.750	0.725	0.732

The evaluation of contact parameters is also one of prime importance of this research-oriented work. For this reason, attempts have been made to evaluate the most used contact parameters such as the contact area dimension, the maximum contact pressure, the maximum deflection at the center of the contacting surfaces, the position of the maximum shear stress under the surfaces etc.

Table.2.5 Calculation of different parameters relating to Hertzian contact stress for experiments on four ball tester

Sr. No	Applied Load (kg)	Contact Area Dimension $X10^{-4}$ (m)	Maximum Contact Pressure (GPa)	Average Contact Pressure (GPa)	Maximum Deflection $X10^{-6}$ (m)	Maximum Shear stress (GPa)	Depth at which maximum Shear Stress occurs $X10^{-6}$ (m)
01	80	3.2484	3.5510	2.3674	16.6132	1.1837	2.0725
02	90	3.3785	3.6930	2.4620	17.9702	1.2131	2.1555
03	95	3.4400	3.7602	2.5068	18.6298	1.2534	2.1947
04	100	3.4993	3.8250	2.5500	19.2778	1.2750	2.2326

The contact area depends on the geometry of the contacting bodies, load and material properties. The contact area is circular when two balls are in contact. Contact pressures and deflections also depend on the geometry of the contacting bodies. Since Hertz originally developed the formulae for contact parameters, terms such as Hertzian contacts or Hertzian Stresses can frequently be found in the literature. Here in our case for calculation of contact parameters like contact area dimension, maximum contact pressures etc, we are using the formulae suggested by Hamrock and Dowson [16]. The calculated results are tabulated below.

The formulae for calculation of these parameters are given in APPENDIX

3. DISCUSSION

Table 3.1. Comparison of Scar Diameters at different loads using selected lubricants

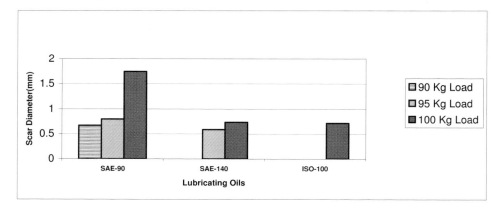

It has been discussed already that surface pitting or generation of a scar is the indication of fatigue failure of a component. From the above table, we find that for the oil SAE-90, the scar comes at the load of 90 Kg, and for the oil SAE-140, the scar comes at 95 Kg but in the lubricating oil ISO-100, the scar is obtained at the load of 100 Kg. From these experiments we have arrived at the conclusion that ISO-100 can withstand higher load without failure. At the same time for a certain load, at 100kg, the measured scar diameter for different lubricant are shown in figure. From this, we can conclude that the diameter is more in case of SAE-90 with respect to other two oils.

In Four Ball Tester M/C the upper ball is rotating and the bottom three balls are stationary. In operation, the upper ball touches the lower three balls and it is necessary to maintain minimum film thickness between the two convex surfaces of balls. When this film breaks then metal-to-metal contacts comes into play and surface pitting fatigue occurs. When load increases the contact stress also increases between two surfaces and accordingly contact area also increases, as shown in the table 2.5. This contact stress generates the scar on the surfaces of balls. So when we gradually increase the load then the chance of separation of film also increases. By this experiment we can say that, for a specific pressure additive, lubricant (like SAE-90) can withstand up to that pressure before scar comes or surface-pitting fatigue occurs.

The result also shows that for the higher viscosity oil the load carrying capacity is also higher and for a certain load the scar diameter also depends upon the viscosity. For 100 kg load, the scar comes for all three lubricants but scar diameter is least in case of ISO-100 and viscosity is highest for this oil among the three. By this way, we can conclude that lubrication, especially viscosity of the lubricant, has a great effect on fatigue life.

APPENDIX

If,
W= applied load (N)
R_1, R_2=radii of ball1 & ball2 (m)
E_1, E_2=Young's Modulas for ball 1 & ball 2 (N/m^2)
v_1, v_2=Poisson's ratio for ball1 & ball2
Then,
Reduced Radius of Curvature
$1/R'=1/R_1+1/R_2$
Reduced Young's Modulas
$1/E'=1/2[(1-v_1^2)/E_1+ (1-v_2^2)/E_2]$
Contact Area Dimension
$a =(3WR'/ E')^{1/3}$
Maximum Contact Pressure
$P_{max}=3W/2\Pi a^2$
Average Contact Pressure
$P_{avg} =W/ \Pi a^2$
Maximum Deflection
$\delta=1.0397(W^2/E'^2R')$
Maximum Shear Stress
$\tau_{max}=1/3\ P_{max}$
Depth at which maximum shear stress occurs
Z=0.638a

REFERENCES

[1] William Batchelor, Andrew; Nee Lam, Loh; Chandrasekaran, Margam.Materials Degradation and its control by Surface Engineering, Imperial College Press, 1999,p.57-58.
[2] Scott Hyde. R, Contact fatigue of Hardened steel.ASM Handbook. Fatigue and Fracture.Vol.19.1996.p.699
[3] H.Czichos, Tribology, Elsevier, Amsterdam, 1978, p.130
[4] H.Czichos and L.Kischke, Investigations into failure (transition point) of lubricated concentrated contacts, wear, 22 (1972) 321-336.
[5] H.Czichos, Failure criteria in thin film lubrication-the concept of a failure surface, Tribology, (Feb. 1974) 14-20.
[6] H.Czichos, Failure modes of sliding lubricated concentrated contacts, Wear, 28 (1974) 95-101.
[7] H.Czichos, Failure criteria in thin film lubrication: investigation of the different stages of film, Wear, 36 (1976) 13-17.
[8] A. Begelinger and A. W. J. De Gee, Boundary lubrication of sliding concentrated steel contacts, Wear, 22 (1972) 337-357.

[9]   A. Begelinger and A. W. J. De Gee, Thin film lubrication of sliding point contacts of AISI 52100steel, Wear, 28 (1974) 103-114.

[10] A. Begelinger and A. W. J. De Gee, Lubrication of sliding point contacts of AISI 52100steel-the influence of curvature, Wear, 36 (1976) 7-11.

[11] A. Begelinger and A. W. J. De Gee, on the mechanism of lubricant film in sliding concentrated steel contacts, Trans. ASME, J. Lubr. Techno. 98 (1976) 575-579.

[12] A. Begelinger and A. W. J. De Gee, Failure of thin film lubrication-the effect of running in on the load carrying capacity of thin film lubricated concentrated contact, Trans. ASME, J. Lubr. Techno. 103 (1981) 203-210.

[13] A. Begelinger and A. W. J. De Gee, Failure of thin film lubrication-a detailed study of the lubricant film breakdown mechanism, Wear, 77 (1982) 57-63.

[14] T. E. Tallian, J. I. McCool and L. B. Sibley, Partial elastohydrodynamic lubrication in rolling contact, Inst. Mech. Eng. Proc., 180 (3B) (1965-1966) 169-184.

[15] T. E. Tallian, On completing failure modes in rolling contact, ASLE Transactions, 10 (1967) 18-439.

[16] B.J.Hamrock & D.Dowson, Ball Bearing Lubrication, The Elastohydrodynamics of Elliptical Contacts, John.Willey & Sons, 1981

The Effect of Degree of Refining of Base Oils on Grease Properties

V. Serra-Holm

Nynas Naphthenics AB, 149 82 Nynashamn, Sweden

ABSTRACT

The selection of base oil affects the process conditions of grease production, as well as several grease properties. While the influence of the oil's low temperature properties on the grease behaviour at low temperatures is well known, the influence of the oil's solvating power on parameters such as soap yield, additive solvency, and grease smoothness has not been extensively studied. The present paper illustrates tests carried out on greases produced from mineral oils (naphthenic and paraffinic) with different solvating power. Properties such as low temperature pumpability, elastomer compatibility, and soap consumptions have been measured.

Keywords: Naphthenic Oil, Grease, Aniline Point, Paraffinic Oil

1. INTRODUCTION

The most common industrial and automotive lubricants are grease and oil. Grease and oil are not interchangeable. The choice of a suitable lubricant for a certain application depends on the machinery design and operating conditions. "The function of grease is to remain in contact with and lubricate moving surfaces without leaking out under gravity or centrifugal action, or being squeezed out under pressure." (1)

Grease is generally used for: (i) machinery that runs intermittently or is in storage for an extended period of time; (ii) machinery that is not easily accessible for frequent lubrication; (iii) machinery operating under extreme conditions such as high temperatures and pressures, shock loads, or slow speed under heavy load; (iiii) worn components.

Grease is a semi-fluid to solid mixture of a fluid lubricant, a thickener and additives. The thickener gives grease its consistency, by forming a three dimensional network of fibres that keeps the oil in place. Common thickeners are soaps and organic or inorganic non-soap thickener. Additives enhance performance and protect the grease and lubricated surfaces. The fluid lubricant can be mineral oil, synthetic oil, or vegetable oil. The most commonly used fluids are by far mineral oils. Since the oil accounts for about 85% of the total grease weight, it is evident that the fluid selection affects several properties of the lubricating grease.

In the present study we have investigated the behaviour of several naphthenic base oils with different degree of refining and of a paraffinic base oil, to verify both the effect of the type of mineral oil as well as the degree of refining of the oil. In particular, tests on solubility of common thickener precursors in oils, soap consumption, response of grease rigidity to oil dilution, elastomer compatibility, and oil separation from grease were carried out. It was observed that the excellent low temperature properties and solvating power of naphthenic oils could significantly affect several important properties of the lubricating grease.

2. EXPERIMENTAL STUDIES

2.1. Properties of the base oils tested

The main properties of the base oils tested are summarized in Table 1. T110, NS100, S100B, S150, BNS150, BT150 and SR130 are naphthenic base oils, while SN500 and SN700 are paraffinic base oils.

Table 1. Main properties of the oils tested.

Characteristics	Test method (ASTM)	Base Oils								
		T110	NS100	S100B	SR130	SN500	SN700	S150	BNS150	BT150
Density 15°C, g/cm^3	D4052	0.917	0.906	0.892	0.908	0.882	0.889	0.905	0.914	0.922
Viscosity 40°C, mm^2/s	D445	111	104	104	144	89	151	150	150	152
Viscosity 100°C, mm^2/s	D445	8.5	8.8	9.1	10.7	10.4	14.5	11.7	11.2	11.1
Flash point PM, °C	D93	215	216	216	228	242	266	242	240	232
Pour point, °C	D97	-24	-27	-27	-27	-9	-12	-33	-27	-27
Aniline point, °C	D611	84	94	103	95	111	113	105	96	89
VGC	2501	0.857	0.843	0.825	0.841	0.812	0.814	0.837	0.850	0.860
C_A %	D2140	11	7	<1	5	3	4	3	7	13
C_N %	D2140	40	41	42	37	27	27	44	42	38
C_P %	D2140	49	52	57	58	70	69	53	51	49

2.2. Grease Production

Based on the oils listed in the paragraph above, NLGI grade 2 greases were prepared, using Lithium 12-hydroxystearate as thickener. A 5 kg steel cooker was used. The formulation was made from oil, 12-hydroxy-stearic acid and lithium hydroxide. Three times as much oil as acid was initially used. At gentle stirring, the acid was dissolved in the oil (~96°C). A slurry of lithium hydroxide in water was slowly added to the oil/acid mixture. After about 20 minutes the temperature was raised to 103°C and the mixture was "cooked" for approximately one hour. The temperature was then gradually raised to 220°C until all the water had evaporated away. The soap at this stage had melted and a clear oil/soap mixture was formed. The temperature was then progressively lowered to 50°C, by oil addition. The grease was finally homogenized between rollers under vacuum. The desired consistency was reached by step-wise dilution with oil. The consistency of the grease was measured after each dilution step and the obtained values were used to build dilution curves for each grease sample.

2.3. Influence of Oil on Grease Properties

All mineral oils are not equivalent when formulating grease. It is well known that the low temperature behaviour of greases is greatly affected by the low temperature characteristics of the base fluids, as will be illustrated in this paper. It is maybe less known that the solvating power of the base fluid is extremely important as far as grease production and properties of the end product are concerned. When it comes to production, the oil's solvating power can influence for instance soap consumption, additive solvency, and overall energy economy of the process. Among the properties of the final grease that are affected by oil's solvating power are soap structure and oil separation.

2.3.1.   Effect of Oil's Solvating Power

The oil's solvating power can be measured with different methods, the most common ones being Aniline Point (AP) and Viscosity Gravity Constant (VGC). The aniline point method (ASTM D611) involves measuring the temperature at which aniline dissolves in the oil. The higher the solvating power, the lower the aniline point. Viscosity Gravity Constant (VGC) is a dimensionless constant that is based on a mathematical processing of the viscosity and density values according to ASTM D2501 and provides a weighted value between the viscosity effect on the solvating power and the chemical nature of the oil. The higher the solvating power, the higher the value of VGC.

As showed in Table 1, all naphthenic oils have a higher solvating power than paraffinic oils having the same viscosity.

2.3.1.1.   Lower Temperature to Dissolve the Fatty Acid

The higher solvating power has several beneficial effects on the grease production. First, when using naphthenic oil, a lower temperature is needed during the cooking stage in order to dissolve the fatty acid, which lowers the risk of oxidation of the grease. Figure 1 shows the solution temperature of 12-hydroxystearic acid in several naphthenic and one paraffinic oil. The chosen concentration of acid in oil was 30% by weight. As shown in the figure, all naphthenic oils have a lower solution temperature compared to the paraffinic oil.

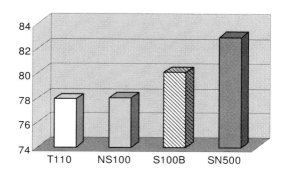

Figure 1. Solution temperature of 12-hydroxystearic acid in different base oils (30 wt.-%)

2.3.1.2.   Lower Bleeding Tendency

It is reported that the oil added to the grease during cooking is the part that is most bonded to the soap network (2). When naphthenic oil is used, stronger bonds between the oil and the soap matrix are established, due to the oil's higher affinity for soap. Moreover, due to the higher oil-soap affinity, in naphthenic-based greases there is a prevalence of physiochemical interaction between the oil and the soap, while in paraffinic-based greases most of the oil is physically trapped in the soap structure. This entails that the naphthenic oil is more intimately bonded with the soap structure and displays lower tendency to separate from the grease. The condition when the oil separates from the thickener (commonly known as bleeding) is particularly negative in certain grease applications, such as applications in centralized lubrication systems or in factory-fill applications. In the case of centralized lubrication systems, oil separation can lead to serious plugging of the pipes; in factory-fill applications, OEMs set very severe limitations on maximum allowed bleeding.

2.3.1.3.   Lower Soap Consumption

A higher solvating power means also a better soap yield, i.e. the soap necessary to reach a certain consistency. Three naphthenic oils with increasing degree of refining (T110, SR130, S100B) and one paraffinic oil (SN500) having approximately the same viscosity were used to produce greases having the same consistency (NLGI grade 2). If one plots the soap content of each grease versus the aniline point of the corresponding base oil, one can see that the solvating power has a clear influence on soap consumption (Figure 2). The lower the aniline point (and therefore the higher the solvating power) the lower the soap consumption. The soap consumption is lowest for the naphthenic T110 and highest for the paraffinic SN500.

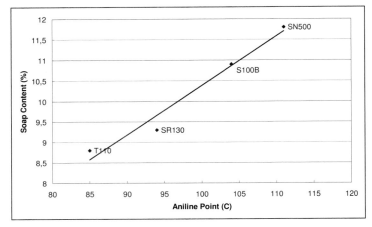

Figure 2. Soap consumption for greases based on different base oils

2.3.1.4.   Faster Response to Oil Dilution

Another effect of the solvating power is the response of greases to dilution. As described in Section 2.2, grease is generally prepared with a harder consistency than the target value, and is subsequently stepwise diluted with base oil until the final consistency is reached. Greases based on oils with higher solvating power give a faster response to oil dilution, thereby significantly reducing the number of steps required to reach the final consistency, which in turn means a shorter and more efficient process. As a parameter to characterize the consistency of greases, σ_{GRIS} was used. σ_{GRIS} is the yield stress value for which the elastic and viscous moduli are equal (loss angle of 45°). That means that above the σ_{GRIS} value, the grease has a prevalently elastic behaviour (it behaves like a solid), while below the σ_{GRIS} value, the grease has a prevalently viscous behaviour. Therefore the higher the σ_{GRIS} value, the higher the consistency of the grease. In Figure 3 the dilution curves for several base oils having different solvating power are reported.

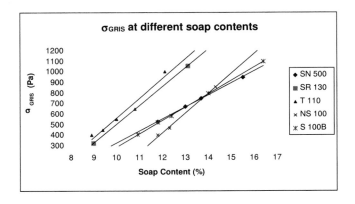

Figure 3. Dilution curves for greases based on different base oils

It can be observed that the impact on grease structure (softening effect) is clearly greater for the oils with higher solvating power, such as T110, SR130 and NS100, while the oils with lower solvating power (S100B and SN500) soften less with addition of more oil.

2.3.1.5. Higher additive solvency

Due to their higher solvating power, naphthenic oils dissolve more easily additives. From a production point of view, since the additives dissolve easier and better, shorter mixing times and lower temperature are necessary, with consequent energy saving.

Moreover, from the point of view of the end product, a better additive solvency means a consistent quality of the grease.

2.3.1.6. Elastomer compatibility

Another property where the oil's solvating power plays a very important role is the grease compatibility with different elastomers. What can be observed is that, depending on the chemical nature of the elastomer, an oil with high or low solvating power should be preferred to find an optimal compatibility.

Rubber interactions with base oils and grease were studied by completely immerging rubber samples in base oils and greases. The ageing was performed at three different temperatures, 80°C, 100°C and 120°C and the test duration was 168 hours. Three naphthenic oils (BT150, BNS150 and S150, see Table 1) and a paraffinic oil (SN700) and greases based on them were used for the tests. The rubbers used were chloroprene rubber (CR) and nitrile butadiene rubber (NBR) with a nitrile content of 28%. For all temperatures the change in hardness and weight for the rubber samples were measured. Hardness was determined by IRHD (International Rubber Hardness Degrees) method, where rubber's resistance to indentation is measured by pressing a rounded steel peak connected to a calibrated spring into the material.

The results for the ageing of NBR at 100°C are reported in Figures 4 and 5, while the results relative to the ageing of CR are displayed in Figures 6 and 7.

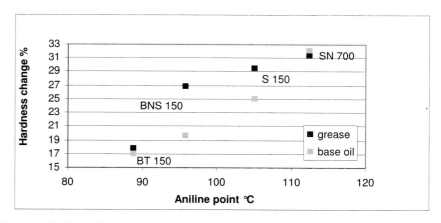

Figure 4. Hardness changes for NBR , aged in greases and base oils for 168 hours at 100°C.

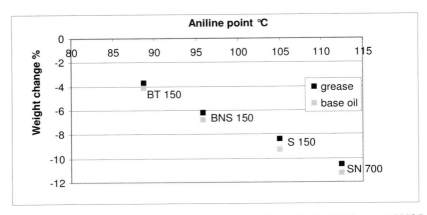

Figure 5. Weight changes for NBR aged in greases and base oils for 168 hours at 100°C.

All NBR samples have become harder and have shrunk during ageing both in the base oils and the greases. The smallest impact is seen on the rubber sample aged in BT150, which is the oil with highest solvating power (lowest aniline point). Another comment that can be made based on these results is that, although there are differences in the absolute values of shrinkage and hardening between the base oils and the greases, still they follow the same trend. This is important, as it means that the behaviour of an elastomer in contact with grease can be predicted by testing the elastomer with the base fluid on which the grease is produced, with evident practical advantages in conducting the tests.

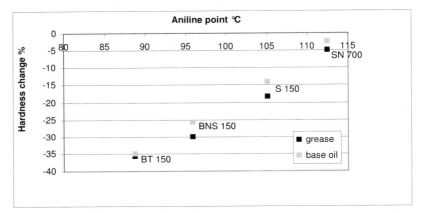

Figure 6. Hardness changes for CR aged in greases and base oils for 168 hours at 100°C.

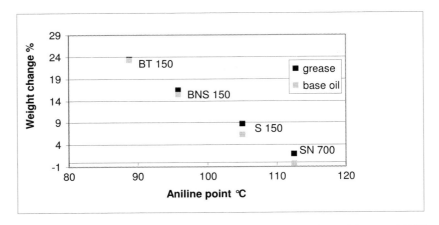

Figure 7. Weight changes for CR aged in greases and base oils for 168 hours at 100°C.

The behaviour of CR during ageing goes in an opposite direction compared to NBR. First, the rubber swells and softens in contact with the lubricants. Secondly, in this case it is the oils with the lowest solvating power (highest aniline point), the paraffinic SN700 and the naphthenic S150, that cause the smallest changes in the rubbers.

What could be observed when measuring other rubber properties before and after ageing, such as tensile strength and glass transition temperature, is that the swelling or shrinkage of the rubber is not sufficient to obtain a complete picture over the interactions between the lubricant and the rubber, but other factors must be taken into account, such as replacement of plasticizer with base oil in the rubber matrix and oxidation of the polymer itself. Another interesting indication emerging from the tests carried out was that approximately the same amount of plasticizer has been extracted out of the rubber during ageing, meaning that the difference in swelling/shrinkage was due to the amount of mineral oil absorbed by the rubber matrix.

2.3.2.   Effect of Oil's Low-Temperature Properties

As mentioned earlier, the low temperature properties of the oils are determining the grease behaviour at low temperatures. The n-alkanes contained in paraffinic oils crystallise upon cooling, which impedes the free flow of the oil. When the cloud point occurs (i.e. the crystallization point is reached), the oil is no longer a Newtonian fluid but becomes a two-phase system. Conversely, naphthenic oils are virtually free from n-alkanes, which means that they have much better low temperature properties than paraffinic oils, which contain n-alkanes. A common way to characterise the oil's low temperature properties is to determine the pour point, i.e. the lowest temperature at which the oil flows (ASTM D97 test method). As shown in Table 1, at equal viscosity, the pour point of naphthenic oils is much lower than that of paraffinic oils, meaning that the low temperature properties of naphthenic oils are clearly superior. In order to verify the influence of the oil on the behaviour of the grease at low temperature, a flow pressure test was performed on all greases based on oils having a viscosity of 150 cSt, namely BT150, BNS150, S150 and SN700. The test was performed according to a standard DIN 51 805 method. The test setup consists of a standard conical nozzle which is filled with deaerized grease. The nozzle is placed in the measuring instrument, equilibrated for 2-3 hours at a desired temperature, and then an increasing pressure is applied to the nozzle. The threshold pressure at which grease starts to flow through the nozzle is recorded as the flow pressure of the grease at the actual temperature. The results are illustrated in Figure 8.

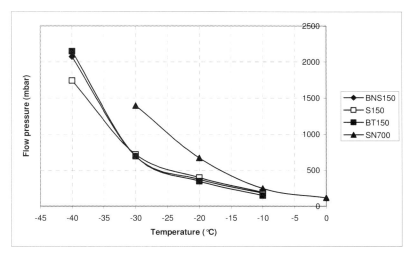

Figure 8. Flow pressure test DIN 51 805 for the paraffinic and naphthenic greases at low temperatures.

As can be observed, at temperatures above 0°C there is no noticeable difference between the paraffinic- and the naphthenic-based greases, but already at -10°C the flow pressure for the paraffinic-based grease is about 30% higher than that of the naphthenic-based ones. This difference is increasing when the temperature decreases, and at -30°C the pressure needed for the paraffinic grease to flow is almost twice as high as that for the naphthenic greases. At -35°C some differences between the naphthenic greases start to show up and it is the grease based on the most refined naphthenic oil (S150) that shows the best result. At -40°C there is a difference of 400 mbar between the grease based on S150 and that based on BT150.

3. CONCLUSIONS

The choice of base fluid has a great importance when formulating grease. Choosing a suitable base oil means improving the production process and obtaining a final product of higher quality. When mineral oils are used, paraffinic and naphthenic oils are the alternatives. The high solvating power and the excellent low temperature properties of naphthenic oils compared to paraffinic oils make them an advantageous choice, both in terms of production process and in terms of quality of the end product.

REFERENCES

[1] Boehringer, R.H., Grease. ASM Handbook, Volume 18, Friction, Lubrication and Wear Technology: ASM International, US; 1992. p. 123.
[2] Ischuk J.L., Composition, Structure and Properties of Plastic Lubricants, Kiew; 1996
[3] Stang G. and Salomonsson L., Rubber Interactions with Grease and Base Oil, NLGI Spokesman, Volume 69, Number 1, US; 2005. p. 20-34.

Session 12
LUBRICATION MANAGEMENT 3

Chair: Prof. Edward H. Smith

Linear Sweep Voltammetry (RULER©) – An innovative approach for Looking Forward to Lubricant Oxidation
J. AMEYE, R. E. KAUFFMAN, J. TERRADILLOS

COMONET – the DTI Knowledge Transfer Network for Condition Monitoring Sensors
T. SPERRING, C. PISLARU

Tribology: A vital ingredient in Asset Management
P. J. HUGGETT

In-Service Wear Assessment of Aircraft Engines
T. SPERRING

Linear Sweep Voltammetry (RULER©) – An innovative approach for Looking Forward to Lubricant Oxidation

J. Ameye [1], R. E. Kauffman [2], J. Terradillos [3]

[1] Fluitec International, Nieuwbrugstraat 73 B-1830 Machelen Belgium, j.ameye@fluitec.com
[2] UDRI, 300 College Park, Dayton, OH 45404, Kauffman@udri.udayton.edu
[3] Fundación Tekniker, Avda. Otaola, 20, 20600 Eibar, Spain

ABSTRACT

Understanding and predicting the oxidation process of in-service industrial lubricants, becomes a vital part of every lubricant condition monitoring program. With the extension of lubricants life, increasing load factors, and introduction of long-life improved base-stocks, it is of extreme high value to know and measure the remaining oxidative life of lubricants.

Until today industry employs oil analysis by trending Acid Number and Viscosity, to identify the lubricant oxidation, and consequently schedule an oil drain (not on condition, but driven by time).

Although the process of oxidation represents a lot of unanswered questions, it starts by understanding the role/function of antioxidants, for different lubricants and conditions, and how they contribute to the oxidative health of lubricants. In the first part of this paper, we will cover this subject, and also introduce you to the linear sweep voltammetric technique (RULER©) as one of the proactive ways of performing remaining oxidative live by trending/monitoring the consumption of the antioxidants during their service life, and safeguard lubricants against oxidative stresses.

In a second part, this paper will present different applications where antioxidant analysis (by means of the RULER© technology) as part of a global oil-diagnostics program is of high added value. End-users and used oil laboratories will understand how this recently certified ASTM Test Method – ASTM D-6971 – will contribute to the value of the oil and grease screening program by allowing for immediate maintenance actions (if required) coupled with reduction in time and with the objective to avoid base oil degradation.

Keywords: Lubrication Management, Lubrication Technology, Lubricants and Additives, Lubricant Testing, Antioxidants, Voltammetry, Oxidation.

1. INTRODUCTION

With the increasing operating temperature of lubricants, extended drain intervals, and high related costs due to equipment downtime, a new parameter has been growing in importance, namely the lubricant oxidation stability, or Remaining Useful Life. As industry recognize the oxidation process as one of the primary lubricant degradation mechanism, the parameter of oxidative stability contributes to the proactive (added) value of Condition Based Maintenance (CBM) programs. Linear Sweep Voltammetric techniques (RULER™) have been addressing and introducing this issue, by their ability to monitor and control antioxidant depletion, and predict the Remaining Useful Life of lubricants on a wide range of applications, and type of lubricants (including greases). Let's first try to understand the role or function of antioxidants.

2. ROLE AND FUNCTION OF ANTIOXIDANTS – THE KEY TO THE RESISTANCE TO OXIDATION

The oxidation process is a chemical reaction from the organic hydrocarbon chain (1,2,4) or more specific the reaction between oxygen and the hydrocarbon base stock. Beside the cleavage reaction of the lubricant chain, this oxidation reaction results also in the formation of reactive oxidation compounds, which will themselves start to attack the oil base stock and form polymers. Chemically this reaction is better known under the formation of oil insoluble sludge, varnishes and other deposits, and will directly result in a significant increase of viscosity. One thing to notice about the antioxidants is that most lubricants are formulated with mixtures of antioxidants, just to increase their resistance to oxidation.

Fundamentally the antioxidants main function will be to react with the reactive oxidation compounds (referred to as free radicals or peroxides), by neutralizing them and turning them into duds. By industrial standards this is referred to as the "oxidation stability", and will extend the operating life of the oil.

So, during use of the fluid the antioxidants (AO) will be depleted until a certain critical level is reached at which the fluid start to degrade / polymerize at a higher rate. At this point the fluid reached its useful life. In order to estimate the Remaining Useful Life (RUL) of a fluid it is therefore important to know its critical antioxidant concentration. In a later stage of this paper, we will come back to this important parameter of RUL.

2.1. Type of antioxidants – a wide variety, but 1 key function

As the role of antioxidants is to protect the type of base oil by either scavenging (alkyl and peroxy) radicals, or decomposing hydroperoxides into stable products, 2 main categories of antioxidants are applied in the industry, better known as:

o   Primary antioxidants - by removing the radicals or better known as radical scavengers. Amines and phenols are characteristic types of primary antioxidants, and a typical concentration used in turbine oils is in the range of 0.3-0.7 wt.% [3].

o   Secondary antioxidants – act by eliminating peroxides (hydroperoxide decomposers) and to form non reactive products which do no participate in further oxidation of the lubricant. Zincdithiophosphates, or better known under the name of ZnDtP or ZDDP, or sulphurized phenols belongs to this class of antioxidants. Typical concentrations applied for ZDDP antioxidants in automotive crankcase lubricants reach up to a maximum of 1.5 wt. % [4].

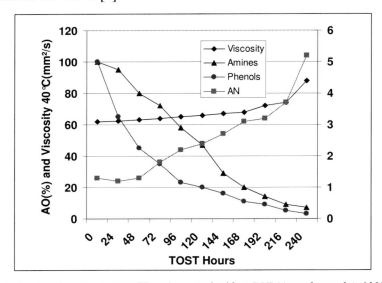

Figure 1. Ageing time Dry-TOST (Hours) vs. Antioxidant RUL% number and Acid Number

o Mixed antioxidant systems. When two or more antioxidants are added to an oil, an antioxidant effect is frequently observed in excess of either additive introduced individually. Antioxidants are often used in synergistic mixtures in modern lubricant formulations, to achieve an extended lubricant life, where one of the antioxidants sacrifices itself in preservation and regeneration of the other. A realistic example is the synergy between amines and phenols [5] whereby the phenols deplete early in the oxidation life whilst the amine concentration remains constant during this period (Figure 1). Another example is the combination between a primary and secondary antioxidant, where both radicals and hydroperoxides will be removed.

In all above cases it's obvious that all antioxidants have to be taken into account, to understand the total antioxidant capacity of the lubricant.

Now that we understand, the oxidation reaction, the role and function of antioxidants, let's have a closer look at oxidation accelerators.

2.2.   What factors or parameters are oxidative accelerators?

The parameters contributing directly to oxidation, better known as oxidative accelerators can be divided in 3 categories:

Temperature stress: elevated temperature is an important accelerator to oil oxidation. This can be due to local hot spots (local bearing effects, dieseling), or overall high operating temperature. The impact of high temperature on the rate of oil oxidation (rule of Arrhenius – for operating temperatures higher than 100°C each increase by 10°C , will double the rate of oxidation or half the oxidative life of the lubricant)

Solid contamination (through wear debris or dirt ingestion) accelerates the oxidation, as being a catalyst, and decomposes hydroperoxides.

Water/wear acting as oxidative accelerators – Moisture/Water contamination (Increase due to ingestion, condensation, and fresh lubricant top-up).

These oxidative accelerators will enhance the fluid degradation and will increase the degradation when they work in combination, like water and metals (see Figure 3 below).

Why measuring lubricant oxidation? Different experiences [5,6,7] have shown that lubricants will quickly start to degrade, once the 10-20% remaining antioxidant concentration is reached, especially with higher temperature applications where large changes in the basestock physical properties will occur, i.e. the useful life of the oil ends. If a lubricant is than used past its end of useful life, excessive basestock degradation can occur, resulting in component wear and eventually equipment/engine malfunction.

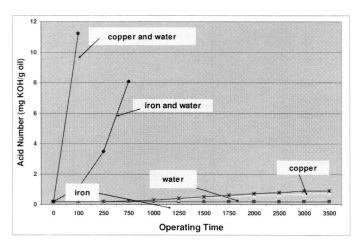

Figure 2. Influence of oxidation accelerators on oxidation (Acid Number) – source: Einschelbaum, M.

From here we can conclude that for all applications where condition based oil changes have become part of maintenance practices, the application and monitoring of the RUL-data will be of great economical value for this program.

That means that every user of lubricant will need to have and use information on antioxidant depletion rates, by trend analysis for oil condition, as part of modern condition based maintenance strategies.

One of the aspects we did not highlight here, beside the economical/financial aspects of lubricants, is the environmental aspect. A good example of this is the reduction of Zinc-based antioxidants, which has been for years a very economical and effective protection against oxidation, as well as anti-wear performance (automotive & industry). ZDDP being replaced by ashless type (amines/phenols) type of antioxidants, in combination with new type of base-oils, like synthetic industrial lubricants, meet the environmental and performance requirements. A few examples of these applications have been trendsetters:

- Industrial gear oils at wind turbines (PAO, PAG, esters)
- Hydraulic oils for injection moulding equipment (ZDDP vs. non-zinc antioxidant formulations)
- Synthetic PAG/PAO compressor lubricants
- Medium –to high temperature greases
- Biodegradable lubricants

3. THE VALUE OF MONITORING ANTIOXIDANTS – TO KNOW THE RUL OR NOT TO KNOW THE RUL, THAT'S THE QUESTION?

The answer to this question has to be found into the basic characteristic of modern Maintenance Techniques, requiring Root Cause Failure analysis. In order to extend fault free machine life, trending of oxidative health or antioxidants concentration, will be able to look at the root causes of lubricant failures.

By monitoring the antioxidants, lubricant operators will detect in advance additive failure and logically avoid oxidation, acid formation, thickening, varnishing, and bearing lubricant starvation.

Organic (weak) acids are produced during oxidation, which will result in corrosion damage on long-term. Typically acid concentration is measured by tests like Acid Number (AN), but has very low proactive value in CBM programs. As a second indicator or signal from heavy lubricant degradation exists the viscosity increase, which is a direct result from the polymerization (chain formation) between hydrocarbon (base-oil) chains, enhanced by the oxidation products.

And herein lays the major benefit by monitoring the antioxidant concentration or the Remaining Useful Life (RUL), as users will be able to look forward, rather than look backward by being reactive on changes of parameters like viscosity, acid number (AN) or oxidation by FTIR (FTIR-Ox).

The main drawbacks of techniques like AN, viscosity and FTIR-Ox is their inability to predict the operating time from when the analyzed fluid was sampled until a fluid change will become necessary due to additive depletion, i.e. these techniques like AN, Viscosity, FTIR-Ox can not predict the remaining useful life of a fluids. In addition to that AN-analyses are affected by the operating conditions of the equipment or by the additives, e.g. ZDDP concentration affects AN values.

This is why in contrast to fluid degradation techniques, techniques which monitor by routine the antioxidant concentration are able to look forward, predict the operating time, depending from the operating conditions.

Each trend of antioxidant depletion will be reflecting the characteristic and different operating conditions, enabling operators to look at the root causes for possible abnormal conditions.

3.1. Linear Sweep Voltammetric Techniques – working principle

The working principle of RULER™ method is based on linear sweep voltammetric analysis [6,7,8] as electro-analytic methods, in which a lubricant sample is mixed with an electrolyte and a solvent, and placed in an electrolytic cell to detect the electrochemical (antioxidant activity). The voltammetric test results are based on current, voltage and time relationships at the cell electrodes.

The cell consists of a 3-electrode sensing system with a small, easily polarized microelectrode, and a large non-polarizable reference electrode (see Figure 3). The reference electrode should be massive compared to the microelectrode so that its behaviour remains essentially constant with the passage of

Figure 3. Voltammetric (RULER) 3- electrode sensing system

small current: it remains un-polarized during the analysis period. In simplistic terms, when performing a voltammetric analysis, the potential across the electrodes varies linearly with time, and the resulting current is recorded as a function of the potential. With increased voltage to the sample in the cell, the various additive species under investigation in the oil oxidize electrochemically. The data recorded during this oxidation reaction can then be used to predict the remaining useful life of the grease or oil type.

A typical current-potential curve produced during the practice of the voltammetric test is illustrated in Figure 3. Initially the applied potential produces an electrochemical reaction with a rate so slow that virtually no current flows through the cell. As the voltage is increased (Figure 3), the electro-active species (such as antioxidants) begin to oxidize at the microelectrode surface, producing an anodic rise in the current. As the potential is increased (from 0 to 1.7 V at a rate of 0.1 V/second), the decreases in the electro-active species concentration at the electrode surface and the exponential increase of the oxidation rate lead to a maximum in the current-potential curve (Figures 4a & 4b); this is the oxidation wave, and will represent each antioxidant in function of its oxidation potential. Additionally to the potential ramp increase, the voltammograph (RULER) can also select the time mode between the short 10 seconds (MODE A) or the longer 17 seconds (MODE V).

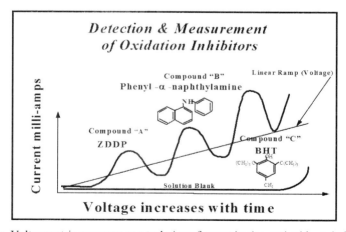

Figure 4a. Voltammetric response as a technique for monitoring antioxidants in lubricants.

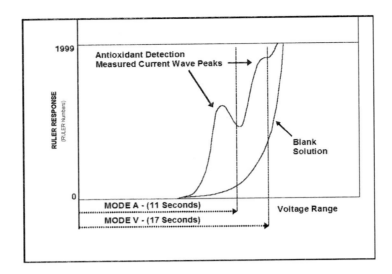

Figure 4b. Voltammetric response with antioxidants response vs. time selection (Mode A or Mode V)

3.2.   Voltage vs. Current for different antioxidants e.g. ZDDP, amine and phenols.

After the lubricant samples (max. 400µl) are been diluted in an acetone/electrolyte prepared mixture, to enhance the extraction of the antioxidants into the solvent phase, the RULER will produce oxidation wave peaks. The peaks produced by the RULER are consequently been used to evaluate the remaining antioxidant additives of the used samples.   The peak of a zinc dialkyl dithio phosphate (ZDDP) [1,4] additive is followed by an amine (PANA), and then by a hindered phenol (BHT) (see Figure 4 above).

3.3.   Voltammetric test procedures

To enhance the extraction of antioxidants out of the oil phase, the following RULER test procedures have to be applied [5,6,7,8, 9,10,11]:

- Dispense 400µl of the oil sample inside the vial, containing the electrolytic solution
- Shake vial for 10 seconds – this procedure will enhance the extraction of the antioxidants into the electrolytic test solutions.
- Let solution settle for about 2 minutes until clear liquid is evident on top of the vial
- Perform RULER test, by inserting the RULER probe into the electrolytic test solutions. The fresh lubricant is saved to be applied as the 100% standard (base-line) and the measurements of the used lubricant samples were expressed as percentage remaining additives (see Figures 5 & 6).
- The repeatability of the percent-remaining additive measurements is between 5 and 7%.

3.4.   Linear Sweep Voltammetry as an ASTM approved technique

Over the last 3 years, Linear Sweep Voltammetric techniques have been part of new test methods development at ASTM Subcommittee 09.00 (oxidation) which resulted in 2 new ASTM methods, ASTM D 6810 and D 6971. While ASTM method D 6810 [12] specifically targets the measurement of phenolic inhibitors in turbine oils, ASTM has approved a second standard, ASTM D 6971 [14], offering the ability to monitor the concentration of phenolic and aromatic amine antioxidants in non-zinc containing turbine oils. The RULER instrument is also perfectly capable of measuring the oxidation stability provided by ZDDP and similar antioxidant/anti-wear additives [7].

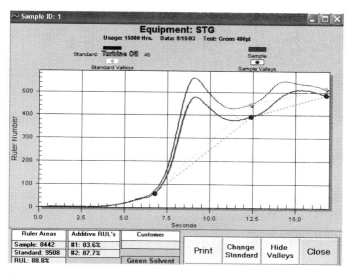

Figure 5. Voltammograph from mineral gas turbine oil formulation, consisting of aromatic amine (additive #1) and phenols (additive #2)

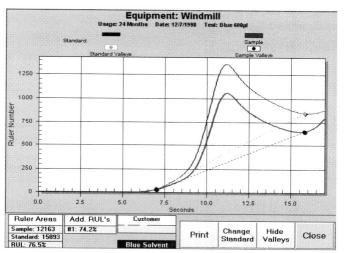

Figure 6. Voltammograph from mineral wind turbine oil formulation, after 24 months of service

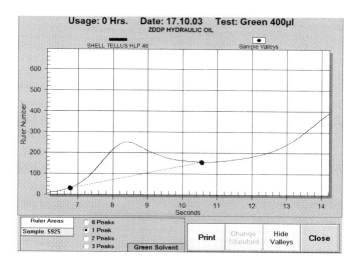

Figure 7. Voltammograph from mineral type of hydraulic oil containing a multifunctional ZDDP type of antioxidant

4. CASE STUDIES USING VOLTAMMETRIC TECHNIQUES

For a wide range of lubricants, mineral or synthetic, Voltammetry has the ability to detect the different type of antioxidants.

Following applications have been shown high interest into the monitoring of antioxidants as part of oxidative health monitoring programs:

➤ *Power generation lubricants*, e.g. steam turbine lubricants, gas turbine lubricants, hydraulic fluids, pump bearing oils – see Figure 5 for a typical voltammogram
➤ *Compressor lubricants*: mineral and synthetic compressor lubricants for screw type compressors
➤ *Wind turbine gear oils:* mineral and synthetic high performance gear oils (containing antioxidants) for new generation type of wind turbines – see Figure 6 for a Voltammogram from a mineral wind turbine gear oil
➤ *Greases:* mid to high temperature applications for bearing assemblies on railroad (see Figure 12 for a typical Voltammogram for a grease)
➤ *Specialty fluids:* transformer oils, phosphate ester, polyglycols etc...

With the following cases we will try to show you the value behind the lubricant oxidative health information, applied at different power generation stations, as part of an on-site oil screening program.

4.1. Case 1: Industrial lube oil oxidation tests

During normal service (even at storage) from any industrial lubricant, antioxidant additives are consumed. For an end-user it will be interesting to monitor and trend at which rate the antioxidants are depleting, rather than having 1 data point with antioxidant concentration. To understand the value behind antioxidant monitoring for industrial lubricants, we have collected data from 2 different oxidation tests, one on a turbine lubricant and one on a compressor lubricant.

For the turbine lubricant oxidation test, sets of 14 glass vials (with each 1ml-sample volume) were heated isothermal in a drilled aluminium block at the following temperatures 140°C oxidation. At prescheduled time intervals (20-25 hours) a glass vial was removed, cooled and diluted with analysis solvent and consequently analysed with the RULER™, as well for carboxyl groups by FTIR, and viscosity test (40°C). The results are summarized in the graph below and results in 2 different clearly phases:

➤ Part 1: primary degradation phase, which can be recognized by the antioxidant concentration higher than 20-25%, in order to keep the C-radical formation reaction under control

➤ Part 2: secondary degradation phase, characterized by the antioxidant concentration less than 20% and lacking to protect the base-oil against the secondary and irreversible degradation. It will be vital for a lubricant operator to avoid working in this degradation phase, especially as part of reconditioning practices.

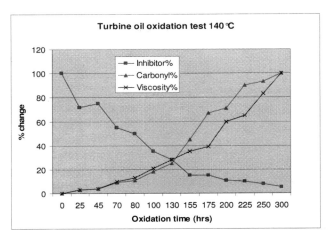

Figure 8. Turbine oil oxidation test result information, with the X-axis the total oxidation time, and in the Y-axis Antioxidant concentration, viscosity (40°C) increase, as well carbonyl component % increase

For the compressor test, different oil samples were collected during the normal field operation from the air screw type compressor. The mineral type of oil consisted of a package of ZDDP and phenol type of antioxidants, and the Figure 9 below. It can be concluded from this trending graph, that the oxidation process is divided in 3 phases:

      Phase 1: RUL% between 100 and 40%

      Phase 2: RUL% between 10 and 40%

      Phase 3: RUL% lower than 10%

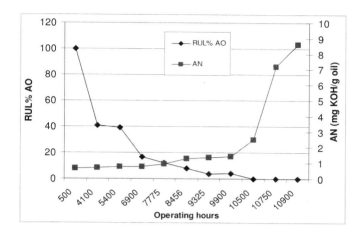

Figure 9. Compressor oil life test graph showing (X-axis) the operating time, vs. Antioxidant concentration, in the Y-axis.

4.2.   Case 2: Power Generation plant

With this case, experiences were taken from a lube screening program at a power station in Europe, with Frame-9 Gas turbines for a total output of 2000 MW. Each turbine is equipped with a 35,000 litter oil reservoir and uses mineral based turbine oil.

The turbine fluids are now more than 4 years in service, approaching the 48.000 hrs of operation. Table 3 summarizes the characteristics of the new oil.

Table 1. Characteristics new gas turbine oil ISO VG32

Measurements	New Oil
TAN (mg KOH/g)	0.07
Colour	L 2.0
RPVOT (min)	> 1500
Viscosity (40°C) mm2/s	32,1
Water (%)	< 0.05
RUL % Amines	100%

Every two months the power station analyzed samples with the RULER equipment to determine their remaining % antioxidant , water content, viscosity, colour, and ISO cleanliness level.

They complement to this data, every 6 months analysis with the oxidative health data by RPVOT (ASTM D-2272). Figure 10 summarizes all the analytical data for one of the five turbines, during the last 4 years of service, whereas Figure 4 presents only the trending graphs of the antioxidants (by RULER measurement) for the 5 gas turbines.

It is important to note that antioxidant trending by RULER and RPVOT are similar. From the operator's (power station) point of view, the RULER field results could be used to screen oils for RPVOT. When the antioxidant concentration stays above 25% and the total acid number remains below the oil company specifications RPVOT is not necessary. This will save the end user money and time.

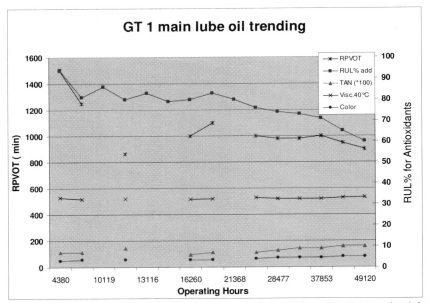

Figure 10. Lube oil analytical data for gas turbine 1, with RPVOT data on the left Y-axis and RUL% on the right Y-axis, as well TAN (black line), Viscosity@40°C (Green line) and Color (purple line).

The 4-years data showed that the parameters (viscosity, color and water) remain relatively stable. The AO concentrations suggest that the fluctuations are probably caused by top-ups of fresh oil, and FTIR data confirmed for all the samples that no oxidation products build-up is occurring yet.

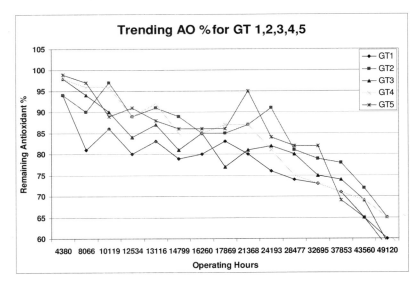

Figure 11. The trending graphs for RULER data (antioxidants concentration) for the 5 gas turbines (GT 1-5) vs. operating hours of gas turbines.

4.3.   Case 3: RULER for greases.

With the latest ability of RULER to measure directly into the grease phase, more specifically the antioxidants, and predict the remaining grease life[9], this case will present the experiences on a grease monitoring program for Motor Operated Valves (MOV) at multiple power stations.

Customers are frequently asking for the remaining life of bearing greases, e.g. if they should re-lubricate a bearing during a maintenance stop or how much longer they can run safely before having to re-lubricate.

The parameters considered by a method found in literature [9,10], which are able to answer customer questions concerning remaining grease life, are: degree of oxidation, antioxidant depletion, oil content and total acid number. For all of these parameters, a grease extraction phase is necessary, which is becoming both complicated and time consuming for a field application.

The RULER method is being used widely measuring the relevant grease life parameters like antioxidant capacity and oil oxidation.

When comparing the RULER technology to existing grease and oil oxidation test [10] methods, such as FT-IR, and HPLC, the following differences are apparent:

- Ease in use: the test procedure consists of sampling the grease, mixing it with the 5 ml prepared test solution, inserting the probe, and measuring;
- Test method requires a very small grease sample volume (max.200 mg);
- Test avoids the extraction phase of oil with solvents;
- Portable technology, allowing on-site analysis;
- Quick test method (less than 5 minutes), which can be used for field analysis;
- Detects all present AOs compared to HPLC or FT-IR analysis method.

The RULER method, which measures remaining lubricant life, is a potential and reliable monitoring routine for grease lubricants, as part of a lube screening program.

The Figure 12 below shows a typical graph from a high temperature, Lithium-hydroxide grease after 1760 hrs of severe oxidation test conditions, which shows significant consumption of the aromatic amines antioxidants.

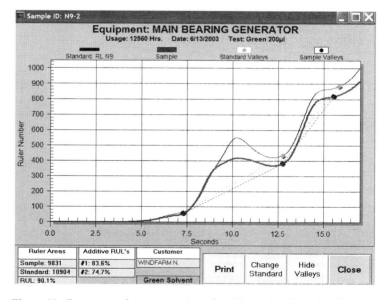

Figure 12. Grease sample power station after 36 months of service life

A total of approx. 20 power stations collected different grease samples (all from MOV Actuators) which were analyzed by the RULER, as well for wear metal analysis.

Data below shows the correlation of remaining antioxidant concentration, for different lifetime of greases (Figure 13)

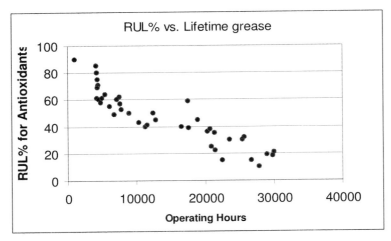

Figure 13. RULER results on greases sampled from 20 power stations with varying operating grease life

5. HOW CAN RULER METHOD FIT INTO A LUBRICANT SCREENING PROGRAM?

As described in the first paragraph, monitoring the lubricant physical and chemical properties along with all possible root cause degradation methods makes an oil analysis program effective and ultimately successful. Financial restraints combined with common sense, provide the limits and/or levels of certain root cause accelerators of oxidation that we must allow to exist, but ultimately affects the lubricant health.

Integrating a method of monitoring the lubricant oxidative health into a lubricant screening program will provide not only the true condition of the lubricant but also assist in estimating the expected service life if the root cause accelerators are maintain within their appropriate ranges.

A lubricant screening program is typically divided into 3 categories of tests:

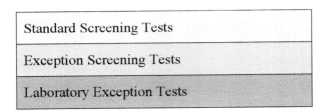

Examples of:

> Standard screening tests – Lubricant Appearance, ISO Particle Count, Water Contamination (crackle and/or saturation), Viscosity,Oxidation (RULER)

> Exception Screening tests – Ferrous Counts, Debris Analysis, Ferrography,

> Laboratory Exception tests – Trace metal analysis, FTIR, TAN, Karl Fischer, RPVOT

Depending on the environmental and operating conditions, the test(s) and/or test frequencies can be altered to ensure competent trending and comparison to other collected data. By providing early warning of any anomalies that effect/cause the limits to be exceeded targets will lead into the ideal combination of on-site exception testing and laboratory testing.

6. CONCLUSIONS

When implementing a lube oil-screening program based on linear sweep Voltammetry, different factors are of importance, to make from the program a cost efficient program, and assure a return on investment:

➢ **Value added information behind lubricant oxidative health**: by offering the end-user the possibility of measuring on-site the remaining antioxidants activity and logically assessing its remaining useful life and integrating this information to provide a proactive added value behind any lube oil screening program. More specific applications for RUL evaluation can be as part of readditization strategies, where specific replenishment with antioxidants can be monitored and controlled.

➢ **Oil sampling frequency**: adapt the oil frequency in function of the application, and as well in function of the condition of the oil. A more degraded oil, will need additional testing to define the correct time of changing the lubricant; not to early, not to late. Here comes the high value of audit programs, as an objective evaluation and assessment of oil frequency for lube oil-screening programs.

➢ **Education**: even though modern on-site equipment requires easy users procedures and operates under platform of performing software, continuous education is necessary to keep the focus of end-users on selecting the correct test equipment, with the appropriate sampling frequency, test procedures and practices (Standard organizations, OEM).

REFERENCES

[1] Mortier, R. and Orszulik, S., "Chemistry and Technology of Lubricants", Blackie and Son, p.94, (1992)

[2] Richard N. Wurzbach, "Learning the basics – Using Oil analysis to Manage Chemical and Physical Stability of Lubricants" – POA 2000 Conference Proceedings, page 140 – 145

[3] Jayaprakash, K. C.,Srivastava, S. P.,Anand, K. S. And Goel, P.K., "Oxidation Stability of Steam Turbine Oils and Laboratory Method of Evaluation," Lubrication Engineering, 40, 2, pp 89-95 (1984)

[4] Born, M., Hipeaux, J. C., Marchand, P. and Parc G., "Relationship between the Chemical Structure and Effectiveness of Some Metallic Dialkyl and Diaryldithiophosphates in Different Lubricated Mechanisms," Engine oils and Automotive Lubrication, Bartz, W.J., ed., Marcel Dekker, NY, p 336

[5] W. van Leeuwen (1999), Use of RULER for the Determination of Critical Antioxidant Concentration in Ester Based Hydraulic Fluids, Proceedings AISE, Sept. 1999

[6] Kauffman, R.E., "Rapid Determination of Remaining Useful Life of Lubricant Life", in CRC Handbook of Lubrication and Tribology, 3, Booser, E.R., ed., CRC Press, Boca Raton, FL,p.89, (1994)

[7] Ameye, J, (2000), "The results of a Program for Quick Determination of Antioxidants on O-160 Helicopter Turbine Lubricants by Using the RULER oil Analysis instrument," in Proc. Technology Showcase 2000, JOAP Int. Condition Monitoring Conf. Mobile, Alabama, pp 86-98

[8] Robert E. Kauffman, Jo Ameye – ASTM STP publication – " Antioxidant Analysis for Monitoring Remaining Useful Life of Turbine Fluids" – Presented at June 2001 ASTM Symposium "Turbine Lubrication in the 21st Century". Published in ASTM STP 1407.

[9] Vandenkommer, A, SKF (2001), Predicting Remaining Grease life – a new approach and method by linear sweep voltammetry – ELGI AGM Bern Switzerland, May 2001

[10] Bryan Johnson, APS Power, Jo Ameye – NLGI Meeting, October 2004 – "Condition Monitoring of Anti-oxidant Chemistry of In-Service Bulk Greases" – NLGI Proceedings, October 2004

[11] ASTM D6810, Standard Test Method for Measurement of Hindered Phenolic Antioxidant Content in HL Turbine Oils by Linear Sweep Voltammetry

[12] ASTM D4378, Standard Practice for In-Service Monitoring of Mineral Turbine Oils for Steam and Gas Turbines

[13] ASTM D6224, Standard Practice for In-Service Monitoring of Lubricating Oil for Auxiliary Power Plant Equipment

[14] ASTM D6971, Standard Test Method for Measurement of Hindered Phenolic and Aromatic Amine Antioxidant Content in non-zinc containing Turbine Oils by Linear Sweep Voltammetry

COMONET – the DTI Knowledge Transfer Network for Condition Monitoring Sensors

T. Sperring, C. Pislaru

Jost Institute for Tribotechnology, University of Central Lancashire, Preston PR1 2HE, UK

ABSTRACT

COndition MOnitoring NETwork (COMONET) is a DTI Knowledge Transfer Network designed to allow industrial companies and the scientific and research base to meet, discuss and direct developments in condition monitoring. This will be achieved through a series of seminars and technical discussion groups which will be held at venues throughout the UK. As well as this, e-activities will be hosted through the web portal. Users from all divisions of the condition monitoring sensor sector are represented - sensor manufacturers, research institutes, governing bodies and end users.

Innovation is essential for any market sector to move forward. COMONET will facilitate dialogue between the users and providers to create new solutions by directing research, enhance existing sensors and develop innovative methods of integrating sensor systems to add value to engineering solutions and cut costs for industry.

Keywords: Condition monitoring, knowledge transfer network, sensor technology.

1. INTRODUCTION

Condition monitoring is essential for any business concerned with the efficient and reliable operation of machinery. Sensors are the engineer's eyes and ears which can help detect current and future problems. With well directed investigation and research, they can also predict failure and prescribe remedial action.

Over the past decade machine condition monitoring techniques have matured to the point where, when employed correctly, the very earliest stages of wear can be detected. As sensor technologies have developed, more information has become available to allow diagnostic action. However, in reality, more data can often lead to confusion, and misinterpretation of the results can lead to mistrust in sensors or even mistrust of condition monitoring as a maintenance tool. By bringing together the condition monitoring community to share good practice, develop analysis techniques and evaluate potential solutions to common issues, robust systems can be produced as the centre of a proactive maintenance programme.

2. AIMS OF COMONET

To compete on a world stage, companies need to make best use of their equipment, running at the lowest cost and with the best availability. With this goal in mind, the Jost Institute for Tribotechnology was established at the University of Central Lancashire (UCLAN) to bring the users and suppliers of technology together. COMONET, a UK-wide Knowledge Transfer Network has been formed to inform users and potential users of the benefits of condition monitoring and nurture innovation of new sensor technologies.

Using the funding from the DTI, a series of seminars will be hosted at various locations around the UK on the hot topics of condition monitoring. An event has already been held at UCLAN in conjunction with the Institute of Mechanical Engineers titled "Use of On-line Sensor Technology in Condition Monitoring to Improve Maintenance". It was well attended and created a variety of opportunities linking businesses with the science and technology base. The event also hosted a successful exhibition which allowed users and suppliers to come together. Similar exhibitions will be held in the future.

COMONET will be advertised though published literature, web-based activities, trade exhibitions and the DTI dedicated web portal. Hosting web-meeting will allow solutions to problems be created through collaboration between COMONET members. The portal will include up-to-date news on condition monitoring, have a specialised database on maintenance issues, and store archived seminar presentations.

Although there are many regional, industry-based groups throughout the country there is no single organisation dedicated to the furtherance of condition monitoring across different industrial sectors. DTI funding will allow the creation this group but in future it is intended to be at least partly self-funding, supported by the members through an annual fee. It is proposed that various sensors groups will meet together to exchange their knowledge and experience and form partnerships to enhance services to industry. These include companies involved with oil analysis, vibrations, acoustic emissions, wear debris analysis and thermography, and will bring together the users and providers of condition monitoring technology.

3. IMPACT

Sensors in condition monitoring are a growing market sector driven by the move to on-line, automated analysis. They are being manufactured and developed in a huge variety of formats; optical measurement of particles, acoustic measurement through air and oil as well as acoustic emissions detected on bearing races, magnetic, capacitance and inductive devices to measuring wear debris, vibration and thermography have all be used to help determine machine health. However, selecting the right tool for the right machine and using it in the correct manner can be difficult to achieve. Utilising the experience of Network members and transferring their knowledge to those who are implementing a condition monitoring regime will help improve company productivity.

By bringing together all those connected with condition monitoring, innovative solutions will be developed to increase the effectiveness of the sensors in this field. This will ensure new technologies are relevant and useful and are integrated in the most effective manner.

To ensure the quality and diversity of the Network, various initial partner organisations were approached to aid in knowledge dissemination, direct research to solve problem areas and relate studies of failures and successes. They are involved in all stages of the condition monitoring chain and have given their backing for the formation of COMONET. Sensor manufacturers welcome the opportunity to hear the need of industry – creating the right sensor is key to their survival, issues of robustness, accuracy and, ultimately, what sensors can say about machine condition are vital for their future. End users need to make certain future research initiatives produce solutions to their problems.

To guarantee excellence is maintained in the series of seminars, it is proposed that the network will draw on people who are world leaders in their fields to give bespoke presentations in line with the theme of the meeting that day. These presentations will be recorded and available as an archive, playable through Interwise, held on the web-portal. As well as seminars and e-activities, COMONET will produce documents outlining the benefits of sensors and condition monitoring. If needed, the research fellow employed by COMONET will visit companies on-site to see how sensor technology can enhance their productivity and safety. The research fellow will also coordinate the creation of common terminology including discussion with the various standard agencies, including ISO.

Compliance with ISO 14001 is becoming a necessity for many UK businesses. Reducing the whole-life impact of operating machinery can be achieved in part by reducing downtime and running more efficiently which will lower the total power requirement, amount of consumables used and extend life. COMONET will help generate, gather and analyse the information that UK industry need to be compliant with environmental legislation by collating members' experiences and by contacting knowledge transfer networks in similar fields.

COMONET will allow industry and the scientific and research base to meet, discuss and direct developments in condition monitoring to build a knowledge-base which can be used throughout the UK and exported worldwide. The UK is in a prime position to become the world leader in condition monitoring sensors and technology. The network will allow any future research and development work to be directed towards industry's needs and to integrate into business quickly and effectively. Sensor systems designed specifically for an engineering solution may have application in other areas such as monitoring the wear of artificial hip replacements or monitoring environmental change.

A recent survey mentions that maintenance costs are a major part of the total operating cost of all manufacturing or production plants. Depending on the industry, maintenance cost can represent a significant part of the cost of goods produced. Recent surveys indicate that one-third of all maintenance costs is wasted because work is either unnecessary or improperly carried out. The impact on productivity and profit is clear. The formation of COMONET will give UK companies the knowledge to integrate condition monitoring sensor technology to reduce this wasted effort.

Condition monitoring can provide significant economic and safety benefits. The economic benefits stem from reductions in fixed periodic preventative maintenance, whilst also reducing the risk of economic loss associated with major plant damage. Safety benefits stem from a reduction in the frequency of faults resulting from plant component failures based on the ability to take planned action on the diagnostic information provided.

Because the field of condition monitoring is vast, and in many cases uncoordinated, the formation of COMONET is critical to UK business. There is a wealth of sensor technology but for UK industry to benefit it must be reliable, robust and fit for purpose. COMONET will help ensure that new and emerging sensors are integrated correctly whilst nurturing innovation in new technology.

4. MANAGEMENT OF COMONET

COMONET has commenced on March 2006 and funding was requested for three years. Membership to this network will be sought through advertising, both web-based and printed media, attending exhibitions and contributing to conferences. An annual fee will give free admittance to four annual, day long seminars which will have cross-industry themes (e.g. Oil analysis sensors, How thermography can help your business etc.). These will be based throughout the UK to spread the burden of travel between members. Members will also be able to set up e-meetings using Interwise through a web-portal set up and managed by COMONET as well as being able to access past presentations. This will further reduce the burden on companies to release personnel.

UCLAN will manage the Network through the Jost Institute for Tribotechnology. In terms of student numbers, UCLAN is the UK's fifth largest university with over 33,000 students. The UCLAN mission statement specifically supports working in partnership with business, the community and other educators, and encourages and promotes research and innovation. UCLAN has a wealth of expertise in all areas associated with this network, including financial controls, conference facilities and technical personnel. This application for a DTI Knowledge Transfer Network Grant is consistent with and supported by institutional strategy and the mission statement.

Dr Crinela Pislaru has been employed as a Research Fellow based at the Jost Institute to manage the COMONET network. Her role is to administer the web-portal, organise the series of seminars and ensure that advertising is well directed and relevant. She will also act in a consultancy role for the network with the emphasis on bringing step-change to companies' maintenance philosophy because she will be the single contact point for all network members. Dr Trevor Sperring, Lecturer in condition monitoring, will oversee the work of the Research Fellow.

The Network will be extensively advertised using regional government agencies and national bodies relevant to the suppliers and users, and also at the UK leading exhibitions. COMONET will also help organise national and international conferences which, in addition to raising finance for future sustainability, will disseminate the expertise we have in the UK around the globe.

Advertising the benefits of membership will be carried out in a variety of formats; published literature (which can be delivered via magazines and at exhibitions, conferences and seminars), by directing people to the web portal and through the innovations created as a result of COMONET collaboration.

COMONET partners come from all branches of the condition monitoring sensor industry – sensor manufacturers, research institutes, educators and end users. It is only by bringing together all these bodies that UK condition monitoring will become a world leader. The initial COMONET partners are:

1. **British Institute of Non-Destructive Testing (BINDT)** has a committee directly responsible for the condition monitoring and organise the bi-annual international Condition Monitoring conference. The committee see the network will increase awareness of their activities and in return they can provide expert speakers in this field. BINDT headquarters in Northampton will be the Midlands location for the Network. Integrating the knowledge base of COMONET and BINDT will further increase the UK influence on International Standards in maintenance.

2. **QinetiQ** in Farnborough will provide the Southern base for the Network. QinetiQ have a wealth of experience in both military and civil applications – their knowledge and experience will be invaluable to all Network members.

3. **UCLAN** in Preston, Lancashire and the **University of Manchester** will be the Northern hosts and are experienced in organising and hosting such events. Both institutions also have researchers with industry-based experience to develop and test emerging sensor technologies.

4. Advances and discussions on oil analysis will be the lead by of **Swansea Tribology Services** who have 25 years of experience in this field.

5. **Kittiwake and Pall** both manufacture sensors for condition monitoring - the network will allow them to educate UK industry on best practice and also take on board their needs, problems and what industry would like to see in the condition monitoring sensor marketplace in the future.

   (Key to all these groups are the end-users since they will purchase and use the technologies developed through the Network. The automotive sector is increasingly demanding on-line engine health monitoring through lubricant condition to increase service interval.)

6. **Castrol, part of BP** and a leading automotive lubricant supplier will advise on the needs of this sector. Plant operators, especially those with large estates, are moving to on-line monitoring.

7. **GSK** will help steer the R&D of sensors to meet the needs of industry.

It is expected that opportunities for collaborative research will arise as a result of discussion between network members. COMONET will actively encourage such activity and be a helping-hand through the period of any such projects. By including good industrial partners from the start, both multinational and SMEs, COMONET can make an impact from the outset of its formation.

DTI funding will launch this network by providing the personnel and web portal that are essential at the early stages of COMONET's existence. The Research Fellow will be a versatile asset who can help in knowledge transfer and be a personal link for all members. The web portal will give all network members access to cutting edge e-activities including e-meetings which will increase the density of communication routes for all users.

Bringing together the users and suppliers, encouraging positive dialogue and directing the future of condition monitoring sensor technology will guarantee that UK maintenance is a world leader, an expertise that can be exported to the global market.

5. WEB PORTAL

Knowledge transfer between members will be encouraged by the readily available web-portal which will have a series of discussion groups managed by Vignette [1]. Responding rapidly to changing business conditions reported through Vignette will ensure that UK industry can perform in the competitive global market. By having a common portal format for all DTI KTNs, COMONET will be able to advertise to other networks. Through cross network cooperation, condition monitoring sensors can be tailored to the needs of all areas of UK industry. The Jost Institute at UCLAN will publish reports on research in sensor technology and condition monitoring which will be available to Network members via the web portal (subject to confidentiality agreements). Case studies, condition monitoring fundamentals, sensor technology and literature surveys will be published held the web portal. This information will allow companies to make informed decisions on implementing new maintenance practices.

5.1. Autonomy Search Engine

The DTI webportal incorporates a specialist search engine. Autonomy automatically categorises and summarises information base on an understanding of the documents. For example, a search for 'penguin' may result in Antarctic birds, chocolate biscuits and references to Batman. Autonomy will group these different concepts based on pattern recognition system of the content of the results. Autonomy can be personalised to assist in future searches. US patent database can be searched and the European patent database will be integrated within the year.

5.2. Conference centre

A key part of the Knowledge Transfer Network webportal is the conference centre. On-line presentation can be delivered in real-time using a combination of a whiteboard and voice. The whiteboard can be used to show presentations, debate results, demonstrate equipment and software or show a website. Getting access to this technology is done via the front page of the sensors webportal at

http://www.sensorsktn.com

There is a brief set up procedure which need only be performed once and the meeting is ready. Meetings can be open or closed and the facilitator can choose to advertise the meeting on the website.

Online conferencing is still relatively new but the advantages are clear. Meeting require very little outlay and reduce the time and travel burden on companies. Meeting can be one-on-one or broadcast to an audience of 100. The conference can be recorded and made available to all or to a special interest group.

5.3. VBCS

Vignette Business Collaboration Services (VBCS) is an on-line tool for setting up and running collaborative projects. Group members can share a web space with access being granted to sub-groups. When setting up a collaborative project document tracking is vital to ensure all members are examining the latest versions.

5.4. News

On the front page of COMONET there is an automated news feed which searches the web for the latest developments in condition monitoring sensors.

The generic activities typical of a KTN, specific roles and skills and the required training courses have been defined in a report [2]. The roles commonly assigned for operating a KTN are: contract manager, site administrator, network leader, network moderator, helpdesk supervisor and trainer, membership manager, editor. These people will ensure a good communication between sensors producers and users.

6. CONCLUSIONS

Innovation is essential for any market sector to move forward and COMONET will facilitate dialogue between the users and providers to create solutions by directing research programmes, enhance existing sensors and develop innovative methods of integrating sensor systems to add value to engineering solutions and cut costs for industry.

There are some uncertainties associated with the setting up of a network. A training budget has been allocated to ensure that personnel are kept up-to-date with the technologies used by COMONET. Technical difficulties will be managed by UCLAN and the difficulties of travel are solved in two ways: having meetings that are located throughout the UK and also by hosting meetings through the web-portal – the appropriate software will be supplied as part of the network.

REFERENCES

[1]   The KTN Internet Platform. KTN Report. June 2005: London, United Kingdom.
[2]   KTN Skills, Training and support - Making sure your team has the skills, training and support to operate your DTI Knowledge Transfer Networks. KTN report, November 2005: London, United Kingdom.

Tribology: A vital ingredient in Asset Management

P. J. Huggett

The Woodhouse Partnership Limited, www.twpl.com

ABSTRACT

Fifty or so years ago it was common practice to have to replace the big-end and main crankshaft bearings in motor cars every few years. Then suddenly in the 1950s and 60s the problem vanished without many people being aware - it was the start of tribology!

Planned maintenance, by its very nature, maintains assets to safely perform their desired functions but it does not encourage change and continuous improvement. However tribology and methodologies such as RCA (Root Cause Analysis), TPM (Total Productive Maintenance) and quality management etc, do!

Maintenance management and tribology are elements of asset management, the latter being a comprehensive strategy to improve the performance of assets and processes to improve profitability and competitiveness.

Tribology, as with other improvement processes and strategies, therefore needs to show satisfactory return on investment. For example, this would necessitate a cost/benefit analysis be done for the introduction of any technique such as improved oil filtration technology.

This paper reviews the structure of a comprehensive asset management programme and how tribology can play a vital role in its development and in so doing, will also give a high level vision of the important elements in a tribology programme.

1. INTRODUCTION

1.1. Where tribology fits in optimising asset performance

Tribology treats the causes of wear and deterioration of components in lubricated systems and therefore aims at improving their expected life cycles. If a tribology programme is focused on critical assets, and correctly applied, financial benefits should be forthcoming. However, operating management have a number of other or different opportunities and processes to choose from to improve asset performance, so the application of tribology and its financial cost/benefit relationship needs to be compared to them and the most profitable processes given priority.

1.2. What is Asset Management?

Asset management is often confused with maintenance management. Maintenance management ensures that assets perform the functions that they were designed and/or selected to perform, whereas asset management ensures that assets perform their required functions in the most cost effective way. There are a number of processes for managers to choose from, in a comprehensive asset management programme. The choice is dependent on which one to concentrate on to bring the greatest benefit in the shortest possible time.

A further key aspect of an asset management programme, is to ensure that the various processes selected dovetail together to maximise the synergy between them, and that each new process builds on the strengths of the other processes, and that they be implemented at a digestible rate for the organisation.

There are three important pillars to asset management:

- ❑ Key Performance Indicators (KPIs) - to focus the management team on the results that are to be achieved and the rate of improvement desired
- ❑ The various processes that will enable improved competitiveness and profitability improvement
- ❑ Leadership that will organise, plan, motivate and structure the direction of the continuous asset management improvement programme.

1.3. Selected Processes in Asset Management

Some of the more common asset management processes that are complementary to tribology are:

1.3.1. Reliability Centred Maintenance (RCM) [1]

RCM ensures that the correct choice of proactive maintenance tasks is made for each asset to maintain its desired systems functions. It has a decision diagram that sets out the logic of choice and there are four main options:

- ❑ Functional failure finding tasks, functional testing of protective devices and standby plant etc
- ❑ Preventive maintenance, the replacement/repair of components/assets at fixed intervals which is based purely on the age of the item eg, the replacement of spark plugs in a motor car at fixed intervals.
- ❑ Predictive maintenance, the replacement/repair of components/assets based on the indication of deteriorating condition (vibration, wear, thinning, heat and/or dirt particles or metals in oil etc)
- ❑ Scheduled corrective maintenance eg, regular inspections of non-critical items such as office light bulbs and replacement thereof when failed.

1.3.2. Total Productive Maintenance (TPM)

TPM is where selective aspects such as autonomous maintenance, activity boards, one-point lessons and improvement projects etc, can dovetail in with a RCM programme to enhance the roll-out of a customised maintenance strategy. Care should be taken to avoid conflict of the latter with the prescriptive nature of planned maintenance programmes suggested by TPM strategists from the East. [2]

1.3.3. Root Cause Analysis (RCA)

RCA (Root Cause Analysis) is not a sharply defined technique/technology and can be found in ISO 9000 programmes and a large variety of providers of logic to which reference in this paper makes use, and can be found on the web through many search engines, searching for 'Root Cause Analysis'.

RCA which is mostly a reactive strategy, which aims to prevent incidents of damage, breakdowns and asset defects from recurring by finding remedies for the root causes of failure. Thus it is a vital element in tribology which also treat the root cause of wear in lubricated systems which can lead to an improved standard in an existing lubrication system. This too can complement the RCM strategies, which aim to reduce the consequences of functional failure, in that it might also be cost effective to reduce the frequency of recurrence, which will reduce the need for maintenance too in the future.

1.3.4. Risk Based Inspection (RBI)

Risk Based Inspection was developed to focus more intensity of inspection and more frequent inspection on more critical assets and less so on less critical assets. Standards to its application have been outlined in publications such as API RP580/1. (American Petroleum Institute – Ruling Practice). [3]

1.3.5. Example of an Asset Management Roadmap

The selection and implementation of asset management processes needs to be co-ordinated and to focus on risk reduction and opportunities for efficiency and profitability improvement (KPIs). They should not all be implemented at the same time, as this is likely to lead to confusion and rushed and ineffective implementation. Thus the capacity of the organisation to change and implement a continuous improvement programme needs to be assessed in order to plan an effective roadmap for the future.

Asset Management Programme Roadmap:

		2006	2007	2008	2009	2010
1	High level Risk & Opportunity Assessment	➡				
2	KPIs		➡ - - -	- - - - -	- - - - -	- - - ➡
3	RCA		➡ - - -	- - - - -	- - - - -	- - - ➡
4	Tribology		➡ - -	- - - - -	- - - - -	- - - ➤
5	RCM		➡➡➡➡➡	- - - - -	- - - - -	- - ➡
6	TPM (Selected tools)				➡ - - -	- - - ➤
7	Cost Risk Optimisation		- - - - -	- - - - -	➡➡➡➡	- - - ➡

Table 1. An example of a formalised roadmap for an asset management improvement programme

Table 1 is an example of a formalised roadmap for an asset management improvement programme. It is important to set out the logical order of implementation for an organisation to work to. Care should be taken not to overload the staff involved, as this could lead to de-motivation and confusion. Each step is fully agreed to by management as they are to implement it. A high level risk and opportunity assessment aims at ensuring that management focuses on the major issues facing the organisation. KPIs will direct focus and measurement of the results that are to be achieved to ensure that any business process that is to be improved will measurably improve the productivity of the organisation. Tribology is linked directly to Root Cause analysis as both processes are likely to bring about change to standards of existing procedures and technology. RCM is followed by the implementation of selected elements of TPM, as the latter will facilitate the roll out of the improved maintenance strategies selected in the RCM programme. Cost Risk Optimisation, uses the strategies selected in the RCM and TPM programme, and optimises intervals and choices thereof, to ensure cost effectiveness and is a quantitative technique. It therefore tends to follow the rest, as illustrated above.

A vital element in the roadmap implementation process is effective leadership, which needs to motivate and drive the overall programme.

1.4. Economics of Asset Management

Two aspects should be considered, macro and micro economics with respect to the organisation decision making process:

1.4.1. Macro Economics

This should be an estimated cost/benefit analysis of the process being considered. The benefits, whether they be reduced failures or longer life of the assets being targeted together with the benefits to operations and product quality etc, should be considered. The annual cost of implementing and maintaining the new AM (Asset Management) programme needs to be less than the benefits that are to be earned.

1.4.2. Micro Economics

Each decision needs to be evaluated to ensure that it contributes positively to the overall cost effectiveness of the improvement programme.

The following example of optimising the oil purification interval on a turbine and its effect on the improved life of the bearings is illustrated in figure 1. The more frequently one purifies the oil the longer the life of the bearings is likely to be. Purifying oil can range from on-line and off-line filtration of dirt from the oil on the one hand, to removing all the dirt and producing ultra-pure oil on the other. The latter technology is not limited to the minimum filter size of filtration technology, as it works on the principle of electrostatic adsorption. This technology, know commercially as ELC (Electrostatic Liquid Cleaning) is able to remove all dirt particles as well as oil oxidation products. Oil additives are soluble in oil and are therefore not removed by either process.

Estimates have been entered into the calculation as illustrated and the net benefits of purifying the oil at two months instead of the existing 4 monthly cycle, produces an estimated £2k benefit per year. There are 24 similar turbines on site and the total benefit for all the turbines would be c.£48k per year. The cost of a second electrostatic oil purifier is c.£80k and the payback is less than 2 years.

The current interval is 4 months but the optimal is at 2 months.

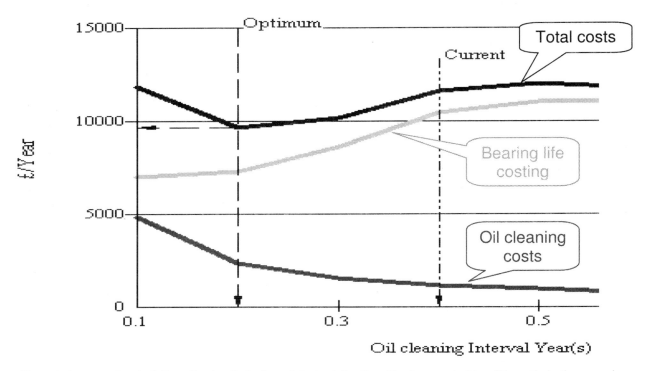

Figure 1. An example calculation of cost optimisation of electrostatic oil purification on a turbine. (The optimisation curve in figure 1 is illustrated here by kind permission of APTOOLS Ltd. (www.APTOOLS.co.uk))

The optimisation of the interval of the 'oil cleaning cycle' in figure 1 above, is an illustration of a system that where it might only be possible to reduce the amount of dirt by off-line oil purification. This costs money and the more frequently one purifies the oil the higher the oil cleaning costs become, as illustrated by the red line above. However, the longer an oil cleaning interval the more wear will result on the equipment which will push up the maintenance cost, as illustrated by the blue line above, 'bearing life costing'. The total of the two costs in this case, illustrates that the optimal (total cost curve in black) oil cleaning interval is fact 0.2 of a year (c.2 months), whereas, the current interval is set at 0.4 of a year (c. 4 months). Thus by cleaning the oil more regularly at half the existing interval, will more than pay for the additional costs of oil cleaning and bring about a total cost saving of c.£2,000 per year per system.

2. CONCLUSION

Finding the balance and relative financial importance when selecting new processes.

The example of the oil purification above, needs to be ranked against the other projects in the organisation, and a further example is illustrated below in figure 2 to show how that could be done.

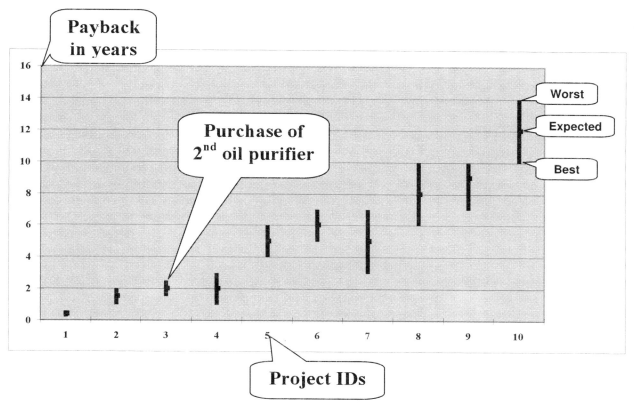

Figure 2. An example ranking 10 improvement projects

The investment in a second oil purifier would rank 3rd out of 10 projects and would have a reasonable undiscounted payback rate of around 2 years. As these calculations are based on estimates of the organisation's staff, sensitivity testing is also illustrated above where the best and worst case estimates are also shown, in each case. All organisations face the same problem of a shortage of good data, however, sensitivity testing usually shows that decisions can be taken and choices made with weak data as the decision options usually 'hold water' under the whole range of likely scenarios, as illustrated.

REFERENCES

[1]   Moubray, J. (1991) "RCM – Reliability Centred Maintenance". Published by Butterworth Heinemann (ISBN 0 7506 02309)
[2]   Smith, A. M. (1993) "Reliability Centered Maintenance". Published by McGraw-Hill Inc. (ISBN 0 07 059046 X)
[3]   API RP580/1: American Petroleum Institute, 2002, API RP580, 1st edition Washington DC. (British Standard BS 7910 (2005)).

In-Service Wear Assessment of Aircraft Engines

T. Sperring

Jost Institute for Tribotechnology, University of Central Lancashire, Preston PR1 2HE, UK

ABSTRACT

Wear debris is a well established tool for determining machine condition. Particle analysis techniques, ranging from simple measurements of the amount of debris using a ferro-magnetic inductive method to a full compositional analysis using EDX-RF from a scanning electron microscope, yield information on whether a piece of equipment has exceeded its working criteria and, in some cases, give a prediction of expected remaining useful life.

In this paper, a summary account is given of the way in which specific test machines have recently been utilised to produce wear debris under controlled test conditions. In particular, the morphological features of wear debris are described in relation to wear characteristics obtained from using three test machines: four-ball, pin-on-disc, and bearing test stand. The results of subsequent microscopic analysis and classification of the debris morphology are described in relation to the corresponding wear modes experienced in the test. The implications for application of a new software-based, wear debris classifier are reviewed and discussed in relation to present-day methods employed in the maintenance of military engines and gear transmission systems.

Keywords: Condition monitoring, wear debris analysis, particles, aircraft

1. INTRODUCTION

Wear debris analysis is used throughout the aircraft industry as a means of engine health monitoring. Analysing particles to assess machine condition has been used since the 1950s [1]. Condition monitoring of critical components allows operators to assess the wear state, diagnose problems and extend the life of a machine.

2. WEAR DEBRIS ANALYSIS

Examination of wear products throughout the life of an engine or gearbox can yield information about the current state of the machine. By measuring the amount of debris a graph can be plotted and would usually follow the typical bath-tub curve (Figure 1), from initially high wear production rates due to run-in followed by a (ideally) long period of relatively low wear, eventually leading to a high rate before the end of the machine life. More detailed examination of the particles using an optical microscope can reveal the type of particles being produced at any given time and, therefore, the wear modes present, which is summarised in Figure 2. For example, initially cutting wear may be found due to machined parts bedding in, but once running-in is over occurrences of these particles may reduce in number.

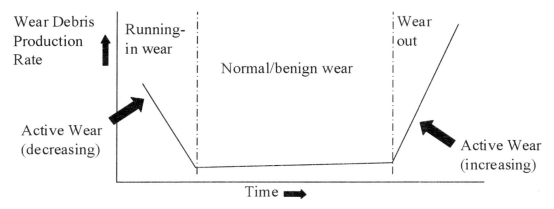

Figure 1. Typical bath tub curve [2]

Further analysis using a scanning electron microscope can examine smaller particles than the optical method and can also give the elemental composition of the particle which helps trace debris back to their source.

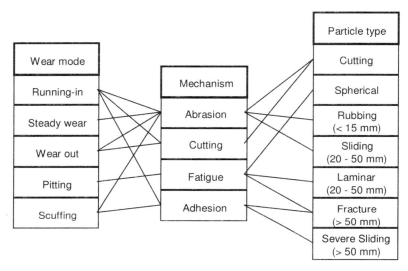

Figure 2. Relationship between wear mode and particle shape [3]

3. TEST APPARATUS

3.1.   Four ball machine

Laboratory conditions allow wear particles to be generated under known controllable parameters such as load, speed, lubrication regime and material specification. The four-ball machine is normally utilised to perform lubricant tests according to internationally recognised standard test procedures, but can also be used to generate a variety of particle types. In the UK, the designated standards are stipulated according to the Institute of Petroleum (IP) as follows: scuffing tests (sliding) - IP239 [4]; pitting fatigue (rolling) – IP300 [5].

Figure 3 shows schematically the four-ball configurations for sliding (a) and rolling (b), respectively. For sliding operation, the three lower balls are clamped in place and the upper fourth ball is rotated against them. For rolling contact, the lower three balls are free to rotate on their own axes and around the 'race' cup under the driving action of the rotating upper ball. Under standard operating conditions the sliding four-ball will experience two wear modes, mild or severe and, hence, two particle types, mild sliding and severe sliding (see later).

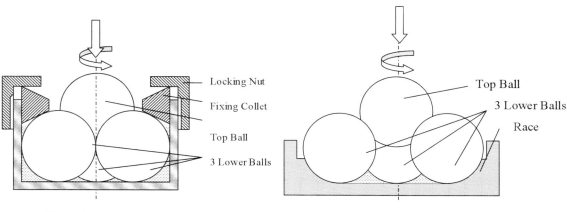

Figure 3. (a) Rolling four-ball test   (b) Sliding four-ball test

When operated in rolling pitting fatigue mode, the lower three balls are free to rotate in a race mimicking the movement of balls in a bearing. In this case much higher loads are applied and the test duration is much longer (typically between 10 minutes and 3 hours). The test is carried out with loads of 600kg.

3.2. Pin-on-disc Machine

A variety of particles can be generated on a pin-on-disk machine (Figure 4) because of the combination of contact geometry and materials changes. Normally, a round ball would be run against a flat disc but this can be changed to a line or surface contact by using a roller on its curved side or flat end. By changing the material of the disc contacts involving dissimilar hardnesses can be tested. As with the four-ball machine both mild and severe wear particles can be generated by altering the lubrication regimes from EHL to boundary which can be achieved by letting the temperature of the oil rise by running the test for a long time or by starving the contact of oil. Cutting particles can be generated by using a ball that is more than 1.3 times the hardness of the disk. This difference in hardness allows the ball to score out material from the disk and produce swarf-like wear debris as is seen on a metal lathe but on a much smaller scale.

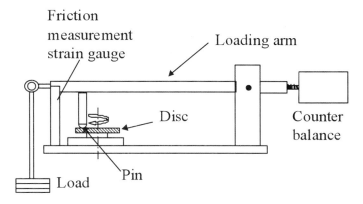

Figure 4. Pin-on-disc machine

3.3. Bearing test stand

The apparatus used for the testing is a bearing standard stand originally designed for determining the L10 life of 7305 and 6305 bearings (shown in Figure 5). The rig has been fitted with a magnetic debris extraction to study the particulate material shred throughout the test duration.

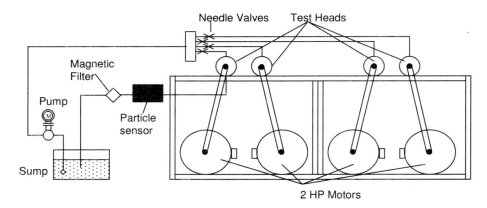

Figure 5. Bearing test stand

Pairs of standard 7305 angular contact bearings were used. Load is applied through dead-weights on a cantilever – 300 lb was applied on the arm which translates as a 17390 N radial load through the bearing pair. The Shaft is rotated at a constant speed of 1500 rpm. The bearings fail through rolling pitting fatigue, often with a spall on the inner race.

3.4. Debris from Military Aircraft

To validate the laboratory experiments wear debris from a variety of military aircraft was sampled. These came from fighter aircraft engines and helicopter gearboxes and included stripdown reports which contained details of any defects found.

3.5. Particle Collection and Preparation

Particles were collected in a variety of methods depending on the test. When using the four-ball machine the balls were removed and washed with solvent into a small collection bottle. Next, the cup and the other apparatus were washed into the bottle as well. A similar procedure was used for the pin-on-disk machine, washing with solvent the component into a collection bottle. Debris from the bearing test stand was captured on a magnetic filter. The debris from military aircraft was removed from the permanent archive.

Once the various samples of oil and debris have been collected it is desirable to view them with a metallurgical microscope. To present the particles in an acceptable manner, the sample bottle is drawn through a 0.8 mm Millipore Isopore® filter using a standard filter assembly with vacuum pump. This particular filter is used because it is transparent when examining the particles in transmitted lighting conditions that can yield silhouette images useful for computer-based analyses.

Images of the particles are captured using a JVC CCD camera mounted on top of an Olympus BX40 metallurgical microscope. This in turn is connected to a computer which captures several images in different focal planes and collaged them together to create a single in-focus picture.

4. WEAR PARTICLE TYPES

Many wear particles were generated throughout the testing period and their form depended on the wear mode of the test. Four main types of debris were observed and can be described as follows. Mild sliding (Figure 6a), small particles with few surface features and low aspect ratio, were present during all test and are the result of the abrasive wear from the surface roughness of the contacting surfaces; severe sliding wear (Figure 6b) was generated from the four-ball sliding tests and pin-on-disc. These particles often exhibit surface striation due to the adhesive conditions under which they are formed. The surface can be rough and dark in colour due to high local temperatures. Fatigue particles (Figure 6c) are the result of cyclic loading causing micro-pitting and sub-surface cracks. These particles can have a pitted surface and normally display radial petal-like cracks. They have a low aspect ratio and are indicative of wear out. Cutting wear (Figure 6d) is formed when two surfaces of dissimilar hardnesses come into contact and the harder acts as a cutting tool on the softer material. This can be the result of either entrainment of a foreign body, such as sand or aluminium oxide, or from the work hardening of one of a pair of like materials.

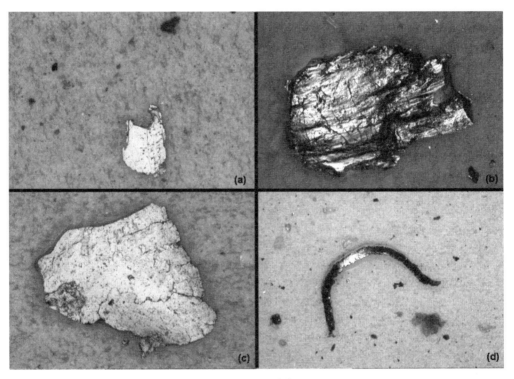

Figure 6. Wear particles types

When comparing the debris from the Royal Air Force archive and that generated under laboratory conditions, no discernable difference was apparent for single wear mode particles. Fatigue debris from the rolling four-ball and bearing test stand was identical to that found from a wearing engine bearing. However, the debris from aircraft was slightly more prone to exhibit multiple wear modes. Primarily, this comprised fatigue debris which had subsequently entered another contact and was expelled with surface striations. This did occur in the bearing test when the fatigue spall was large. The difference is due to the complexity of the engine system and lubrication route.

5. ASSESSING MILTARY AIRCRAFT

The UK Royal Air Force currently uses staff based at Early Failure Detection Centres (EFDC) to conduct wear debris analysis on all its aircraft. Debris is captured onto magnetic detector plugs (MDP) which are located throughout the lubrication system. The MDPs are subsequently removed from the aircraft, washed in solvent and examined under a microscope to determine wear particle types.

To assist in identifying wear particles, the Royal Air Force used a library of know particles published in a manual known as a wear particle atlas. The data gathered from this research enabled an electronic wear particle atlas to be generated. To further assist personnel an automated classifier, SYCLOPS, was written utilizing a Bayesian belief network which asked the operator a series of questions about the morphology of a particle and subsequently automatically characterized it into one of the types above. SYCLOPS also included a useful training package which increased user confidence in identifying specific features of wear debris. A full account of this development is given in a paper by Sperring and Nowell [6].

6. CONCLUSIONS

Wear debris analysis is a powerful tool for condition monitoring and fault diagnosis. Improvements in image analysis have allowed this methodology mature almost to the point of full automation. By determining debris type an assessment of wear mode can be concluded and, hence, the fault in the tribological contact.

Future systems will require less human interaction to avoid the subjectivity of wear debris analysis. The move to on-line systems already incorporates some debris analysis – for the most part based on particle size distribution. It is hoped that the lack of information on morphology will be offset by the amount of data and immediate response that an on-line sensor can give.

REFERENCES

[1]   Dawson D, 'History of Tribology', Professional Engineering Publishing, 1998
[2]   Roylance, B.J., Williams, J.A. & Dwyer-Joyce, R., "Wear debris and associated wear phenomena – fundamental research and practice", Proc Inst. Mech. Engrs, Vol 214. Part J, pp 79 – 105, 2000.
[3]   Roylance B and Hunt T.M., 'Wear Debris Analysis -Machine and Systems Condition Monitoring Series', Coxmoor Publishing Co. 1999.
[4]   IP Standards for Petroleum and Its Products, Part 1 'Extreme Pressure and Wear - Four-ball', Vol. 1, pp 239.1-239.16, Institute of Petroleum, London, John Wiley and Sons, 1986.
[5]   IP Standards for Petroleum and Its Products, Part 1, 'Rolling Contact Fatigue Test for Fluids in a Modified Four-Ball Machine', Vol. 2, pp 300.1-300.11, Institute of Petroleum, London, John Wiley and Sons, 1986.
[6]   Sperring T P and Nowell T J, 'SYCLOPS—a qualitative debris classification system developed for RAF early failure detection centres', Tribology International, 2005.

Session 13
LUBRICANTS & ADDITIVES 5

Chair: Mr. Bob Cutler

The Role of Bubbles in Gaseous Cavitation
E. H. SMITH

Lubricant Additives Effects on the Hydrodynamic Lubrication of Misaligned Conical-Cylindrical Bearings
A. A. ELSHARKAWY

The Role of Bubbles in Gaseous Cavitation

E. H. Smith

Jost Institute for Tribotechnology, University of Central Lancashire, United Kingdom

ABSTRACT

This paper examines the behaviour of a hydrodynamic bearing where the lubricant contains entrained bubbles of air. It is shown that a critical lubricant pressure can be determined, below which bubbles will expand uncontrollably and raise the pressures in the outlet region of the bearing. However, a solution of the Reynolds equation with compressibility included, demonstrates that in the configurations examined, the bubbles expand sufficiently to keep the minimum pressure above this critical value. Indeed, in heavily-loaded configurations the bubbles expand and contract significantly and the pressure profile closely resembles that predicted using the Reynolds boundary condition. In very lightly loaded contacts, the bubbles grow or shrink very little, and the lubricant behaves as an incompressible one. It is possible, therefore, that entrained bubbles could be part of the mechanism of gaseous cavitation in hydrodynamic bearings.

1. INTRODUCTION

Gaseous cavitation occurs in most hydrodynamic bearings that exhibit a divergent clearance space. The effect of cavitation is to prevent large sub-ambient pressures being developed in the outlet region of the bearing, thus producing a positive load-carrying capacity. Without it, journal bearings, for example, could not operate. There are a number of competing theories [1] to describe the mechanism of gaseous cavitation: flow separation, entrained bubbles and streamers. In highly-loaded contacts, predictions of performance usually employ the Reynolds boundary condition. Whilst this approach does not explain the mechanism of cavitation, it satisfies flow continuity, and predicts pressures that agree with practice.

However, there still remains the influence of suspended bubbles, which most lubricants will contain. This paper seeks to further the understanding of their effect, following on from earlier work [2].

2. THEORETICAL ANALYSIS

Bubble Dynamics

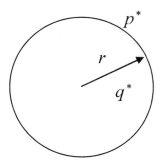

Consider a spherical bubble, of radius r, as shown in Figure 1. The Rayleigh-Plesset equation of motion for a symmetrical bubble of radius, r, in a liquid of density, ρ_L, is:

$$\rho_L \left\{ r\frac{d^2r}{dt^2} + 1.5\left(\frac{dr}{dt}\right)^2 \right\} = q^* - p^* - \left\{\frac{2T}{r}\right\} - \left\{\frac{4\eta}{r}\frac{dr}{dt}\right\}$$

$$\underbrace{\qquad\qquad\qquad}_{\text{inertia term}} \qquad\qquad \underbrace{\qquad\qquad}_{\text{viscosity term}}$$

Figure 1. A bubble

Smith [6] undertook a dimensional analysis of this equation. In most situations, he shows that the group $(\eta U / T)(h_{min} / l) \ll 10$. Because of this situation, and also because the Reynolds number is small, the equation of motion reduces to:

$$q^* - p^* = 2T / r$$

where the surface tension of the liquid is T Nm^{-1}.

At some initial position (usually at the bearing's inlet),

$$p^* = p_0^* \; ; \; r = r_0$$

Hence,

$$q_0^* = p_0^* + 2T / r_0$$

At some arbitrary position, when the liquid's absolute pressure is p^*,

$$q^* = p^* + 2T / r$$

The two internal pressures will be related according to:

$$q_0^* V_0^{\gamma} = q^* V^{\gamma}$$

(1)

where V_0 and V are the volumes of the bubbles at the respective positions, and are given by:

$$V_0 = \frac{4}{3} \pi r_0^3 \; ; \; V = \frac{4}{3} \pi r^3$$

If the constant, γ, is unity, then equation (1) reduces to:

$$(p_0^* + 2T / r_0) r_0^3 = (p^* + 2T / r) r^3$$

(2)

Introducing the non-dimensional terms, $\overline{p}^* = p^* r_0 / T$; $\overline{r} = r / r_0$, equation (2) becomes:

$$(\overline{p}_0^* + 2) = (\overline{p}^* + 2 / \overline{r}) \overline{r}^3$$

(3)

From which we obtain:

$$\overline{p}^* = (\overline{p}_0^* + 2) / \overline{r}^3 - 2 / \overline{r}$$

This expression is plotted overleaf in Figure 2. The curves indicate that as the absolute pressure is reduced outside the bubble, the radius increases until a critical pressure $\overline{p}_{crit}^*$ is attained, at which point the bubble will grow uncontrollably.

The radius ratio at this point is $\overline{r}_{crit}$, and the relationship between these two variables is given by:

$$\overline{p}_{crit}^* \overline{r}_{crit} = -4 / 3 \quad \text{and} \quad \overline{r}_{crit} = \sqrt{1.5(\overline{p}_0 + 2)}$$

It is instructive to determine from this relationship, the critical value, p_{crit}, of the gauge pressure.

The earlier expression,

$$\bar{p}^*_{crit} \bar{r}_{crit} = -4/3$$

can be rearranged to yield

$$p^*_{crit} = -\left[(4/3)/\bar{r}_{crit} \right] T / r_0$$

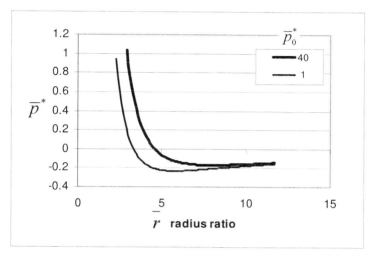

Figure 2. Variation of bubble radius with lubricant pressure

Hence the critical gauge pressure = $p_{crit} = -\dfrac{4/3}{\sqrt{1.5(\bar{p}_0 + 2)}} \dfrac{T}{r_0} - p^*_0$

and since $\bar{p}_0 = p^*_0 r_0 / T$,

$$p_{crit} = -\dfrac{4/3}{\sqrt{1.5(\bar{p}_0 + 2)}} \dfrac{p^*_0}{p_0} - p^*_0$$

This relationship is plotted in Figure 3 below, for $p^*_0 = 0.1$ MPa.

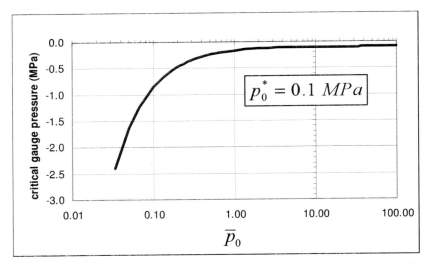

Figure 3. Variation of critical gauge pressure with initial non-dimensional absolute pressure of the lubricant

In the analysis in this paper, we have taken a value of $\overline{p}_0 = p^*_0 r_0 / T = 40$, and T = 0.03 Nm^{-1}, implying a value for r_0 of 40 x0.03/10^5 m = 12 μm. Thus the critical gauge pressure is approximately -0.1 MPa. With these values for p^*_0 and T, the bubble radius can be plotted against critical gauge pressure as shown in Figure 4.

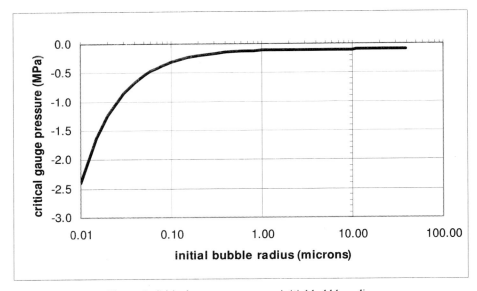

Figure 4. Critical gauge pressure vs initial bubble radius

Determining the bubble radius

In this study, we need to determine the radius of the bubble once the pressure in the liquid is known. Thus equation (3) must be arranged to yield:

$$a\bar{r}^3 + b\bar{r}^2 + d = 0$$

(4)

where

$$a = \bar{p}^* \quad ; \quad b = 2 \quad ; \quad d = -(\bar{p}_0^* + 2)$$

This equation can be solved analytically with the values of a, b and d which pertain.

Reynolds Equation

The one-dimensional Reynolds equation with variable density and constant viscosity is:

$$\frac{d}{dx}\left(\frac{\rho h^3}{12\eta}\frac{dp}{dx}\right) = \frac{U}{2}\frac{d}{dx}(\rho h)$$

Introducing the following non-dimensional terms:

$$H = h/h_{min} \quad ; \quad X = x/l \quad ; \quad P = ph_{min}^2/(\eta U l) \quad ; \quad \bar{\rho} = \rho/\rho_L$$

yields the non-dimensional Reynolds equation:

$$\frac{d}{dX}\left(\bar{\rho}H^3\frac{dP}{dX}\right) = 6\frac{d}{dX}(\bar{\rho}H)$$

Pressures

The non-dimensional pressures, P, in the Reynolds lubrication equation and the dimensionless pressures, $\bar{p}^*$, in the bubble equation are related by the following relationship:

$$\bar{p}^* = P\phi + \bar{p}_0^* \quad ,$$

where $\phi = (\eta U/T)(r_0/h_{min})(l/h_{min})$

In most lubrication situations, $1 \leq \phi \leq 20,000$.

Determining the density of the mixture

If the bubbles occupy a fraction, V_O, of the lubricant mixture at the reference pressure, then the density of the mixture, ρ_O is obtained from:

$$\rho_O = \rho_L(1 - V_O) + \rho_G V_O$$

where ρ_L, ρ_G are the densities of the pure liquid and gas, respectively.

Since $\rho_G \ll \rho_L$,

$$\rho_O \approx \rho_L (1 - V_O)$$

And therefore,

$$\overline{\rho}_O = 1 - V_O$$

The dimensionless density, $\overline{\rho}$, at any other pressure is therefore:

$$\overline{\rho} = 1 - V$$

Where V is the volume fraction of bubbles at that pressure, and is given by

$$V = n(4/3)\pi \, r^3,$$

where n is the number of bubbles per unit volume of mixture.

Since $V_O = n(4/3)\pi r_O^3$, V can be expressed as:

$$V = V_O (\overline{r})^3$$

and thus

$$\overline{\rho} = 1 - V_O (\overline{r})^3$$

The dimensionless bubble radius, $\overline{r}$, is obtained from the equation (5).

Solving the Reynolds equation

The pressure equation $\dfrac{d}{dX}\left(\overline{\rho}H^3 \dfrac{dP}{dX}\right) = 6\dfrac{d}{dX}(\overline{\rho}H)$ can be solved for the pressure term, P, using finite differences provided that $\overline{\rho}, H$ are known as function of X. H is a property of the geometry of the conjunction and can be easily determined. $\overline{\rho}$ is calculated in the manner discussed above. The overall procedure is a simple one:

1. Input known geometry, volume fraction, initial pressures and ϕ
2. Calculate bubble radii
3. Determine dimensionless densities
4. Solve Reynolds equation by finite differences
5. Calculate new bubble radii
6. Determine new densities
7. .... and so

3. RESULTS AND DISCUSSION

To study theoretically the effect of bubbles on hydrodynamic lubrication, an infinitely-wide, parabolic slider was employed. The ratio of inlet to minimum film-thickness was 1.75. The volume fraction of gas was taken to be 0.1, the ambient pressure as 0.1 MPa, and the surface tension of the oil as 0.03 Nm^{-1}.

As a test of the finite-difference representation, the full Sommerfeld conditions were applied, with zero bubbles entrained. This is compared with the theoretical solution in Figure 5.

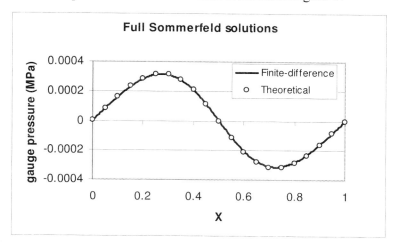

Figure 5. Comparison of theoretical and numerical full-Sommerfeld solutions

In Figures 6 and 7, the variation of liquid pressure in MPa are plotted against the position in the contact..

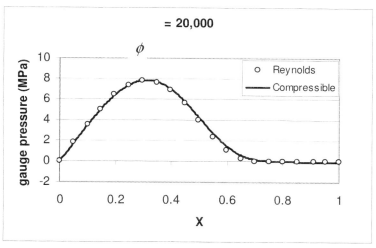

Figure 6. Pressure distribution in a heavily-loaded, bubbly contact

When $\phi = 20,000$ (which is representative of a heavily-loaded contact), the pressure reaches a maximum of 7.9 MPa, and a minimum value of -77,400 Pa. The sub-ambient pressure loop is clearly insignificant. However, in the very lightly-loaded arrangement illustrated in Figure 7, where $\phi = 1$, a peak value of 314 Pa obtains, with a minimum value of -312 Pa. It can be seen that the pressure distribution in this lightly loaded contact is very similar to the theoretical full Sommerfeld solution.

These two behaviours can be explained as follows. In the heavily loaded contact, the bubbles are expanding in the sub-ambient region and are acting to raise the pressures in this area. Figure 8 illustrates this clearly, where the radius ratio is plotted against the position in the contact. The bubbles grow by approximately 60% in the outlet region of the conjunction, and do not reach the critical value in the arrangement studied.

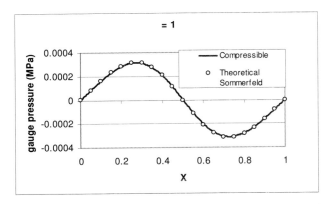

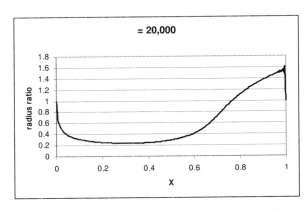

Figure 7: Pressure distribution in a lightly-loaded, bubbly contact

Figure 8. Variation of bubble radius in a heavily-loaded, bubbly contact

The presence of entrained bubbles clearly produces pressure profiles which accord with those obtained in practice. It is possible, therefore, that a full understanding of the mechanisms of gaseous cavitation should include the effects of gas entrainment. Further work will be pursued to examine this concept.

4. CONCLUSIONS

This paper has examined the behaviour of a hydrodynamic bearing where the lubricant contains entrained bubbles of air. It is shown that a critical lubricant pressure can be determined, below which bubbles will expand uncontrollably and raise the pressures in the outlet region of the bearing. However, a solution of the Reynolds equation with compressibility included, demonstrates that in the configurations examined, the bubbles expand sufficiently to keep the minimum pressure above this critical value. Indeed, in heavily-loaded configurations the bubbles expand and contract so much that the pressure profile closely resembles that predicted using the Reynolds boundary condition. In very lightly loaded contacts, the bubbles grow or shrink very little, and the lubricant behaves as an incompressible one. It seems possible, therefore, that entrained bubbles could be part of the mechanism of gaseous cavitation in hydrodynamic bearings. Further work will be pursued to examine this.

REFERENCES

[1]   Dowson, D and Taylor, C M, "Cavitation in Plain Bearings", *I Mech E Cavitation Conference*, Edinburgh, Sept 1974.
[2]   Smith, E H, , "The Influence of Surface Tension on Bearings Lubricated with Bubbly Liquids", *Jour Lubric Technol*, Vol 102, 1980, pp 91-96

Lubricant Additives Effects on the Hydrodynamic Lubrication of Misaligned Conical-Cylindrical Bearings

A. A. Elsharkawy

Department of Mechanical Engineering, College of Engineering & Petroleum
Kuwait University, P. O. Box 5969, Safat 13060, Kuwait

ABSTRACT

A non-Newtonian rheological model to theoretically investigate the effects of lubricant additives on the performance of misaligned conical-cylindrical bearings is proposed in this study. In this model, the non-Newtonian behavior resulting from blending the lubricant with polymer additives is simulated by the Stokes couple stress fluid model. The formed boundary layer at the bearing surface is described through the use of a hypothetical porous medium layer that adheres to the bearing surface. The Brinkman-extended Darcy equations are utilized to model the flow in the porous region. A stress jump boundary condition is applied at the porous media/fluid film interface. The misalignment of the cylinder rod is also considered. A modified form of the Reynolds equation is derived and solved numerically using a finite difference scheme. The effects of bearing geometry and non-Newtonian behavior of the lubricant on the steady-state performance characteristics such as pressure distribution, load carrying capacity, and coefficient of friction are presented and discussed. The results showed that lubricant additives significantly increase the load carrying capacity and reduce the coefficient of friction as compared to the Newtonian lubricants. Furthermore, the misalignment of the piston rod has significant effects on the performance of conical-cylindrical bearings.

Keywords: Conical-Cylindrical Bearing; Non-Newtonian Fluids; Lubricant Additives; Hydrodynamic Lubrication; Porous Media.

1. INTRODUCTION

Figure 1 shows the physical configuration of a conventional conical-cylindrical bearing, which is usually used in electro-hydraulic servo cylinder to improve control accuracy, eliminate static friction, and increase the normal load carrying capacity. This type of bearings involves a combination of slider and journal bearings. Yang and Jeng (2001) studied the thermal effects including isothermal, adiabatic, and thermohydrodynamic boundary conditions on the performance of this type of bearing. They extended their study to investigate the effects of non-Newtonian behavior of the lubricant using a power-law fluid model (Yang and Jeng, 2003). Their results showed that the normal load carrying capacity is enhanced by higher values of flow behavior index, higher eccentricity ratios and larger misalignment factors. Yang and Jeng (2004) further extended their previous work to incorporate the variation of the lubricant viscosity with pressure and temperature into the thermohydrodynamic lubrication analysis. To the author's knowledge not many other studies on the lubrication of the cylindrical-conical bearings are available in the literature. The present study is an attempt to investigate how much the selection of the proper lubricant as a design variable can influence the performance of this type of bearing.

Additives are used extensively in lubricants to improve lubricating properties. One of the roles of the additives is to thicken the protective lubricant film thickness, through the mechanism of hydrodynamics. However, another important function of an additive is the formation or enhancement, by either a chemical or physical activity, of a boundary layer on the opposing surfaces. This layer protects the surfaces from degradation and reduces the shear or frictional force required to slide relative to each other. Oliver (1988) showed experimentally that an additive of dissolved polymer in a lubricant improves the load carrying capacity and reduces the friction coefficient in short journal bearings. Spikes (1994) examined base oil blended with some additives to balance the behavior of the lubricant in elastohydrodynamically-lubricated contacts and consequently reduce friction and surface damage. Furthermore, Durack et al. (2003) observed a substantial reduction of friction in engine journal bearings when oil fortifier (oil additives) was added to the base oil.

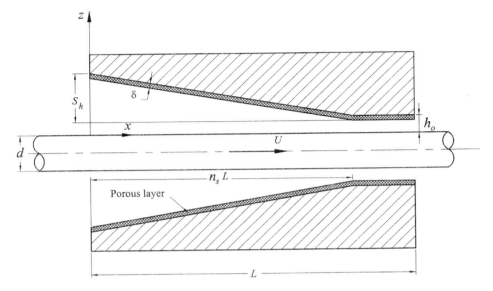

Figure 1. Conical-cylindrical bearing configuration

Non-Newtonian behavior is generally a function of the structural complexity of fluids. Lubricants containing additives should be treated as non-Newtonian fluids. In the literature, two models are widely used to describe the non-Newtonian behavior of the lubricant in hydrodynamically lubricated conformal conjunctions. The first rheological model is the well-known power-law fluid model [Dien and Elrod (1983), Li et al. (1996), Yang and Jeng (2003)]. The second model consists of the couple stress fluid model based on micro-continuum theory derived by Stokes (1966). Stokes theory is the simplest generalization of the classical theory of fluids, which allows for the polar effects such as the presence of non-symmetric stress tensor, the couple stresses and the body couples. The couple stresses might be expected to appear in noticeable magnitudes in liquids containing additives with large molecules. For this model, the continuity and momentum equations governing the motion of the lubricant in the absence of body forces and body couples are

$$\nabla \cdot V = 0 \tag{1}$$

$$\rho \frac{DV}{Dt} = -\nabla p + \mu \nabla^2 V - \eta \nabla^4 V \tag{2}$$

where V is the velocity vector, ρ is the density, p is the pressure, μ is the classical viscosity coefficient, and η is a material constant for couple stress with the dimensions of momentum. Many investigators have used couple stress theory of fluids to study static and dynamic characteristics of various bearings [for example see: Gupta and Sharma (1988), Lin et al. (2001) Wang et al. (2002)]. These studies have led to the predictions such as larger load carrying capacity, lower coefficient of friction, and delayed time of approach compared with Newtonian case.

From slow squeezing of a thin film between two crossed molecularly smooth mica cylinders, Chan and Horn (1985) found that the squeeze rate can be predicted by the classical Reynolds equation down to about 30 nm. They obtained good correlation between theory and experiment by simply adding a fictitious rigid layer of 0.7 nm to the mica surface. Based on these experimental observations, Tichy (1995) was able to develop a rheological model, which can be applied to boundary lubrication. He considered the fictitious rigid layer considered by Chan and Horn (1985) as a solid porous layer adhered to the solid surfaces due to the lubricant microstructure. Darcy's law, which states that the local flow velocity relative to the porous medium is proportional to the pressure gradient, and inversely proportional to the viscosity, was used to describe the fluid flow through the porous medium. Li (1999) modified Tichy's model by using the Brinkman extended Darcy model, which takes into account the viscous shear effects and the viscous damping effects, to describe fluid flow in a porous medium. The Brinkman-extended Darcy model is also appropriate for thin porous media with high permeability. A shear stress jump condition was applied at the porous/fluid film interface. The experimental observations by Nield (1991) and the study of Ochoa-Tapia and Witaker (1995) supported the idea of inclusion of the stress jump boundary condition at the porous media/fluid film interface.

In the present study, both the porous media model, which was developed by Tichy (1995) and modified by Li (1999), and the couple stress model are utilized to study the effects of lubricant additives on the performance of misaligned conical-cylindrical bearings. A modified form of Reynolds equation using the Brinkman extended-Darcy model with the stress jump boundary condition at the porous media/fluid interface and the couple stress model is derived. A finite difference scheme is implemented to solve for the pressure distribution within the lubricated conjunction. The effects of bearing geometry and non-Newtonian behavior of the lubricant on the steady-state performance characteristics such as pressure distribution, load carrying capacity, and coefficient of friction factor are presented and discussed.

2. MATHEMATICAL FORMULATION

The geometric details of a conical-cylindrical bearing system of length L, shoulder height s_h, shoulder length ratio n_s, and outlet film thickness h_o are illustrated in Fig. 1. The cylinder rod is moving axially to the right with velocity U without circumferential rotation. A porous layer of thickness δ is attached to the stationary bearing surface. The porous film thickness is assumed to be smaller than the thickness of the lubricant. Physically, the thickness of the porous layer represents presumably known molecular scale of the lubricant, Tichy (1995). The fluid inertial forces are negligible with respect to viscous effects. The flow in the oil film clearance is steady, laminar, and unidirectional. The porous matrix is homogenous and isotropic and the variation of the pressure across the porous liner and the fluid film is negligible. Thermal effects are not considered in the present study.

The lubricant flow in the film region ($0 \leq z \leq h - \delta$) obeys Stokes couple stress model (1966). Under the usual assumptions of lubrication applicable to thin films, the flow equations in this case can be written as

$$\frac{\partial p}{\partial x} = \mu \frac{\partial^2 u}{\partial z^2} - \eta \frac{\partial^4 u}{\partial z^4} \ , \qquad \frac{\partial p}{\partial y} = \mu \frac{\partial^2 v}{\partial z^2} - \eta \frac{\partial^4 v}{\partial z^4} , \qquad \frac{\partial p}{\partial z} = 0 \qquad (3)$$

where p is the pressure in the film region, u and v are the flow velocities in the x and y directions within the film region, respectively.

The lubricant flow in the porous region ($h - \delta \leq z \leq h$) is governed by the Brinkman equation, Brinkman (1984), which accounts for the viscous shear effects and the viscous damping effects (Darcy resistance)

$$\frac{\partial p^*}{\partial x} = -\frac{\mu}{k} u^* + \mu^* \frac{\partial^2 u^*}{\partial z^2}, \qquad \frac{\partial p^*}{\partial y} = -\frac{\mu}{k} v^* + \mu^* \frac{\partial^2 v^*}{\partial z^2}, \qquad \frac{\partial p^*}{\partial z} = 0 \qquad (4)$$

where μ^* and μ are the effective viscosity of the lubricant within the porous layer and the film region, respectively, p^* is the pressure of the lubricant within the porous layer, u^* and v^* are the local mean (ensemble-averaged) velocities in the x and y directions within the porous layer, respectively.

The boundary conditions are that the velocities match at the porous medium/fluid film interface, that the coupled stress vanishes at the interface, and that no-slip boundary conditions at the impermeable surface:

(a) at the piston rod-fluid film interface ($z = 0$): $u = U$, $v = 0$ $\qquad\qquad\qquad$ (5)

(b) at the porous liner-fluid film interface ($z = h - \delta$): $u* = u$, $v* = v$, $\mu * \dfrac{du*}{dz} - \mu \dfrac{du}{dz} = \beta \dfrac{\mu}{\sqrt{k}} u *$,

$$\frac{\partial^2 u}{\partial z^2} = 0, \ \frac{\partial^2 v}{\partial z^2} = 0 \tag{6}$$

where β is the stress jump parameter.

(c) at the rigid housing-porous layer interface ($z = h$): $u* = v* = 0$ \hfill (7)

From Eqs. (3) to (7), the flow velocities can be derived in the following dimensionless form:

(a) within the fluid film ($0 \le Z \le H - \Delta$):

$$\bar{u} = 1 + \frac{Z}{H-\Delta}(F_1 - 1) - \frac{\partial P}{\partial X}\left[\left(\frac{Z}{H-\Delta}\right)F_2 - \frac{Z^2}{2} + \frac{Z(H-\Delta)}{2} \ -\bar{\ell}^2 + \bar{\ell}^2 \frac{\sinh\left(\frac{H-\Delta-Z}{\bar{\ell}}\right) + \sinh\left(\frac{Z}{\bar{\ell}}\right)}{\sinh\left(\frac{H-\Delta}{\bar{\ell}}\right)}\right] \tag{8}$$

$$\bar{v} = -2\lambda \frac{\partial P}{\partial \theta}\left[\left(\frac{Z}{H-\Delta}\right)F_2 - \frac{Z^2}{2} + \frac{Z(H-\Delta)}{2} \ -\bar{\ell}^2 + \bar{\ell}^2 \frac{\sinh\left(\frac{H-\Delta-Z}{\bar{\ell}}\right) + \sinh\left(\frac{Z}{\bar{\ell}}\right)}{\sinh\left(\frac{H-\Delta}{\bar{\ell}}\right)}\right] \tag{9}$$

(b) within the porous layer ($H - \Delta \le Z \le H$)

$$\bar{u}* = F_1 \sinh\left(\frac{H-Z}{\alpha\sqrt{K}}\right) / \sinh\left(\frac{\Delta}{\alpha\sqrt{K}}\right) - \frac{\partial P}{\partial X}\left[KC_1(Z) + F_2 \sinh\left(\frac{H-Z}{\alpha\sqrt{K}}\right) / \sinh\left(\frac{\Delta}{\alpha\sqrt{K}}\right)\right] \tag{10}$$

$$\bar{v}* = -2\lambda \frac{\partial P}{\partial \theta}\left[KC_1(Z) + F_2 \sinh\left(\frac{H-Z}{\alpha\sqrt{K}}\right) / \sinh\left(\frac{\Delta}{\alpha\sqrt{K}}\right)\right] \tag{11}$$

where

$$C_1(Z) = 1 - \left[\sinh\left(\frac{H-Z}{\alpha\sqrt{K}}\right) - \sinh\left(\frac{H-\Delta-Z}{\alpha\sqrt{K}}\right)\right] / \sinh\left(\frac{\Delta}{\alpha\sqrt{K}}\right) \tag{12}$$

$$F_1 = \frac{1}{(H-\Delta)\left[\frac{\alpha}{\sqrt{K}}\coth\left(\frac{\Delta}{\alpha\sqrt{K}}\right) - \frac{\beta}{\sqrt{K}} + \frac{1}{H-\Delta}\right]} \tag{13}$$

$$F_2 = \frac{\alpha\sqrt{K}\left[\coth\left(\frac{\Delta}{\alpha\sqrt{K}}\right) - \text{csch}\left(\frac{\Delta}{\alpha\sqrt{K}}\right)\right] + \frac{H-\Delta}{2}}{\frac{\alpha}{\sqrt{K}}\coth\left(\frac{\Delta}{\alpha\sqrt{K}}\right) - \frac{\beta}{\sqrt{K}} + \frac{1}{(H-\Delta)}} + \frac{\bar{\ell}\left[\text{csch}\left(\frac{H-\Delta}{\bar{\ell}}\right) - \coth\left(\frac{H-\Delta}{\bar{\ell}}\right)\right]}{\frac{\alpha}{\sqrt{K}}\coth\left(\frac{\Delta}{\alpha\sqrt{K}}\right) - \frac{\beta}{\sqrt{K}} + \frac{1}{(H-\Delta)}} \tag{14}$$

where $H = h/h_o$, $Z = z/h_o$, $\lambda = L/d$, $P = ph_o^2/\mu UL$, $\bar{u}* = u*/U$, $\bar{v}* = v*/U$, $\bar{u} = u/U$, $\bar{v} = v/U$, $\bar{\ell} = \left(\sqrt{\eta/\mu}\right)/h_o$, $\alpha = (\mu*/\mu)^{1/2}$, $K = k/h_o^2$, $\Delta = \delta/h_o$.

It is worth noting that, since the piston rod is moving in the axial direction and there is no rotation in the circumferential direction, it is expected that the main flow will be in axial direction. Furthermore, the other velocity components will be much smaller than the velocity in the axial direction. The couple stress parameter $\bar{\ell}$ arises from the presence of polar additives in the lubricant. The dimension of the ratio

(η/μ) is of length squared and this length is of the same order of magnitude as the chain length of the polar additives in the lubricant. Hence, the couple stress parameter $\bar{\ell}$ provides the mechanism of interaction of the fluid with the bearing geometry. The additives effects are more prominent when either the chain length of the polar additives is large or the minimum film thickness is small, i. e., when $\bar{\ell}$ is large. The couple stress parameter can be obtained experimentally, Stokes (1984), and it can be predicted from the pressure measurements using the inverse technique proposed by Elsharkawy and Guedouar (2001).

The bearing oil film thickness varies along axial and circumferential directions depending on the geometric configuration of the bearing, and the effects of shoulder length ratio, eccentricity ratio, and tilted angles. The geometry of eccentric and asymmetric film thickness in this study is illustrated in Fig. 2, where e is the eccentricity, γ_1 and γ_2 are the titled angles, and $x = 0$ is the reference point at the oil entrance. From Figs. 1 and 2, the film thickness equation can be written in the following dimensionless form

$$H = \begin{cases} 1+\varepsilon\cos\theta+\dfrac{1}{\bar{h}_o}\left(1-\dfrac{X}{n_s}\right)-\dfrac{X}{\bar{h}_o}(\sigma_1\cos\theta-\sigma_2\sin\theta) & 0 \le X \le n_s \\[4mm] 1+\varepsilon\cos\theta-\dfrac{X}{\bar{h}_o}(\sigma_1\cos\theta-\sigma_2\sin\theta) & n_s \le X \le 1 \end{cases} \tag{15}$$

where $X = x/L$, $\theta = 2y/d$, $\varepsilon = e/h_o$, $\bar{h}_o = h_o/s_h$, $\sigma_1 = (L/s_h)\tan\gamma_1$, $\sigma_2 = (L/s_h)\tan\gamma_2$. From the geometry of the bearing, the misalignment factor σ_1 should be less than $\bar{h}_o(1+\varepsilon-\Delta)$ to prevent the contact between the piston rod and the bearing surface at the trailing edge of the bearing.

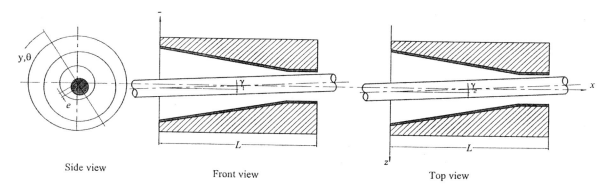

Side view   Front view   Top view

Figure 2. Eccentric and asymmetric geometries

Substituting Eqs. (8) to (11) into the continuity equation and integrating across the film thickness using the boundary conditions, Eqs. (5) and (7), the modified Reynolds equation can be written in the following dimensionless form

$$\frac{\partial}{\partial X}\left[G\frac{\partial P}{\partial X}\right]+4\lambda^2\frac{\partial}{\partial\theta}\left[G\frac{\partial P}{\partial\theta}\right]=6\frac{\partial B}{\partial X} \tag{16}$$

where

$$G = 12F_2H^* + 12K(\Delta-2H^*) + 6(H-\Delta)F_2 + (H-\Delta)^3 - 12(H-\Delta)\bar{\ell}^2 + 24\bar{\ell}^3\frac{\cosh\left(\dfrac{H-\Delta}{\bar{\ell}}\right)-1}{\sinh\left(\dfrac{H-\Delta}{\bar{\ell}}\right)} \tag{17}$$

$$B = (H-\Delta)(F_1+1)+2F_1H^* \tag{18}$$

$$H^* = \alpha\sqrt{K}\left[\coth\left(\frac{\Delta}{\alpha\sqrt{K}}\right)-\operatorname{csch}\left(\frac{\Delta}{\alpha\sqrt{K}}\right)\right] \tag{19}$$

If $\bar{\ell} \to 0$, and $\Delta \to 0$, then $G \to H^3$, $B \to H$, and Eq. (16) reduces to the classical Reynolds equation. The following boundary conditions are used when solving the modified Reynolds equation: $P(0,\theta) = P(1,\theta) = 0$ (in motion direction), $P(X,0) = P(X,2\pi)$ (in the circumferential direction). Furthermore, the pressure is constrained to be positive throughout the oil film.

Equation (16) can be solved numerically using a finite difference scheme. The Tri-diagonal Matrix Algorithm (TDMA) was used along X-direction with a line-by-line sweep in the θ-direction to obtain the pressure distribution within the lubricant film. For the results presented in this paper, the mesh sizes were 123 points in the X-direction, 81 points in the θ-direction. The iterative scheme will continue until the convergence criteria is satisfied. The load carrying capacity, and the friction force are obtained by integrating the pressure, and the shear stress fields over the surface of the piston rod, respectively.

3. RESULTS

The present model contains five parameters to describe the non-Newtonian behavior of the lubricant: couple stress parameter $\bar{\ell}$, dimensionless porous layer thickness Δ, stress jump parameter β, viscosity ratio parameter α, and permeability parameter K. The design parameters that describe the bearing configuration are: shoulder length ratio n_s, length to diameter-ratio λ, dimensionless outlet film thickness $\bar{h}_o$, eccentricity ratio ε, and misalignment factors σ_1 and σ_2. Results presented in this section were obtained for $n_s = 0.8$, $\lambda = 1$, $\bar{h}_o = 0.8$, $\sigma_2 = 0.05$. To verify the accuracy of the present model, the oil film pressure distribution is compared with the existing theoretical results. Figure 3 shows a comparison between the pressure distributions, at the section of maximum pressure, for three different cases obtained from the present analysis when $\bar{\ell} \to 0$ and $\Delta \to 0$ (i.e. Newtonian lubricant) and those reported in Yang and Jeng (2003) when the power law exponent $n \to 1$. Results exhibit good agreement although thermal effects are not considered in the present study. Considering the thermal effects will lead to a reduction in the oil viscosity within the conjunction resulting in a reduction in the film pressure.

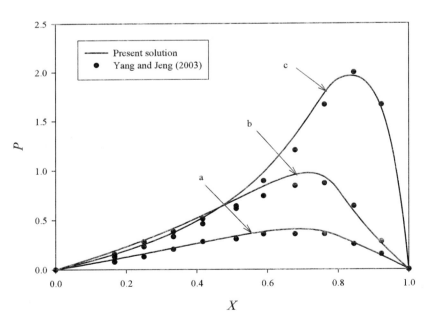

Figure 3. Comparison between pressure distributions for three different cases obtained from the present analysis when $\bar{\ell} \to 0$ and $\Delta \to 0$ (i.e. Newtonian lubricant) and those reported in Yang and Jeng (2003) when the power law exponent $n \to 1$.

(a): $\varepsilon = 0$, $\sigma_1 = 0.1$, $(\theta = 0^\circ)$,

(b): $\varepsilon = 0.6$, $\sigma_1 = 0.1$, $(\theta = 180^\circ)$, (c): $\varepsilon = 0$, $\sigma_1 = 0.6$, $(\theta = 0^\circ)$.

Figures 4 and 5 show the variations of the dimensionless load carrying capacity $W_z = w_z h_o^2 / (\mu URL^2)$, and the friction factor $\bar{f} = fL / h_0$ as functions of misalignment factor σ_1 for various values of the couple stress parameter $\bar{\ell}$ with $\varepsilon = 0.1$, $\Delta = 0.2$, $\beta = 0.5$, $K = 0.001$, and $\alpha = 1$. It is observed that the load carrying capacity is minimum and the friction factor is maximum when $\sigma_1 = 0.08$. For $\sigma_1 > 0.08$, the load carrying capacity increases and the friction factor decreases as the misalignment factor σ_1 increases. This can be explained from the minimum film thickness equation at the trailing edge, which can be derived from the geometry of the bearing shown in Fig. 2 and can be written as $H_{\min} = \varepsilon - \sigma_1 / \bar{h}_o + 1 - \Delta$. The minimum film thickness $H_{\min}$ has its maximum value when $\sigma_1 = \varepsilon \bar{h}_o$ and if $\sigma_1 > \varepsilon \bar{h}_o$ its value decreases by increasing σ_1. The results presented in these figures show the significant effect of the tilt angle γ_1 and the eccentricity of the piston rod on the performance of the cylindrical-conical bearing. Furthermore, increasing the couple stress parameter $\bar{\ell}$ increases the load carrying capacity and decreases the coefficient of friction.

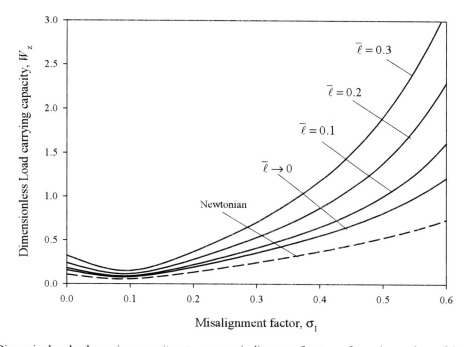

Figure 4. Dimensionless load carrying capacity W_z versus misalignment factor σ_1 for various values of the couple stress parameter $\bar{\ell}$ when $\varepsilon = 0.1$, $\Delta = 0.2$, $\beta = 0.5$, $K = 0.001$, $\alpha = 1$.

The effects of the thickness and permeability of the porous layer (Δ and K) on the variations of the dimensionless load carrying capacity W_z, and friction factor $\bar{f}$ with the misalignment factor σ_1 are depicted in Figs. 6 and 7. The couple stress parameter was held fixed at $\bar{\ell} = 0.2$. It is observed that load carrying capacity is strongly increased by the layer thickness and decreased by porosity. The load increase is much more pronounced at higher values of the misalignment factor σ_1. The friction factor is strongly decreased by the layer effect and slightly increased by porosity. Similar results in the case of slider bearing were reported in Tichy (1995). It can be concluded that additives that increase the lubricant ability to adhere to the bearing surface and form a thin solid layer will significantly enhance the load carrying capacity and reduce the friction coefficient.

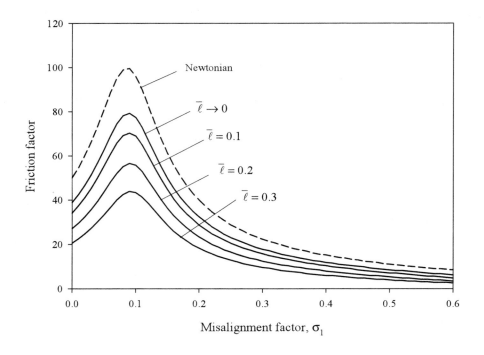

Figure 5. Friction factor versus misalignment factor σ_1 for various values of the couple stress parameter $\bar{\ell}$ when $\varepsilon = 0.1$, $\Delta = 0.2$, $\beta = 0.5$, $K = 0.001$, $\alpha = 1$.

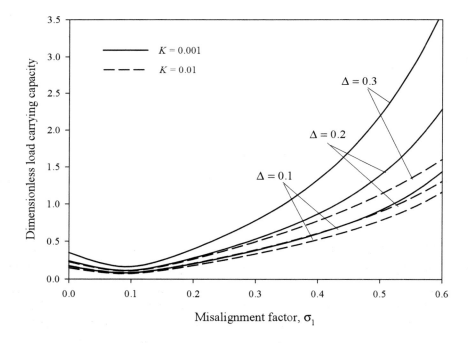

Figure 6. Dimensionless load carrying capacity W_z versus misalignment factor σ_1 for various values of porous layer thickness Δ when $\varepsilon = 0.1$, $\bar{\ell} = 0.2$, $\beta = 0.5$, $\alpha = 1$.

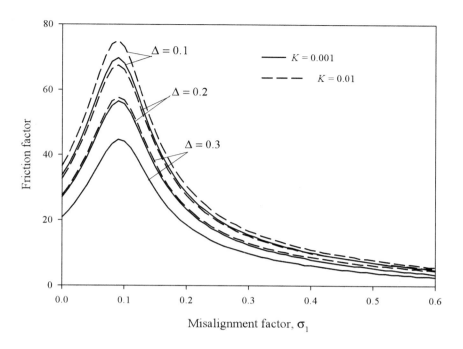

Figure 7. Friction factor versus misalignment factor σ_1 for various values of porous layer thickness Δ when $\varepsilon = 0.1$, $\bar{\ell} = 0.2$, $\beta = 0.5$, $\alpha = 1$.

Figures 8 and 9 show the variations of the dimensionless load carrying capacity W_z and friction factor $\bar{f}$ with the dimensionless porous layer thickness Δ for three values of the viscosity ratio parameter α and two values of the stress jump parameter β. Solid curves in the figures correspond to $\beta = 0.5$ and dashed curves to $\beta = 0.9$. The other parameters were held fixed at $\varepsilon = 0.0$, $\bar{\ell} = 0.3$, $\sigma_1 = 0.4$, $K = 0.001$. It can be seen that as the porous layer attached to the bearing surface becomes thicker, the load carrying capacity increases and the friction coefficient decreases significantly. Therefore, additives that form a thicker boundary layer attached to the bearing surface will improve the lubrication performance of conical-cylindrical bearings. The viscosity ratio parameter α indicates the value of the lubricant viscosity within the boundary layer μ^* relative to the viscosity within the fluid film μ (i.e., $\alpha = 1$ means $\mu^* = \mu$ and $\alpha = 2$ means $\mu^* = 4\mu$). Physically, it is expected that the viscosity of the lubricant within the porous layer will be higher than the viscosity of the lubricant within the fluid film (i.e. $\alpha > 1$). The results presented in Figs. 8 and 9 show the effect of the viscosity ratio parameter on the load carrying capacity and the friction factor. It is observed that as α increases, the load carrying capacity increases and the friction factor decreases. It is expected that the stress jump parameter β will have significant influence on the velocity at the interface between the porous layer and the fluid film and consequently will affect the lubrication performance of the bearing. It can be seen from the figures that the load carrying capacity for $\beta = 0.5$ is higher than that for $\beta = 0.9$. The increase in the stress jump parameter provides a decrease in the load capacity and an increase in the coefficient of friction. Similar observations in the case of journal bearings were reported in Chen et al. (2002).

4. CONCLUSIONS

A non-Newtonian rheological model to theoretically investigate the effects of the lubricant additives on the hydrodynamic lubrication of misaligned conical-cylindrical bearings has been presented. The proposed model combines the thin porous media model, which was developed by Tichy (1995) and

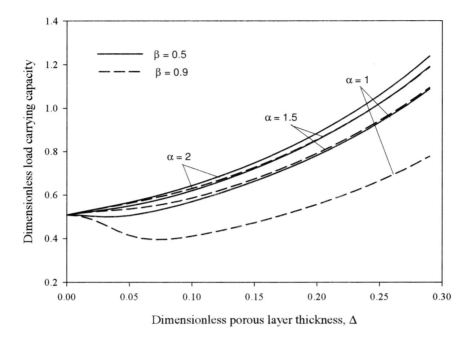

Figure 8. Dimensionless load carrying capacity W_z versus dimensionless porous layer thickness Δ for various values of viscous ratio parameter α when $\varepsilon = 0.0$, $\bar{\ell} = 0.3$, $\sigma_1 = 0.4$, $K = 0.001$.

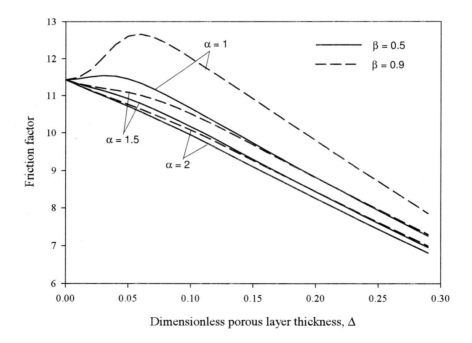

Figure 9. Friction factor versus dimensionless porous layer thickness Δ for various values of viscous ratio parameter α when $\varepsilon = 0.0$, $\bar{\ell} = 0.3$, $\sigma_1 = 0.4$, $K = 0.001$.

refined by Li (1999) to simulate the microstructure of the lubricant, and the couple stress model to incorporate the effects due to the presence of polar additives in the lubricant. A modified form of Reynolds equation has been derived and solved numerically using a finite difference scheme. The present analysis exhibits additive effects through five parameters. These parameters are: couple stress parameter $\bar{\ell}$, dimensionless porous layer thickness Δ, stress jump parameter β, viscosity ratio parameter α, and permeability parameter K. The results showed that additives that increase the lubricant ability to form a thin solid layer adhered to the bearing surface can significantly enhance the load carrying capacity and reduce the friction coefficient. Furthermore, additives with larger chain length molecules can also enhance the load carrying capacity and reduce the coefficient of friction. The misalignment of the piston rod has significant influence on hydrodynamic effect due to wedge action and consequently on the performance characteristics of conical-cylindrical bearings.

5. REFERENCES

[1] Yang, Y. K., and Jeng, M. C. (2001), "Analysis of Thermal Effects on the Misaligned Hydraulic Servo Cylinder," Tribology International, Vol. 34, pp. 95-106.

[2] Yang, Y. K., and Jeng, M. C. (2003), "Thermohydrodynamic Analysis of the Misaligned Conical–Cylindrical Bearing with Non-Newtonian Lubricants," STLE, Tribology Transactions, Vol. 46, No. 2, pp. 161-169.

[3] Yang, Y. K., and Jeng, M. C. (2004), "Analysis of Viscosity Interaction on the Misaligned [4]Conical-Cylindrical Bearing," Tribology International, Vol. 37, pp. 51-60.

[4] Oliver, D. R. (1988), "The Load Enhancement Effects due to Polymer Thickening in a Short Journal Bearing," Journal of Non-Newtonian Mechanics, Vol. 31, pp. 185-196.

[5] Spikes, A. H. (1994), "The Behavior of Lubricants in Contacts: Current Understanding and Future Possibilities," J. Proc. Instn. Mech. Engrs., Vol. 28, pp. 3-15.

[6] Durak, E., Kurbanoglu, C., Biyiklioglu, A., and Kaleli H. (2003), "Measurement of Friction Force and Effects of Oil Fortifier in Engine Journal Bearings Under Dynamic Loading Conditions," Tribology International, Vol. 36, pp. 599-607.

[7] Dien, I. K., and Elrod, H. G. (1983), "A Generalized Steady-State Reynolds Equation for Non-Newtonian Fluids, With Application to Journal Bearings," ASME, Journal of Lubrication Technology, Vol. 105, pp. 385-390.

[8] Li, W. L., Weng, C.I, and Lue, J. I. (1996), "Surface Roughness Effects in Journal Bearings with Non-Newtonian Lubricants," STLE, Tribology Transactions, Vol. 39, No. 4, pp. 819-826.

[9] Stokes, V. K. (1966), "Couple Stresses Fluids," Physics of Fluids, Vol. 9 , pp. 1709-1715.

[10] Gupta, R. S., and Sharma, L. G. (1988), "Analysis of Couple Stress Lubricant in Hydrostatic Thrust Bearing," Wear, Vol. 125, pp. 257-270.

[11] Lin, J. R., Yang, C. B., and Lu, R. F. (2001), "Effects of Couple Stresses in the Cyclic Squeeze Films of Finite Partial Journal Bearings," Tribology International, Vol. 34, pp. 119-125.

[12] Wang, X. L., Zhu, K. Q., and Wen, S. Z. (2002), "On the Performance of Dynamically Loaded Journal Bearings Lubricated with Couple Stress Fluids," Tribology International, Vol. 35, pp. 185-191.

[13] Chan, D. Y. C., and Horn, R. G. (1985), "The Drainage of Thin Liquid Films Between Solid Surfaces," Journal of Chemical Physics, Vol. 83, No. 10, pp. 5311-5324.

[14] Tichy, J. A. (1995), "A Porous Media Model for Thin Film Lubrication," Trans. ASME, Journal of Tribology, Vol. 117, pp. 16-21.

[15] Li, W. L. (1999), "Derivation of Modified Reynolds Equation- A Porous Media Model," Trans. ASME, Journal of Tribology, Vol. 121, pp. 823-829.

[16] Nield, D. A. (1991), "The Limitation of the Brinkman-Forchheimer Equation in Modeling Flow in Saturated Porous Medium and at an Interface," International Journal of Heat and Fluid Flow, Vol. 12, pp. 269-272.

[17] Ochoa-Tapia, J. A., and Whitaker, J. (1995), "Momentum Transfer at the Boundary Between Porous Medium and a Homogenous Fluid I: Theoretical Development," International Journal of Heat and Mass Transfer, Vol. 38, pp. 2635-2646.

[18] Brinkman, H. C. (1984), "A calculation of the Viscous Force Exerted by a Flowing Fluid on a Dense Swarm of Particles," Applied Science Research, A1: 27-34.

[19] Stokes, V. K. (1984), Theories of Fluids with Microstructure- An Introduction, Springer-Verlag, Berlin, Heidelberg, New York, Tokyo.

[20] Elsharkawy, A. A., and Guedouar, L. H. (2001), "An Inverse Solution for Finite Journal Bearings Lubricated with Couple Stress Fluids," Tribology International, Vol. 34, pp. 107-118.

[21] Chen, M. D., Chang, K. M., Lin, J. W., and Li, W. L. (2002), "Lubrication of Journal Bearings-Influence of Stress Jump Condition at the Porous-Media/Fluid Film Interface," Tribology International, Vol. 35, pp. 287-295.

6. SYMBOLS

d	cylinder rod diameter, m
e	eccentricity, m
f	coefficient of friction
h	film thickness, m
h_o	outlet film thickness, m
n_s	shoulder length ratio
k	permeability of bearing material, m^2
L	length in x-direction, m
p	pressure of lubricant film, Pa
$p*$	pressure of the lubricant within the porous layer, Pa
s_h	shoulder height, m
u	velocity of the lubricant film in x-direction, m/s
$u*$	local mean (ensemble-averaged) velocity of the lubricant within the porous matrix in x-direction, m/s
U	axial velocity of the piston rod, m/s
w	velocity of the lubricant film in z-direction.
w_z	load, N.
W_z	dimensionless load, $W_z = w_z h_o^2 /(\mu URL^2)$
v	velocity of the lubricant film in y-direction, m/s
$v*$	local mean (ensemble-averaged) velocity of the lubricant within the porous matrix in y-direction, m/s
x	coordinate system in the moving direction, m
y	coordinate system in circumferential direction, m
z	coordinate system across the film, m
α	viscosity ratio parameter, $\alpha = (\mu*/\mu)^{1/2}$
Δ	dimensionless porous layer thickness, $\Delta = \delta/c$
ε	eccentricity ratio, e/h_o
σ_1, σ_2	misalignment factors
γ_1, γ_2	tilt angles, rad
θ	angular coordinate, $\theta = 2y/d$, rad
μ	viscosity of the lubricant in the film region, Pa s
$\mu*$	effective viscosity of the lubricant in the porous matrix, Pa s
β	stress jump parameter
λ	length-to-diameter ratio, $\lambda = L/d$
δ	porous layer thickness, m

Plenary Session 3
Keynote Address

Chair: Mr. Javier Barriga

The Life Cycle of a Lubricant in an Automotive Engine
M. PRIEST, M. F. FOX

The Life Cycle of a Lubricant in an Automotive Engine

M. Priest, M. F. Fox

School of Mechanical Engineering, The University of Leeds, Leeds, LS2 9JT, UK

ABSTRACT

Life cycle analysis, essentially a "cradle-to-grave" approach, is a technique being ever more frequently applied to a range of engineering applications as environmental concerns and sustainability grow in importance in modern society. Tribology, dealing as it does with efficiency and durability, is an important aspect of life cycle assessment and the automotive sector is an important case study with globally escalating pressures on effective resource utilisation and limiting environmental impact.

The contribution of engine lubricants to sustainability derives directly from their performance requirements to reduce friction (reduce energy consumption), control wear (conserve resources by extending engine life) and increase oil-drain intervals (dramatically extending service life to conserve oil resources). Tribology is key to establishing the optimum useful life of an engine oil and to determining how complex and high quality an engine oil needs to be; simpler oils are more amenable to recycling and are less harmful to the environment through exhaust emissions and final disposal. Ongoing research at the institution of the authors is helping to answer these crucial questions and is discussed through exemplars in this paper.

Keywords: life cycle analysis, automotive, tribology, engine, lubricant, fuel economy, durability, extended oil drain.

1. INTRODUCTION

Life Cycle Analysis (LCA) attempts to objectively analyse the environmental impact of an operation or system [1]. It arises from the concept of "sustainability" developed by International Conferences on the World Environment held in Kyoto and Rio de Janeiro where national governments committed themselves to reducing environmental degradation of the world and move towards a sustainable lifestyle. LCA is increasingly applied to assess the environmental impacts of engineering applications and their implications for sustainability. A complete LCA of a process seeks to deal with all of the contributing operations which come together to make that process work, as illustrated in Figure 1 [2]. Whilst the concept of LCA is simple, an overall analysis is complex and very few analyses have ever been truly completed. Nevertheless, the concept is useful and informative when applied to current issues such as fuel efficiency and lubrication of automobiles.

A very important environmental impact is the number of motor vehicles in use, their construction and consumption of fuel. In 2005 in the UK, there were 33 million motor vehicles and a national population of 60 million people [3]. From the same data source it can be observed that in 2002, there were 533 million road vehicles in service in Europe, Japan and the USA. Furthermore, the main competitor to the reciprocating internal combustion engine, the fuel cell, is developing at a far slower pace than originally anticipated. Our focus in the medium term must therefore remain upon optimising the performance of the reciprocating internal combustion engine to meet environmental, resource utilisation and customer demands.

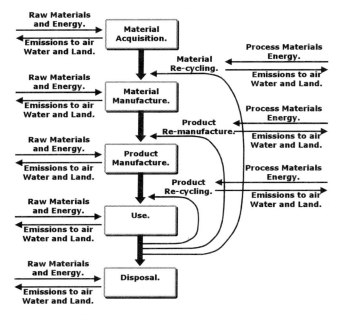

Figure 1. Life Cycle Analysis, after [2]

The technology, legislative and consumer drivers of fuel and lubricant consumption are complex, as evidenced by recent reviews by Ford [4] and General Motors [5]. What is clear, however, is that tribology has a central role in the efficient use of energy and the durability of such machines by effective lubrication. Figure 2 is an attempt to overview the tribology of the reciprocating internal combustion engine using a modified Stribeck diagram. This is a plot of two non-dimensional groupings: the coefficient of friction (μ) on the ordinate and the specific film thickness ratio (λ) on the abscissa. The specific film thickness is defined as the ratio of the film thickness (calculated through the application of classical thin film analysis taking the surfaces to be smooth) to the composite surface roughness of the two bounding solids.

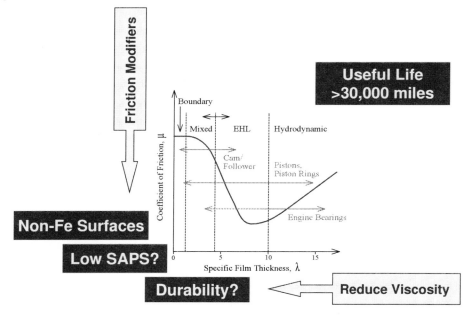

Figure 2. Engine Lubricant Trends on a Modified Stribeck Diagram

The regimes of lubrication conventionally associated with the major tribological components of the engine, namely the piston and piston rings, cam/followers and the engine bearings (on the crankshaft and camshaft), are shown in Figure 2 [6]. These components rely upon different modes of lubrication for satisfactory performance, indeed each may experience more than one form of lubrication during one cycle, and they must all be lubricated by one single engine oil. This makes the task of the tribologist very complex in attempting to improve the performance and environmental impact of the engine. For example, recent years have seen dramatic reductions in the viscosity of engine oils to reduce the hydrodynamic friction losses associated with the pistons, piston rings and engine bearings. However this lowers the general levels of specific film thickness for these components with consequent concerns for increased wear and inferior durability, highlighted in Figure 2. At the same time the lubrication of the cam/followers has been pushed more towards the boundary lubrication regime with a greater dependency on surface active friction modifiers to lower friction and anti-wear additives to protect the surfaces.

In parallel, environmental pollution concerns and the functional requirements of catalytic exhaust aftertreatment devices have placed major restrictions on engine lubricant formulations with the demand for low SAPS (sulphated ash, phosphorous and sulphur) products. Ironically, phosphorus and sulphur are key components of well-established anti-wear and friction modifier additives for engine oils, such as zinc dialkyldithiophosphate (ZDDP) and molybdenum dithiocarbamate (MoDTC). Further complications are the growing use of surfaces and coatings in engines that do not contain any iron when most surface active additives in engine lubricants are specifically designed to function on iron-rich surfaces and also environmental and customer demands to increase the usage period or service interval between oil changes. In effect, the problem of lubricant formulation is a classic design compromise with many competing and contradictory factors.

2. LIFE CYCLE ANALYSIS

2.1. Inputs and Outputs

The LCA of lubricating oils needs an analysis of the inputs and outputs, as shown in Figure 1. The global input of all lubricants, including industrial oils and hydraulic fluids, is approximately 37 Million tonnes per annum (Mt/pa); of this UK consumption is approximately 0.75Mt/pa. With improvements in formulation giving more effective and long-lasting lubrication, the global trend is level or slightly decreasing with time. Increased motor vehicle numbers, the major use of lubricants, has been offset by increased service intervals. Lubricants have made, and continue to make, a major contribution to sustainability. In 1950 a family car required 9 litres of engine lubricant, to be changed every 1600 km with different winter and summer grades, plus transmission lubricants. Currently, a similar car requires around 5 litres of lubricant to be changed every 30,000 km, often including the transmission fluids. Service intervals continue to increase with 50,000 km service intervals readily achievable. Heavy duty construction and truck vehicle manufacturers have set a target of 400,000 km service intervals. In these ways, lubricants have responded to the first stage of the European Union's 'Waste Hierarchy Strategy', shown schematically in Figure 3, in reducing 'Use' by reducing consumption [2].

2.2. Waste Hierarchy and Recycling

In addition to drastically reducing consumption, lubricants contribute to sustainability in the Waste Hierarchy Pyramid of Figure 3 by reducing friction and wear and also, at the end of their useful life, by being recycled.

Whilst developments in lubricant formulation have drastically extended their useful service intervals and reduced wear, the lubricant must eventually be replaced. Of the 0.75Mt/pa consumed in the UK, only around 0.3-0.4 Mt/pa of lubricant is recovered. Whilst in the past recycled lubricant could be used after minimal 'refining', as Recycled Fuel Oil (RFO), with a £40/t fuel excise rebate, this route has been blocked by removal of the rebate and the use of RFO banned except in specialist incinerators requiring a specific authorisation under the Control of Pollution Act (1990). The emphasis is now on recycling used lubricants as base oils. In the past, the low cost of base oils, say £190/t, undermined recycled base oil at £200/t. This has now changed and substantial recycling facilities have developed in Europe and are beginning to open in the UK.

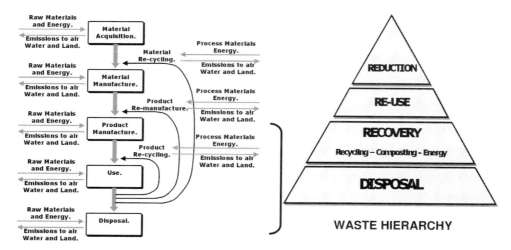

Figure 3. Life Cycle Analysis and Waste Hierarchy Pyramid, after [2]

Of the three separate techniques of recycling lubricants into base oil, namely acid treatment and filtration, liquid-liquid extraction and vacuum distillation, the last produces an oil of low odour and colour that is acceptable as a Group I base oil. Hydrogenation/hydrofinishing produces a better quality oil which can be of Group II quality. These facilities require substantial investment, but there is no doubt that they can produce recycled base oils of high quality. The problem is of manufacturer and consumer acceptance. Recycling of base oils is most developed in Europe, where most major automotive manufacturers will accept them when incorporated into lubricant formulations.

Acceptance into the market is the key issue for recycled base oils, as indeed it is for other recycled products which have to face and overcome the perception of being 'second best'. Paper recycling has already faced this issue and overcome it. Recycled base oils now have to face the same challenge. Whilst the technical aspects of their physical properties are well established as being acceptable and within specification, their performance aspects have yet to be extensively tested.

3. INFLUENCE OF TRIBOLOGY

Reflecting on the above considerations, one can distil a number of issues related to LCA of an engine lubricant and the Waste Hierarchy Pyramid, as illustrated in Figure 4. In reducing the quantity of material in use there have been major gains in terms of reduced sump oil volumes and oil consumption in modern engines. Also, as noted previously, oil drain intervals are increasing in all market sectors. All of these contribute significantly to reducing the quantity of material in the LCA. To progress much further, however, requires a quantitative and definitive method to determine the "useful life" of an engine oil. Tribology is crucial here in scientifically establishing criteria to evaluate the deterioration in performance with time of an engine lubricant and thereby defining the end of useful life. Current practice for oil changes revolves around known duty cycles for engine and vehicles and condition monitoring based around historic trends. This is unlikely to produce optimum usage of lubricants as it does not monitor key performance criteria of the oil in any way. It will generally yield very safe results for vehicle performance but undoubtedly produces unnecessarily large quantities of used engine oil with some remaining useful life.

Moving down the pyramid of Figure 4, re-use of engine lubricants is simply not an option due to their poor physical and chemical condition after first use. So in seeking to minimise waste the focus moves down to recycling where logistical and business pressures of collection, processing and disposal of waste come to bear. These pressures could be alleviated somewhat if the original engine lubricants were not so compositionally complex and the industry demanded less in terms of the quality of the re-refined base stock. This raises questions for tribology with respect to the optimum functionality of engine lubricants in terms of base oils and additive treatments.

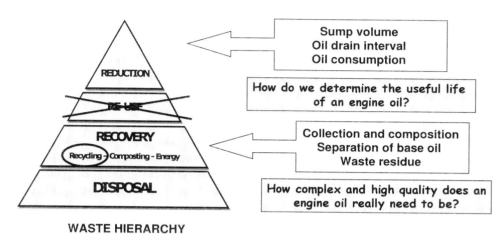

Figure 4. Key Tribological Issues for the Waste Hierarchy Pyramid for Engine Lubricants

The following sections show how ongoing research at the institution of the authors is helping to answer these crucial questions.

3.1. Lubricant Degradation in the Piston Assembly

The useful life of an engine lubricant is undoubtedly determined by the severity of the operating conditions experienced in the piston-piston ring-cylinder system close to the combustion chamber. Within the piston ring pack the lubricant is exposed to the highest temperatures and most chemically aggressive environment offered by the internal combustion engine. Oil can be extracted from this region by drilling a small hole in the back of the piston ring groove and using the gas pressure in the system to push tiny quantities of oil as a mist in a high speed gas flow through a tube to a collection vial outside the engine. Like many experimental techniques this novel methodology, proposed by Saville et al [7], is simple in concept, but very complex in implementation. Several years of development at the institution of the authors has produced a robust and reliable technique to sample oil in this way [e.g. 8, 9].

Assuming that the sump oil is at a temperature below that at which thermal degradation occurs then the engine may be considered as a reactor, shown schematically in Figure 5, where the large volume of oil in the sump is contaminated by the small volume of degraded oil in the piston ring pack when it returns to the sump. The rate of bulk oil degradation in the sump is thereby a function of the quantity of oil passing through and its residence time in the ring pack, the temperature and chemical environment in the ring pack and flow rates between the ring pack and the sump. A full description of this large body of research is beyond the scope of this paper and the reader is referred to Stark et al [8] and Lee et al [9] for further details. Focus here will be on the measurement of carbonyl groups in the oxidised samples using infrared absorption as a measure of degradation, being indicative of ketones and carboxylic acids in the oil, and the calculated total acid number (TAN) that results. In Figure 5 the increase in carbonyl with time for oil samples taken from the ring pack and sump are shown for a highly refined base oil with no additive package, Shell Extra High Viscosity Index (XHVI) 8.2™, which was used for simplicity of chemical analysis at this early stage of the research. The engine used was a Ricardo Hydra single cylinder gasoline research engine based on a General Motors 2.0 L, 4-cylinder production engine (c. 1988) of 86mm bore, 86mm stroke and indirect injection of standard unleaded gasoline. It was operated at 1500 r/min, half load and with sump oil temperature controlled at 70°C for the purpose of the reported test.

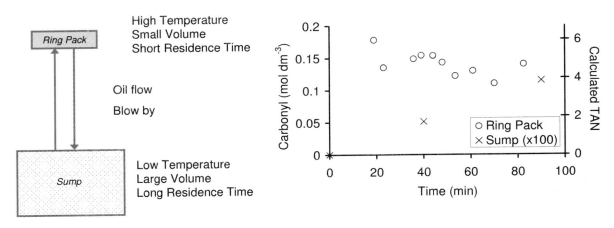

Figure 5. Degradation of Engine Oil with Time in a Gasoline Engine Piston Assembly, after [8]

It can be seen that the carbonyl concentration rises to a high level very quickly in the ring pack and slowly accumulates in the sump oil, which is plotted multiplied by 100 in Figure 5 to enable graphical comparison with the ring pack samples, consistent with the proposed reactor model. In Figure 6, later longer term testing with fully formulated engine oil is shown at the same operating conditions [9]. The carbonyl concentration rises in the ring pack (top ring zone or TRZ) samples as the load is increased, and thereby the temperature and hostility of the environment, and during the aggressive cold start conditions. Again the sump is operating at a reduced level of carbonyl consistent with the reactor model.

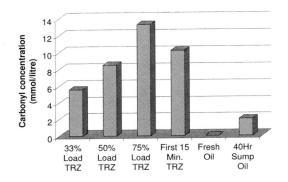

Conditions for six oil samples collected

Oil sample name	Oil sample conditions
33% load TRZ*	33% maximum engine load at 1500 r/min
50% load TRZ	50% maximum engine load at 1500 r/min
75% load TRZ	75% maximum engine load at 1500 r/min
First 15 min	First 15 min from cold start at 1500 r/min
Fresh oil	Fresh Shell Helix Super 15W-40
40 h sump oil	Used sump oil after 40 h at 50% maximum engine load 1500 r/min

*TRZ = top ring zone

Figure 6. Longer Term Degradation of Engine Oil with Time in a Gasoline Engine Piston Assembly, after [9]

Measuring carbonyl and thereby degradation is important, but is far from conclusive as the ramifications for the tribology of the system must be established. One obstacle in this regard is the extremely small volume that is collected using the ring zone sampling system. For example, in the experiments reported in Figure 6 only 25ml of sample was obtained from the top piston ring zone in 40 hours of engine running. Physical and tribological testing must therefore be able to operate with very small quantities of lubricant. Another problem is that the samples are heavily diluted with fuel and its derivatives as shown by gas chromatography in Figure 7(a) for the same samples as Figure 6. The volatiles result from quenching of the combustion process on the cylinder wall and are representative of soot precursors as well as the heavier mass fuel elements [9]. So simply measuring the viscosity of the samples can be quite misleading as any increase in viscosity due to oxidation will be swamped by low viscosity volatile dilution. In Figure 7(b) the frictional performance of the samples in a Plint TE77™ reciprocating tribometer at conditions designed to simulate piston ring and cylinder tribology in the severe portion of the cycle following combustion is shown. There are very clear differences in performance between the samples and in particular it is important to note that the performance of the sump sample is very different from the oil in the top ring zone which actually lubricates this critical part of the engine. The reader is referred to Lee et al [9] for a far more complete consideration of these results and companion tests undertaken on PCS HFRR™ and MTM™ tribometers.

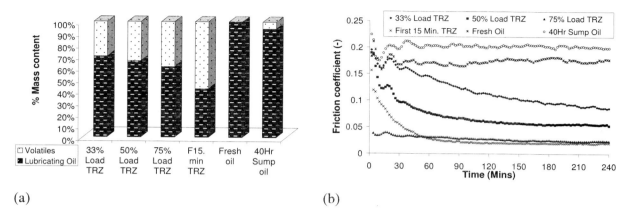

(a)   (b)

Figure 7. Chemical and Tribological Performance of the Oil Samples of Figure 6: (a) Gas chromatography and (b) Plint TE77 reciprocating tribometer (flat cast iron pin on cast iron plate, 2.6MPa, 5mm stroke, 25Hz, 100°C), after [9]

Although there is much research left to do in this field, it has been established that the tribological performance of the engine requires detailed knowledge of the physical, tribological and chemical properties of the actual lubricant within the ring pack of the engine. Simply drawing conclusions from sump oil samples is far from optimum.

3.2. Simpler Engine Oils and Fuel Administered Friction Modifiers

In automotive engines resistance to the motion of the piston within the cylinder is the single largest source of frictional power loss, typically accounting for 40-60% of the mechanical losses of the engine. Fuel economy engine oils of low viscosity have the potential to reduce the losses significantly for the piston skirt sliding against the cylinder wall and for the piston rings when operating with fluid film lubrication. However, the piston rings also experience mixed and boundary lubrication, as indicated in Figure 2, and the extent of this poorer lubrication into the engine cycle from the dead centres increases as the lubricant viscosity falls. So there is a need for effective friction modifiers in fuel economy formulations. As noted previously, there are concurrent demands alongside this for compositionally simpler lubricants that do not poison or inhibit catalytic exhaust aftertreatment devices. The lubricant industry aspires to "CHON" or "NOCH" oils to lubricate engines containing only Carbon, Hydrogen, Oxygen and Nitrogen. Such a hugely ambitious target requires at least major lateral thinking and more likely significant technological breakthroughs to stand any chance of coming to reality [4].

One notion is to use the irritating problem of fuel dilution of the lubricant in the cylinder to our advantage to administer friction modifiers to the piston ring pack via the fuel. Unlike their counterparts in the lubricant, which are complex in their action and long-lived, these could be relatively simple boundary lubricants. Longevity is not an issue as they would be replaced every time the fuel injector opens.

Research is ongoing into this hypothesis at the institution of the authors, the early stages of which have been reported by Smith et al [10, 11]. Initial ring zone and cylinder wall lubricant sampling experiments demonstrated that fuel administered additives can be accumulated in significant quantities in the lubricant films of the piston ring pack in a firing gasoline engine [10]. Subsequently, a Plint TE77 reciprocating tribometer was used to investigate classical boundary lubricants such as fatty acids at conditions designed to simulate piston ring and cylinder tribology in the severe mixed and boundary lubrication regime using real piston ring and cylinder liner sections, as illustrated in Figure 8 [11]. The test oil was Shell Extra High Viscosity Index (XHVI) 4™, a low viscosity highly refined base oil without an additive package to simulate a relatively heavily fuel-diluted lubricant.

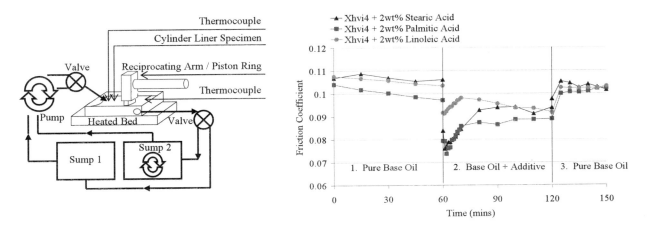

Figure 8. Piston Assembly Coefficient of Friction Variation for Three Model Fuel Additives in a Plint TE77 Reciprocating Tribometer (Ricardo Hydra top piston ring and cylinder sections, 120°C, 170 N, and 2000 r/min) after [11]

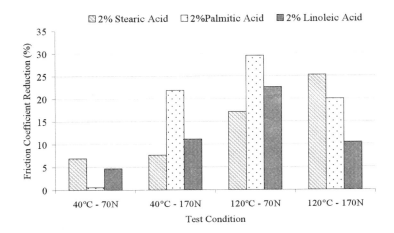

Figure 9. Coefficient of Friction Reduction Averaged over the First Ten Minutes of Additive Influenced Friction in the Test Cycle of Figure 8, after [11]

In Figure 8, a three-stage test can be seen with (1) pure base oil followed by (2) base oil plus the candidate additive and then (3) a return to the base oil. Significant reductions in friction coefficient are observed upon the introduction of the additive and the low tenacity of the boundary lubricant films is evidenced by the rapid loss of this benefit upon return to the base oil alone. The benefits of such additives in this simulation are summarised for a range of tribometer conditions in Figure 9 and clearly show promise as fuel administered friction modifiers.

3.3. Detailed Engine Friction Mapping

The majority of the mechanical frictional losses generated in an automobile can be attributed to the main tribological components of the engine, namely the valve train, piston assembly and engine crankshaft bearings. To this end, a novel experimental system has been developed to evaluate experimentally the frictional losses in all of the three main tribological components of an engine simultaneously under fired conditions [12].

A specially designed pulley torque transducer was used to measure valve train friction [13], an improved IMEP (Indicated Mean Effective Pressure) technique was developed to determine piston assembly friction [14] and crankshaft bearing losses were obtained indirectly by subtraction. This novel methodology has been implemented in the Ricardo Hydra single cylinder gasoline research engine described in Section 3.1.

One key aspect is the sensitivity to lubricant formulation, in terms of both viscometrics and additive packages across a range of operating conditions. Figure 10 shows an example for the piston assembly in the Ricardo Hydra engine [14], with clear benefits in using low viscosity lubricant at lower temperatures (larger film thicknesses), but with disturbing rises in friction at higher temperatures (thinner oil films). This is indicative of an earlier transition into mixed and boundary lubrication and raises durability concerns for the use of low viscosity lubricants.

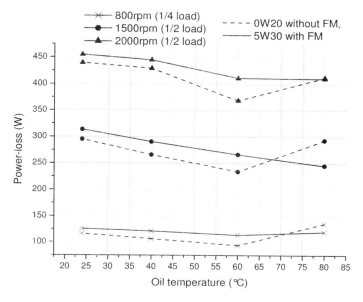

Figure 10. Comparison of piston assembly friction power loss for
SAE 0W20 without FM (friction modifier) and SAE 5W30 lubricants, after [14]

This highly flexible and powerful experimental technique can be applied to evaluate the overall performance of engine lubricants in the key tribological sub-systems of the engine. It can evaluate directly the deterioration in performance of the degraded lubricants discussed in Section 3.1 and the frictional synergy of the simpler oil and fuel administered friction modifiers of Section 3.2.

4. FUTURE PERSPECTIVE

Whilst the reciprocating internal combustion engine remains the principal prime mover for the automotive engine, demands on its performance in terms of environmental protection, efficient use of our finite hydrocarbon resources and customer satisfaction will grow relentlessly. The life cycle of the lubricant in the engine forms a key part of the success of this device and ever more efficient usage will be demanded together with an inevitable growth in recycling. Advanced and innovative tribology research of the type reported in this paper will be an important factor in this process.

5. CONCLUSIONS

- Life Cycle Analysis (LCA) is simple in concept, but complex in practice.

- Tribology is an important contributor to LCA of engine lubricants.

- Key areas relate to usage (fuel economy, durability and emissions), service drain intervals and recycling.

- Current tribology research is able to answer questions beyond the basic performance of the lubricant and inform key decisions about environmental impact and sustainability.

ACKNOWLEDGEMENTS

The research studies discussed in this paper were funded by a range of sponsors including the EPSRC (Engineering and Physical Sciences Research Council, UK), Federal Mogul, Ford, Infineum, Jaguar and Shell. Many thanks go to co-workers at Leeds, in industry and in the Department of Chemistry at the University of York, UK.

REFERENCES

[1] Clift, R. A role for tribology in life cycle design, Tribology for Energy Conservation, Proc. 24th Leeds-Lyon Symposium on Tribology, London, 1997, Tribology Series, Elsevier, Amsterdam, ISBN 0 444 50033 2, 1998, Vol. 34, pp.3-9.

[2] Fox, M.F. Environmental implications and sustainability concepts for lubricants, Handbook of Lubrication and Tribology: Volume 1 Application and Maintenance, Second Edition, G.E. Totten ed., CRC Press LLC, Boca Raton, ISBN-10: 0-8493-2095-X, 2006, Chapter 32, pp.32-1 – 32-31.

[3] Department for Transport, UK, http://www.dft.gov.uk/pgr/statistics/ [accessed June 2006].

[4] Korcek, S., Sorab, J., Johnson, M.D. and Jensen, R.K. Automotive lubricants for the next millennium, Industrial Lubrication and Tribology, 2000, 52(5), 209-220.

[5] Tung, S.C. and McMillan M.L. Automotive tribology overview of current advances and challenges for the future, Tribology International, 2004, 37, 517-536.

[6] Priest, M. and Taylor, C.M. Automobile engine tribology – Approaching the surface, Wear, 241, No.2, 2000, pp.193-203.

[7] Saville, S. B., Gainey, F.D., Cupples, S. D., Fox, M. F., and Picken, D. J. The study of lubricant condition in the piston ring zone of single cylinder diesel engines under typical operating conditions. SAE technical paper 881586. International Fuels and Lubricants Meeting, 10–13, October 1988. 1988.

[8] Stark, M.S., Gamble, R.J., Hammond, C.J., Gillespie, H.M., Lindsay-Smith, J.R., Nagatomi, E., Priest, M., Taylor, C.M., Taylor, R.I. and Waddington, D.J. Measurement of lubricant flow in a gasoline engine, Tribology Letters, 2005, Vol. 19, No.3, 163 - 168.

[9] Lee, P.M., Priest, M., Stark, M.S., Wilkinson, J.J., Lindsay Smith, J.R, Taylor, R.I. and Chung, S. Extraction and tribological investigation of top piston ring zone oil from a gasoline engine, Proc. Instn. Mech. Engrs., Part J: J. Engineering Tribology, 2006, 220(J3), pp. 171-180.

[10] Smith, O., Priest, M., Taylor, R.I., Price, R. and Cantlay, A. In-cylinder fuel and lubricant effects on gasoline engine friction, Proc. World Tribology Congress III (September 2005, Washington DC, USA), Abstract WTC2005-64265, CDROM ISBN 0-7918-3767-X, 2005, 2pgs.

[11] Smith, O., Priest, M., Taylor, R.I., Price, R., Cantlay, A and Coy, R.C. Simulated fuel dilution and friction modifier effects on piston ring friction, Proc. Instn. Mech. Engrs., Part J: J. Engineering Tribology, 2006, 220(J3), pp. 181-189.

[12] Mufti, R.A. Total and component friction in a motored and firing engine, PhD thesis, University of Leeds, 2004, 276pgs.

[13] Mufti, R.A. and Priest, M. Experimental and theoretical study of instantaneous engine valve train friction, Jour. Tribology, ASME, Vol. 125, 3, 2003, pp.628-637.

[14] Mufti, R.A. and Priest, M. Experimental evaluation of piston assembly friction under motored and fired conditions in a gasoline engine, Jour. Tribology, ASME, Vol. 127, 4, 2005, pp.826-836.